IQ Puzzles

Joe Cameron

ARCTURUS

This edition published in 2008 for Index Books Ltd
by Arcturus Publishing Limited
26/27 Bickels Yard, 151–153 Bermondsey Street,
London SE1 3HA

ISBN: 978-1-84193-816-5

Printed in Singapore

Typeset by MATS, Southend-on-Sea, Essex

Welcome to **IQ Puzzles**, a collection of over 500 puzzles to challenge and test your mental agility and problem-solving powers.

The book is organised into twenty levels of ascending difficulty – the first chapters are easier than the later ones. Each level is clearly marked down the side of the page. We advise that you work through each one in a methodical order and resist the temptation to dip in and out at random. If you find the first few chapters easy, please be patient and use them as a warm-up excercise for the more challenging puzzles later on.

When you finish each chapter take time to study the answers and go back over the questions until you fully understand the logic behind them. You will find, as you progress through the book, that certain mathematical patterns seem to re-occur or visual clues overlap. Be warned: these can help but just when you think you can recognize a pattern it changes!

Think laterally, don't just look at the obvious, look at the puzzles from all angles. The rewards can be hours and hours of fun.

Over the page we have listed a few tables which you might find helpful. These contain some basic mathematical formulas to help you do battle with the puzzles.

Good luck and enjoy!

Multiplication Table

×	1	2	3	4	5	6	7	8	9	10	11	12
1	1	2	3	4	5	6	7	8	9	10	11	12
2	2	4	6	8	10	12	14	16	18	20	22	24
3	3	6	9	12	15	18	21	24	27	30	33	36
4	4	8	12	16	20	24	28	32	36	40	44	48
5	5	10	15	20	25	30	35	40	45	50	55	60
6	6	12	18	24	30	36	42	48	54	60	66	72
7	7	14	21	28	35	42	49	56	63	70	77	84
8	8	16	24	32	40	48	56	64	72	80	88	96
9	9	18	27	36	45	54	63	72	81	90	99	108
10	10	20	30	40	50	60	70	80	90	100	110	120
11	11	22	33	44	55	66	77	88	99	110	121	132
12	12	24	36	48	60	72	84	96	108	120	132	144

Cube Numbers

1	1
2	8
3	27
4	64
5	125
6	216
7	343
8	512
9	729
10	1000
11	1331
12	1728
13	2197
14	2744
15	3375
16	4096
17	4913
18	5832
19	6859
20	8000

Square Numbers

1	1
2	4
3	9
4	16
5	25
6	36
7	49
8	64
9	81
10	100
11	121
12	144
13	169
14	196
15	225
16	256
17	289
18	324
19	361
20	400

Numerical Values

1	A	26
2	B	25
3	C	24
4	D	23
5	E	22
6	F	21
7	G	20
8	H	19
9	I	18
10	J	17
11	K	16
12	L	15
13	M	14
14	N	13
15	O	12
16	P	11
17	Q	10
18	R	9
19	S	8
20	T	7
21	U	6
22	V	5
23	W	4
24	X	3
25	Y	2
26	Z	1

Prime Numbers

2
3
5
7
11
13
17
19
23
29

PUZZLE 1

Which number replaces the blank and completes the sequence?

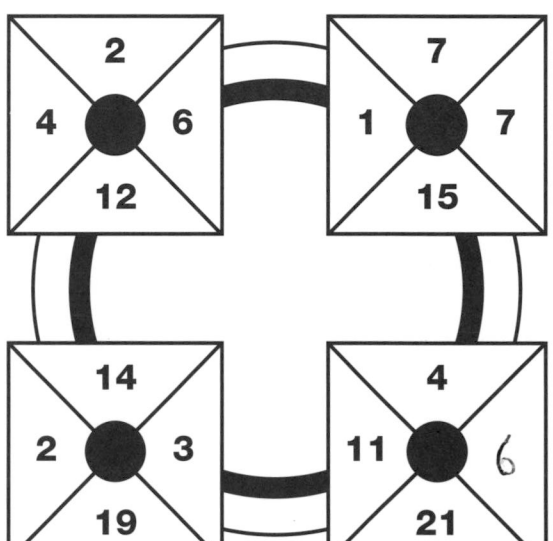

PUZZLE 2

Which letter replaces the blank and completes the puzzle?

 2
 17
 15

 6
 16
 10

 21
 24

3 PUZZLE

Which number is missing from the chain?

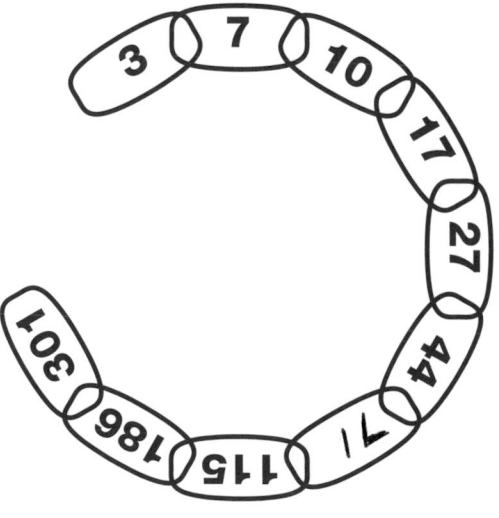

4 PUZZLE

Which number goes in the empty box?

| 2 | 3 | 9 |

| 7 | 6 | 2 |

| 16 | 11 | 12 |

| 25 | 20 | 23 |

8

Which letter completes the third circle?

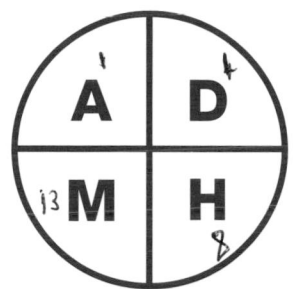
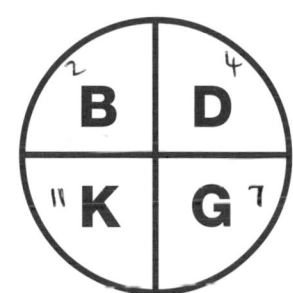

Which number goes in the empty box?

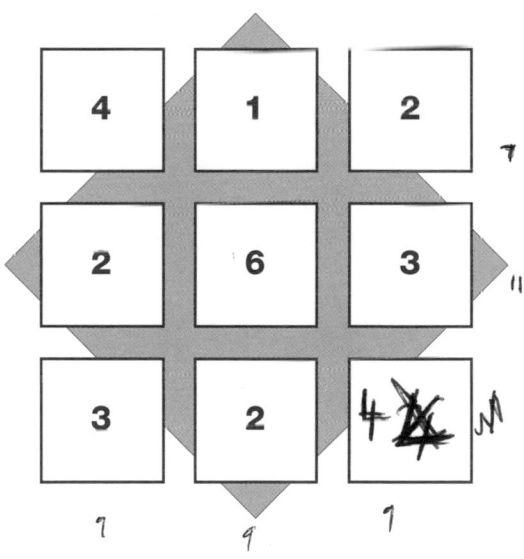

Remove three matches to leave just three squares.

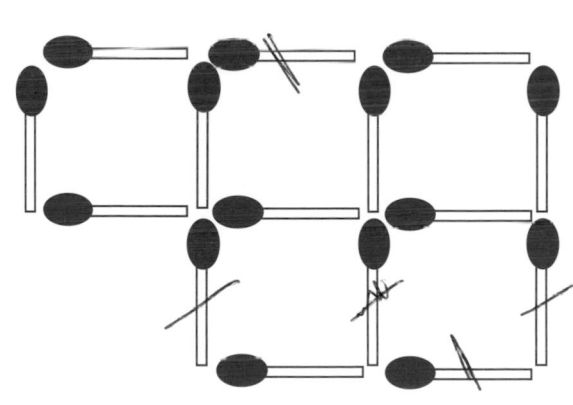

Which letter follows next?

 B  F  K  Q ... X

L E V E L 1

9

PUZZLE 9

Which letter goes in the empty square?

2 **B**	7 **G**	6 **F** 15
10 **J**	12 **L**	15 **O** 27
12 **L**	19 **S**	*21*
24	38	

PUZZLE 10

Following a logical pattern, complete this puzzle.

5	3	8
4	9	13

2	7	9
3	1	4

3	6	9
7	1	*8*

PUZZLE 11

Which number replaces the blank and completes the sequence?

7	2	9
9	3	12
12	4	16

PUZZLE 12

Which number is missing?

3	**9**	3	15
5	**7**	1	13
7	**1**	-3	
15	17		

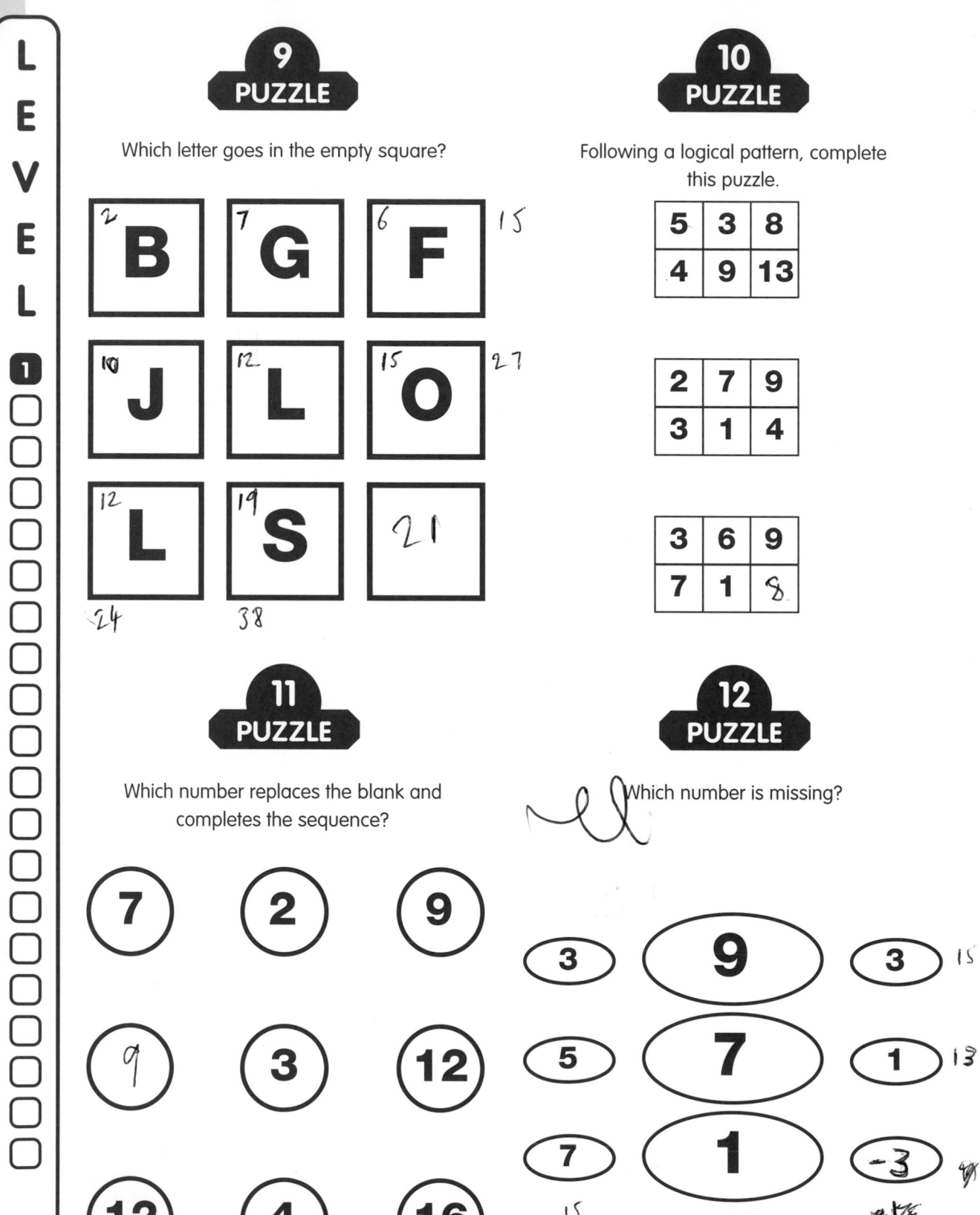

PUZZLE 13

Which number replaces the blank and completes the sequence?

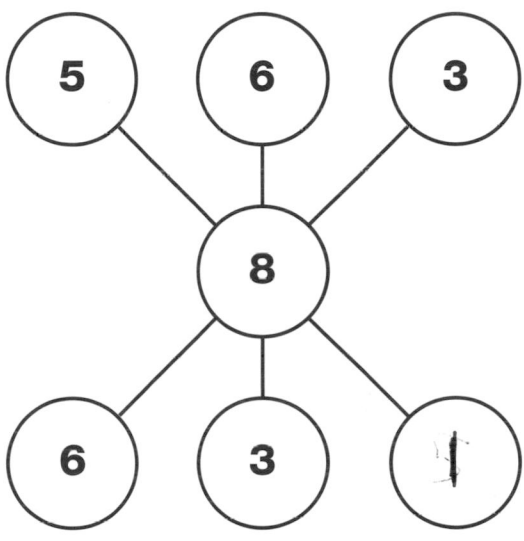

5 6 3

8

6 3 1

PUZZLE 14

Which number is missing from this sequence?

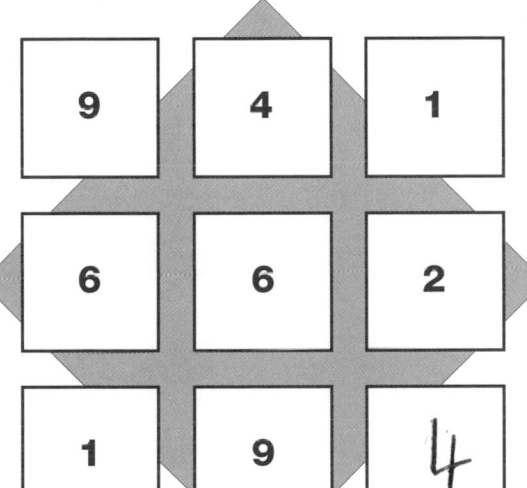

9	4	1
6	6	2
1	9	4

PUZZLE 15

Draw the face in the empty box which continues this pattern.

PUZZLE 16

Which number goes in the empty circle?

6+2

2 4 12

3 1 8

4 5 18

PUZZLE 17

Which number completes the puzzle?

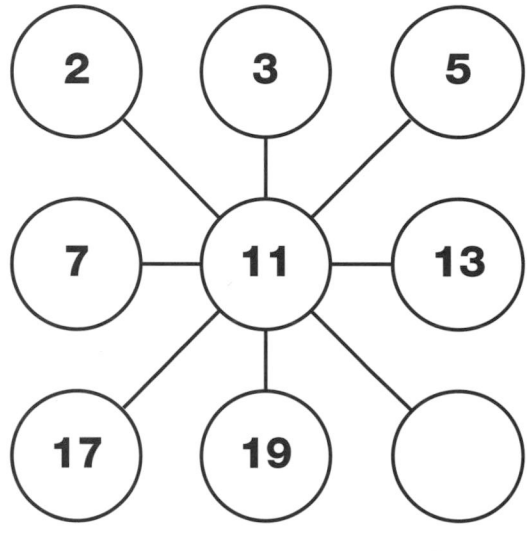

PUZZLE 18

Which number replaces the question mark in the bottom square?

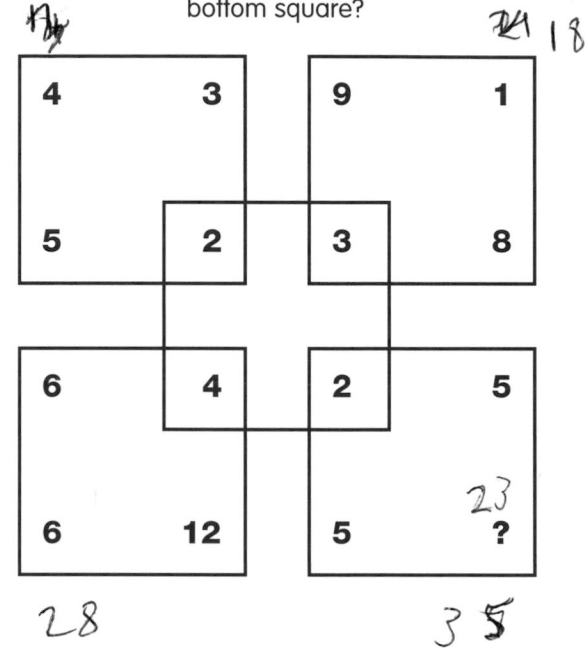

28   3 5

PUZZLE 19

Which letter is the odd one out in each shape?

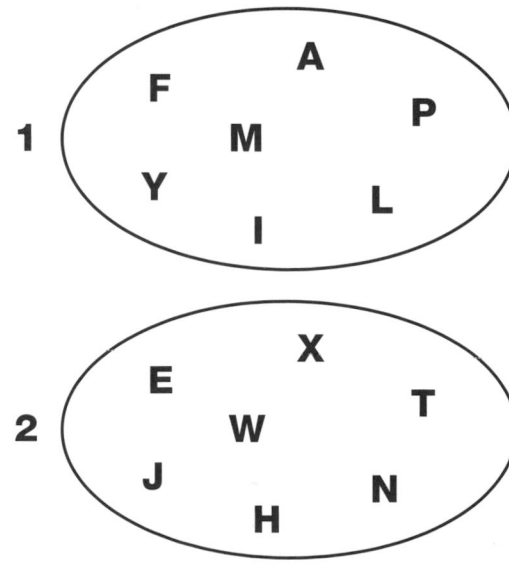

PUZZLE 20

Which number is missing from the empty segment?

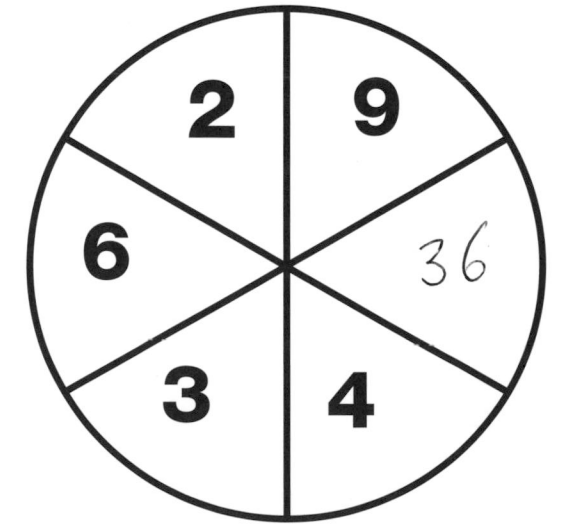

12

What is missing from the last grid?

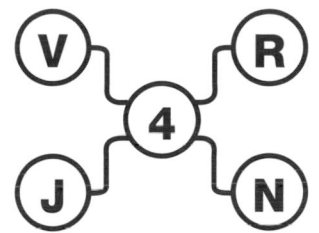  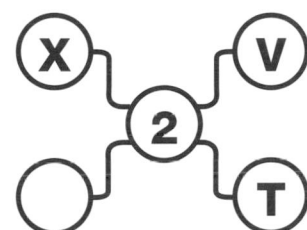

Can you work out which letter is missing?

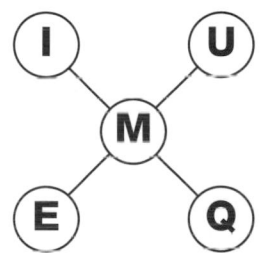 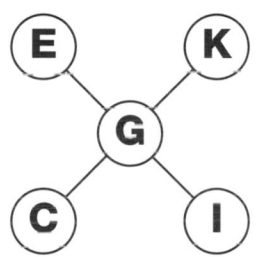 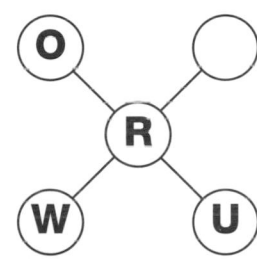

Enter the correct number into the empty square.

Following a logical pattern, complete this puzzle.

4	9	20	*33*
8	5	14	*27*
10	3	*11*	

22   *17*

1	5	7	13
15	5	4	6
3	8	2	13
12	5	2	

LEVEL 1

13

25 PUZZLE

By following this series of cogs attached to the float, can you work out if the flood warning works correctly?

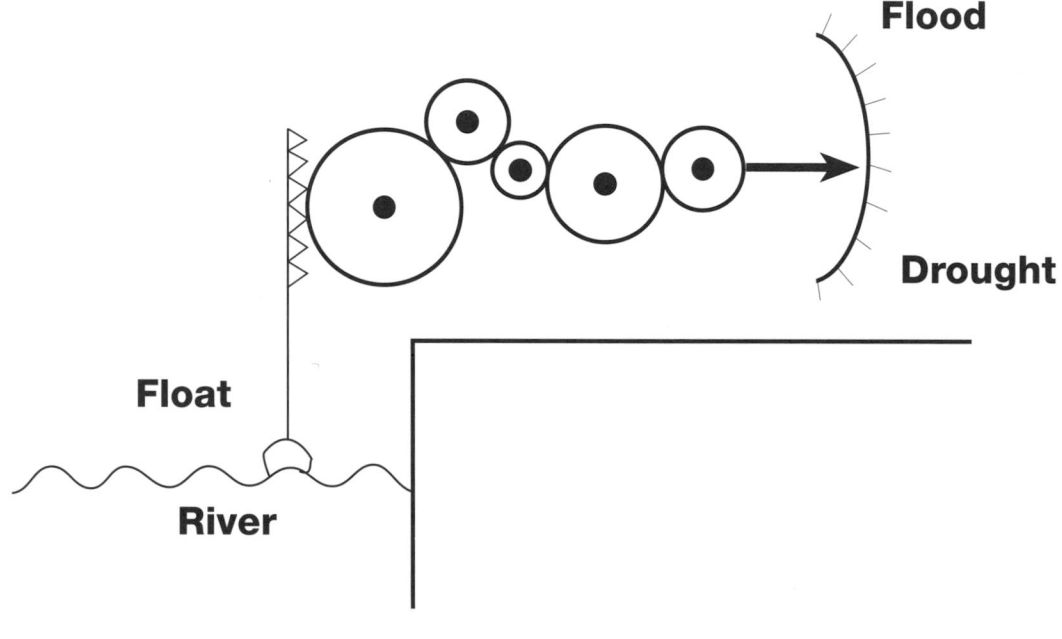

Flood

Drought

Float

River

26 PUZZLE

Which letter replaces the blank and completes the sequence?

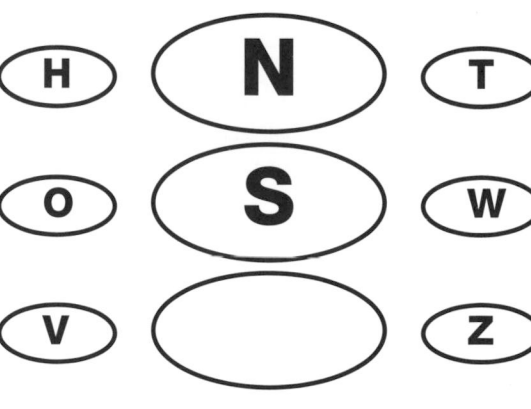

H   N   T

O   S   W

V   Z

27 PUZZLE

What is missing from the empty segment of the wheel?

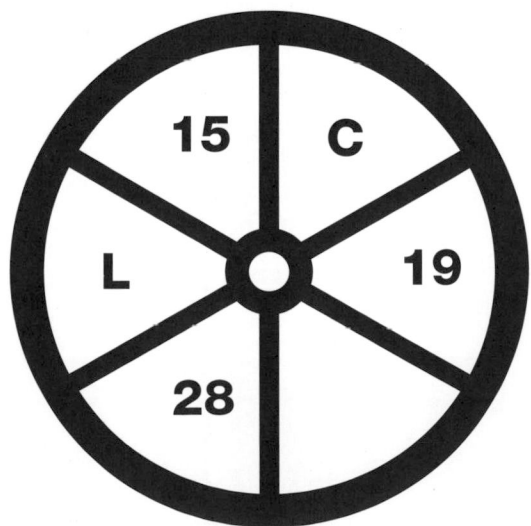

15   C

L   19

28

PUZZLE 28

Which playing card completes the sequence?

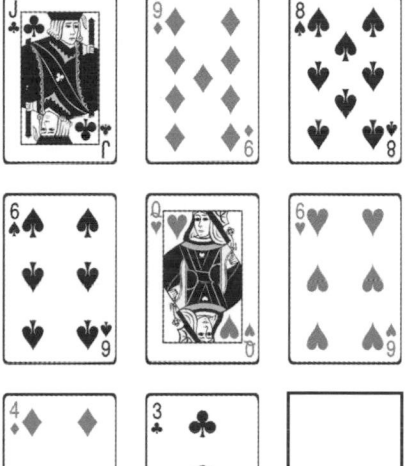

PUZZLE 29

Which two letters are missing?

A	W
C	U
G	Q
I	O
K	M

PUZZLE 30

Draw the dot in the correct segment of the last circle.

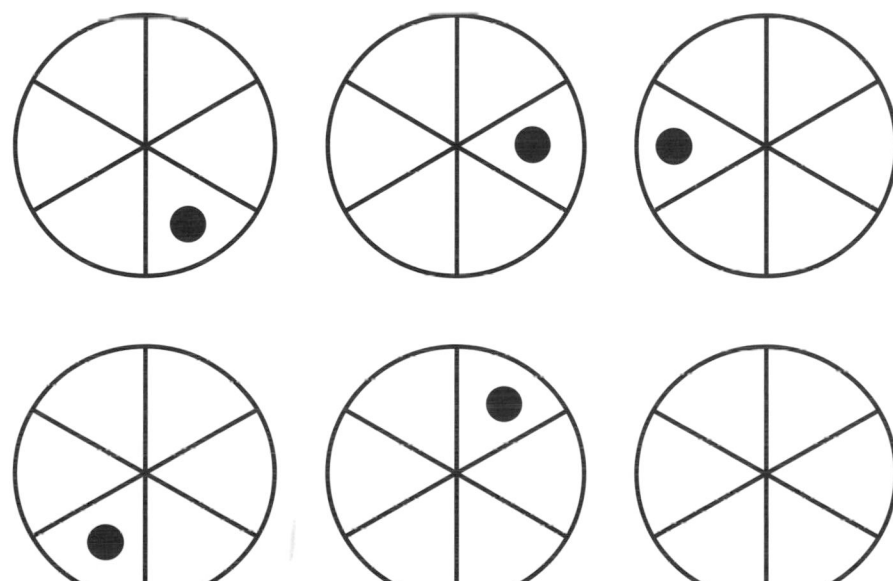

PUZZLE 31

Which number is missing from the third circle?

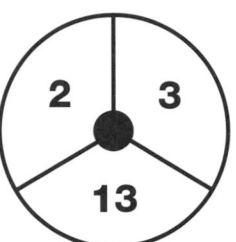
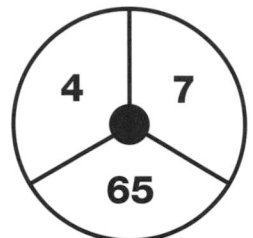
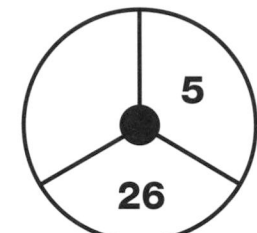

PUZZLE 32

Complete the last star.

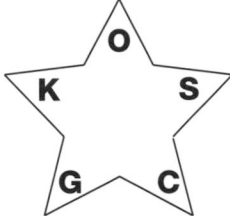

PUZZLE 33

Which two letters will complete this puzzle?

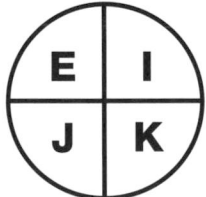

34 PUZZLE

Which number is missing?

 3　 5　 2

 6　 11　 5

 2　 9　 ( )

35 PUZZLE

Which number fits into the empty link?

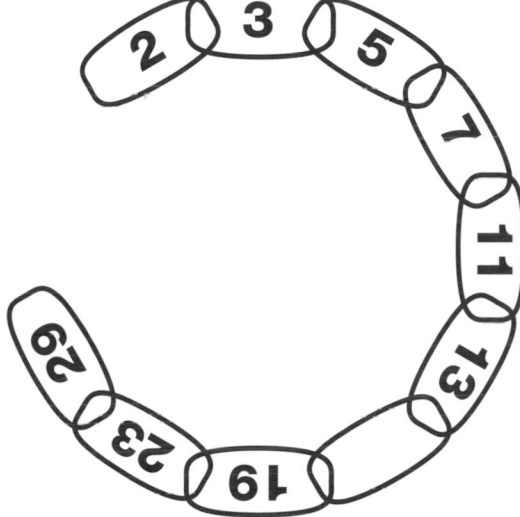

2　3　5　7　11　13　19　23　29

36 PUZZLE

Which letter completes the sequence?

K	Q	F
R	Y	G
M	B	K
O	E	

37 PUZZLE

Which number goes in the centre?

6	9	11
21		12
18	17	15

PUZZLE

Remove two matches to leave just four squares.

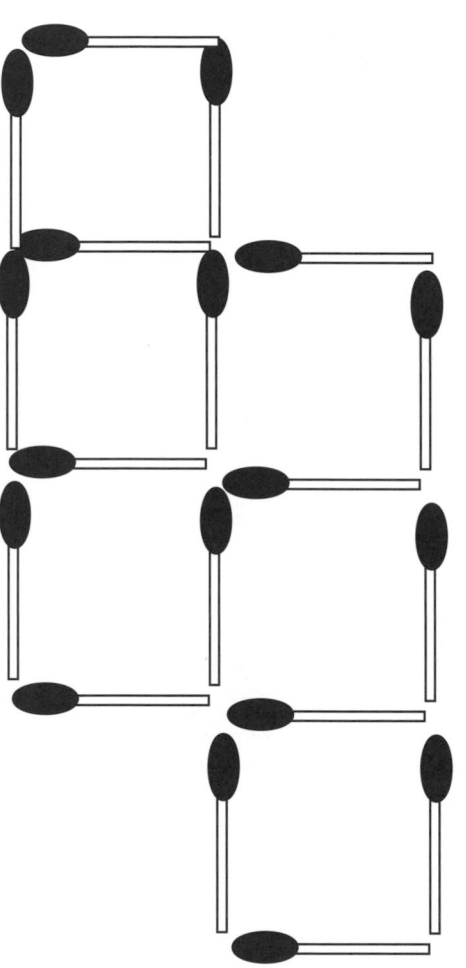

PUZZLE

If the bottom cog is turned anticlockwise will the flag at the top be raised or lowered?

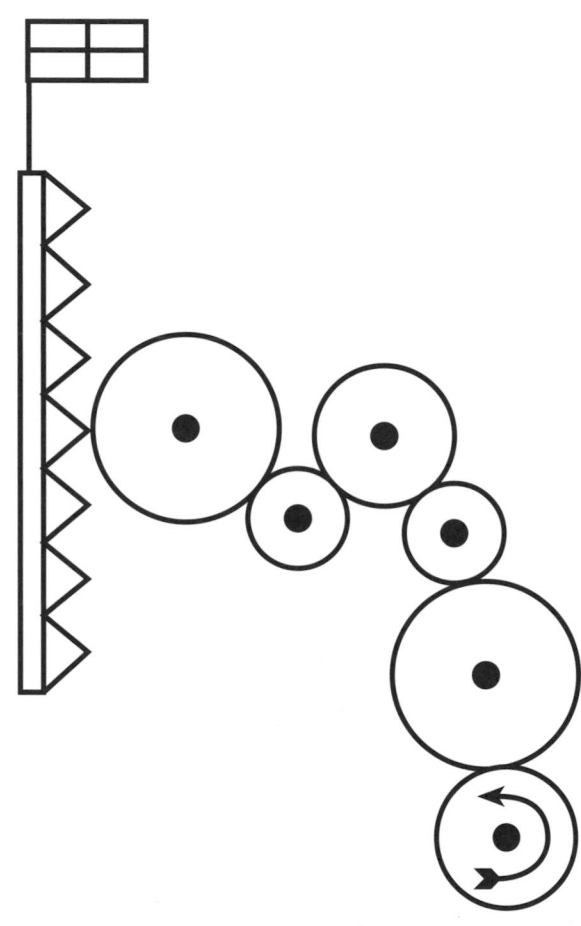

3
PUZZLE

Which number continues this sequence?

18	20	24	32	

Which number will complete this teaser?

10	**8**	6
3	**7**	11
2		4

Which letter goes into the last square of the bottom grid?

B	H	J
K	F	Q

T	A	U
G	H	O

L	N	Z
R	C	

Which number is missing from the box?

8	3	4
1	5	
6	7	2

Fill in the final box to complete the sequence.

D	W

2	7

U	L

3	3

G	O

2	

Which letter is missing from the last star?

9 PUZZLE

Which letter replaces the blank and completes the sequence?

D

P

B

N

10 PUZZLE

Which letter goes in the empty circle?

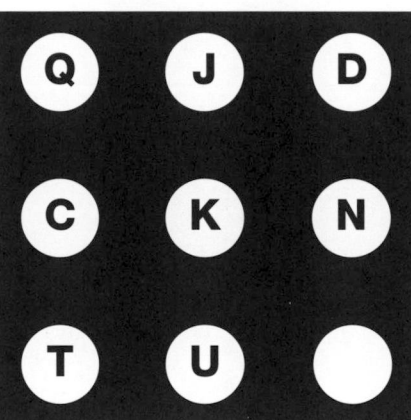

11 PUZZLE

Which number completes the last triangle?

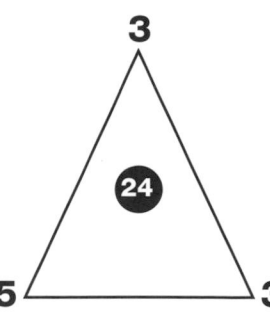 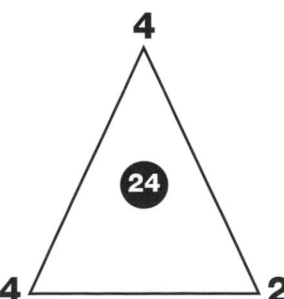 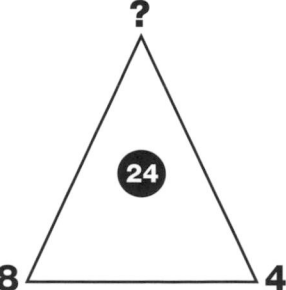

PUZZLE 12

Following a logical sequence, can you complete this puzzle?

5	13	4
6	10	2

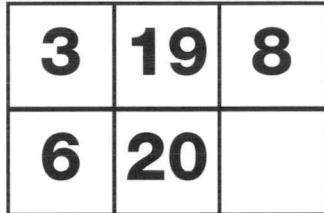

3	19	8
6	20	

PUZZLE 13

Which letter replaces the question mark?

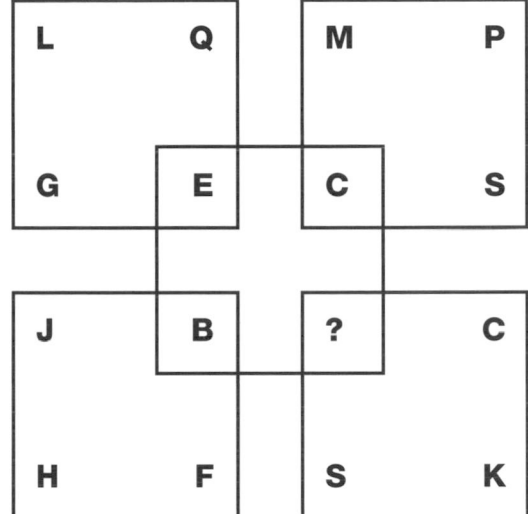

PUZZLE 14

Fill in the empty box.

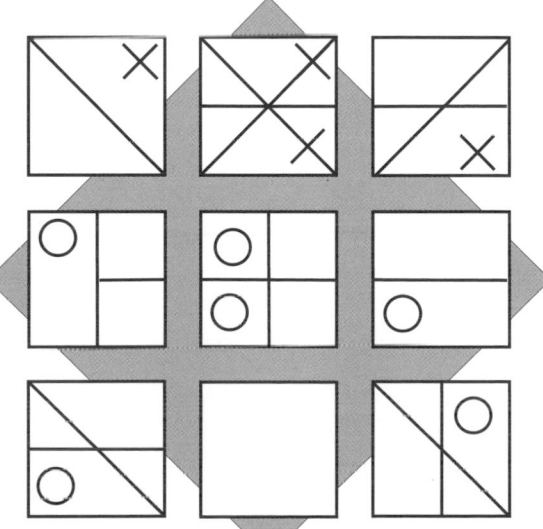

PUZZLE 15

Which number completes this sequence?

123
117
108
99

2

Which of the four squares at the bottom completes the pattern?

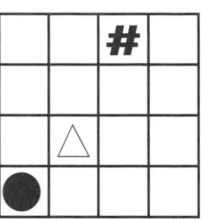 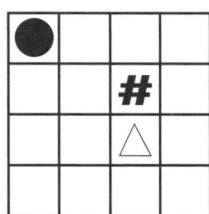 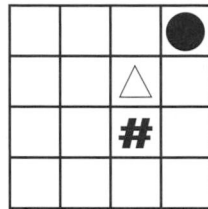 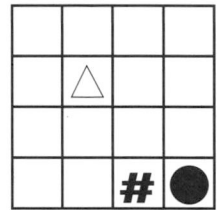

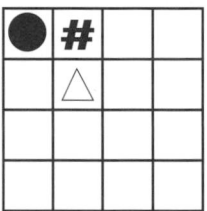 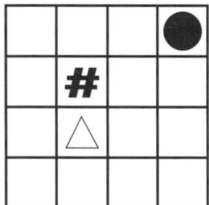 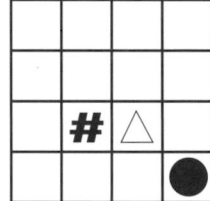 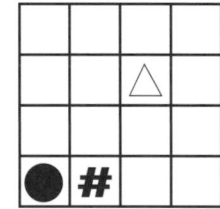

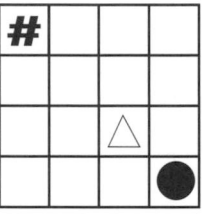 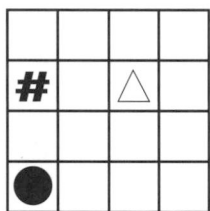 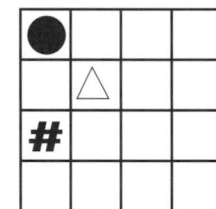 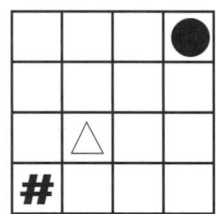

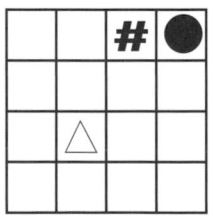 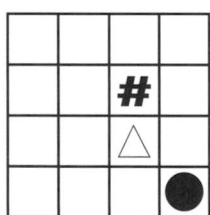 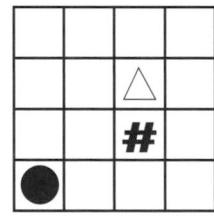 ?

A 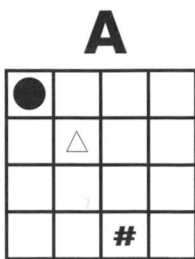 **B** 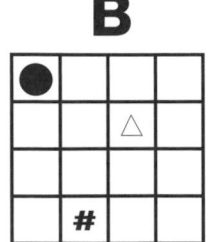 **C** 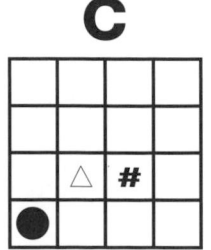 **D**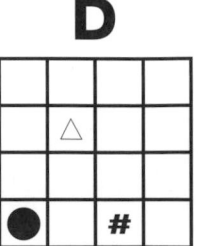

17 PUZZLE

Which number completes this puzzle?

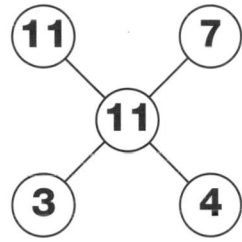 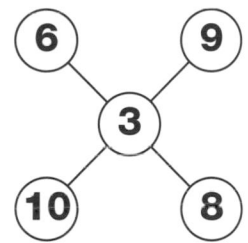 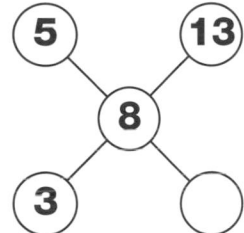

18 PUZZLE

Which pattern completes the grid?

1	2	3	4	5

19 PUZZLE

Which number is missing?

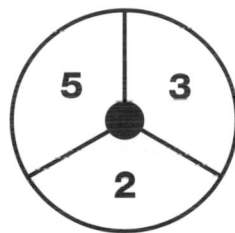  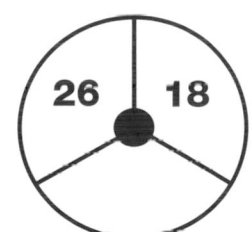

LEVEL

2

23

PUZZLE 20

Using every number between 1 and 9, fill in the spaces on this triangle so that the numbers on each side add up to 20.

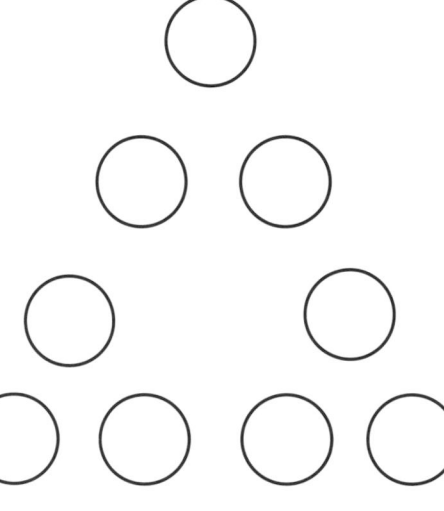

PUZZLE 21

Which number is missing?

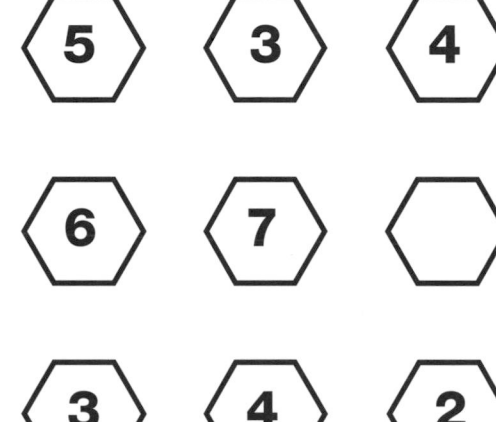

PUZZLE 22

Which number is missing from the third wheel?

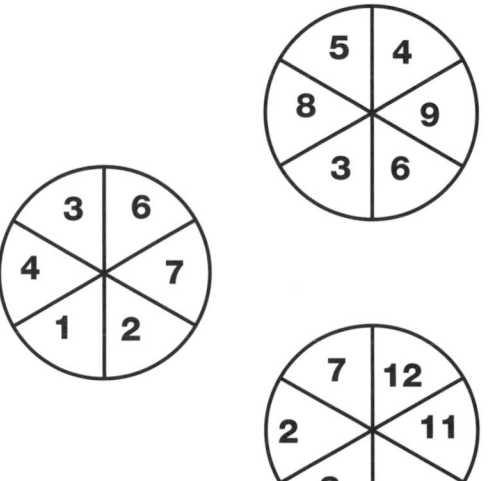

PUZZLE 23

Which number goes in the empty segment?

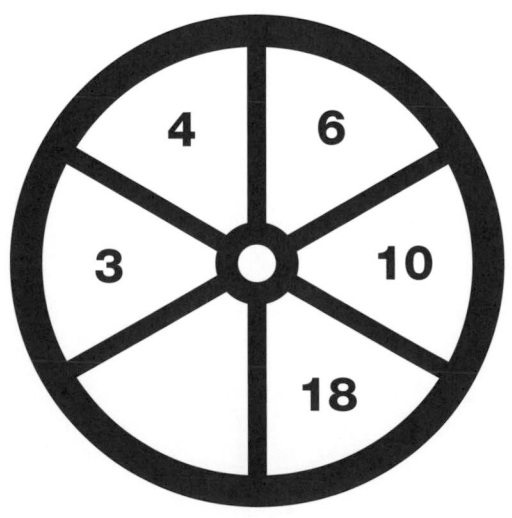

Sean caught a prize fish last weekend. He was going to measure it but realized that his ruler was not long enough. He was able to measure the head and discovered that it was 9cm long, he then measured the tail and found that it was the length of the head plus half the length of the body. If the body was the length of the head plus the tail, what is the total length of the fish?

Which number completes the chain?

1 2 3 5 8 68 55 34 21

Which letter replaces the blank and completes the sequence?

B F C

G G A

E ___ D

Which number logically goes in the centre of this puzzle?

3 11 19

5 ___ 23

7 17 29

LEVEL

2

25

28 PUZZLE

Which of the bottom six grids completes this pattern?

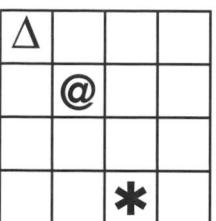

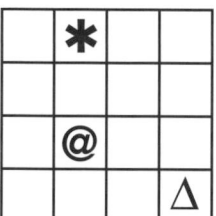

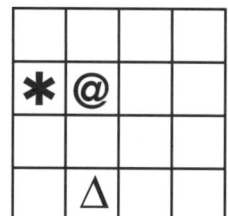

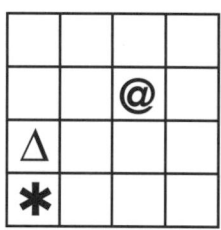

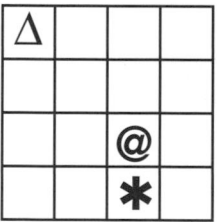

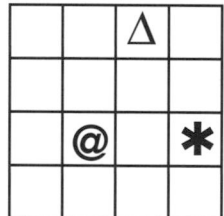

?

A

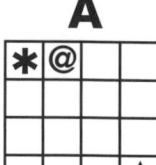

B

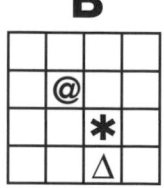

C

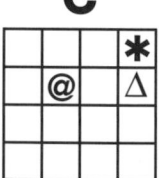

D

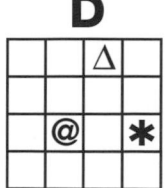

E

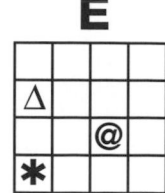

F

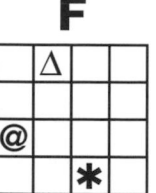

Which number is missing?

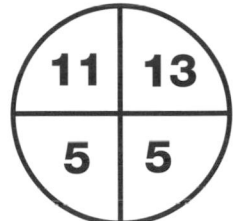 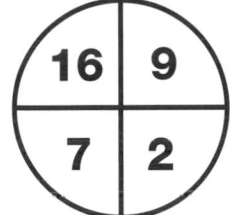 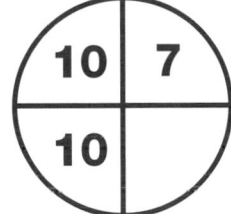

Which letter goes in the empty segment?

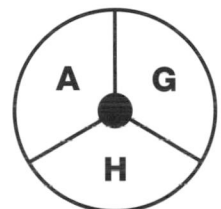 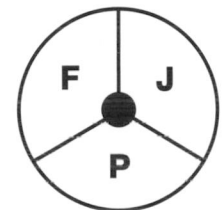 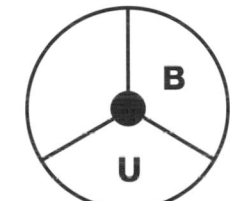

Which letter replaces the blank and completes the sequence?

Which letter completes this puzzle?

PUZZLE 1

Which letter tops the third triangle?

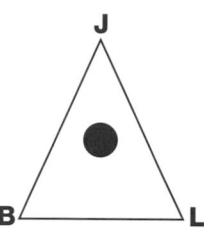
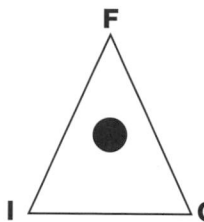
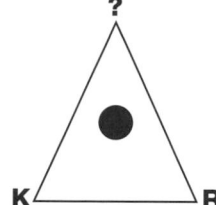

PUZZLE 2

Which number goes in the third star?

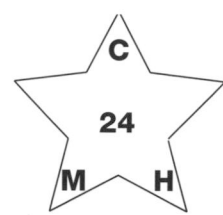
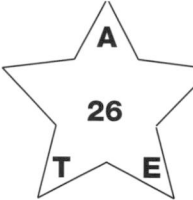
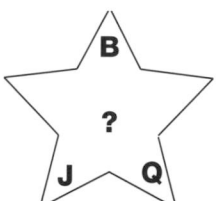

PUZZLE 3

Which letter replaces the blank and completes the sequence?

B	A
C	E
D	F
G	H
J	I
O	

PUZZLE 4

If two painters can complete two rooms in two hours, how many painters would it take to do 18 rooms in 6 hours?

28

PUZZLE 5

Which letter goes in the empty segment?

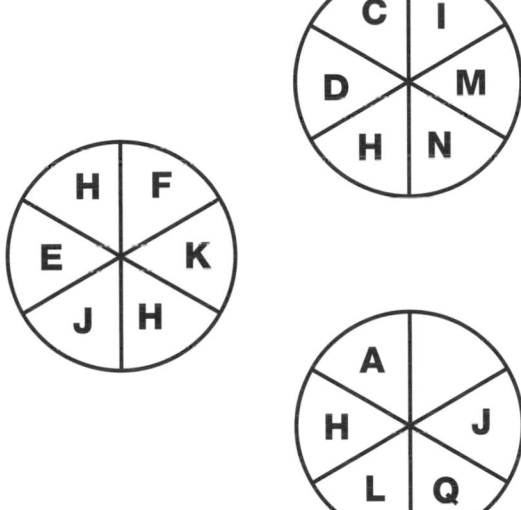

PUZZLE 6

Which number links all these?

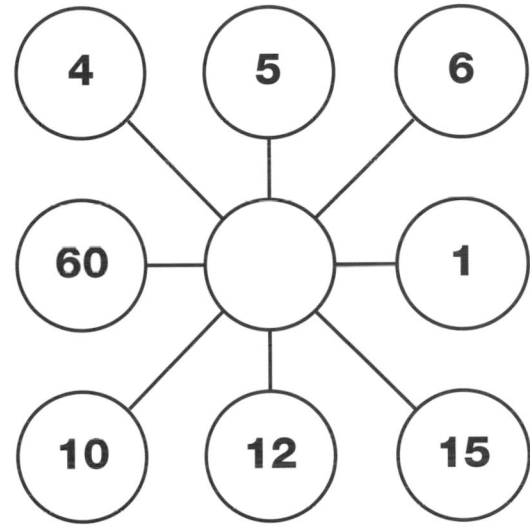

PUZZLE 7

Which number logically finishes this puzzle?

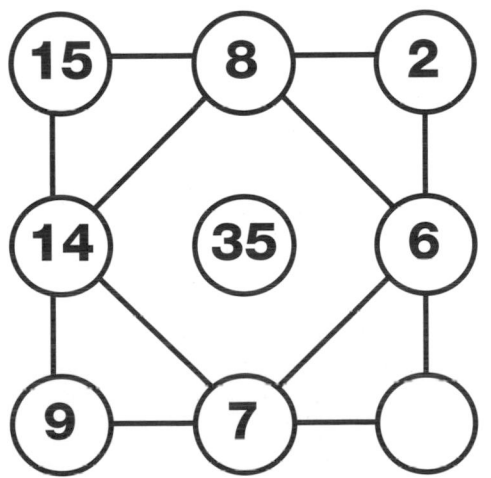

PUZZLE 8

Which number replaces the question mark?

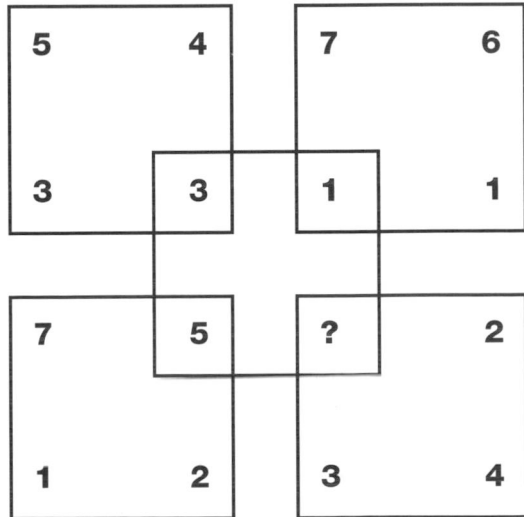

PUZZLE 9

Which number goes in the empty circle?

15   21   18

3   7   6

5   3   ( )

PUZZLE 10

Which number completes this sequence?

2	5
7	3
10	4
14	6
20	8
28	

PUZZLE 11

Which number finishes this grid?

2	6	3
5	3	3
7	2	

PUZZLE 12

Which letter replaces the blank and completes the sequence?

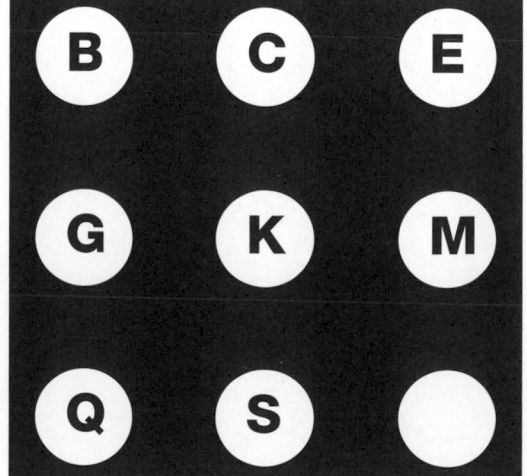

PUZZLE 13

Which playing card is missing?

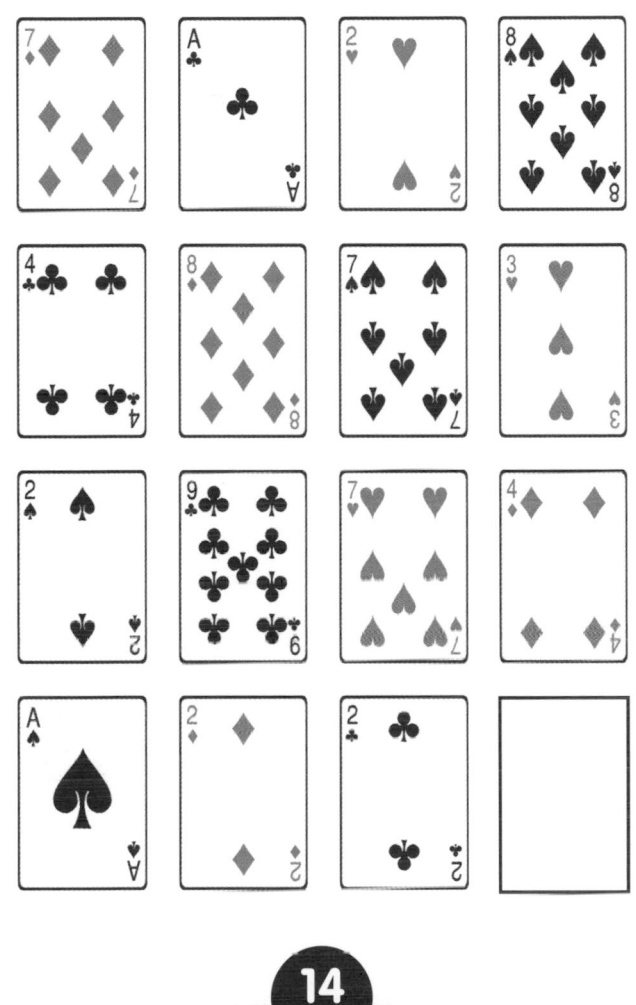

PUZZLE 14

Which character is missing from the point in the last star?

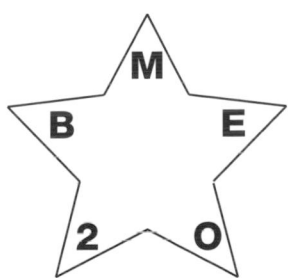
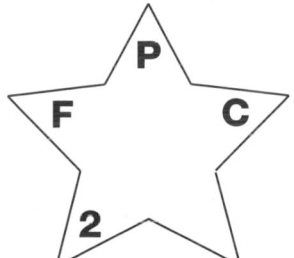

LEVEL

3

3

PUZZLE 15

Which letter goes in the final link to complete the chain?

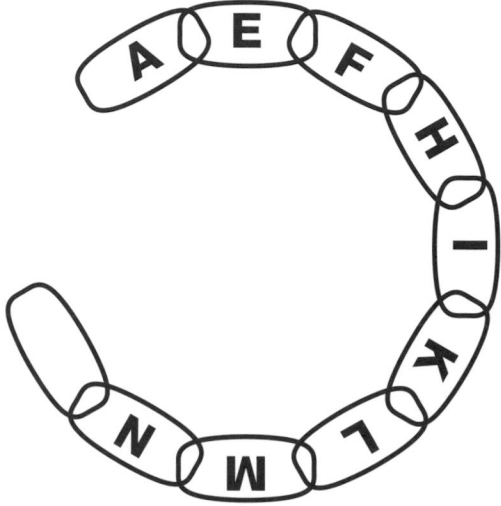

PUZZLE 16

Which number finishes this puzzle?

PUZZLE 17

Which number goes in the empty segment?

PUZZLE 18

Which letter replaces the blank and completes the sequence?

Which number goes in the middle of the last triangle?

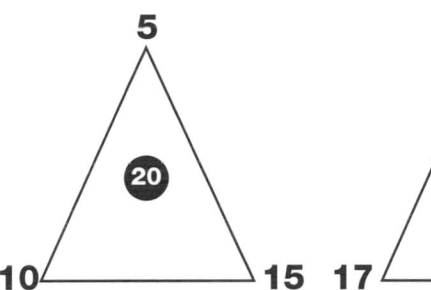
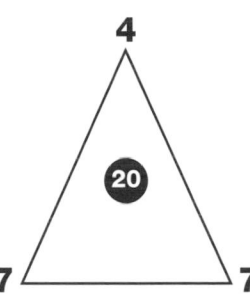
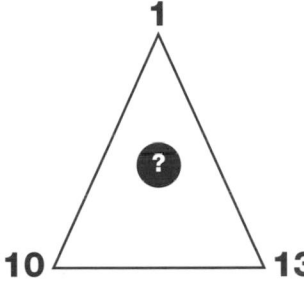

Which number completes the chain?

Which letter replaces the blank and completes the wheel?

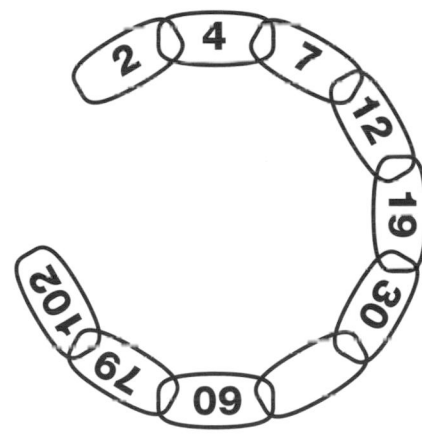

Which number goes in the blank segment of the last circle?

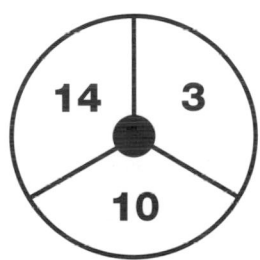
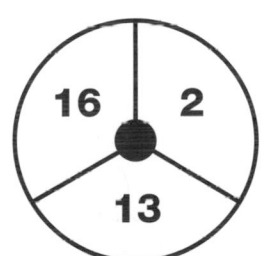
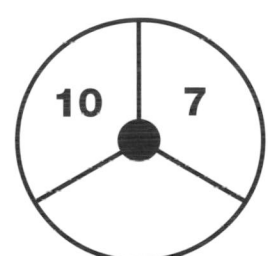

LEVEL

3

PUZZLE 23

Which number goes in the empty circle?

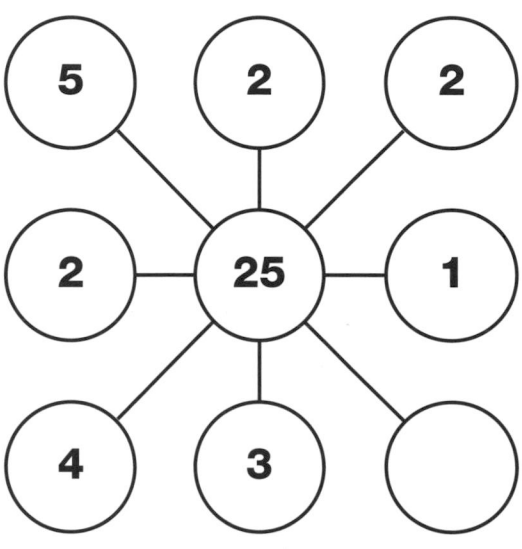

PUZZLE 24

Which character logically completes this sequence?

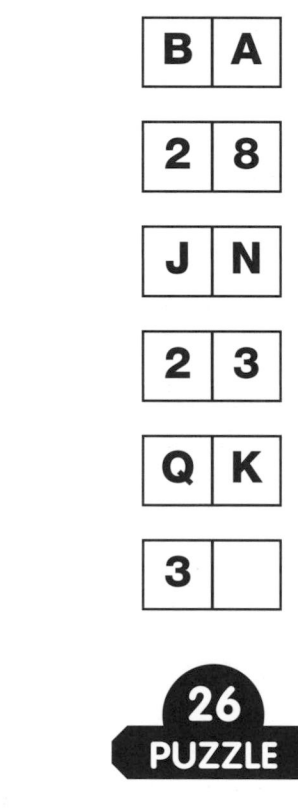

PUZZLE 25

Which letter goes in the empty segment?

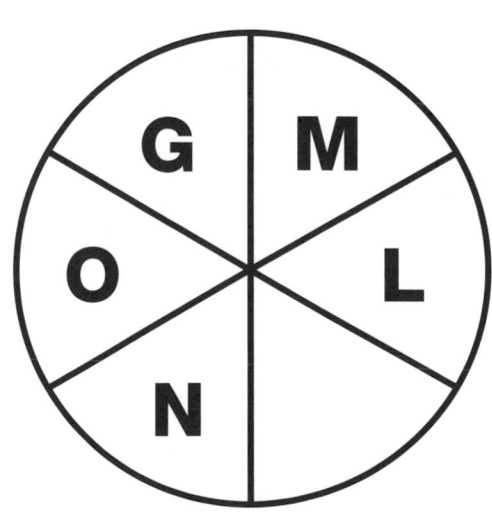

PUZZLE 26

Which number will finish this grid?

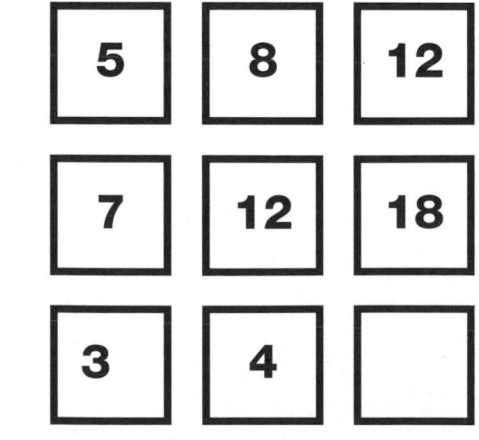

Which number does not fit in this sequence?

1 - 2 - 3 - 6 - 7 - 8 - 14 - 15 - 30

Which number is the odd one out in each shape?

A
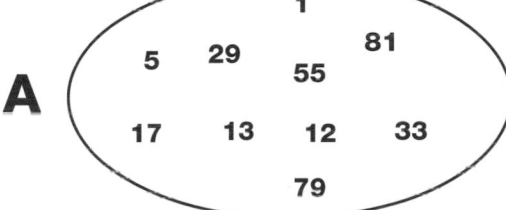

B
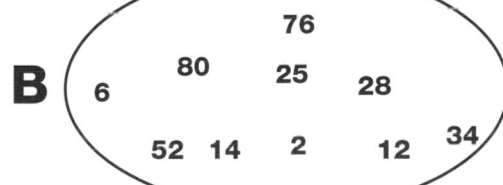

Which number is missing from the puzzle?

Which number is missing in the last grid?

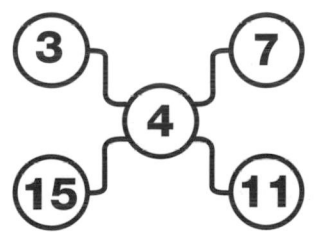

L
E
V
E
L

3

35

PUZZLE 31

Which letter replaces the blank and completes the sequence?

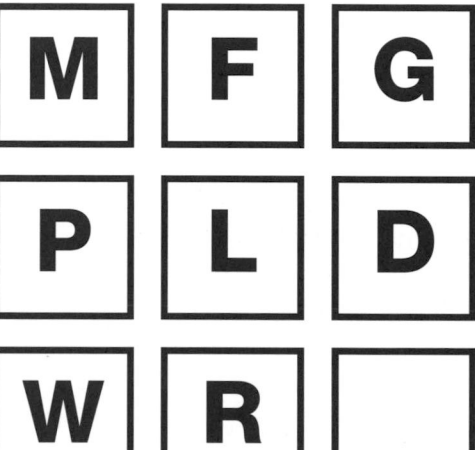

M	F	G
P	L	D
W	R	

PUZZLE 32

Which letter goes in the empty circle and completes this puzzle?

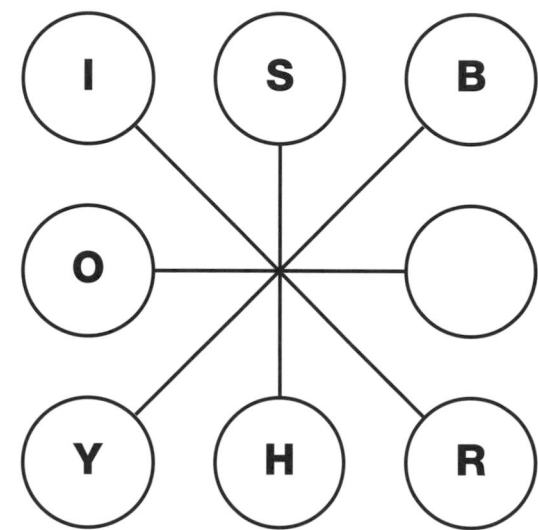

I S B

O

Y H R

PUZZLE 33

Jacob is 12 years old. He is 3 times as old as his brother. How old will Jacob be when he is twice as old?

PUZZLE 34

Which number goes in the empty segment and completes the wheel?

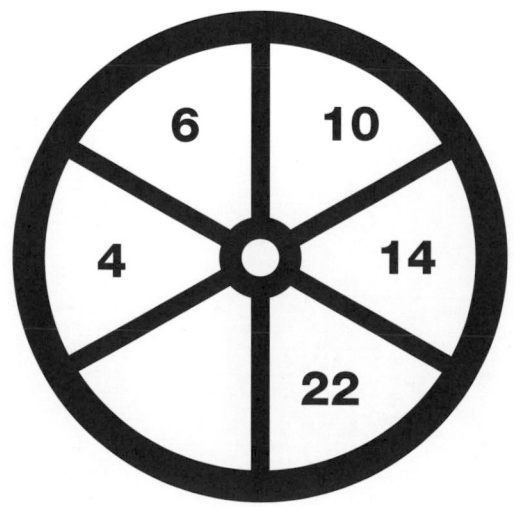

6   10

4   14

22

Which number goes in the empty square?

J	F	N
8	4	0

B	G	P
2	2	4

O	D	I
5	4	

Which number goes in the empty circle and finishes the puzzle?

 4    6    2

 7    8   1

 1   4   ◯

Which character is missing from this puzzle?

B | I
W | P

D | J
V | P

A | F
P | K

 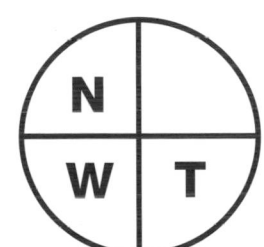

J | N
V | R

N |
W | T

L
E
V
E
L

3

37

PUZZLE 1

Which letter replaces the blank and completes the sequence?

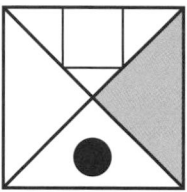 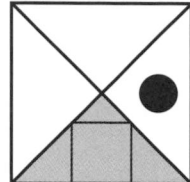 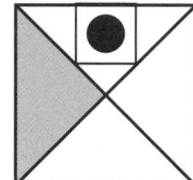

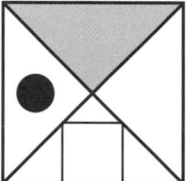 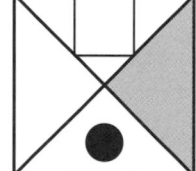

A	B	C	D	E	F
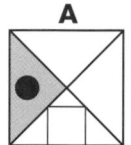	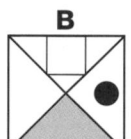	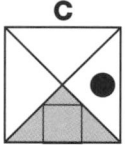	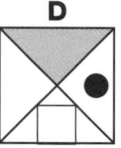	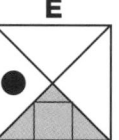	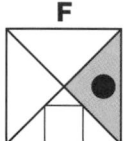

PUZZLE 2

Which number goes in the empty square?

3	7	10
4	11	15
6	4	

PUZZLE 3

Which number completes the sequence?

G	M
2	0

N	T

3	4

U	B

2	

PUZZLE 4

Draw the correct pattern in the empty box to complete the pattern.

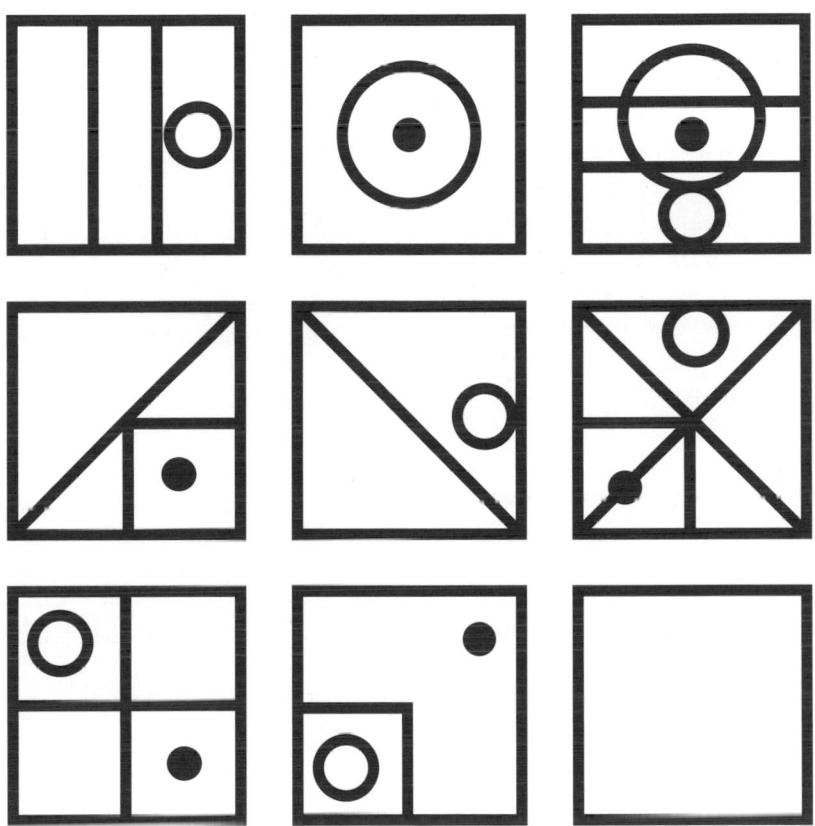

PUZZLE 5

Which number goes in the empty circle?

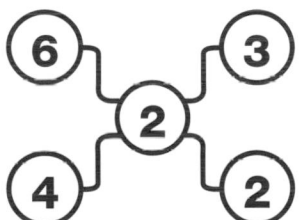

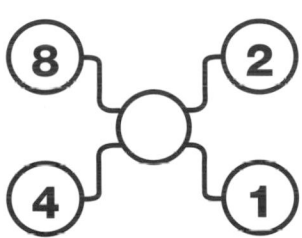

PUZZLE 6

Which letter replaces the blank and completes the sequence?

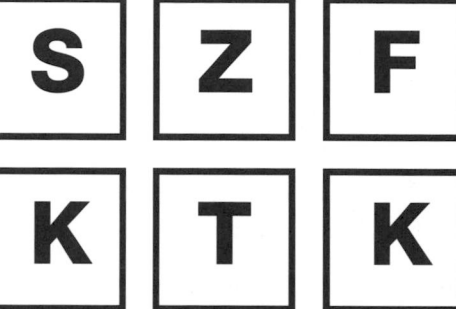

S	Z	F
K	T	K
B	R	

PUZZLE 7

If the price of a dress was cut by 20% for a sale, by what percentage of the sale price must it be increased by to resell it at the original price?

PUZZLE 8

Which number goes at the bottom to start the sequence?

6

11

15

18

20

PUZZLE 9

Which characters complete this grid?

J	Q
1	0
P	K
1	6
T	G

Which of the bottom numbers goes in the centre circle?

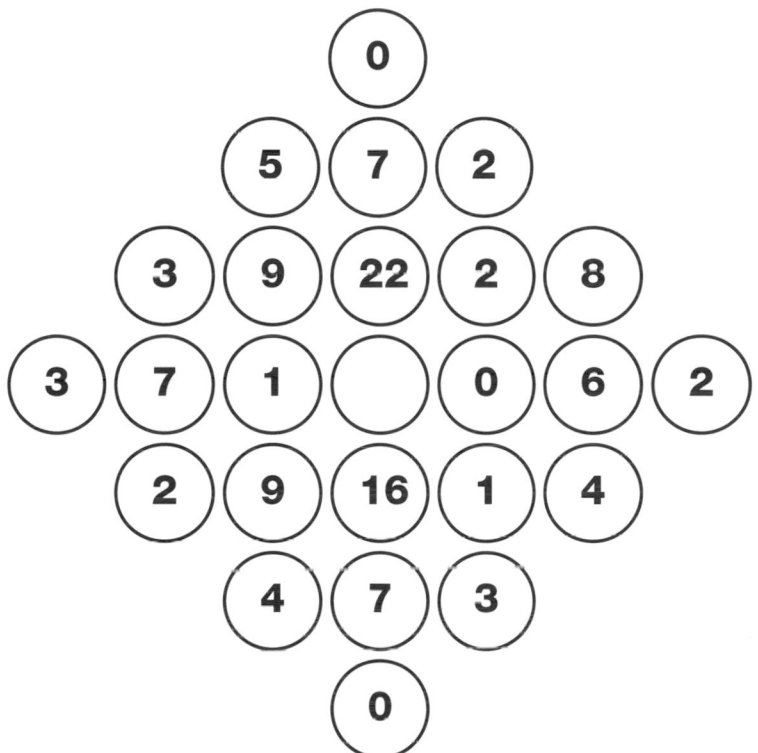

13 15 17 19 21 23 25 27

Which letter finishes off the third triangle?

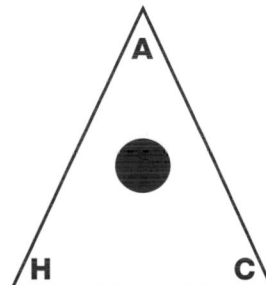
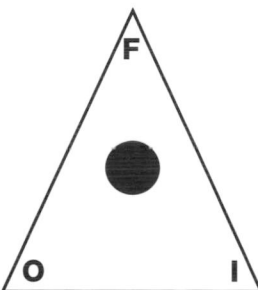
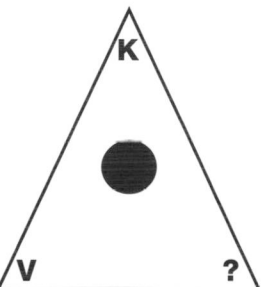

LEVEL

4

12 PUZZLE

Which number is missing from the bottom grid?

4	15	6
7	27	11

6	33	16
3	12	

13 PUZZLE

Which letter logically completes the last box of letters?

H	X	O
Q	A	J

Z	R	K
F	N	U

S	G	D
A	M	

14 PUZZLE

Which number goes in the empty segment?

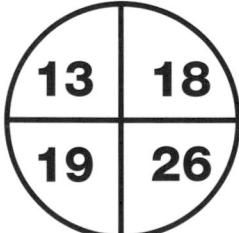

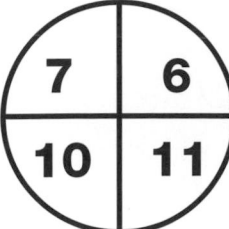

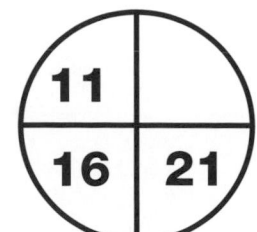

PUZZLE 15

Which letter replaces the blank and completes the third wheel?

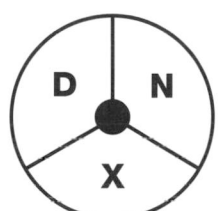 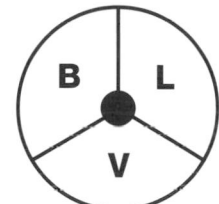 

PUZZLE 16

Which number replaces the blank and completes the sequence?

4	5	6	10
4	3	3	2
4	5	6	0
11	7	6	

PUZZLE 17

George has a square plot of land, but the corner of his house takes up $1/4$ of the available space as the picture shows. He wants to divide the remaining space into 4 equal plots, of the same area and basic shape. It was difficult to do as the plots were not arranged in the most practical way but can you work out how George managed it?

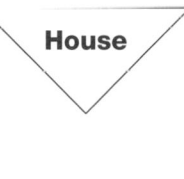

PUZZLE 18

Which letter replaces the blank and completes the sequence?

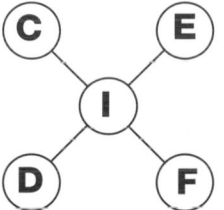 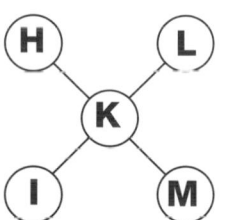 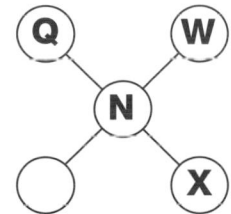

19
PUZZLE

Which number is missing from the last triangle?

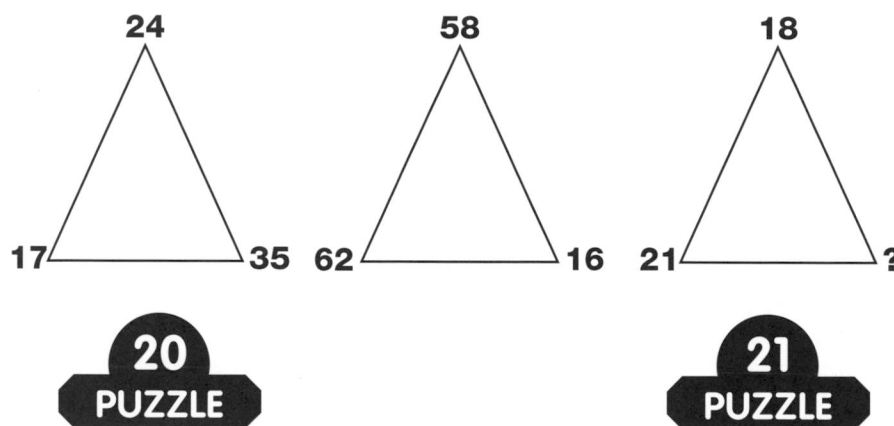

24

17   35   62   16   21   ?

58

18

20
PUZZLE

Which number replaces the question mark?

3	4	5	2
1	26	30	1
3	49	?	7
6	2	1	2

21
PUZZLE

Which playing card is missing from this puzzle?

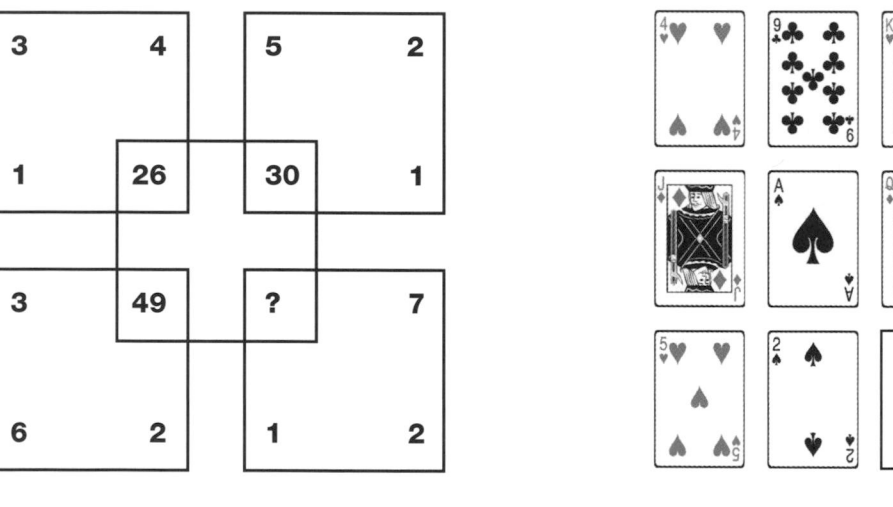

22
PUZZLE

Which letter replaces the question mark and completes the sequence?

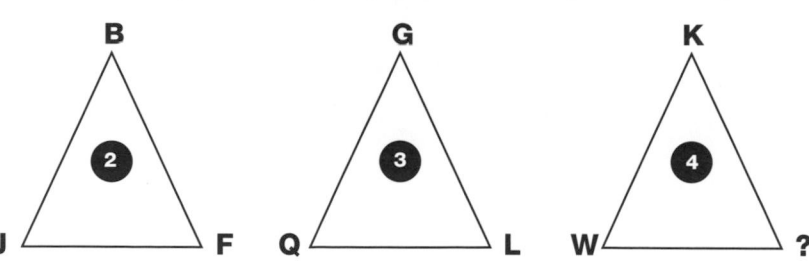

B   G   K

2   3   4

J   F   Q   L   W   ?

PUZZLE 23

If it takes 2 garage mechanics 3 hours to repair 6 cars, how many mechanics would it take to repair 22 cars in 5 hours?

PUZZLE 24

What is the fewest number of matches that need to be moved in order to make the fish swim in the opposite direction?

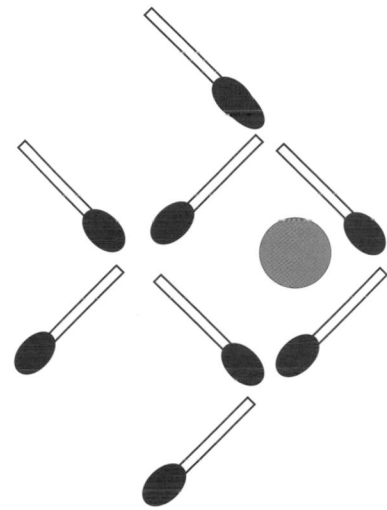

PUZZLE 25

Which number should appear at the bottom of this pile?

11
12
14
18
26

PUZZLE 26

Which number goes in the empty segment?

8
13
18
24
39

27 PUZZLE

Which number is missing?

3	4	7	2	9	3
2	2	1	9	1	6
5	6	9	2	0	9

1	7	8	6	3	2
4	3	2	8	1	1
6	1	1	4	4	

28 PUZZLE

Move just 4 matches to make 3 equilateral triangles.

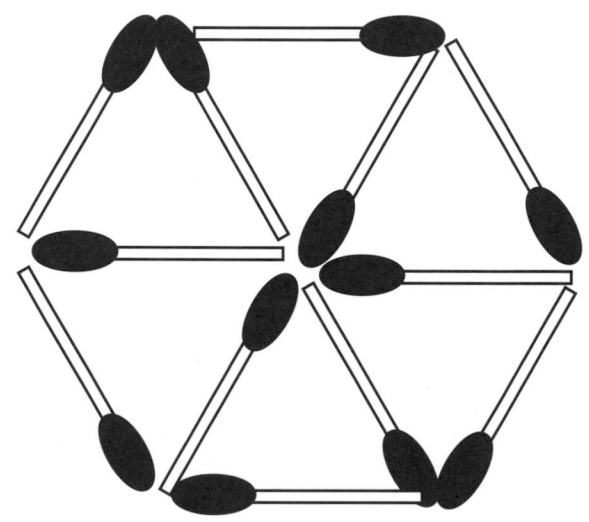

29 PUZZLE

Which letter is missing from the web?

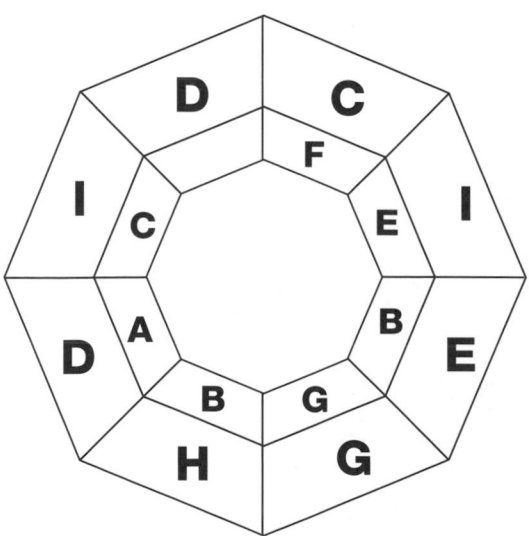

30 PUZZLE

Which letter is the odd one out in each shape?

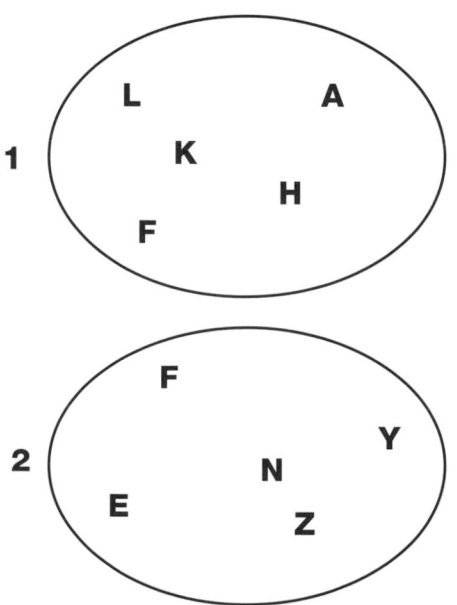

PUZZLE 1

Gill's puppy was growing fast. In the first five days since she got it it had eaten 100 dog biscuits. If each day it had eaten 6 more than the previous day, how many biscuits had it eaten on the first day?

PUZZLE 2

Which two numbers continue this sequence?

1 - 10 - 3 - 9 - 5 - 8 - 7 - 7 - 9 - 6 - ? - ?

PUZZLE 3

Which number follows on from these three?

| 2 | 5 | 26 | |

PUZZLE 4

Which letter goes in the middle of the third triangle?

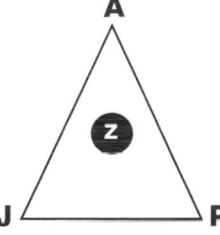
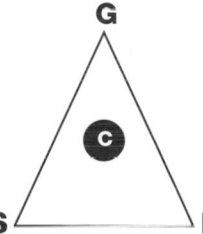
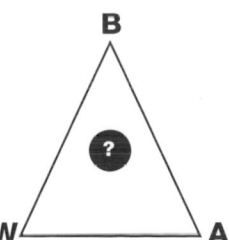

5 PUZZLE

Which number continues this sequence?

| 6 | 10 | 18 | 34 | |

6 PUZZLE

Which number is missing from the last puzzle?

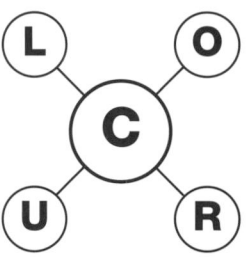
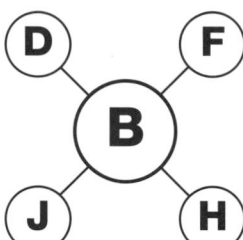
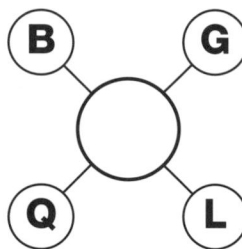

7 PUZZLE

Which number replaces the blank and completes the sequence?

1	1
2	1
3	2
5	3
8	5
	8

8 PUZZLE

Which letter is missing from the empty segment?

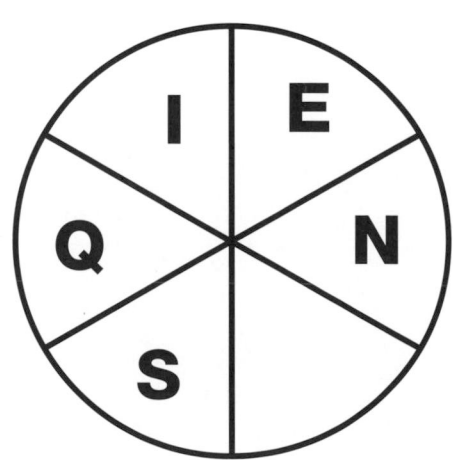

PUZZLE 9

Which number goes in the blank link and completes the chain?

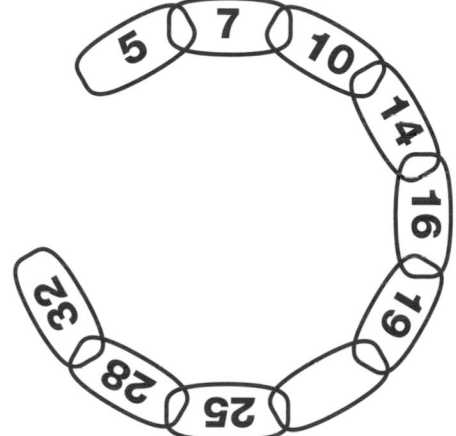

5 7 10 14 16 19 25 28 32

PUZZLE 10

Which number replaces the question mark?

11 6
5 22
3 U L 3
D A
4 P F 7
14 ?
2 24

PUZZLE 11

Which letter is missing?

B	D	G
D	O	K
T	A	P
K	C	

PUZZLE 12

Alex is crossing the desert with his dog, Lucky. He starts off with a full waterbottle and drinks ¹/₃ of the contents during the first day. He then lets Lucky drink half of what is left. The next day, Alex drinks a ¹/₄ of what has been saved from the previous day. What fraction of the original amount did he save for Lucky?

PUZZLE 13

Which number continues this sequence?

| 1 | 8 | 16 | 25 | |

PUZZLE 14

Which number fills the empty circle?

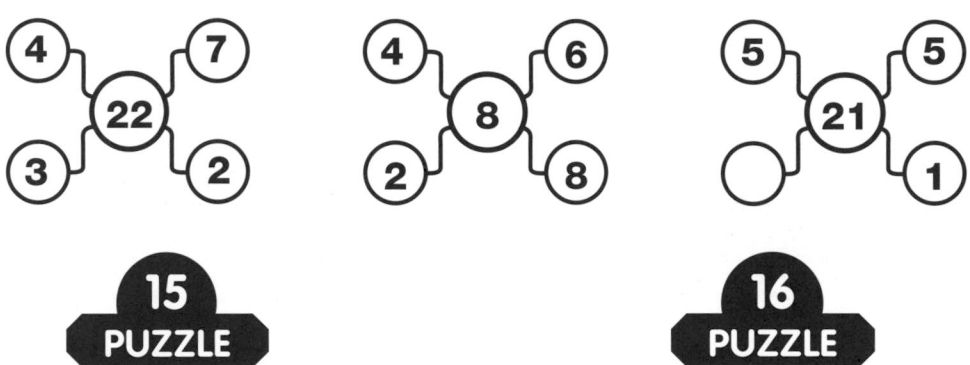

PUZZLE 15

Here is a set of cogs connected via drive belts. If the top left cog is turned clockwise will all the cogs turn freely?

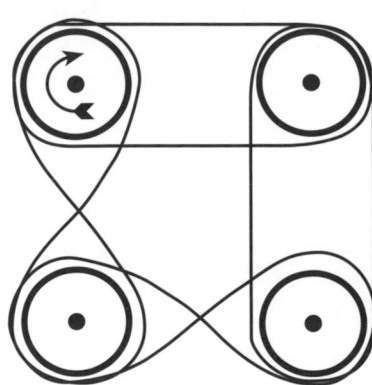

PUZZLE 16

Which number goes in the empty square?

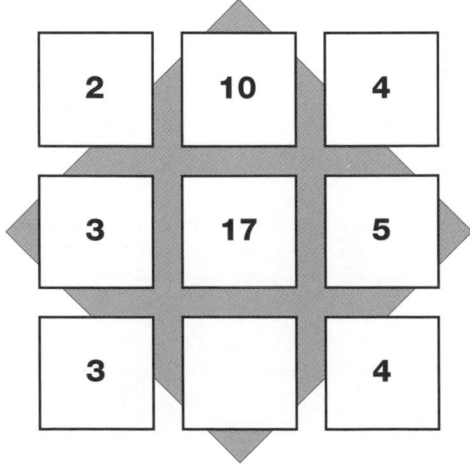

PUZZLE 17

Which number fills the empty segment?

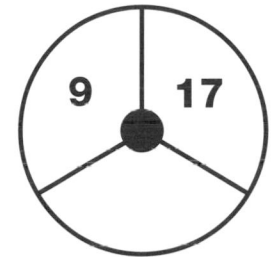

PUZZLE 18

Which of the bottom squares fits logically with the pattern?

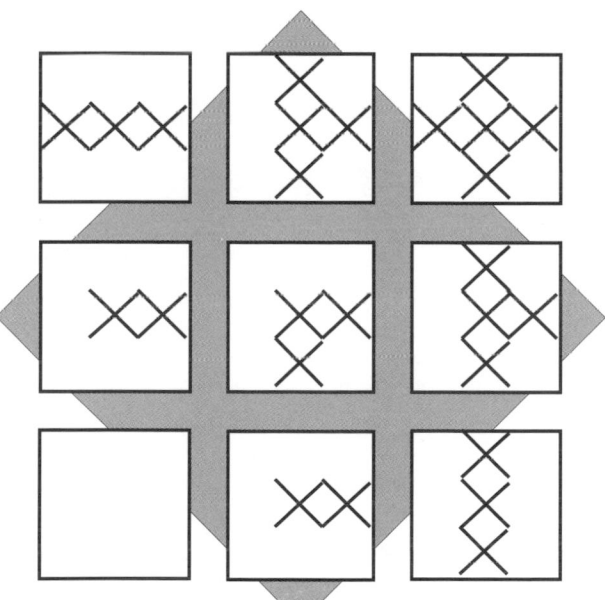

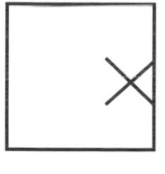

A

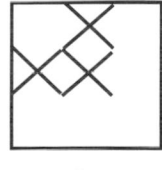

B

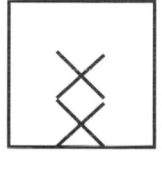

C

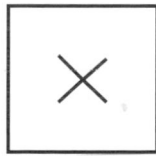

D

E

Which watch fits on the end of this sequence?

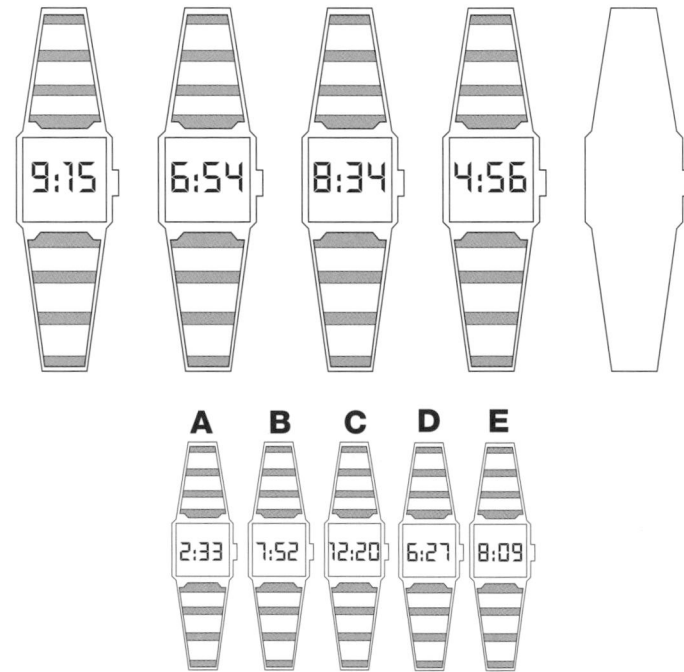

A   **B**   **C**   **D**   **E**

Which number fills the gap in the last circle?

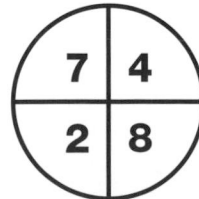 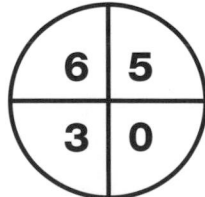

 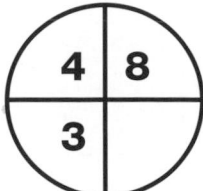

Which number completes this puzzle?

2	8

4	9

3	7

6	9

6	8

3	

LEVEL

5

Which of the bottom shapes fits on the end of the top line?

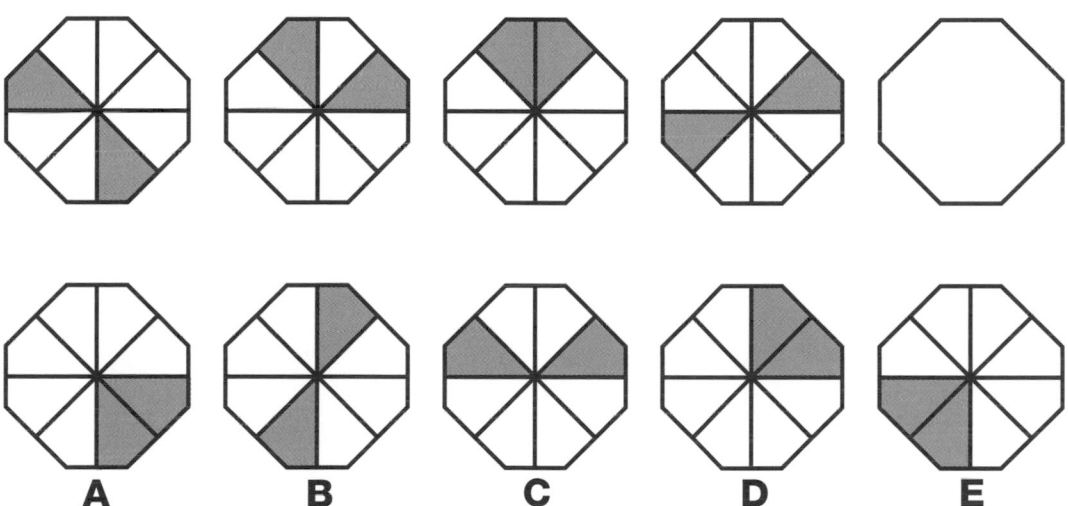

A   **B**   **C**   **D**   **E**

Fill in the empty segment to complete the puzzle.

Which number is missing?

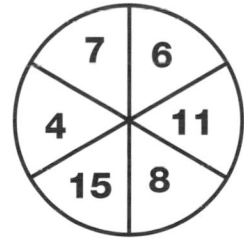

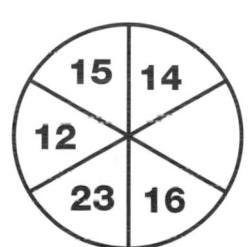

25 PUZZLE

Draw the correct symbols in the empty box.

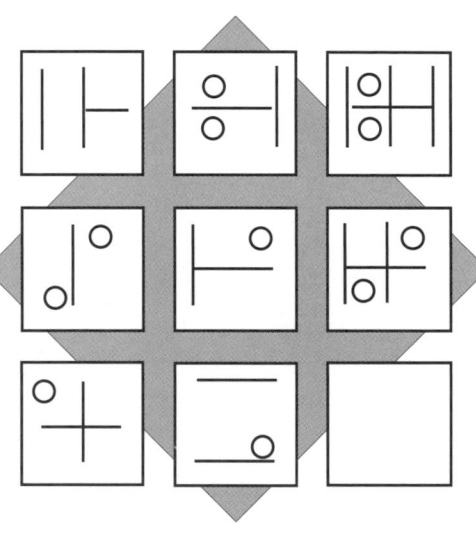

26 PUZZLE

Which number replaces the blank and completes the sequence?

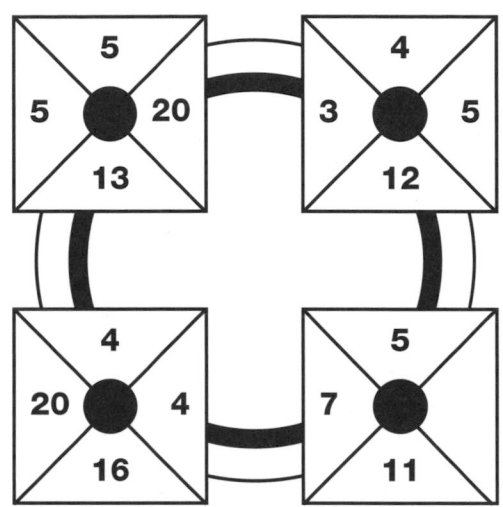

27 PUZZLE

Which number is missing from the empty box?

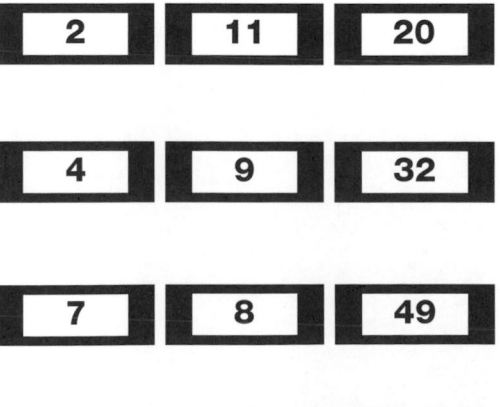

28 PUZZLE

Which letter should be entered into the empty segment?

PUZZLE 29

Which letter replaces the blank and completes the sequence?

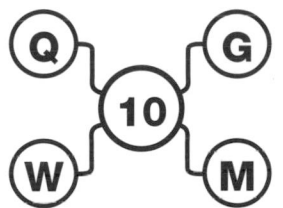  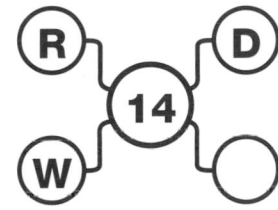

PUZZLE 30

Which number goes in the empty segment?

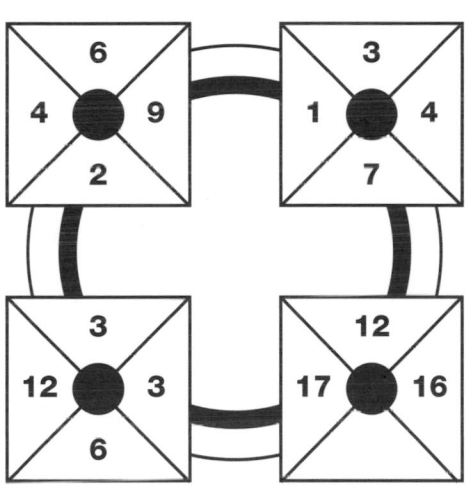

PUZZLE 31

Which number should be written in the empty circle?

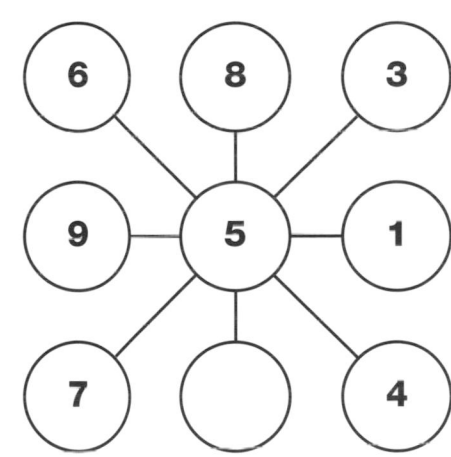

PUZZLE 32

Which number completes the middle star?

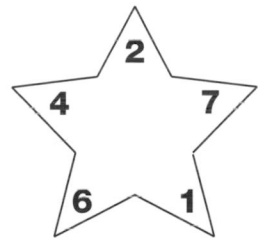  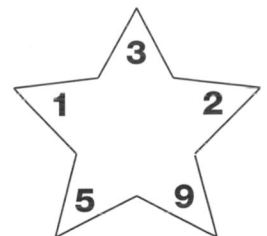

PUZZLE 1

Which number completes this puzzle?

11   2   18

5   2

12   5   14

PUZZLE 2

Fill in the missing letter to complete the chain.

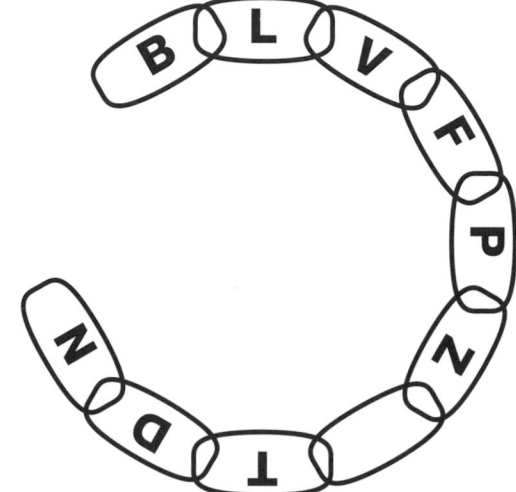

B L V F P Z T D N

PUZZLE 3

Which number is missing?

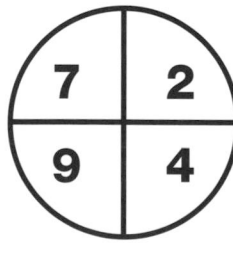
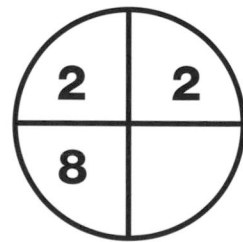

7 | 2
9 | 4

2 | 2
8 |

6 | 1
5 | 11

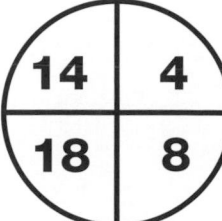
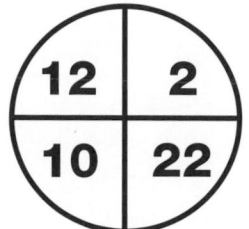

14 | 4
18 | 8

12 | 2
10 | 22

PUZZLE 4

Which number is missing from the empty segment?

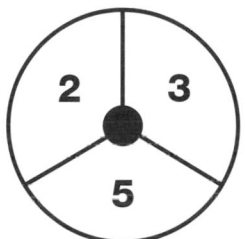

PUZZLE 5

These 12 matches are arranged to give 4 equal areas. Can you rearrange the matches to give 6 equal areas, without adding, removing or breaking any matches?

PUZZLE 6

Which letter should be added to the empty segment?

PUZZLE 7

Which number finishes this grid?

PUZZLE 8

Which number is missing?

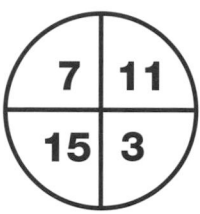
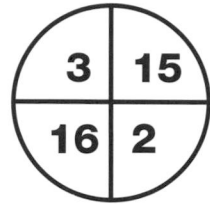
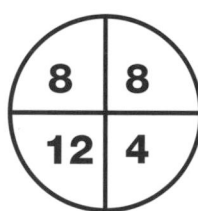
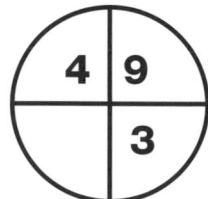

PUZZLE 9

Which number is needed to complete the wheel?

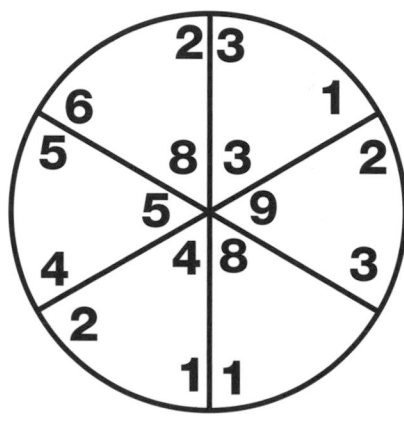

PUZZLE 10

Enter every number between 1 and 8 inclusive in this grid so that no two consecutive numbers are in adjacent squares.

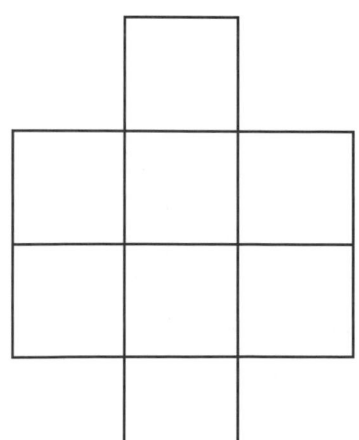

PUZZLE 11

Which letter replaces the blank and completes the sequence?

F	I

J	G

N	Q

R	O

V	Y

Z	

PUZZLE 12

Which letter should be placed in the empty square?

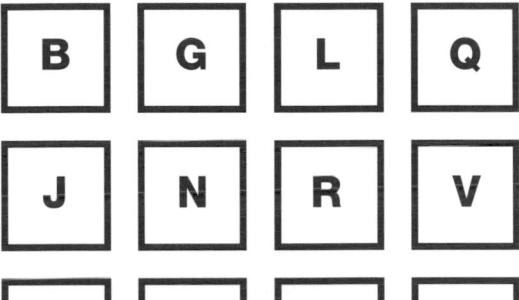

B	G	L	Q
J	N	R	V
K	N	Q	T
R	T	V	

PUZZLE 13

Which number is missing from this wheel?

PUZZLE 14

Enter the correct numbers in the blank segments and complete this puzzle.

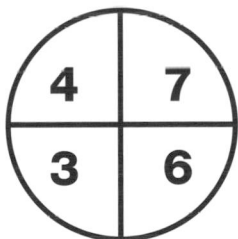

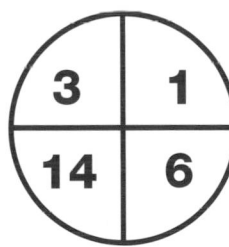

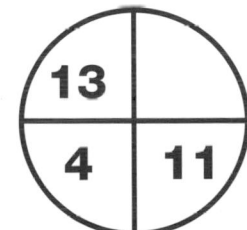

LEVEL

6

PUZZLE 15

Which number is needed to complete the third grid?

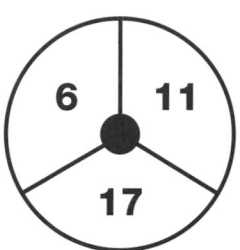  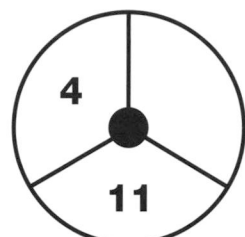

PUZZLE 16

Which number is the odd one out in each shape?

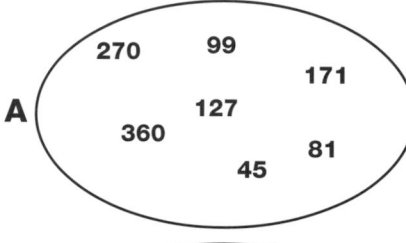

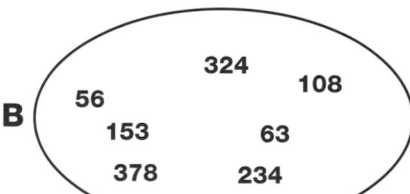

PUZZLE 17

Which number needs to added to the last oval?

PUZZLE 18

Which number is missing from the last triangle?

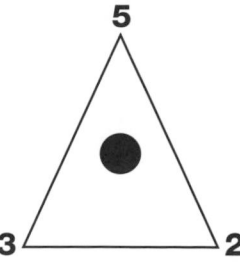 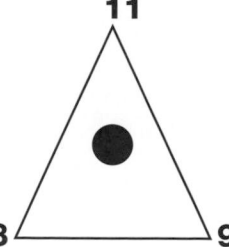 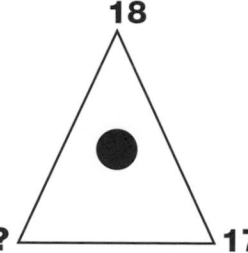

PUZZLE 19

Which letter replaces the blank and completes the sequence?

A	G	L
P	S	U

B	I	O
T	X	A

D	L	S
Y	D	

PUZZLE 20

Which number is missing?

1	3

3	4

4	7

7	11

11	18

18	

PUZZLE 21

Which character is needed to fill the blank segment?

 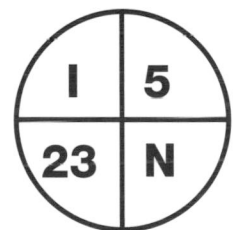 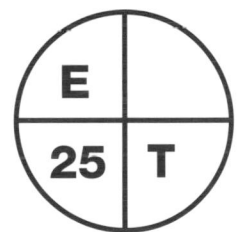

PUZZLE 22

Which number is missing from the last grid?

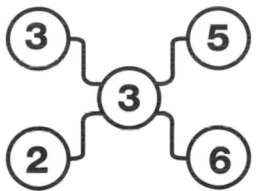 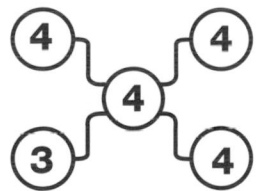 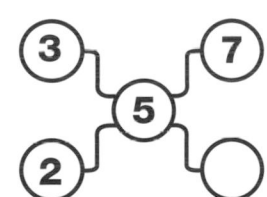

PUZZLE 23

Which number is missing from the final ellipse?

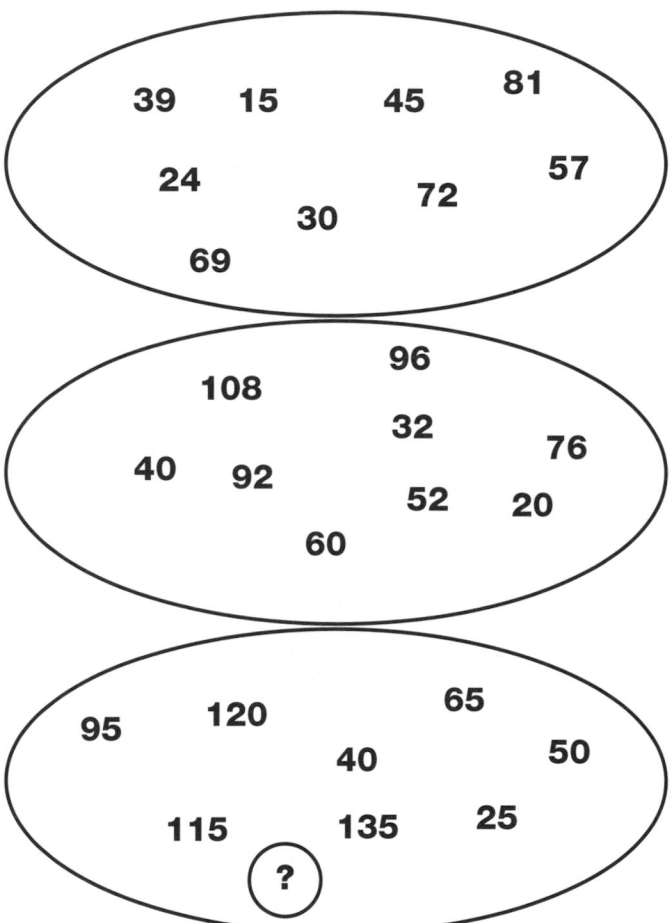

39   15   45   81

24   72   57

30

69

96

108   32

40   92   76

52   20

60

95   120   65

40   50

115   135   25

?

PUZZLE 24

Fill in the missing letter.

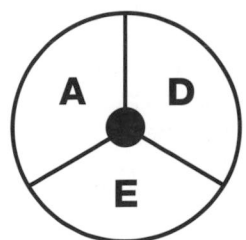

A   D

E

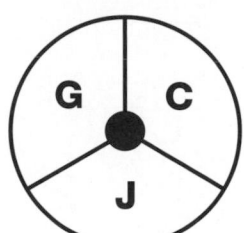

G   C

J

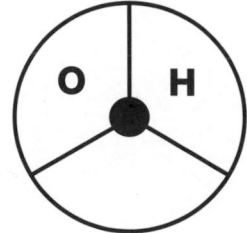

O   H

PUZZLE 25

Which letter is missing from the bottom circle?

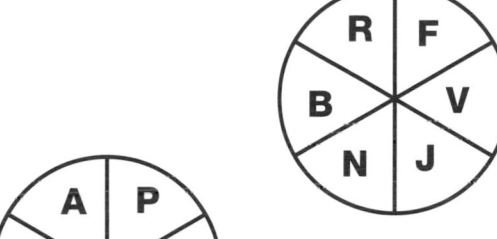

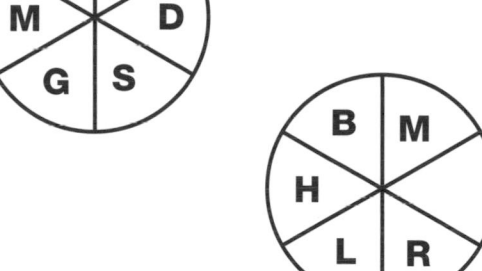

PUZZLE 26

What goes in the empty circle?

PUZZLE 27

Which number is missing from this wheel?

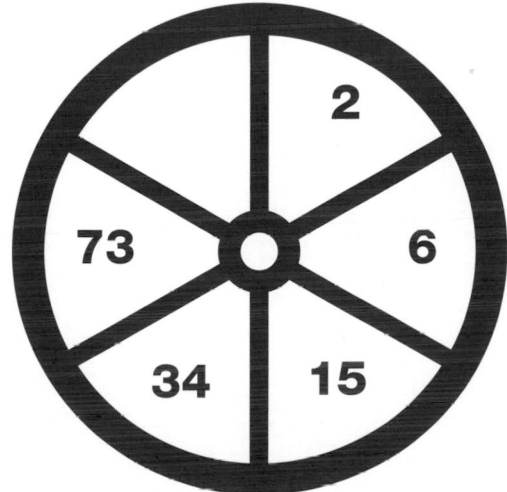

PUZZLE 28

Enter the missing number to complete this grid.

5	21	2
4	20	6
8	55	

L E V E L

6

Which of the bottom grids logically goes in the centre of this puzzle?

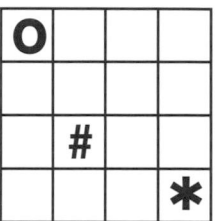

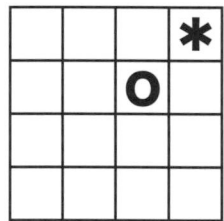

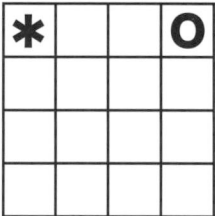
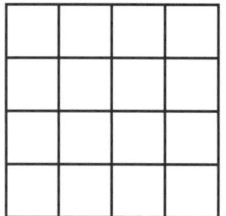
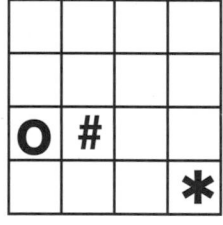

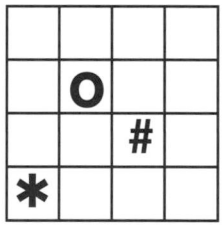
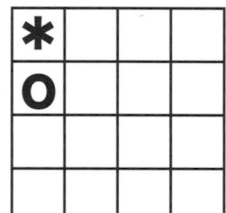

A
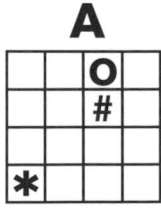

B
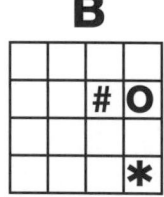

C
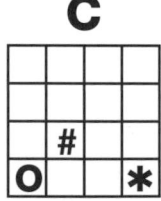

D
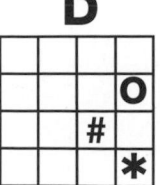

E
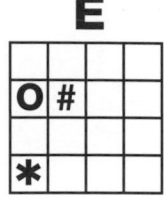

F
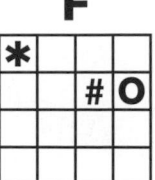

PUZZLE 1

Which number needs to be added to complete the last wheel?

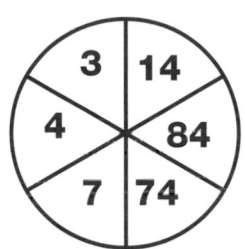

PUZZLE 2

Which number continues this sequence?

| 0 |
| 2 |
| 8 |
| 18 |
| |

PUZZLE 3

Which letter goes in the empty link?

PUZZLE 4

Which number is missing?

2		6	8		4
5	2		6		7
9	14		?		11
8	14		8		6

PUZZLE 5

Which domino will complete the third row?

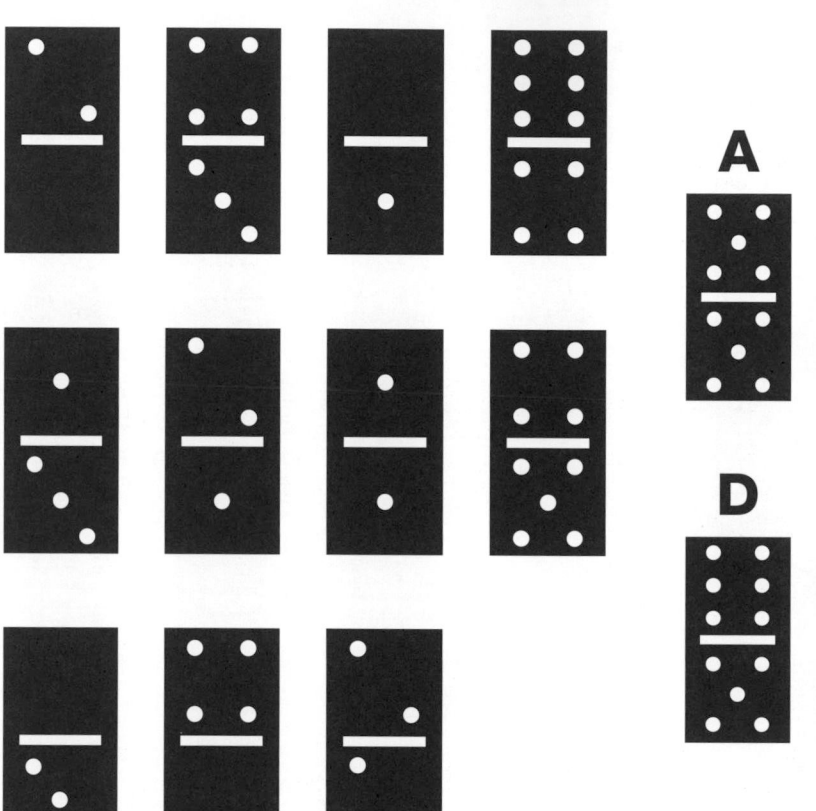

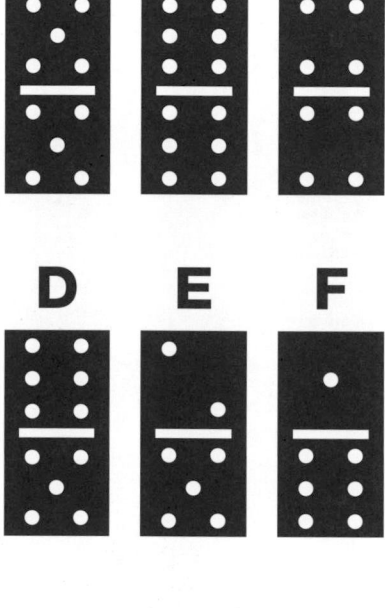

PUZZLE 6

Which letter tops the third triangle?

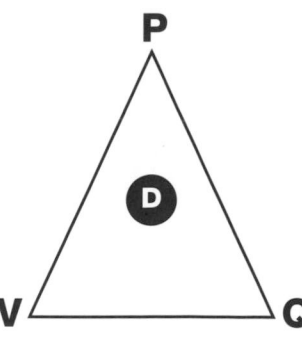

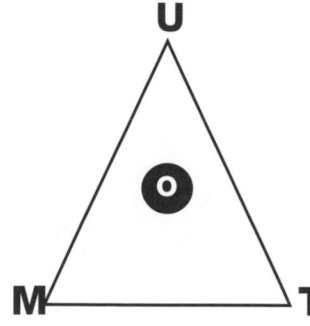

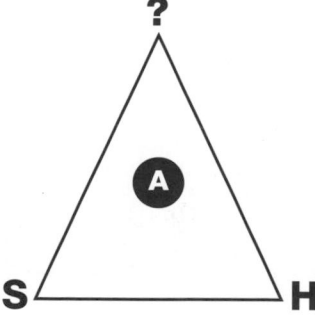

PUZZLE 7

Which number is missing from the grid?

6	2	5
10	3	16
18	6	60
34	15	

PUZZLE 8

Which number goes in the empty circle?

PUZZLE 9

Which number is needed to complete the puzzle?

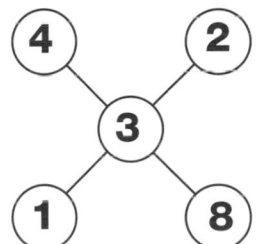 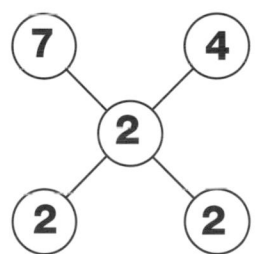 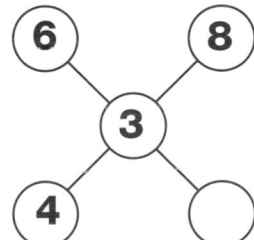

PUZZLE 10

Fill in the blank circle.

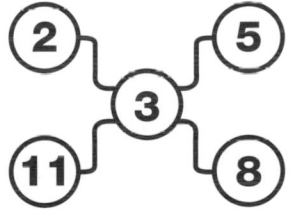  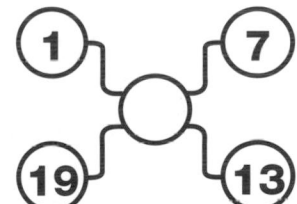

LEVEL

7

67

PUZZLE 11

Which number completes this puzzle?

4	3	2	8
3	7	1	2
8	2	8	2
1	2	5	

PUZZLE 12

Which number is missing?

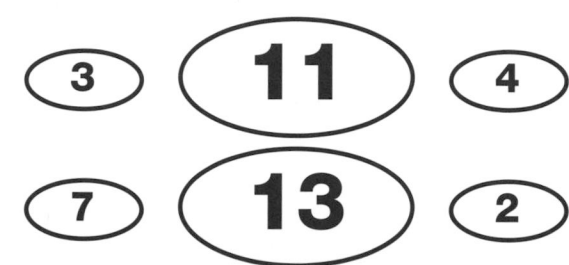

3 **11** 4

7 **13** 2

4 **23**

PUZZLE 13

Which letter is the odd one out in each ellipse?

1 I O X I C R M

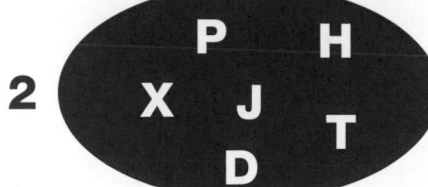

2 P H X J T D

PUZZLE 14

Which number goes in the empty box?

46	85	12

13	48	71

81	54	63

61		53

68

15 PUZZLE

Which playing card is missing from this pattern?

LEVEL

7

69

PUZZLE

Which number needs to go in the blank segment?

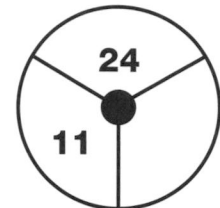

17 PUZZLE

Which number finishes the sequence?

18 PUZZLE

Which letter replaces the blank and completes the puzzle?

19 PUZZLE

Which letter needs to go in the blank circle?

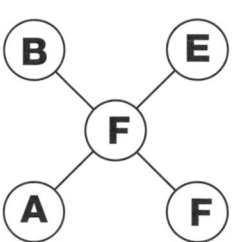
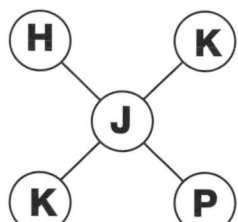
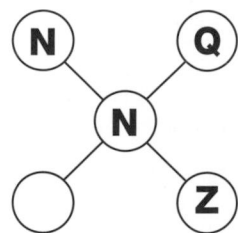

Fill in the empty box with the correct letter.

H	C	N
26	15	20
R	L	

Which number is needed to finish this puzzle?

4
2
9
7
14

Which letter goes in the empty circle?

B   F   H

O   G   V

Y   A   ◯

Which number goes in the empty box
and finishes the grid?

5	2	3
12	6	6

4	2	3
8	8	13

6	5	11
18	6	

LEVEL

7

71

PUZZLE 24

Which number goes in the blank segment?

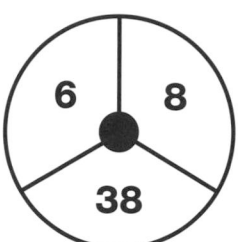 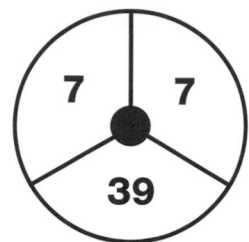 

PUZZLE 25

Which letter completes the sequence?

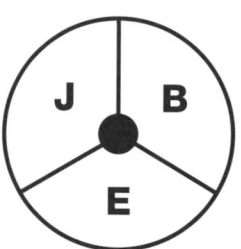 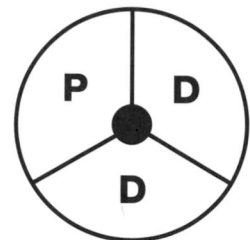 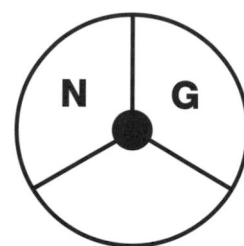

PUZZLE 26

Which number goes in the empty segment?

PUZZLE 27

Which number should be added to the empty circle?

Which letter replaces the blank and completes the sequence?

B	Z	W	U
E	Q	O	R
G	J	L	P
F	H	K	

Can you finish this sequence?

What goes in the empty box?

W	B	4
C	U	9

N	L	5
S	F	1

Z	Q	7
T	I	

Which letter is missing?

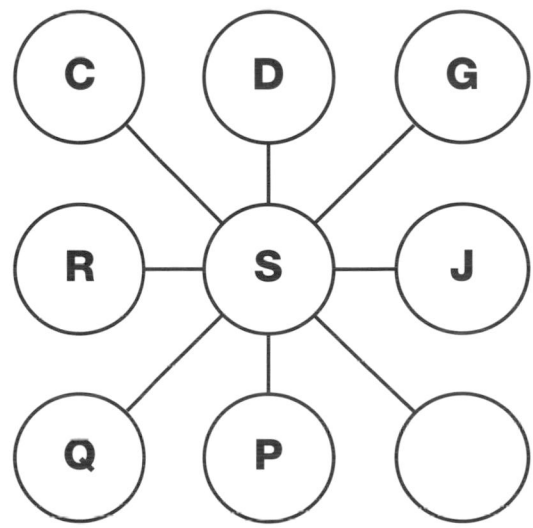

C D G
R S J
Q P

LEVEL 7

73

PUZZLE 1

Which number fits into the empty box?

5	6	8
12	20	36

4	5	7
11	19	35

3	4	6
10	18	

PUZZLE 2

Which letter replaces the blank and completes the sequence?

| M | P | S |

| J | N | R |

| B | G | L |

| D | J | |

PUZZLE 3

Which number would logically complete this grid?

9	3	4	11
5	17	18	3
3	16	21	8
4	9	6	

PUZZLE 4

What goes in the empty circle?

5	4	S
4	2	Z
2	3	

5 PUZZLE

Which piece fits back into the grid?

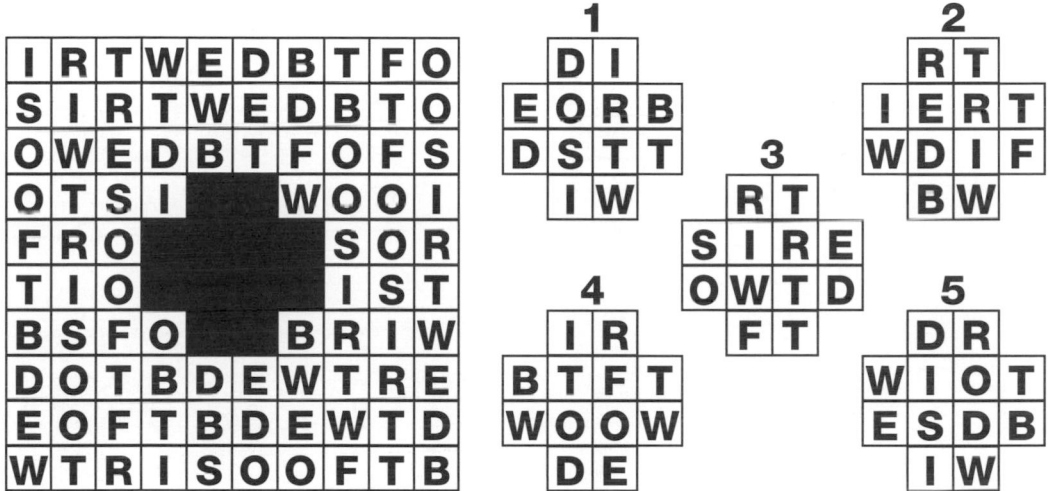

I	R	T	W	E	D	B	T	F	O
S	I	R	T	W	E	D	B	T	O
O	W	E	D	B	T	F	O	F	S
O	T	S	I				W	O	O	I
F	R	O					S	O	R
T	I	O					I	S	T
B	S	F	O				B	R	I	W
D	O	T	B	D	E	W	T	R	E
E	O	F	T	B	D	E	W	T	D
W	T	R	I	S	O	O	F	T	B

1

D	I	
E	O	R	B
D	S	T	T
I	W	

2

	R	T
I	E	R	T
W	D	I	F
	B	W

3

	R	T
S	I	R	E
O	W	T	D
	F	T

4

	I	R
B	T	F	T
W	O	O	W
	D	E

5

	D	R
W	I	O	T
E	S	D	B
	I	W

6 PUZZLE

If two men stand back to back, walk in opposite directions for 4 metres, turn to the left and walk another 3 metres, what is the distance between them when they stop?

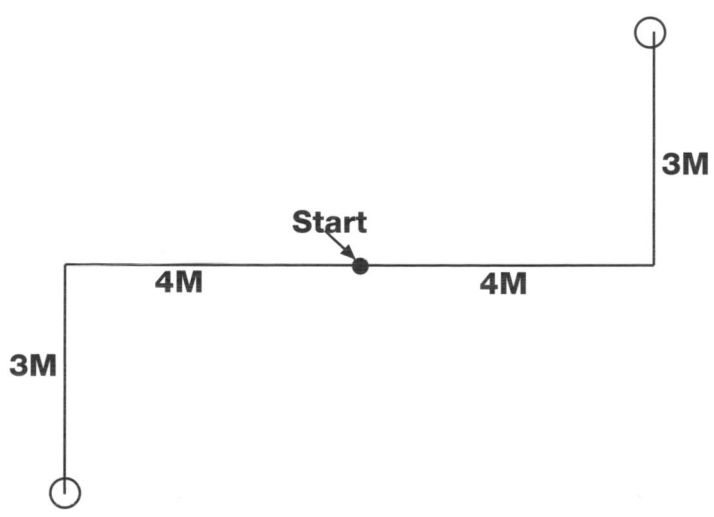

Start

4M   4M

3M

3M

Which of the bottom squares fits logically at the end of this puzzle?

 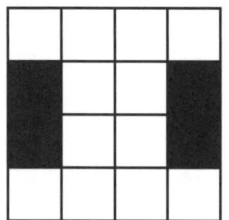 

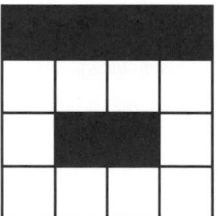  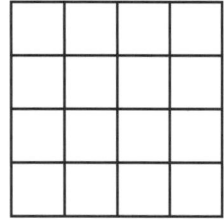

A **B** **C**

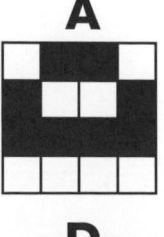 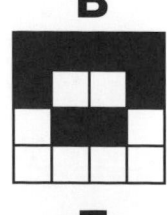 

D **E** **F**

 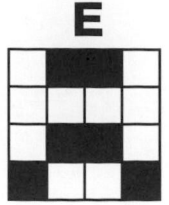 

PUZZLE 8

Which number is missing from this sequence?

1	3

2	4

2	6

3	5

4	12

4	

PUZZLE 9

Which number replaces the question mark and completes the puzzle?

3	11		6	9
5	13	8	11	

7	15	?	13
9	17	12	15

PUZZLE 10

Which two characters go into the empty boxes at the bottom of the table?

3	B

5	C

7	E

11	G

13	K

PUZZLE 11

Joan is extremely fussy about everything, particularly her numbers. She likes 225, but not 224. She prefers 900 to 800, and she absolutely loves 144, but loathes 145.

From this information can you tell if she would like 1600 or 1700?

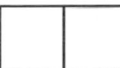

12 PUZZLE

Luke challenged his twin sister Lucy to remove 8 matches to leave 2 squares whose edges do not touch, can you see how she managed it?

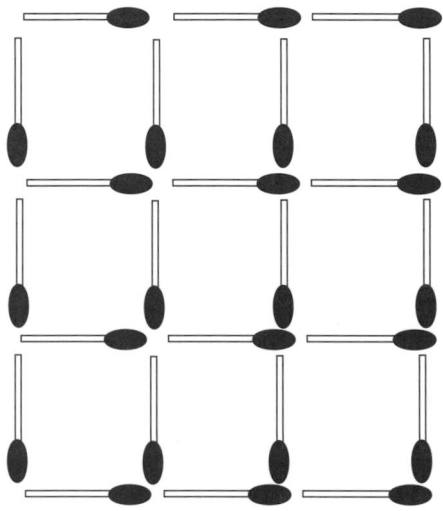

13 PUZZLE

Which number is missing from this puzzle?

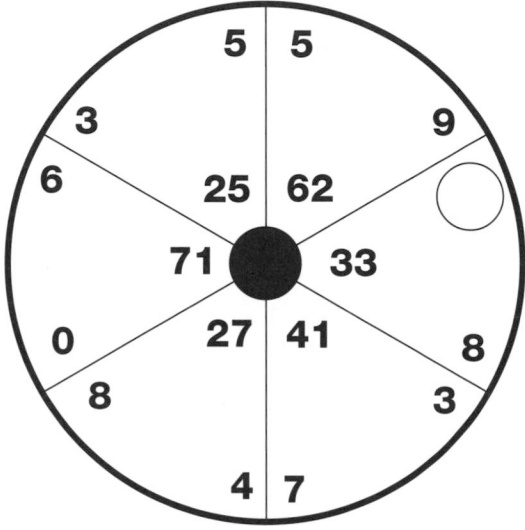

14 PUZZLE

Which number continues the sequence?

15 PUZZLE

Which number replaces the question mark and completes the sequence?

7	12		11	16
15	7		3	3
9	7		?	15
8	17		21	6

78

16 PUZZLE

Simon showed Jason an arrangement of 9 matches which made 4 identical triangles. Jason then showed Simon how to use only 6 matches to produce the same 4 identical triangles. How is this possible?

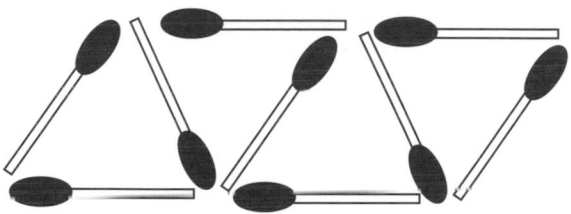

17 PUZZLE

Which number is missing?

18 PUZZLE

Which letter replaces the blank and completes the sequence?

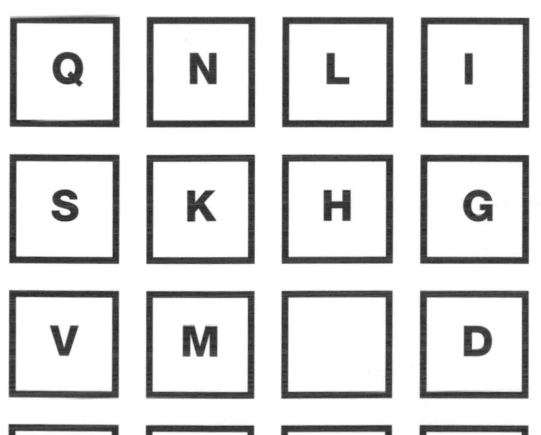

19 PUZZLE

Complete this puzzle by drawing what you think should appear in the empty box.

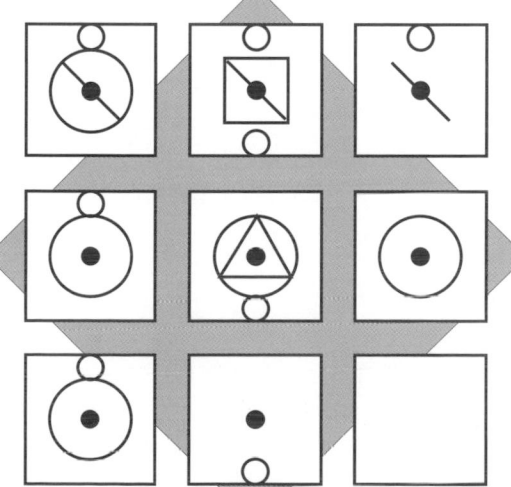

PUZZLE 20

Which number is missing from the middle of the last triangle?

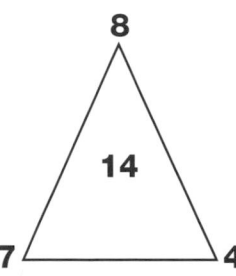
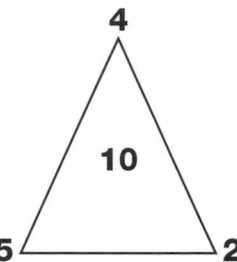
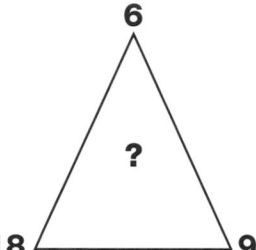

PUZZLE 21

Which number replaces the blank and completes the sequence?

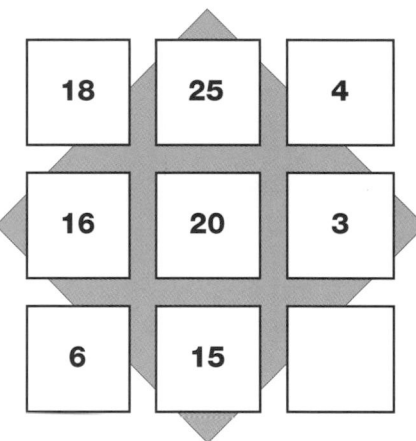

PUZZLE 22

Which number is missing from the empty circle?

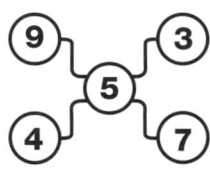
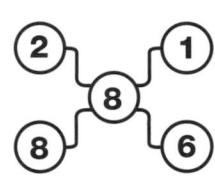

PUZZLE 23

Which number follows next?

Which box is the odd one out?

A

B

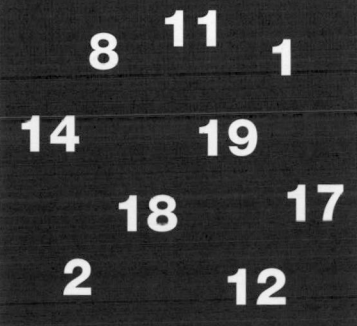

C

D

Which letter is missing?

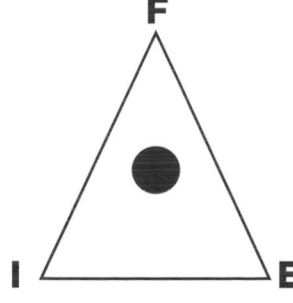

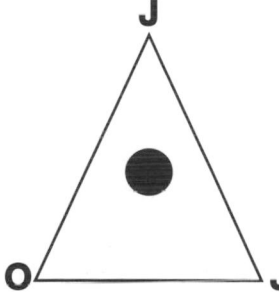

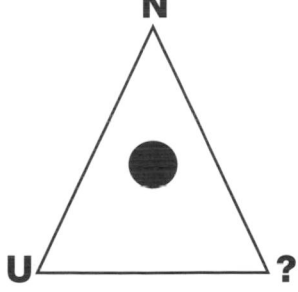

26 PUZZLE

Which letter goes in the empty segment to complete the sequence?

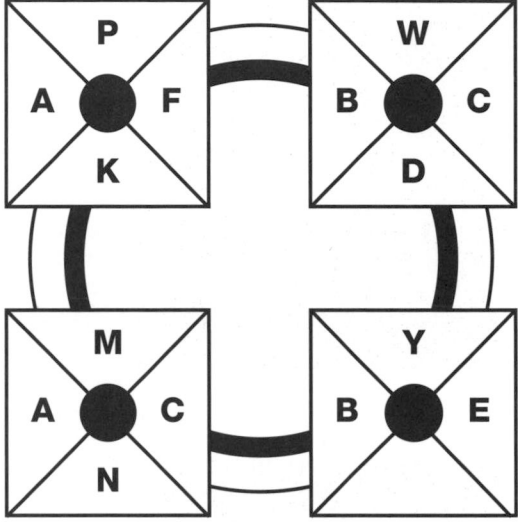

27 PUZZLE

Which number should go in the empty box?

4	7

2	2

6	9

8	12

3	1

7	

28 PUZZLE

Which letter goes in the empty circle?

29 PUZZLE

Melinda and her father love puzzles. When Melinda's cousin asked her how old she was she told her:

"If I doubled my age and subtracted 1, it would be the same as my father's age – and if you reverse the digits of his age, you get my age."

Can you work out their ages?

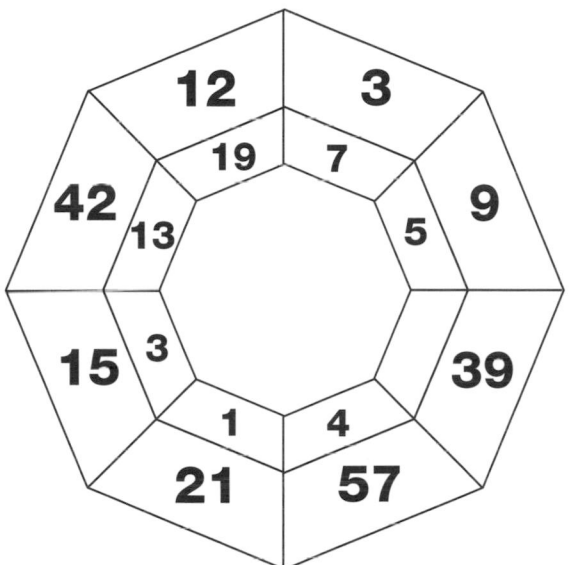

30 PUZZLE

Which number goes in the empty segment?

12 3
19 7
42 9
13 5
15 3 39
1 4
21 57

31 PUZZLE

Which number goes in the empty box?

| 4 | 2 | 6 |

| 7 | 3 | 4 |

| 9 | 3 | 12 |

| 6 | 1 | |

32 PUZZLE

Which letter is missing from the bottom triangle?

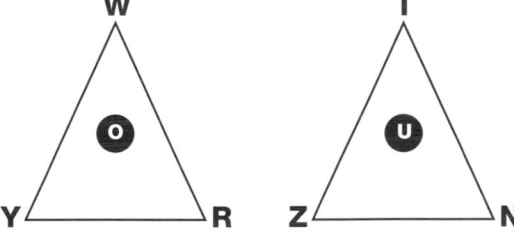

W
O
Y   R

T
U
Z   N

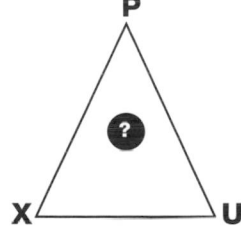

P
?
X   U

33 PUZZLE

Which number is missing from the last row?

7   8   17

3   11   16

5   13

Which number is missing from the centre of the last star?

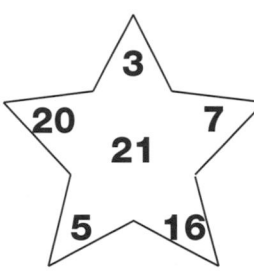

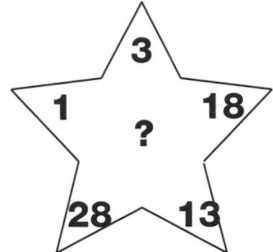

Which number comes next in this sequence?

9 - 7 - 8 - 6 - 7 - 5 - 6 - ?

Which letter is missing from the blank segment?

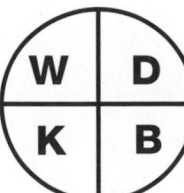

PUZZLE 4

Which number completes this puzzle?

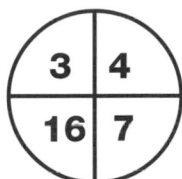
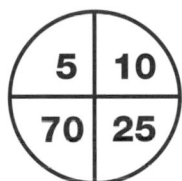

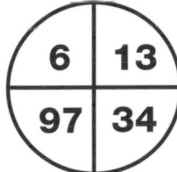
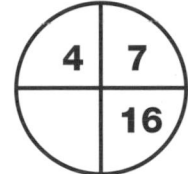

PUZZLE 5

Which number is missing from the last wheel?

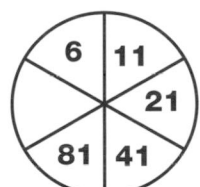

PUZZLE 6

Fill in the blank point of the third star.

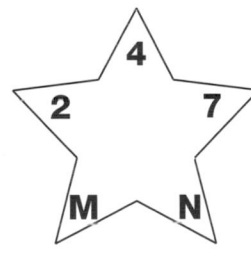
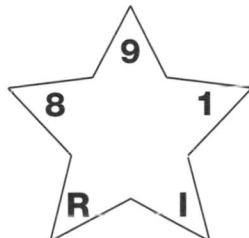
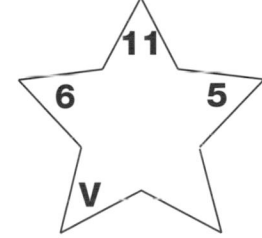

PUZZLE 7

Which number is missing from the last triangle?

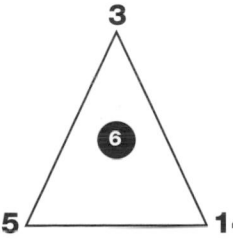
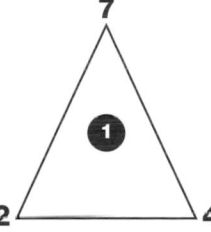
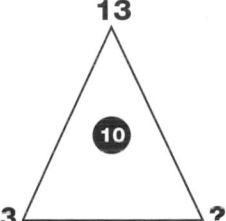

PUZZLE 8

Which number goes in the middle of the grid?

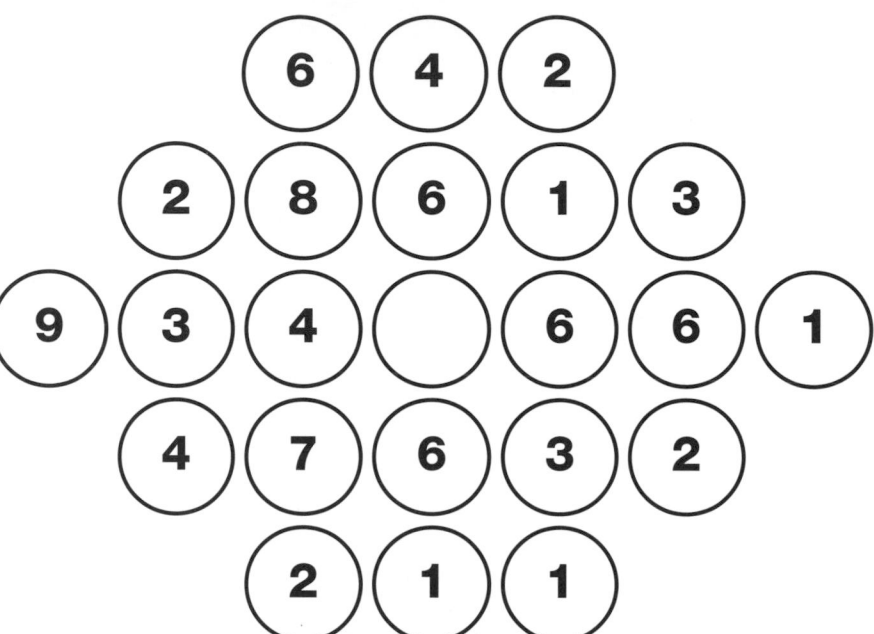

PUZZLE 9

Which number is missing?

10 PUZZLE

Which letter replaces the blank and completes the sequence?

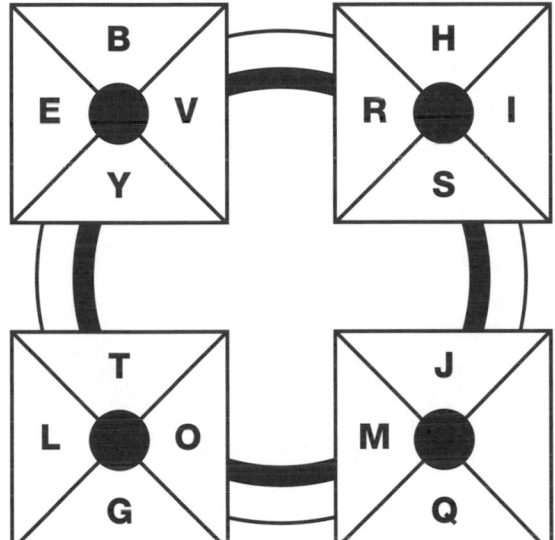

11 PUZZLE

Which number logically completes the grid?

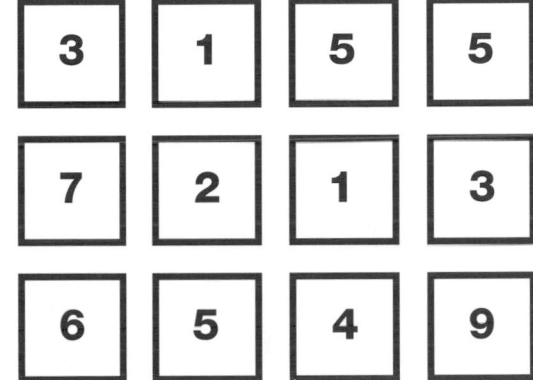

12 PUZZLE

Which letter is missing from around the centre of the wheel?

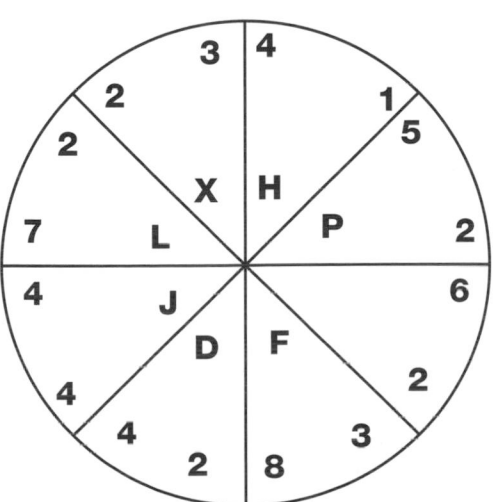

13 PUZZLE

Which letter goes in the empty box?

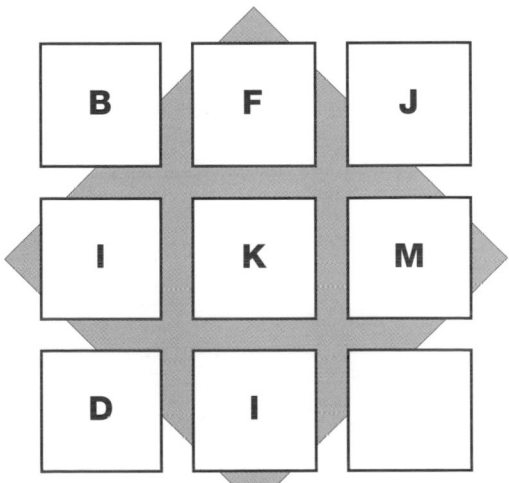

LEVEL

9

87

PUZZLE 14

Which letter goes in the centre?

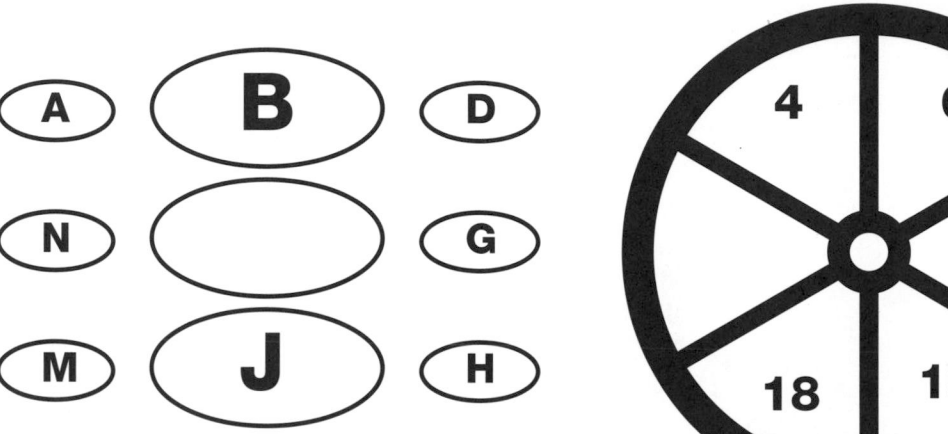

A　**B**　D

N　　　G

M　**J**　H

PUZZLE 15

Which number is missing from the wheel?

4　6

9

18　13

PUZZLE 16

Which of the bottom boxes completes the sequence?

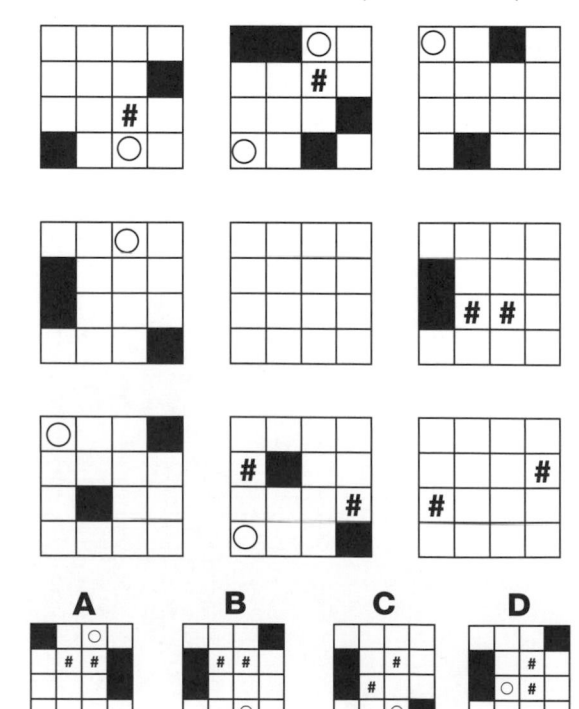

A　B　C　D

Which playing cards complete the sequence?

9

89

18 PUZZLE

Which of the bottom boxes completes this sequence?

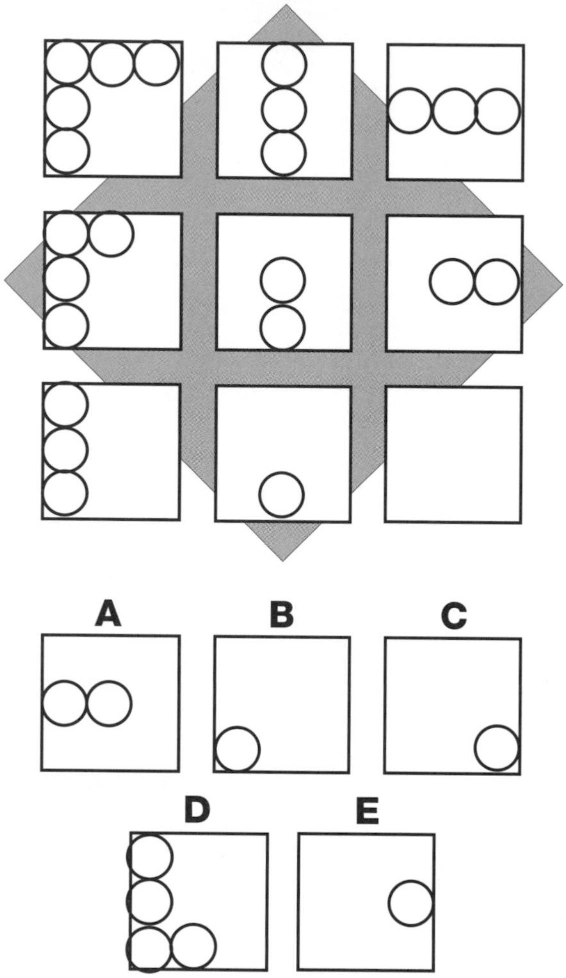

A   **B**   **C**

D   **E**

19 PUZZLE

Which number is missing?

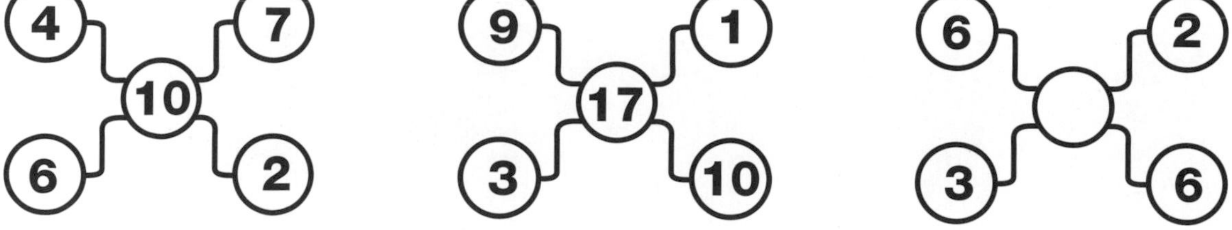

4 — 7
10
6 — 2

9 — 1
17
3 — 10

6 — 2
3 — 6

PUZZLE 20

Which letter replaces the blank and completes the puzzle?

A C F

J L O

S U ( )

PUZZLE 21

Find the missing value.

24	63	24	21	
@	@	@	!	33
!	Σ	!	Ω	?
Ω	Σ	Ω	Ω	33
!	!	!	@	27

PUZZLE 22

Using these six matches, make three squares all the same size.

PUZZLE 23

Which number is missing from the empty segment?

4   6   34   18   10

24 PUZZLE

Which number is missing?

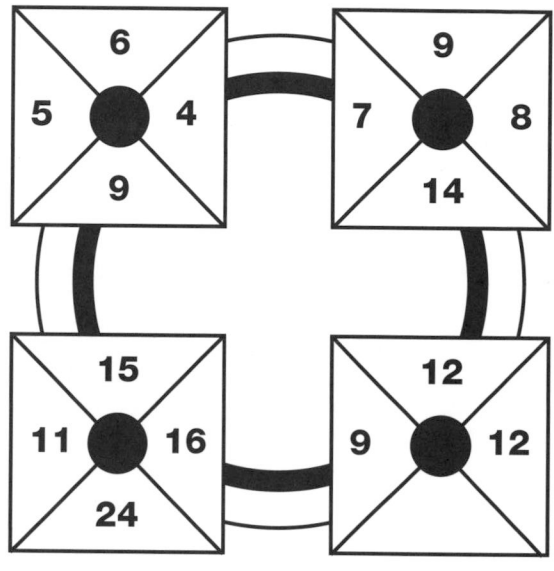

	6	
5	●	4
	9	

	9	
7	●	8
	14	

	15	
11	●	16
	24	

	12	
9	●	12

25 PUZZLE

Becky had a large packet of biscuits. After eating the first one she gave half of what she had left to her friend Ella. After eating another one, she gave half of what was left to Chelsea, leaving her with just 5 biscuits.

How many biscuits were in the packet to start with?

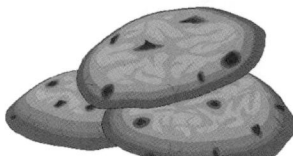

26 PUZZLE

Which letter is missing from the last star?

B Z H T N   G I N B U   J P R H

27 PUZZLE

Which letter replaces the question mark?

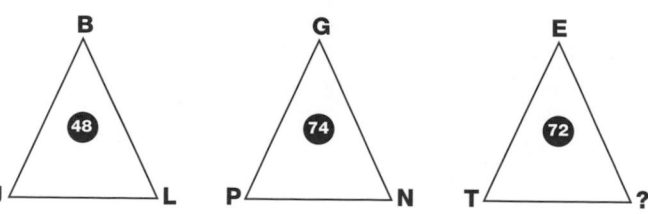

B 48 J L   G 74 P N   E 72 T ?

LEVEL 9

PUZZLE 1

Which letter goes in the empty circle?

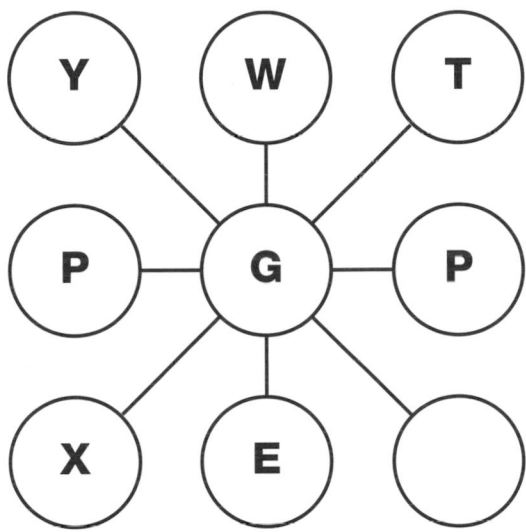

PUZZLE 2

Which letter goes in the empty box at the bottom of the pile?

A	C
D	G
G	K
J	O
M	S
P	

PUZZLE 3

Which number is missing from the empty segment?

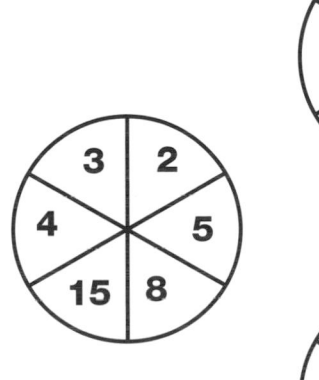

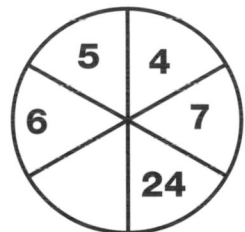

PUZZLE 4

Which number comes next to continue this sequence?

11

36

71

116

171

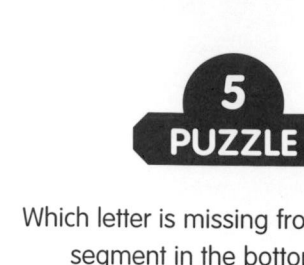

PUZZLE 5

Which letter is missing from the empty segment in the bottom circle?

PUZZLE 6

Which number replaces the question mark?

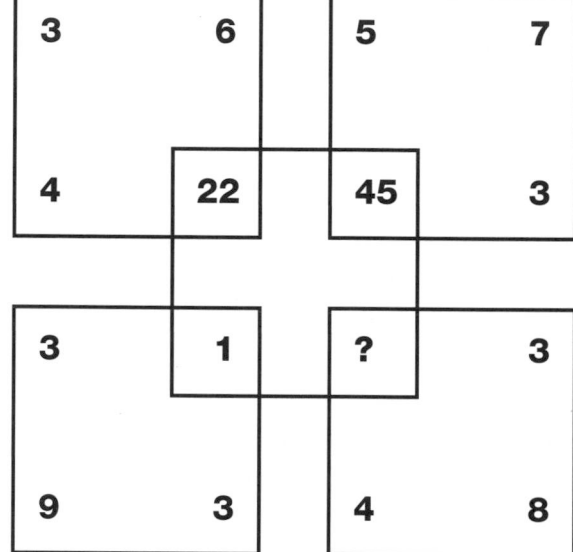

PUZZLE 7

Which number goes in the blank box and completes the puzzle?

| 7 | 3 | 5 |

| 12 | 8 | 10 |

| 11 | 7 | 9 |

| 16 | 12 | |

PUZZLE 8

Which letter goes in the empty segment?

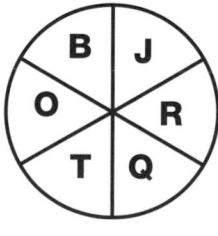

PUZZLE 9

Which letter finishes the third circle?

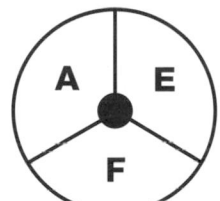 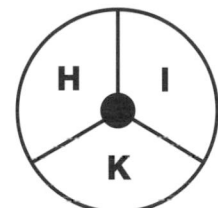 

PUZZLE 10

Which number is missing from the last grid?

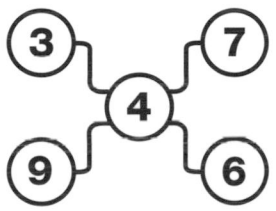  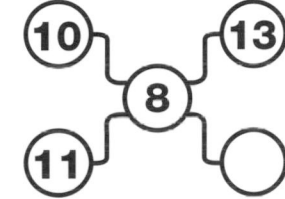

PUZZLE 11

Which number replaces the question mark?

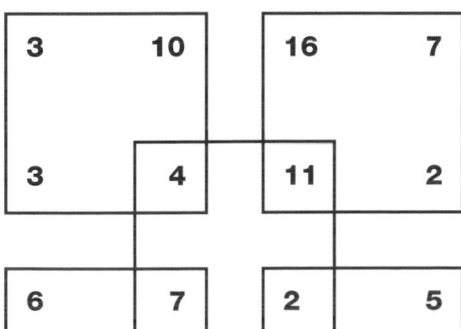

PUZZLE 12

Complete this puzzle.

Which of the bottom boxes completes this sequence?

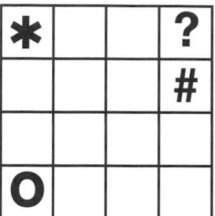
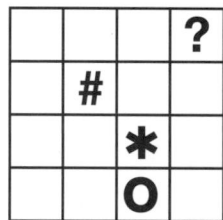
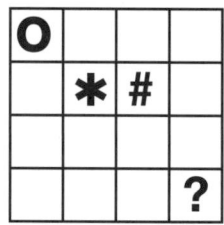

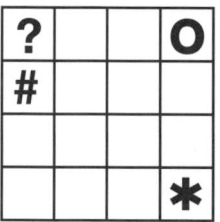
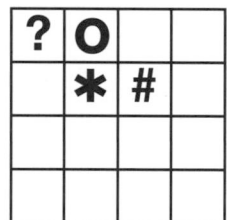
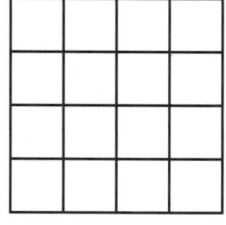

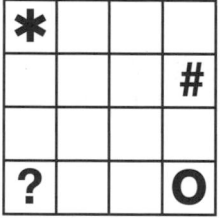

A

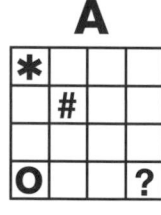

B

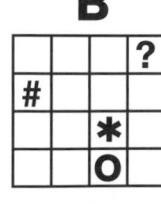

C

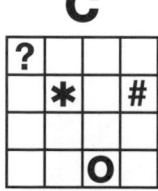

D

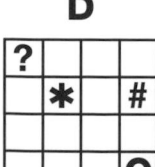

E

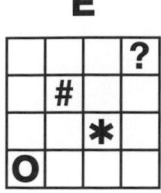

F

LEVEL

10

PUZZLE 14

Which letter finishes the third circle?

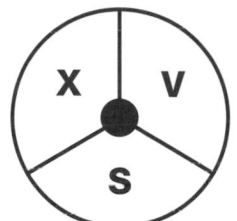

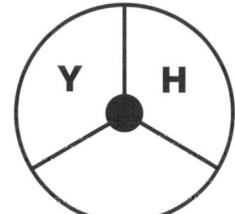

PUZZLE 15

Which number completes the last grid?

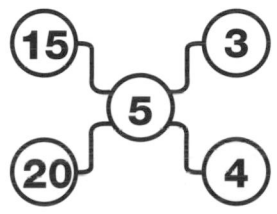
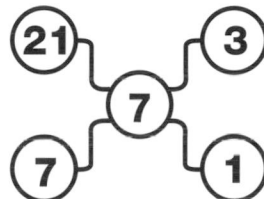

PUZZLE 16

Which number goes in the empty box?

3	11	7
4	14	6
9	7	2
10	62	

PUZZLE 17

Which letter completes this puzzle?

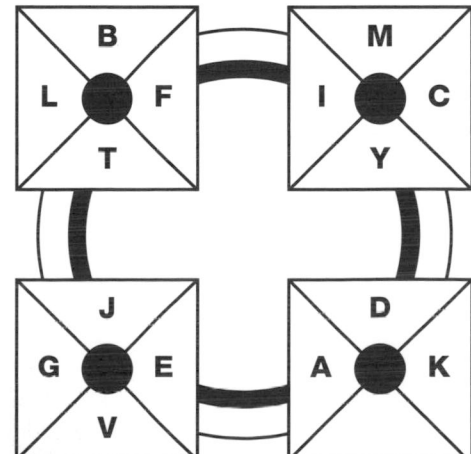

PUZZLE 18

Which letter goes in the empty box?

C	L
H	Q
F	O
K	T
I	R
N	

PUZZLE 19

Which letter completes the wheel?

PUZZLE 20

John arranges 4 matches to make an upside down glass and puts a small coin to one side. He promises to buy Gary a drink if he can put the coin inside the glass just by moving two matches and nothing else.

Can you see how he did it?

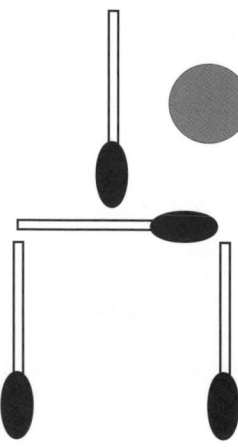

PUZZLE 21

Which number comes next in this sequence?

7
13
24
45

PUZZLE 22

Which number is missing from the last grid?

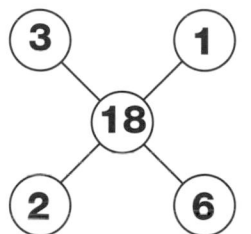 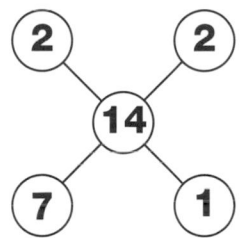 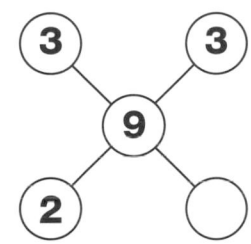

PUZZLE 23

Which number is missing?

  ( )

(36) (38) (39)

PUZZLE 24

Fill in the empty ellipse.

(8) (7) (6)

(11) (11) ( )

PUZZLE 25

What shape will replace the question mark?

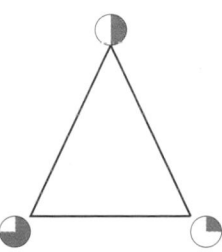 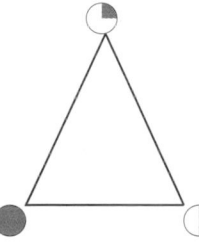 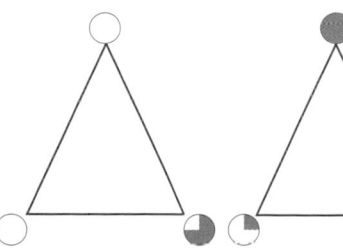 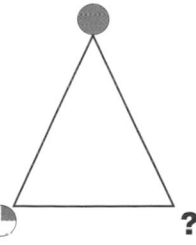 ?

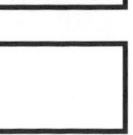

100

Which letter goes in the empty link and completes the chain?

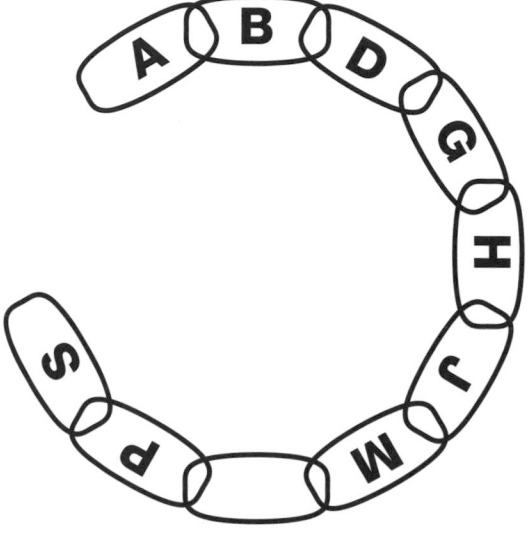

Which number is missing from the middle of the last grid?

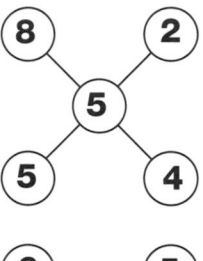
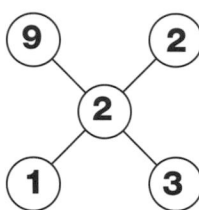
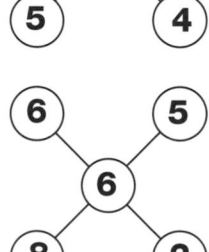
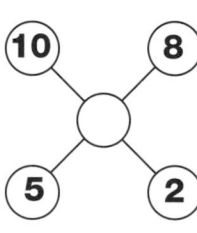

Which number continues the sequence?

8

10

16

34

Draw the correct markings in the last box.

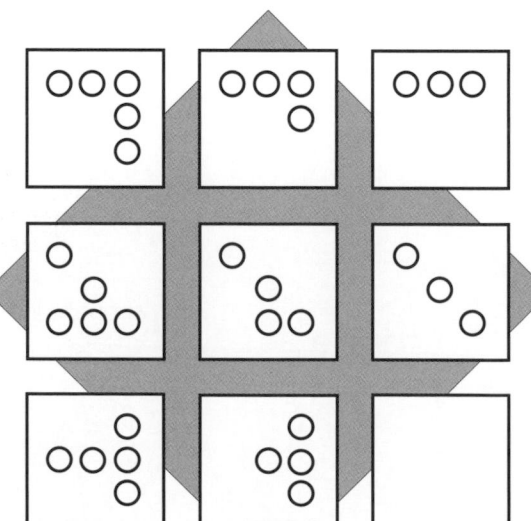

Which shape is the odd one out and why?

PUZZLE 1

Which number goes in the middle of the third triangle?

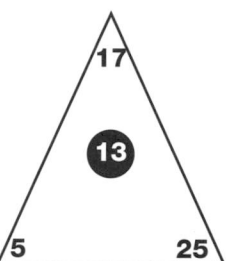 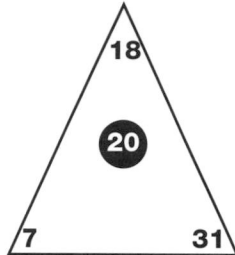 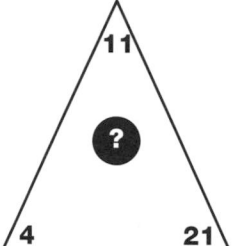

PUZZLE 2

Move one match and make this sum correct.

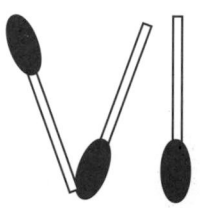 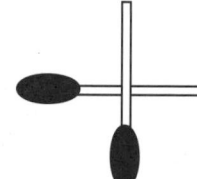 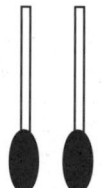 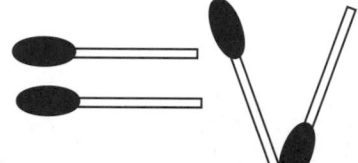

PUZZLE 3

Which number goes in the empty box and completes the puzzle?

3	6	3
10	3	7
8	1	

PUZZLE 4

Which number is missing from the bottom grid?

9	4	6
0	4	3

7	1	3
0	3	1

5	0	4
0	2	

PUZZLE 5

Which number completes the grid?

2	**5**	1
3	**13**	2
2	**20**	

PUZZLE 6

Move just four matches to make seven squares.

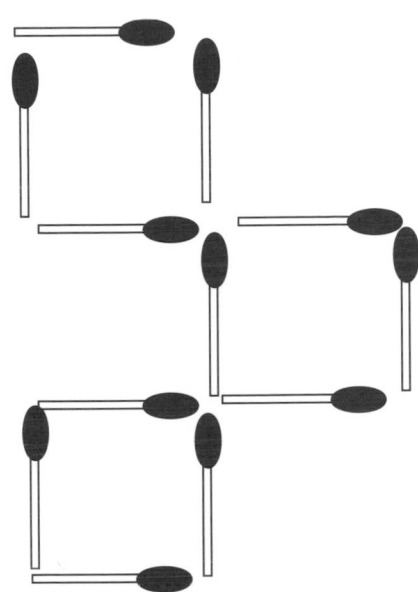

PUZZLE 7

Which number replaces the question mark?

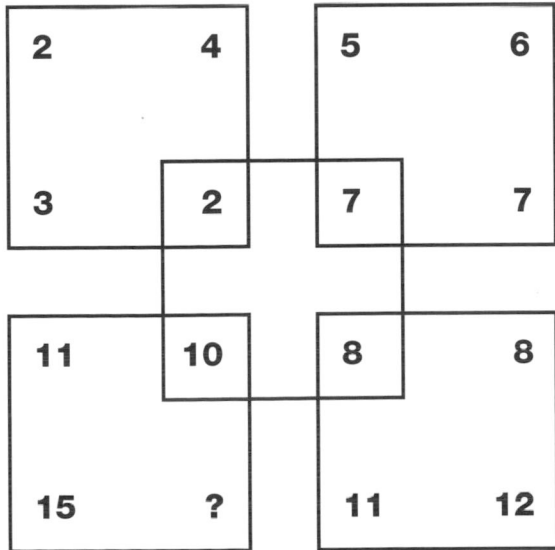

2		4
3	2	7	7
11	10	8	8
15	?	11	12

PUZZLE 8

Which letter goes in the bottom box?

 J

 O

 S

 V

L E V E L

11

103

PUZZLE 9

What is missing from the empty box?

1	0
J	Q
1	8
R	I
2	4
X	

PUZZLE 10

Which number continues the sequence?

| 1 |
| 5 |
| 13 |
| 29 |
| |

PUZZLE 11

What time should the blank watch be showing?

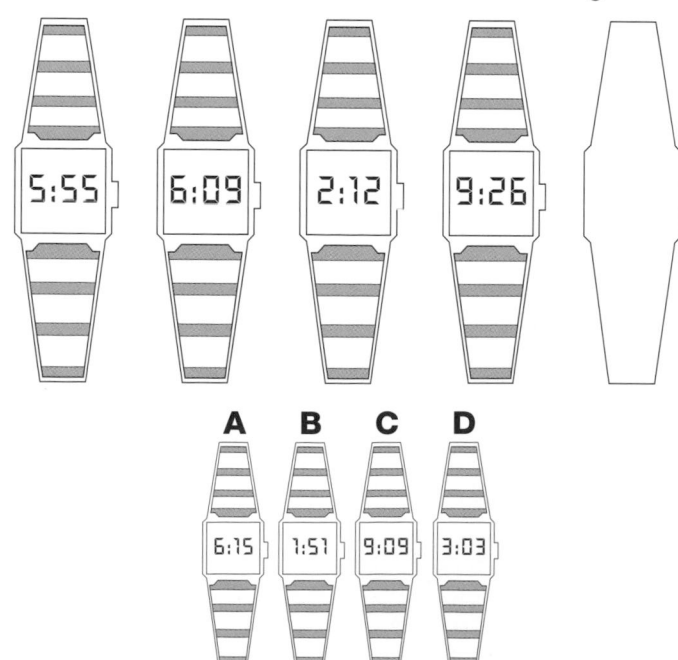

5:55   6:09   2:12   9:26

A   B   C   D

6:15   1:51   9:09   3:03

PUZZLE 12

Which letter should go in the empty circle?

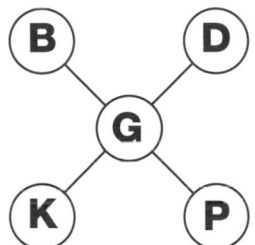
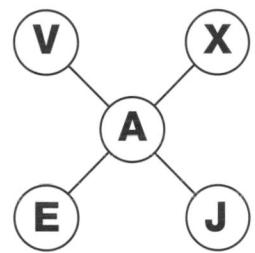
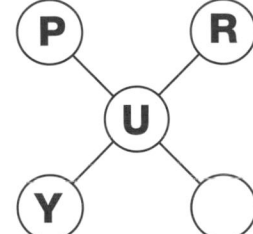

PUZZLE 13

Which number should replace the question mark?

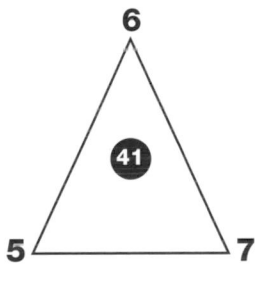
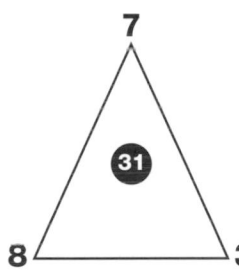
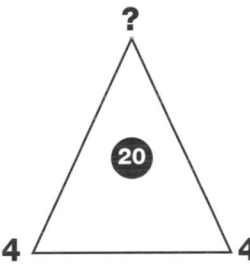

PUZZLE 14

Which of these numbered pieces will fit in the centre of the grid?

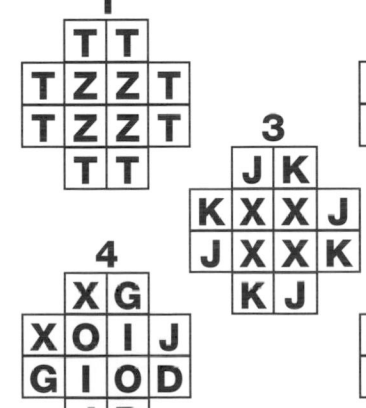
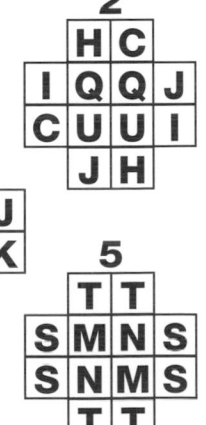

LEVEL

11

Which of the bottom boxes finishes this puzzle?

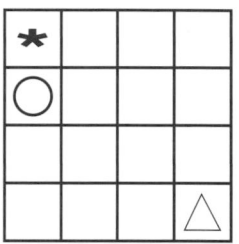 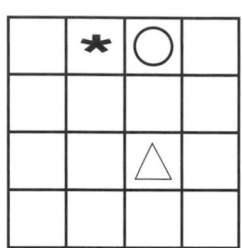 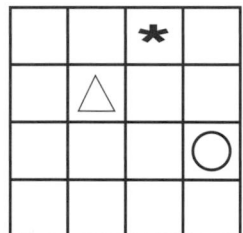 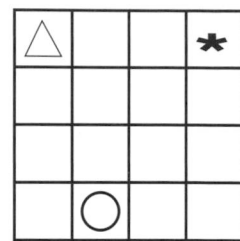

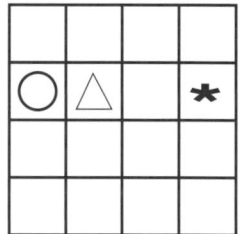 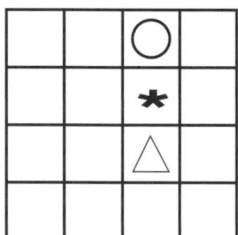 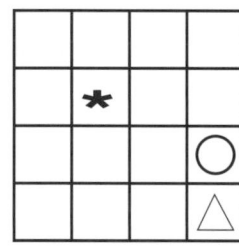 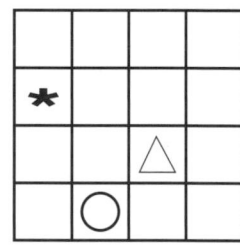

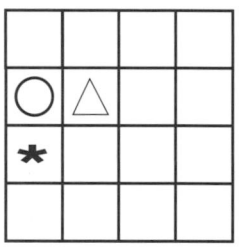 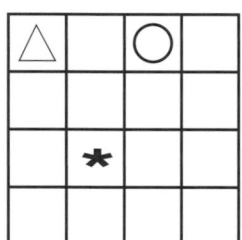 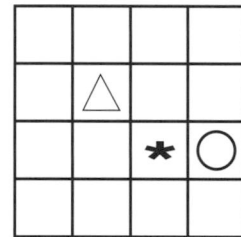 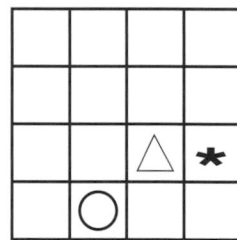

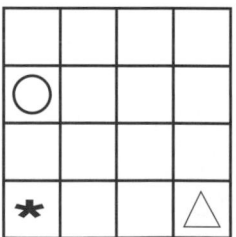 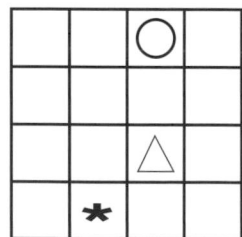 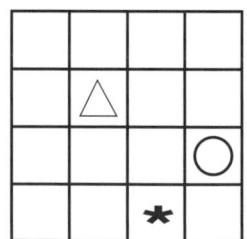 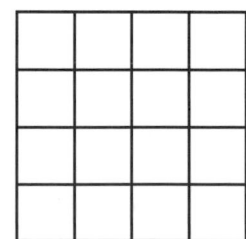

A **B** **C** **D**

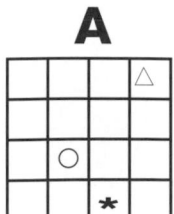 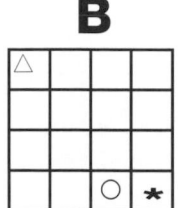 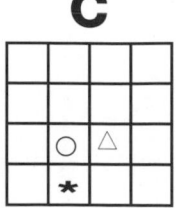 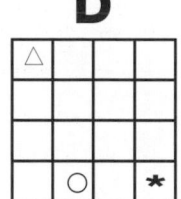

L E V E L

11

PUZZLE 16

What time should be showing next?

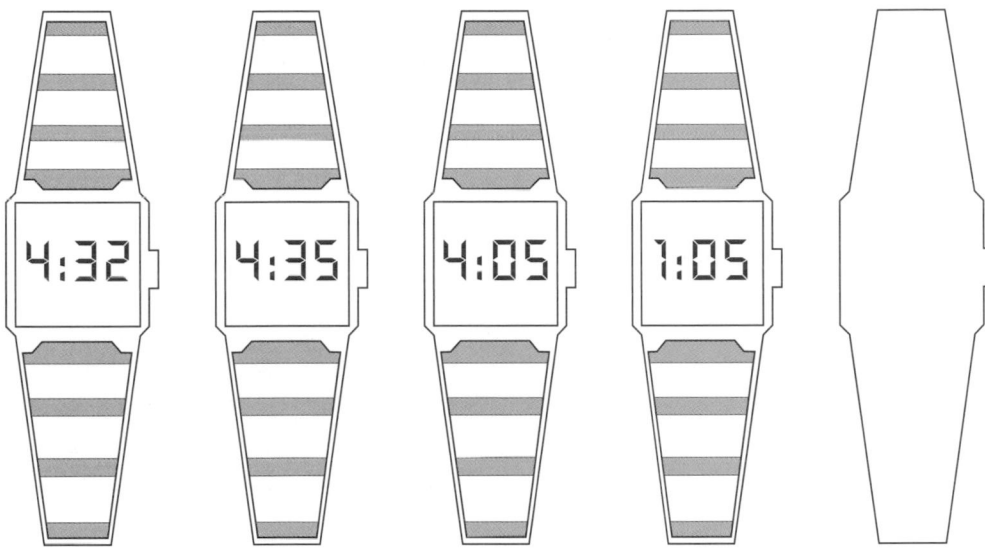

PUZZLE 17

Which letter goes in the empty corner?

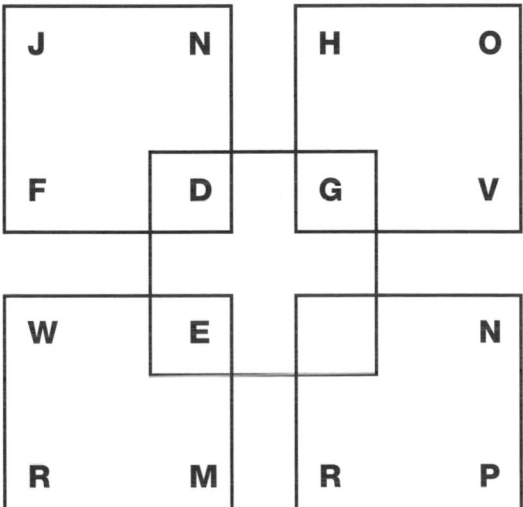

J	N		H	O
F	D	G		V
W	E			N
R	M		R	P

PUZZLE 18

Each number from 1-25 inclusive is to be put in the grid so that each row, column and corner to corner line adds up to 65.

21				1
	8			
		13		
				16
25			2	

Which of the bottom playing cards completes the top line?

     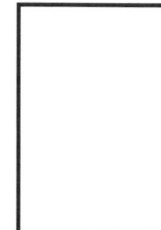

LEVEL

11

108

Which number is missing from the empty segment in the web?

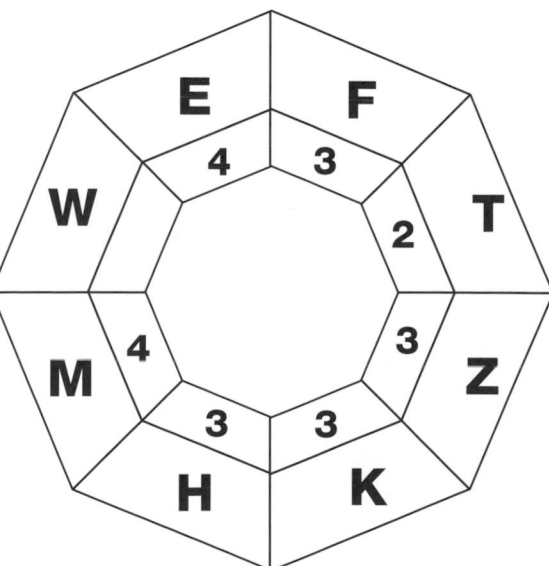

Which number is needed to complete the puzzle?

3

3

6

9

15

PUZZLE 22

Which playing card completes the puzzle?

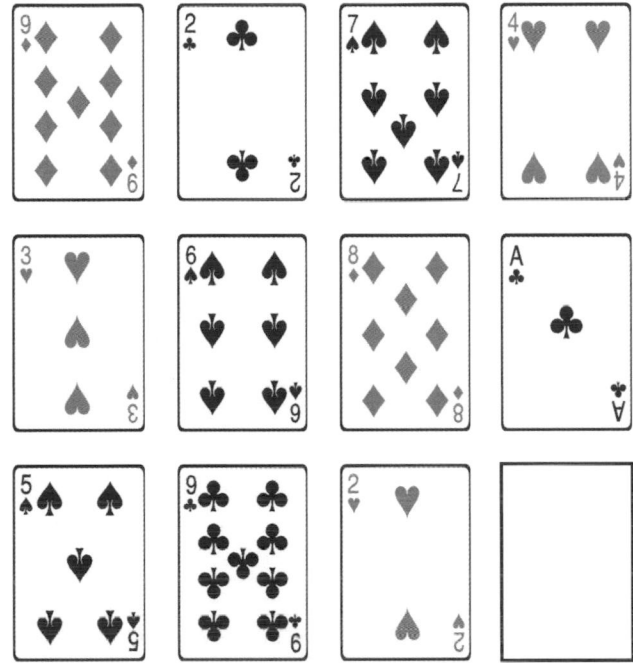

PUZZLE 23

Fill in the empty box.

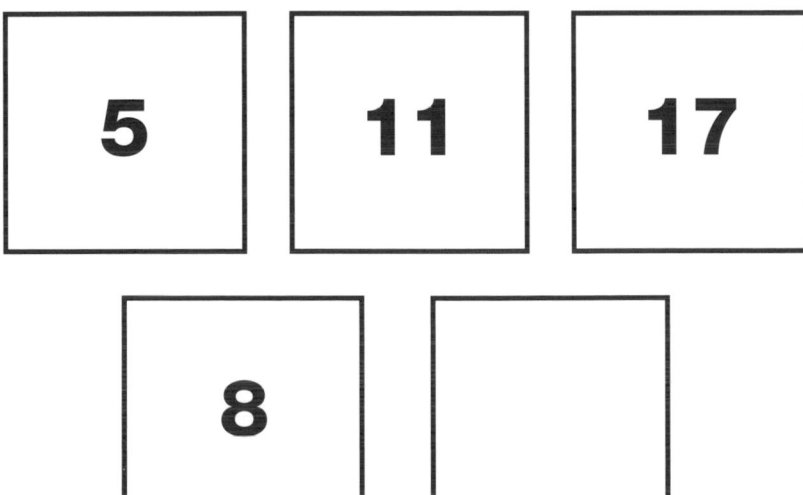

PUZZLE 24

Which number is missing from the bottom circle?

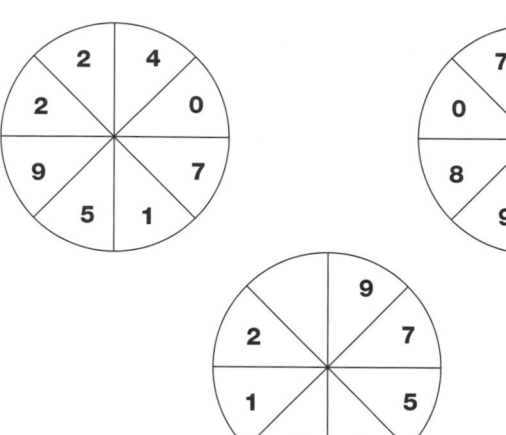

PUZZLE 25

Simon, Steve and Stewart are all apple farmers who pool their crop each year to make cider. For this year's harvest, Steve supplied three times as many apples as Stewart, and Simon supplied twice as many apples as Steve.

If the total number of apples supplied is 900 tonnes, how many did each of them contribute?

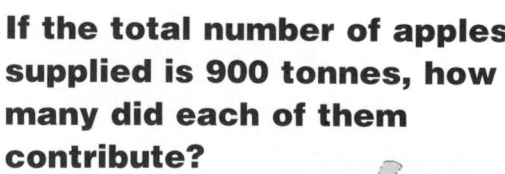

PUZZLE 26

Which letter is missing from the empty circle?

Edward spent $21 on drinks for a party. If the bottle of vodka he purchased was twice the price of the case of beer, and the lemonade was half the price of the beer, how much did Edward spend on the beer?

Which number replaces the blank?

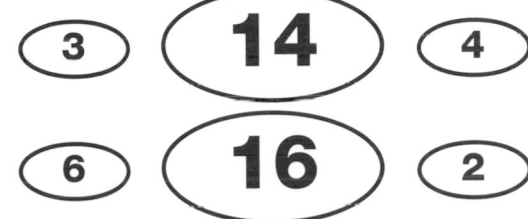

| 3 | **14** | 4 |

| 6 | **16** | 2 |

| 8 | | 3 |

Which numbers are missing from this puzzle?

14	1	12	7
11	8		2
5	10	3	16
		6	

Move two matches to make seven squares.

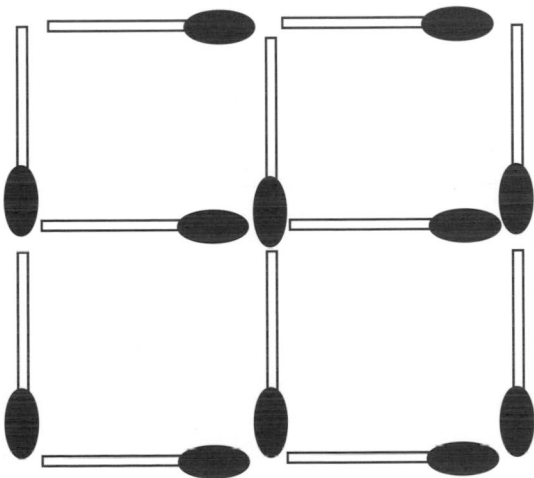

L E V E L

11

PUZZLE 1

Which two playing cards are needed to complete this puzzle?

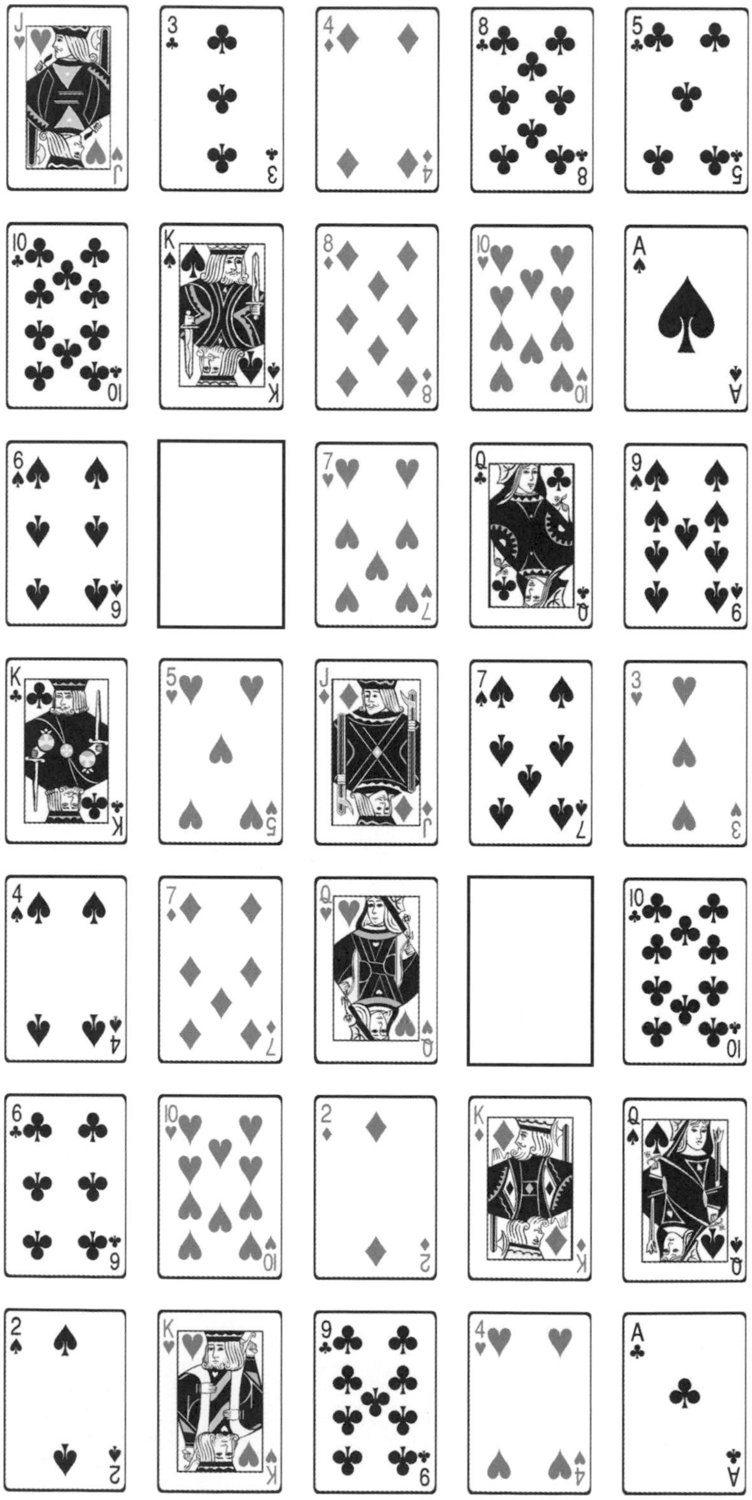

PUZZLE 2

Rearrange these coins into a five-line shape, with each line containing 4 coins.

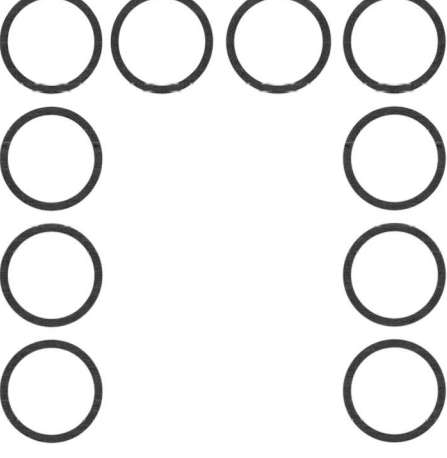

PUZZLE 3

Which number goes in the empty shape?

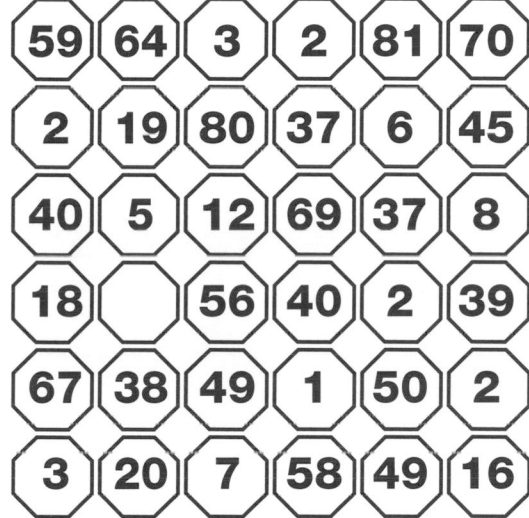

PUZZLE 4

Which number is the odd one out in each ellipse?

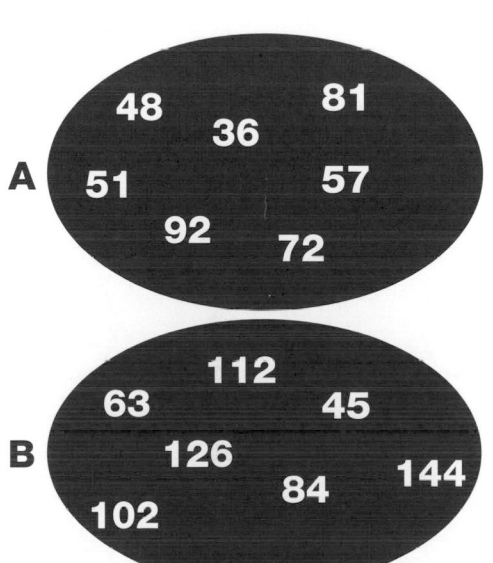

PUZZLE 5

Which number is missing?

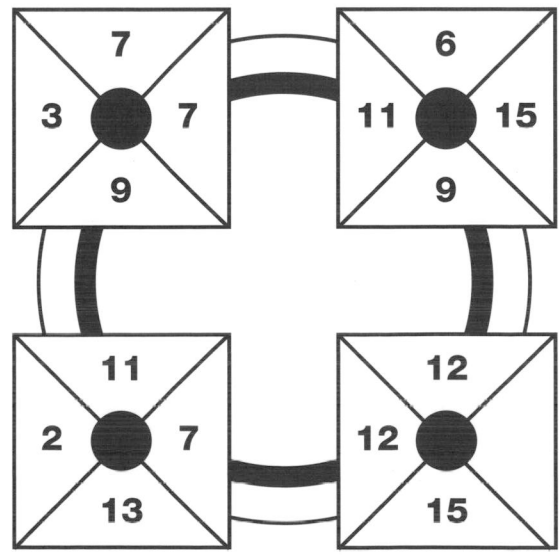

PUZZLE 6

Which of the three letters at the bottom completes the puzzle?

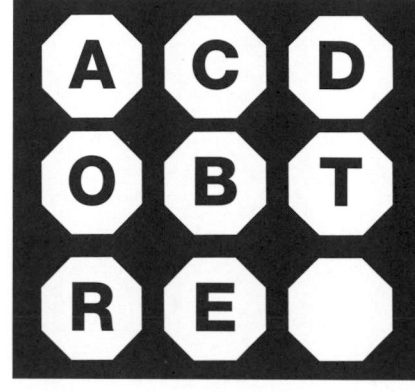

| 1 | 2 | 3 |
| S | W | G |

PUZZLE 7

Which number is missing?

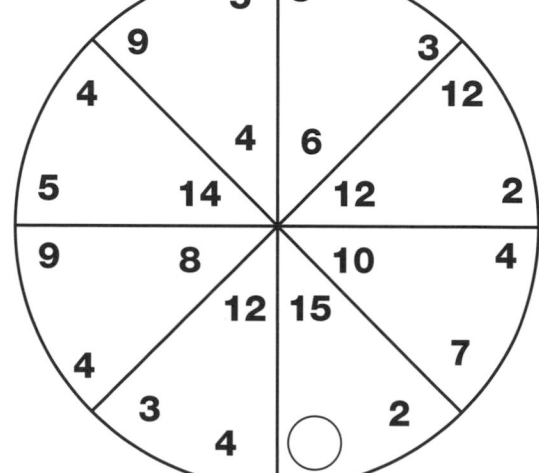

PUZZLE 8

Which number continues the sequence?

3

5

9

15

PUZZLE 9

Which letter replaces the blank and completes the sequence?

J   E   N

O   S   G

A   B   ◯

PUZZLE

Which playing cards are needed to fill in the blanks?

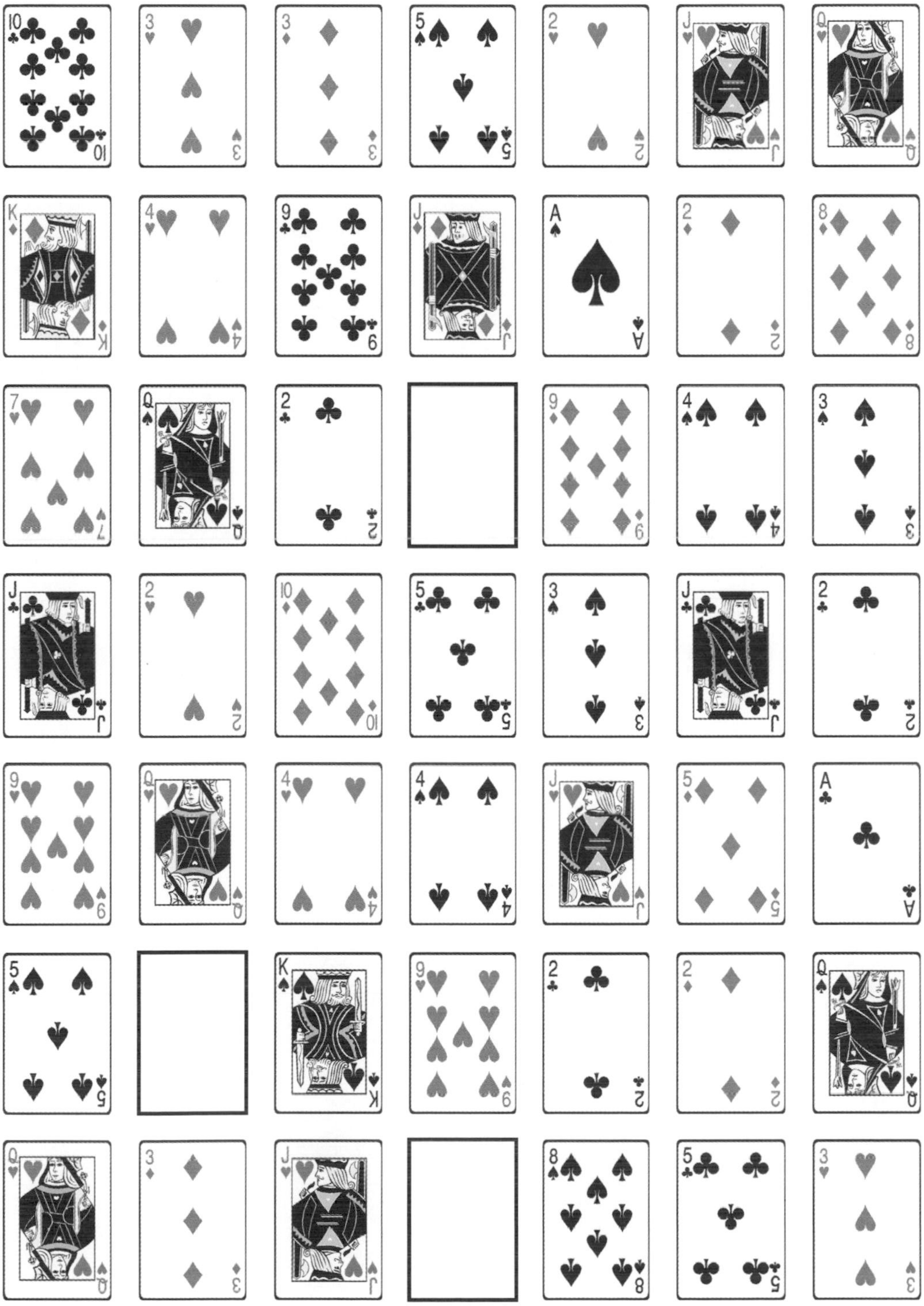

115

11 PUZZLE

Which number goes in the empty box?

10	5	6
1	12	8
7	9	5
17	1	

12 PUZZLE

What is the missing line value?

35	47	38	24	
⊙	▲	▲	▲	?
#	⊙	⊙	#	40
#	*	#	#	21
*	*	*	*	48

13 PUZZLE

Which letter goes in the middle?

F

D   S   G

C   R   B   T   H

B   Q   Z   ( )   C   V   J

P   Y   D   W   K

N   X   L

M

A   B   C   D   E   F   G   H

14 PUZZLE

Which number comes next?

1 - 2 - 5 - 10 - 13 - 26 - 29 - ?

15 PUZZLE

Which number goes in the middle of the last star?

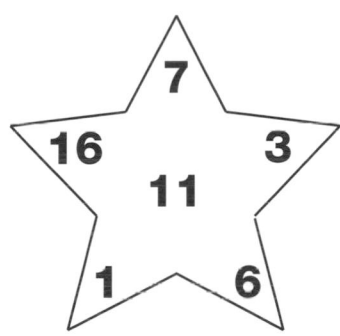 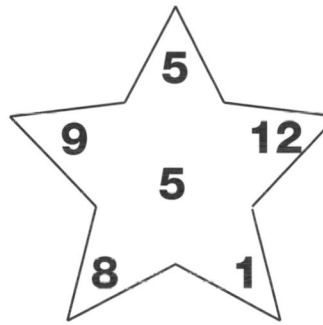 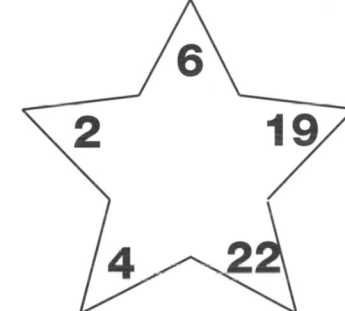

16 PUZZLE

Complete the puzzle.

E	L	Q
H	A	I
D	O	S
S	F	

17 PUZZLE

What is the missing line value?

36	23	24	?	
@	*	#	▲	27
@	▲	▲	#	29
@	*	*	*	24
@	#	#	*	26

PUZZLE 18

Fill in the empty circle.

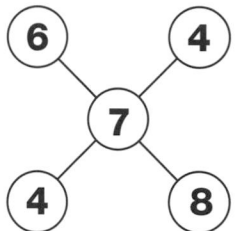 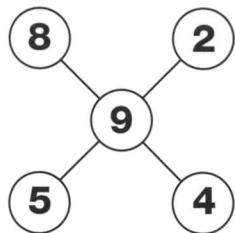 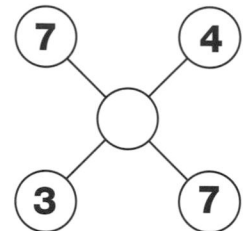

PUZZLE 19

Which letter goes in the empty circle?

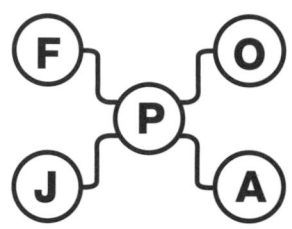 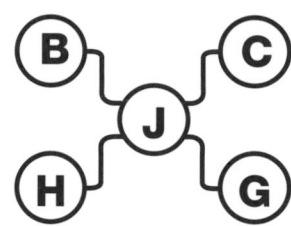 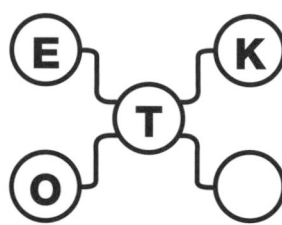

PUZZLE 20

What is the missing line value?

36	40	50	23	
♥	x	#	@	38
x	x	x	@	41
♥	♥	x	@	?
♥	♥	#	♥	37

PUZZLE 21

What goes in the blank corner of the middle square?

5		2	4		10
7	N		Q		3
1	G				9
2		4	1		2

PUZZLE 22

Which number is missing from this column of boxes?

3	1

2	5

8	4

7	12

17	

16	23

PUZZLE 23

Helen's watch needs repairing. She sets it correctly at 4:12pm but three hours later it shows 8:00pm. After a further two hours she notices that it reads 10:32pm.

She goes to bed early and gets up when her watch shows 6:46am.

What time is it really?

PUZZLE 24

What is missing from the blank segment?

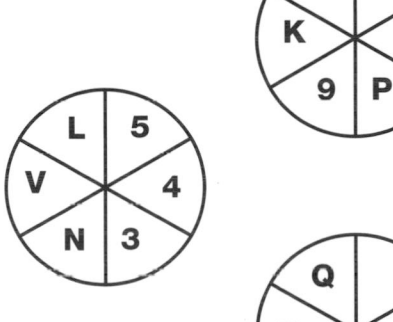

PUZZLE 25

Which number is needed to finish the puzzle correctly?

2	5	3	7
9	8	2	1
4	8	0	8
5	3	4	

PUZZLE 26

Which number needs to be added to the last grid?

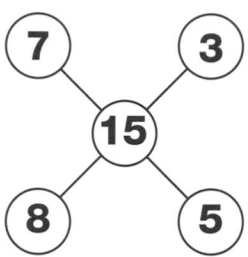 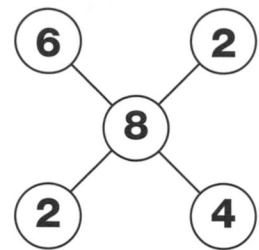 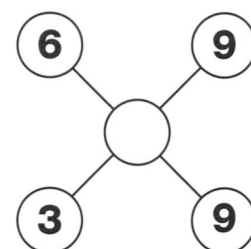

PUZZLE 27

Which number goes in the blank segment?

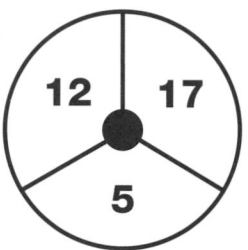  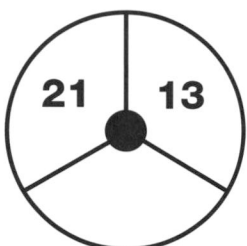

PUZZLE 28

Which number completes the puzzle?

PUZZLE 29

Which number replaces the question mark?

Which of the bottom boxes goes in the middle of this sequence?

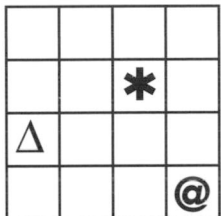
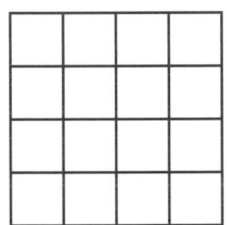
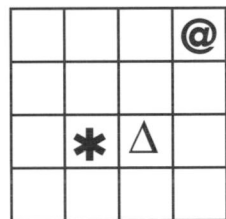

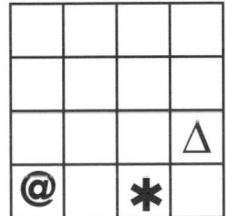
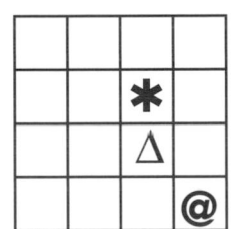
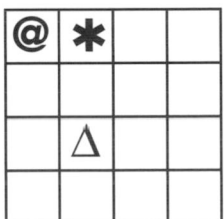

A

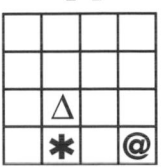

B

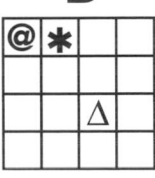

C

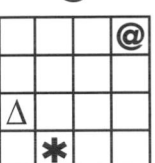

D

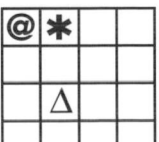

E

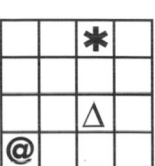

F

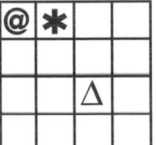

LEVEL

13

2 PUZZLE

Which domino fits into the empty space in this arrangement?

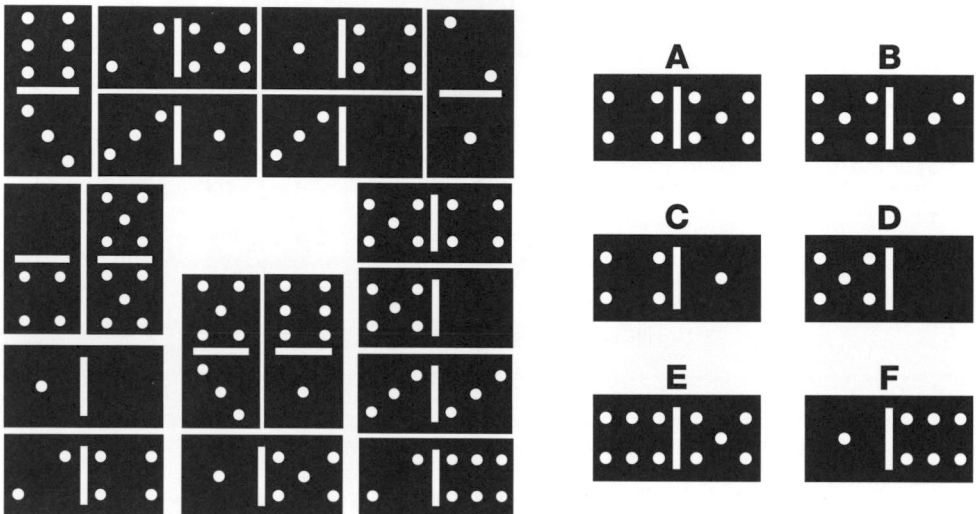

A   B   C   D   E   F

3 PUZZLE

Which number goes in the middle?

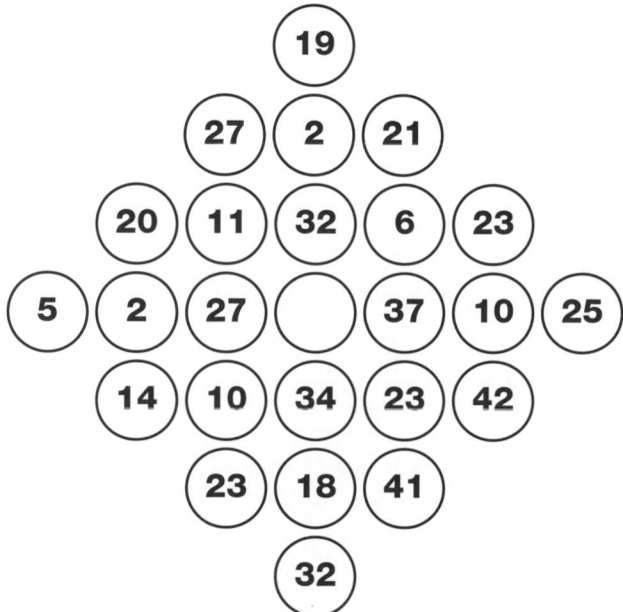

19

27 2 21

20 11 32 6 23

5 2 27 ⬚ 37 10 25

14 10 34 23 42

23 18 41

32

PUZZLE 4

Which number is missing from the web?

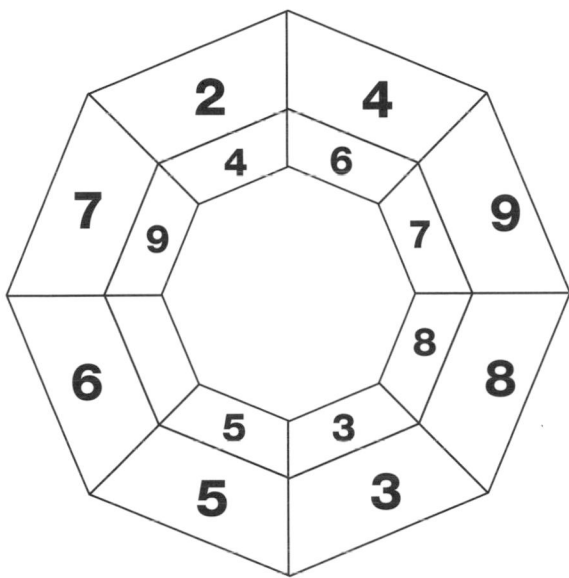

PUZZLE 5

Which number is missing from the wheel?

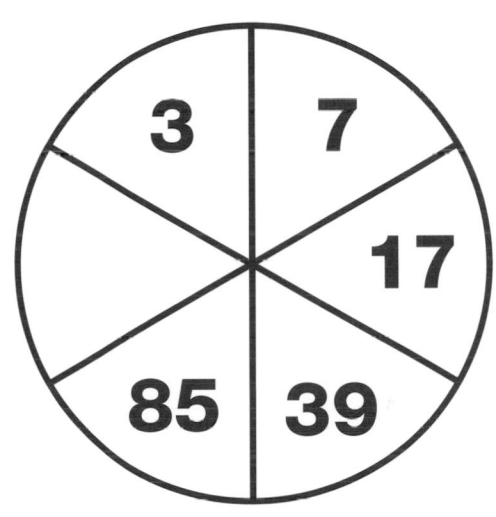

PUZZLE 6

Which watch is the odd one out?

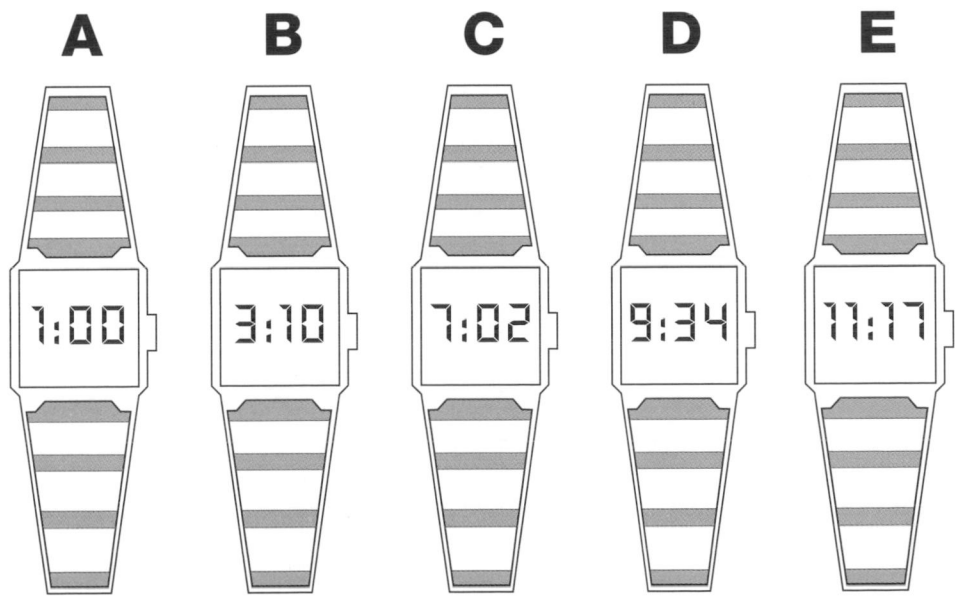

A   B   C   D   E

A: 1:00   B: 3:10   C: 7:02   D: 9:34   E: 11:17

PUZZLE

Which playing cards are needed to fill in the blanks?

PUZZLE 8

Which number completes the third triangle?

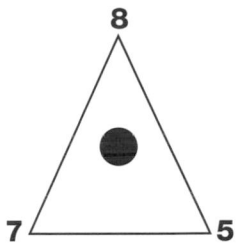
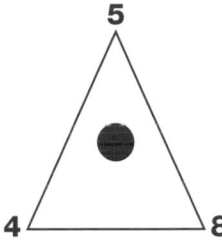
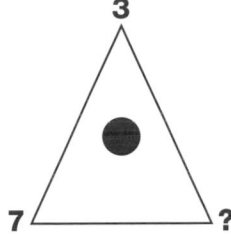

PUZZLE 9

What time should the blank clock show?

PUZZLE 10

What is missing from the empty segment?

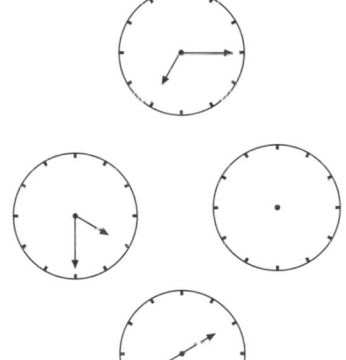
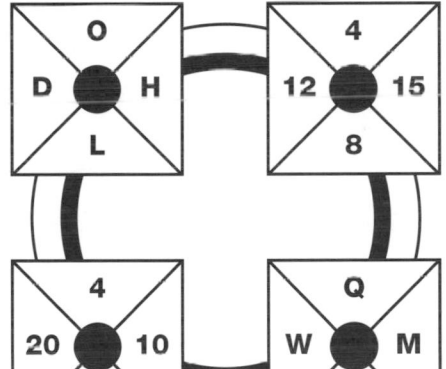

PUZZLE 11

What goes at the bottom of the last triangle?

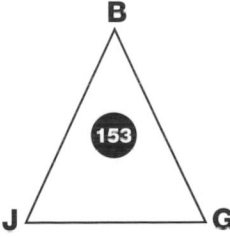
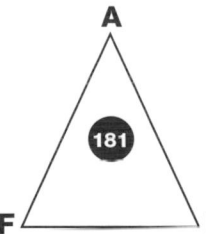
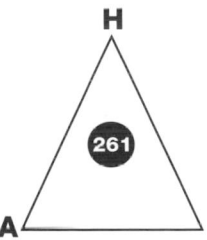

12 PUZZLE

Which letter replaces the blank and completes the sequence?

I   L   O

R   U   X

A   ( )   G

13 PUZZLE

Which letters finish the grid?

H	X	J	Z
U	O	D	H
	G	V	P
I	Y	I	

14 PUZZLE

Which number goes in the empty circle?

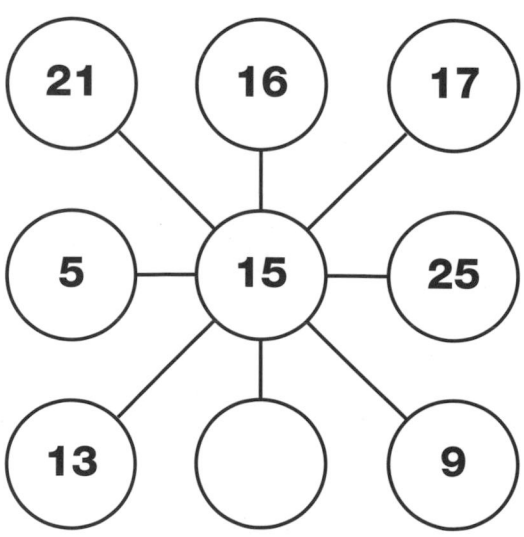

21   16   17

5   15   25

13   ( )   9

15 PUZZLE

Which letter completes the wheel?

F   I

O

R   U

126

16 PUZZLE

Which two letters are missing from the bottom grids?

17 PUZZLE

Fill in the correct number.

3	5	8	7
10	2	7	13
6	6	14	22
9	2	5	

18 PUZZLE

Fill in the empty segment.

LEVEL

13

19
PUZZLE

Which number is missing from the last circle?

20
PUZZLE

Which number goes at the top of the third star?

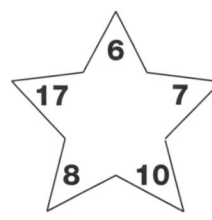
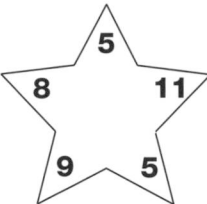
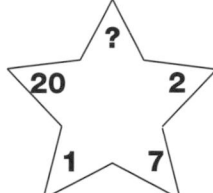

21
PUZZLE

22
PUZZLE

Which letter logically goes in the blank segment?

Complete the bottom grid.

3	8	18
5	10	20

4	10	22
6	12	24

7	16	
9	18	

23 PUZZLE

Which number is needed to complete this puzzle?

3	5	2
1	13	7
4	23	

24 PUZZLE

Finish the chain by filling in the blank link.

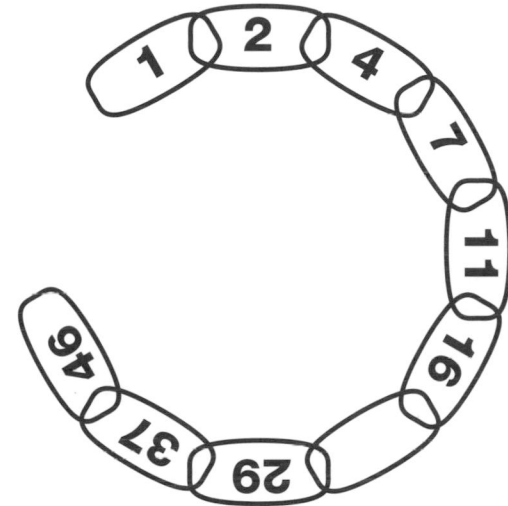

1 2 4 7 11 16 29 37 46

25 PUZZLE

Which letter goes at the bottom?

B
D
G
K
P

26 PUZZLE

Which number goes in the empty box?

2	5	

29	34

Farmer Giles has sent his livestock to market for sale but the farmhand has forgotten how much he was to sell each animal for. The farmer though had drawn him some pictures which showed the equivalent value of each of the animals but didn't finish it. Can you solve the problem for the luckless farmhand?

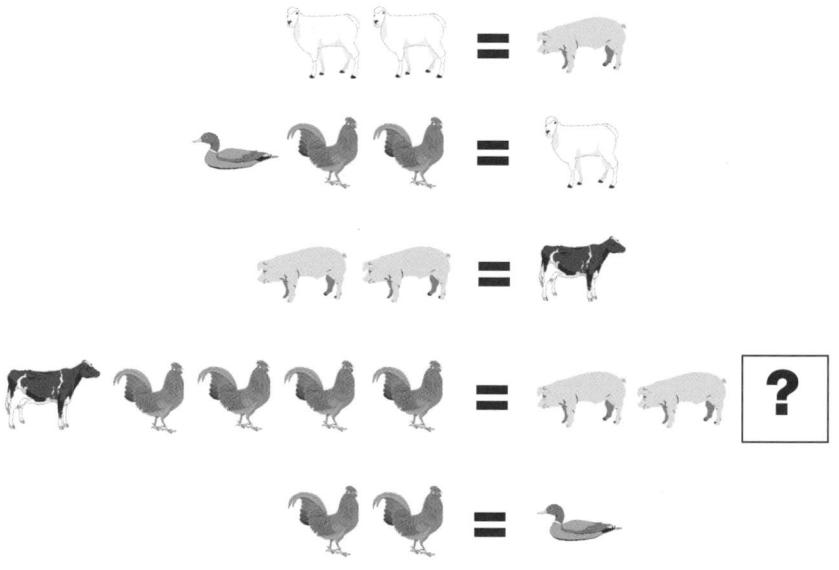

28
PUZZLE

Which letter goes in the empty square and completes the puzzle?

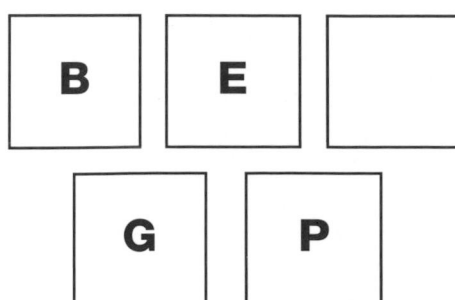

29
PUZZLE

Which letter replaces the blank and completes the sequence?

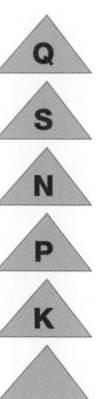

PUZZLE 1

Which letter is missing from the chain?

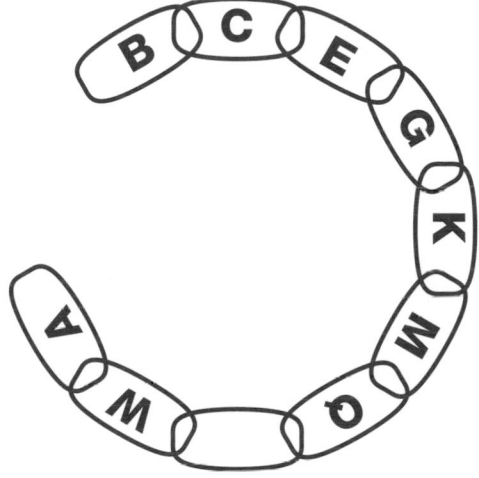

PUZZLE 2

Which number is needed to complete the puzzle?

5	7	10
25	19	
32	40	49

PUZZLE 3

Roy, Molly, Frank and Maude are all keen gardeners. As the diagrams show, they each have room for 10 plants in their plots so they can grow either flowers, trees or vegetables.

Ray grows more flowers than Maude, and Molly has more trees in her garden than Frank. Together Maude and Molly have more vegetables than the men.

Which garden belongs to each gardener?

1

2

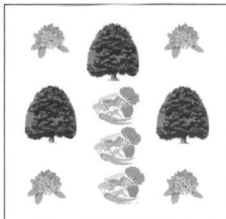

3

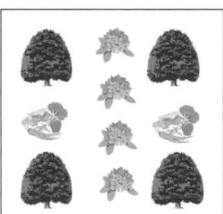

4

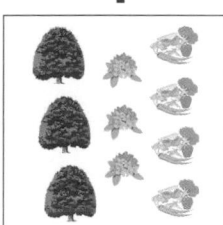

PUZZLE 4

Here is a 4 x 3 grid with twelve matches defining a triangle which takes up half of the area. Move just 4 matches to reduce the area by a half.

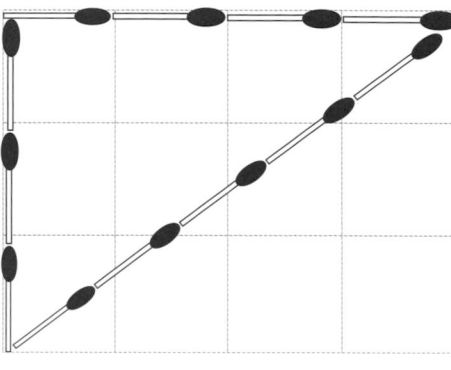

PUZZLE 5

Using the digits 0-5 inclusive, write one number in each small circle so that the values around each large circle add up to ten.

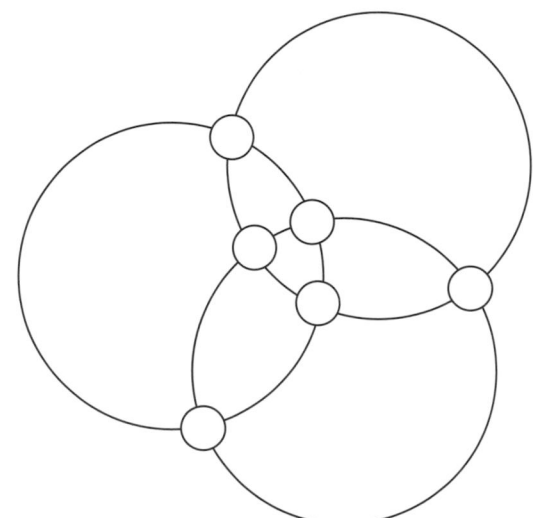

PUZZLE 6

Which letter replaces the blank and completes the sequence?

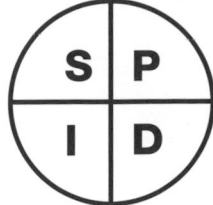
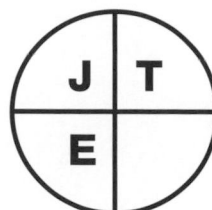

PUZZLE 7

Which letter goes at the bottom of the column?

8
PUZZLE

Which number is missing from the last circle?

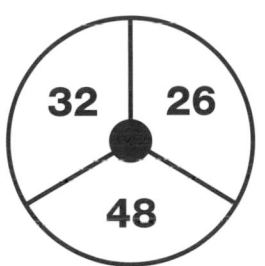

9
PUZZLE

Which playing card completes this puzzle?

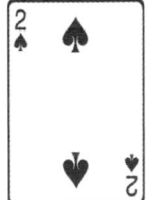   

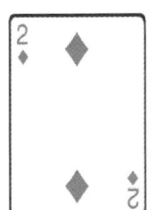   

10 PUZZLE

Which watch goes in the blank space?

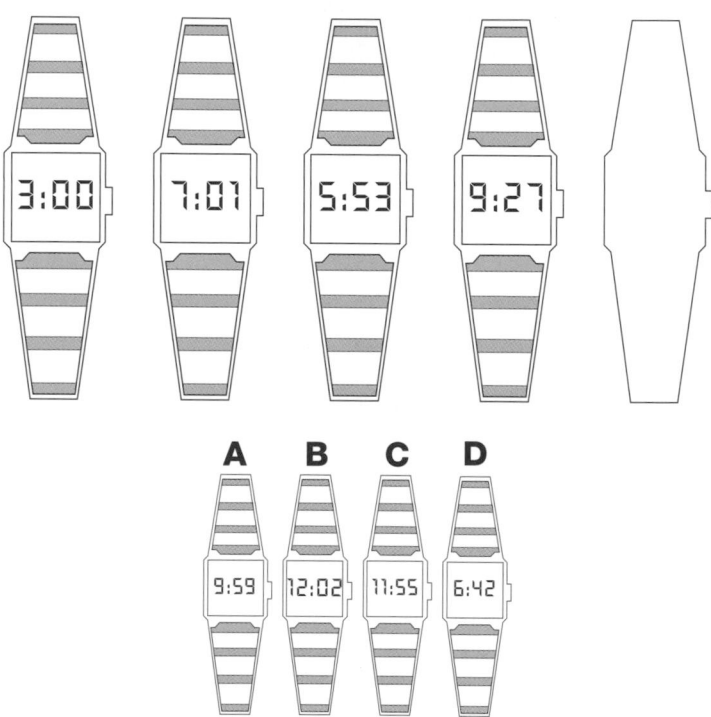

A   **B**   **C**   **D**

11 PUZZLE

Which number is missing?

1

5

9

15

12 PUZZLE

Complete this puzzle.

48   **7**   21

531   **5**   72

54   51

Which playing card finishes the puzzle?

Which letter replaces the blank and completes the sequence?

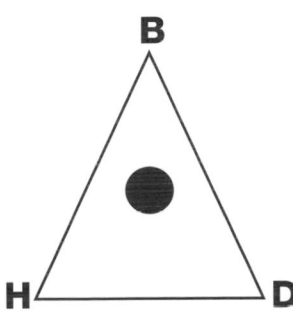 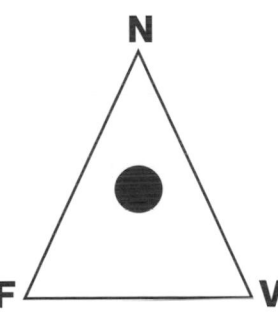 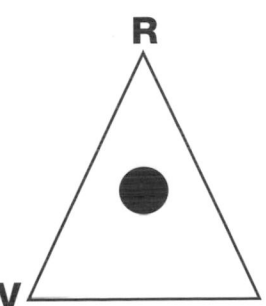

PUZZLE 15

Which letter replaces the blank and completes the sequence?

J   M   P

C   G   K

J   O   ___

PUZZLE 16

Which number will complete this grid?

2	1	2	7	3	2	4
5	1	4	2	9	2	7
4	1	6	6	2	2	7
1	1	1	6	4	4	2
1	1	4	2	5	0	4
4	1	2	9	3	4	

PUZZLE 17

Which of the numbered pieces fits into the middle of the grid?

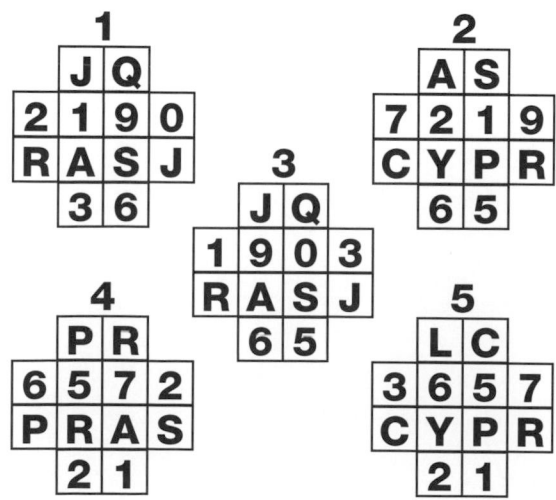

Which playing card is missing?

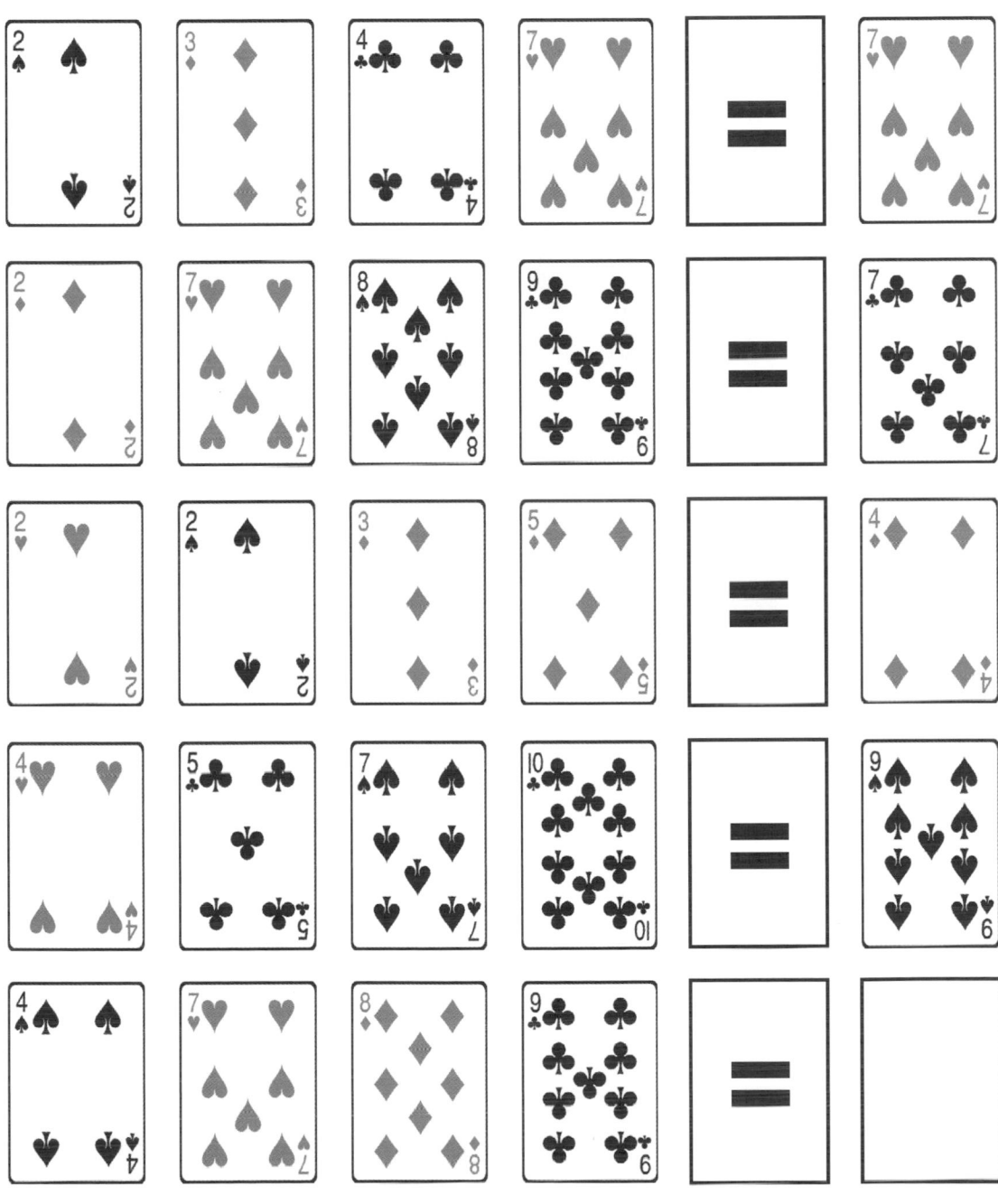

PUZZLE 19

What is the missing value?

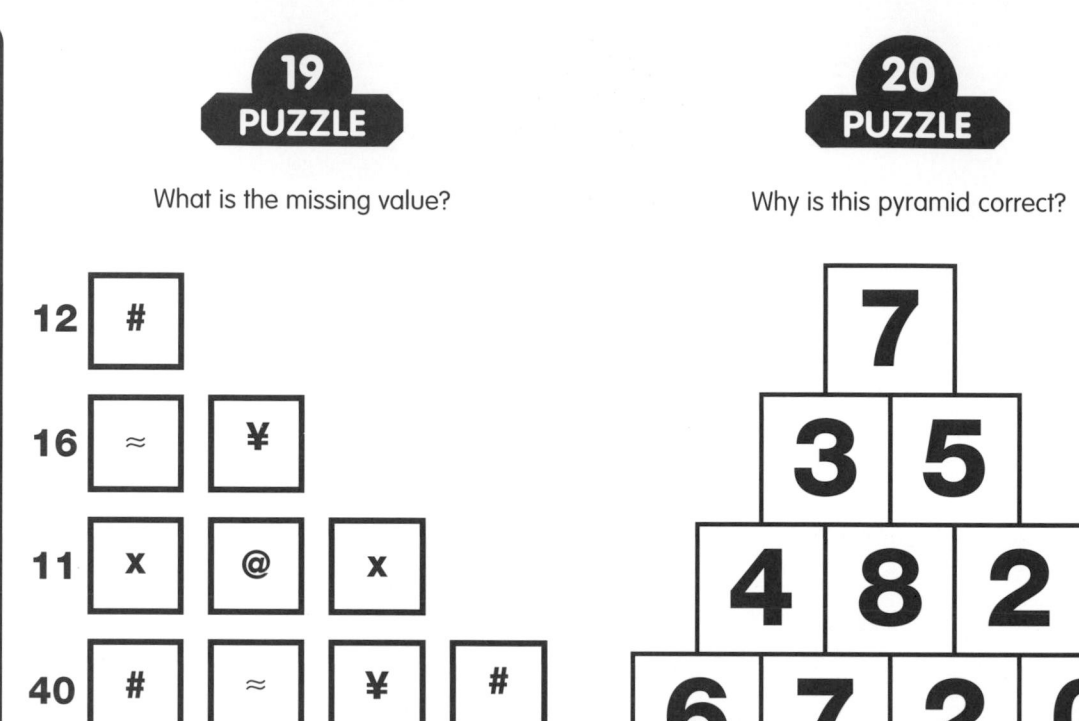

12	#			
16	≈	¥		
11	x	@	x	
40	#	≈	¥	#
	36		10	12

PUZZLE 20

Why is this pyramid correct?

```
        7
      3   5
    4   8   2
  6   7   2   0
```

PUZZLE 21

Which of the numbered pieces fits into the middle of the grid?

```
2 3 9 5 4 2 3 9 5 4
7 0 2 6 3 7 0 2 6 3
9 6 4 2 8 9 6 4 2 8
7 2 6 8       2 6 8 3
8 9 1         1 2 6
2 3 9         9 5 4
7 0 2 6       0 2 6 3
9 6 4 2 8 9 6 4 2 8
7 2 6 8 3 7 2 6 8 3
8 9 1 2 6 8 9 1 2 6
```

1
```
  3 7
2 6 8 9
5 4 2 3
  3 7
```

2
```
    9 6
4 0 2 6
4 2 8 3
    7 2
```

3
```
    2 6
3 7 8 9
2 3 5 4
  7 3
```

4
```
  2 3
9 5 4 7
0 2 6 3
  4 2
```

5
```
  0 2
6 3 4 2
9 6 4 6
  2 8
```

138

Which playing card completes the puzzle?

Which number is the odd one out?

What is the time now if 2 hours later it would be half as long until midnight as it would be if it were an hour later?

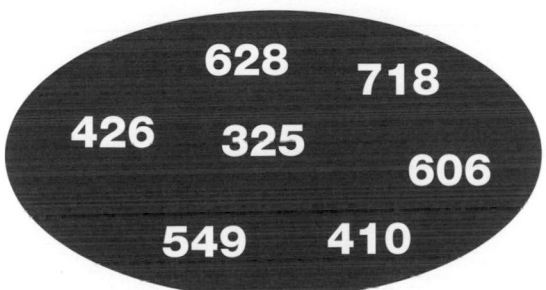

628 718
426 325
606
549 410

LEVEL

14

25
PUZZLE

Which cards are missing?

PUZZLE 1

Which number is missing?

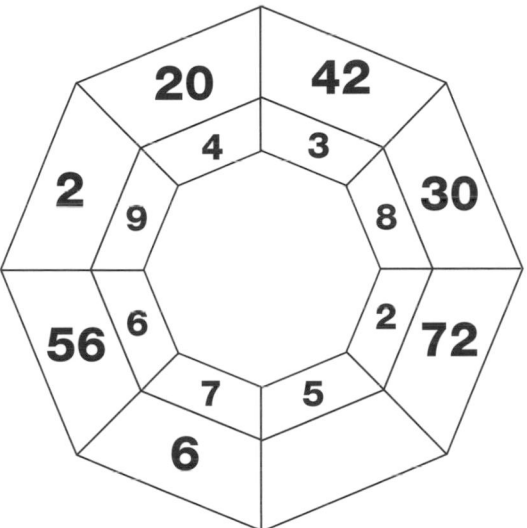

20 42
4   3
2   30
9   8
56 6   2 72
7   5
6

PUZZLE 2

Which number goes in the empty box?

| 5 | 6 | 4 |

| 12 | 2 | |

| 7 | 4 | 6 |

| 8 | 3 | 10 |

PUZZLE 3

Which watch comes next?

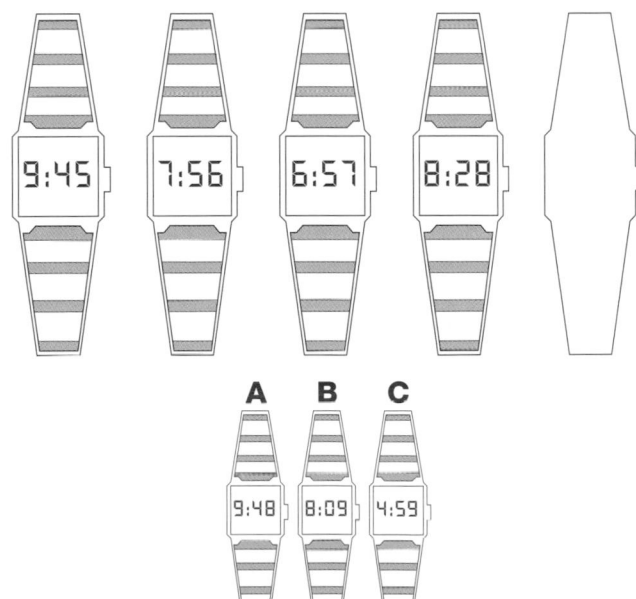

9:45   7:56   6:57   8:28

A   B   C
9:48   8:09   4:59

PUZZLE 4

Which playing cards are missing?

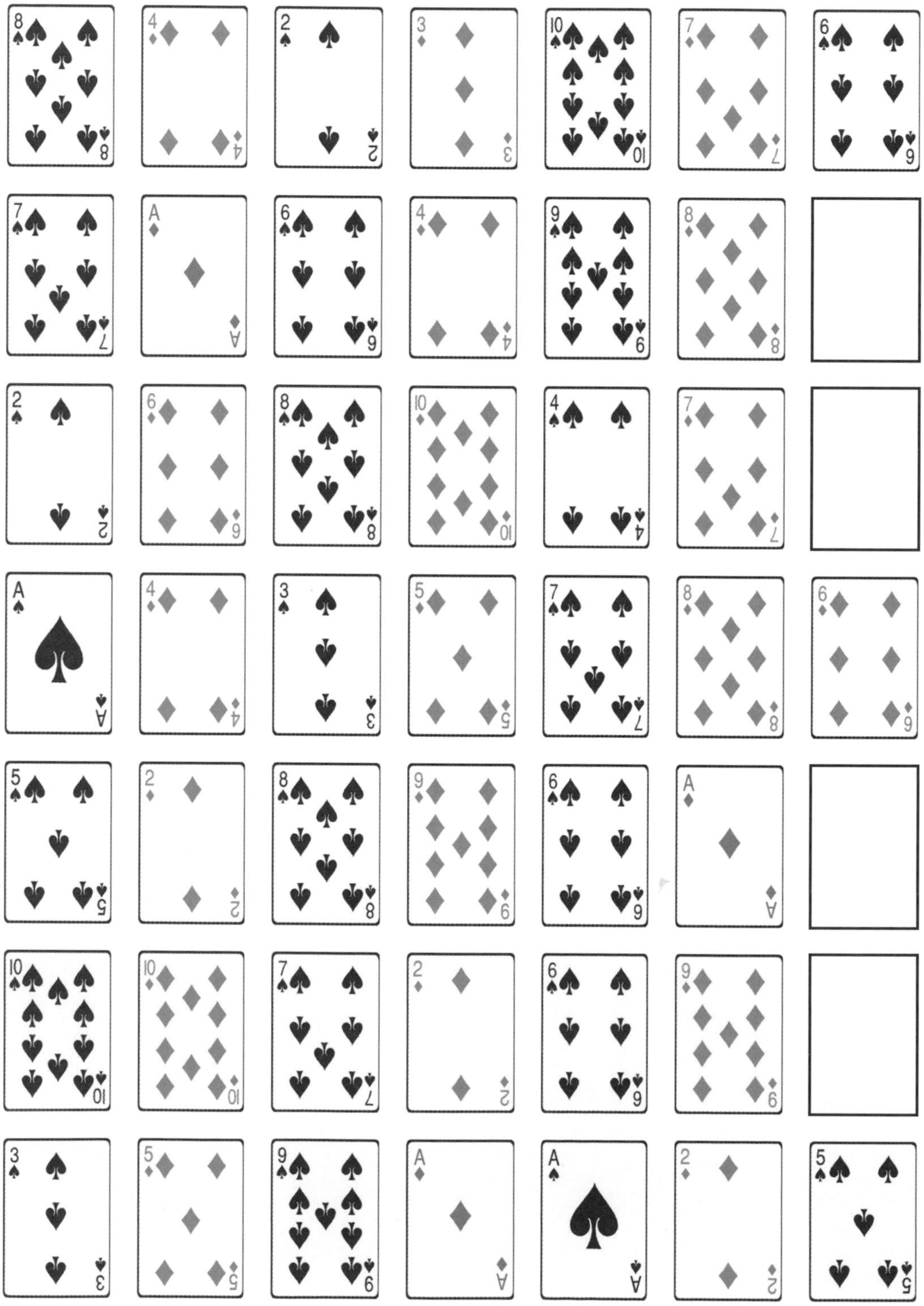

PUZZLE 5

Which number is missing from the last circle?

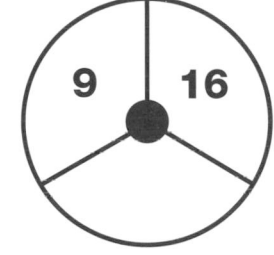

PUZZLE 6

Which of the bottom boxes finishes the sequence?

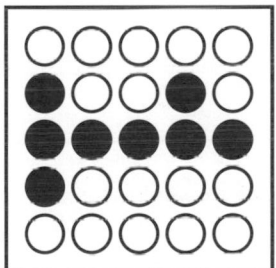
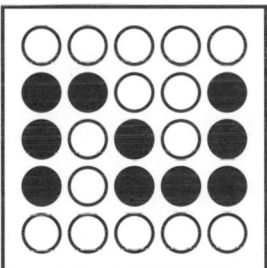
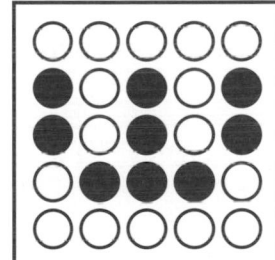

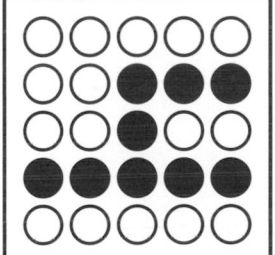
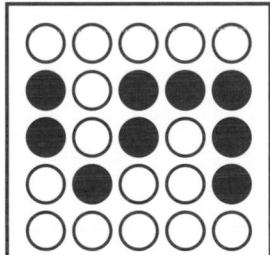
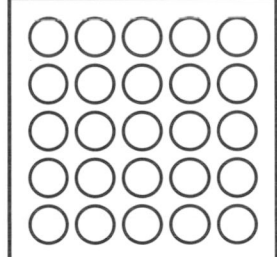

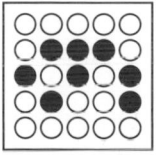
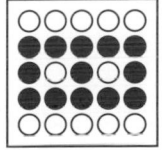
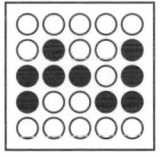
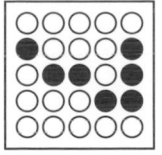
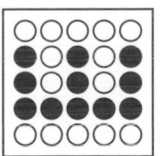
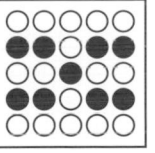

A   **B**   **C**   **D**   **E**   **F**

Which card is missing?

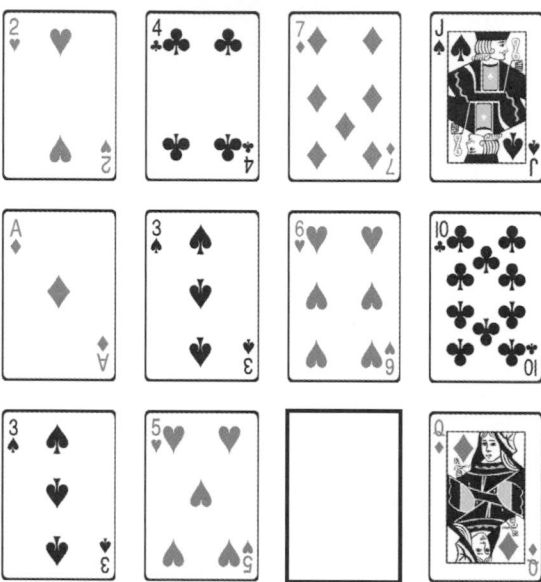

8 PUZZLE

What is the sum of the dots on the hidden faces of these dice?

9 PUZZLE

Which number is missing from the chain?

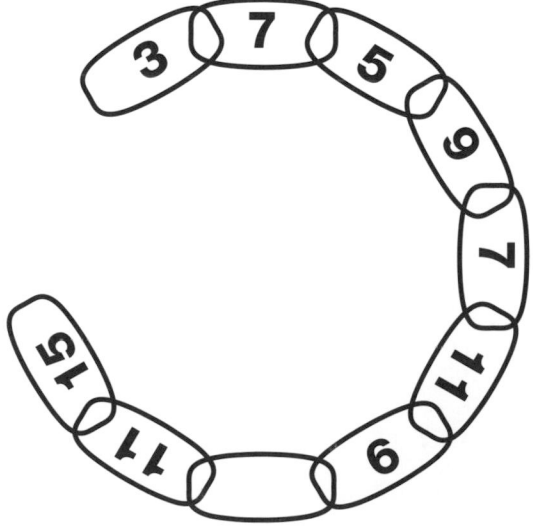

10 PUZZLE

Which numbers need to be placed in the circles in the bottom two boxes?

6	12
93	
7	3

2	5
64	
9	6

3	4
78	
11	6

8	2
◯	
7	3

4	10
◯	
5	1

11 PUZZLE

Which number goes in the empty circle?

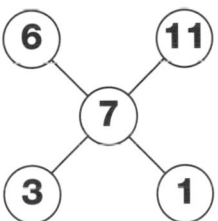

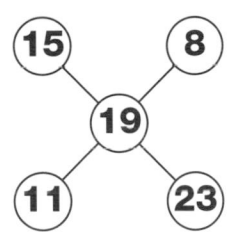

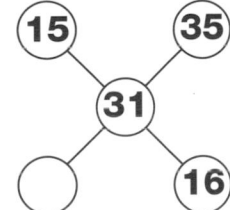

12 PUZZLE

Which number replaces the question mark?

3	7
?	
4	5

8	4
20	
4	3

9	4
22	
7	2

4	5
14	
2	3

L E V E L

15

13 PUZZLE

Which playing cards are missing from this puzzle?

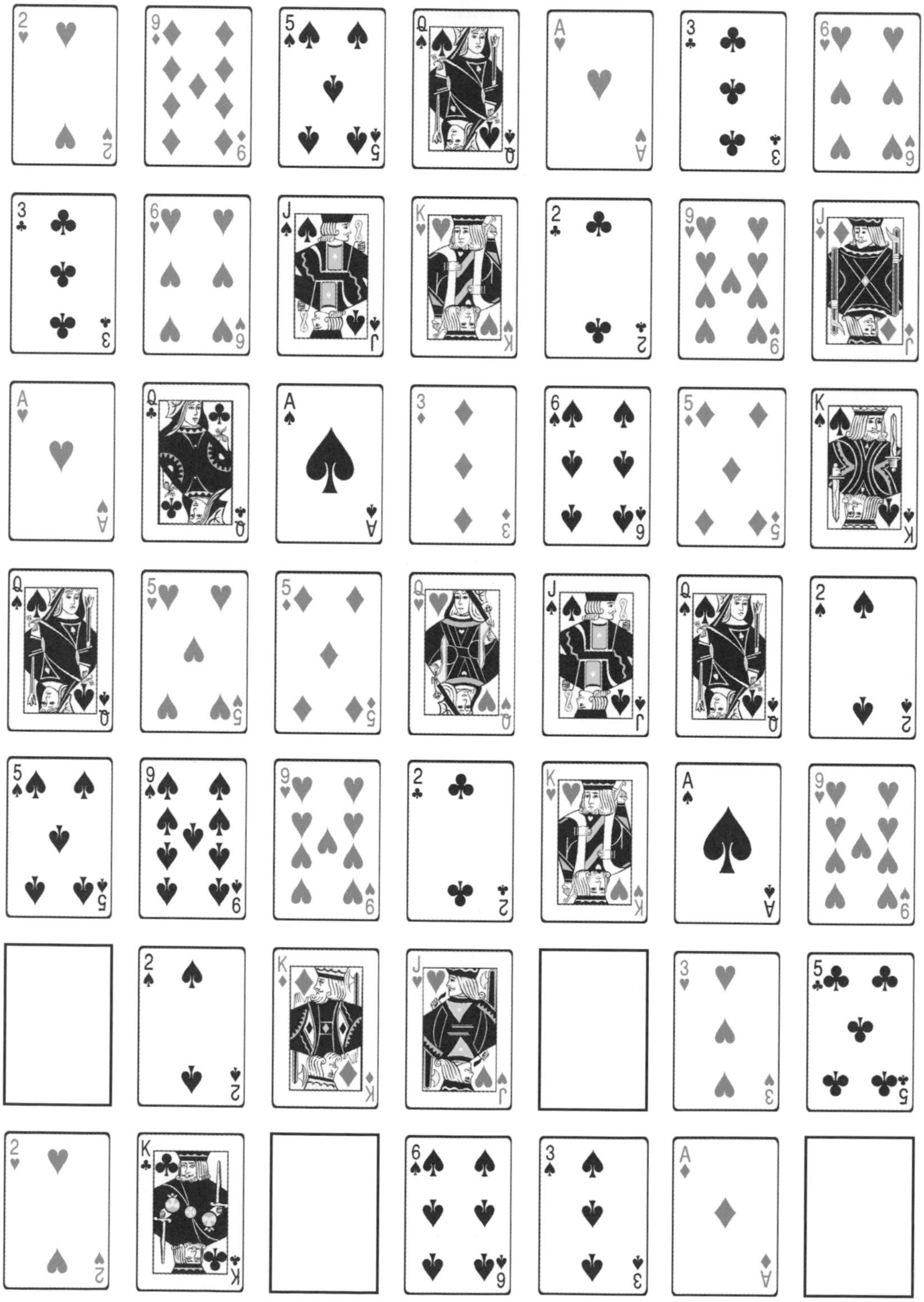

14 PUZZLE

Which letter replaces the blank and completes the sequence?

B	B

F	G

J	L

M	Q

Q	V

T	

15 PUZZLE

Which number goes at the bottom of the column?

5

12

18

23

27

16 PUZZLE

What is missing from the empty ellipse?

(I) **31** (E)

(O) **17** (Y)

(   ) **23** (O)

17 PUZZLE

Fill in the empty box.

5	5	11
3	8	7

6	10	14
7	10	13

2	10	12
6	7	

L
E
V
E
L

15

147

PUZZLE 18

What is missing from the empty segment?

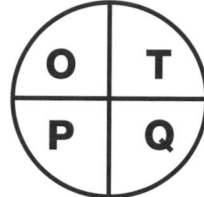

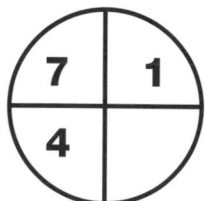

PUZZLE 19

Which letter goes in the middle of the third triangle?

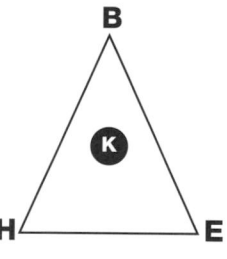
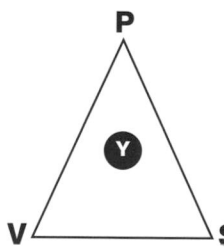
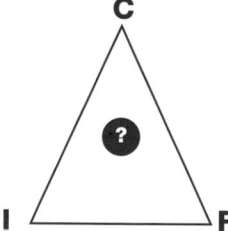

PUZZLE 20

Which letter goes in the empty segment?

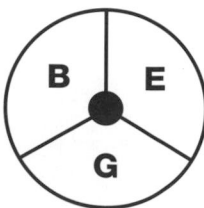

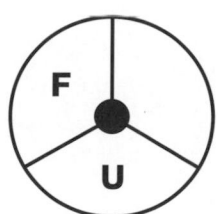

15

PUZZLE 21

Which letter goes in the empty segment?

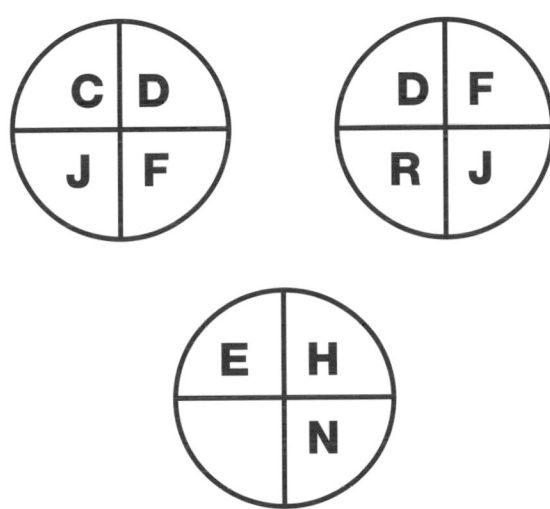

PUZZLE 22

Which number replaces the blank and completes the puzzle?

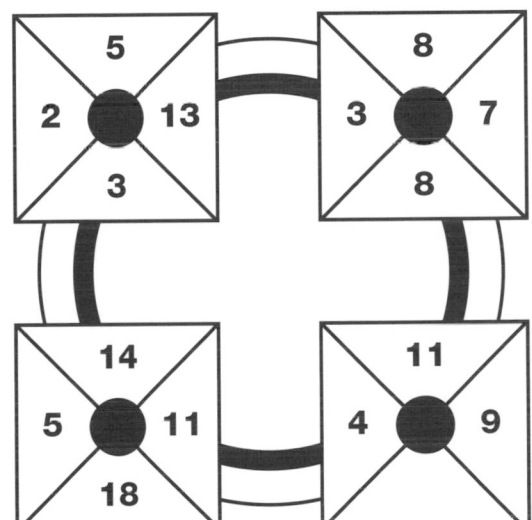

PUZZLE 23

Which of the smaller grids fits into the middle of the larger one?

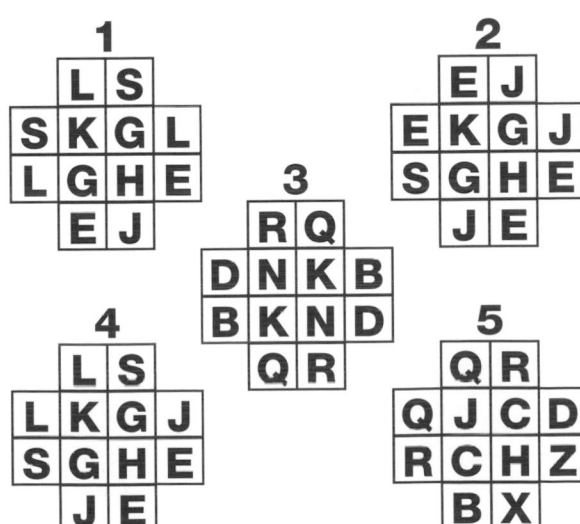

L E V E L

15

149

PUZZLE 1

Which number is missing from the last grid?

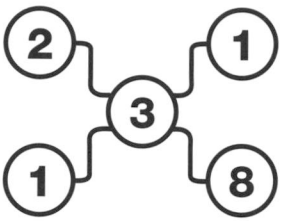 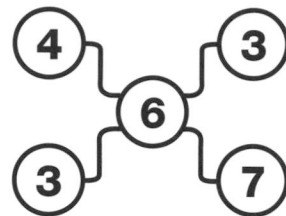 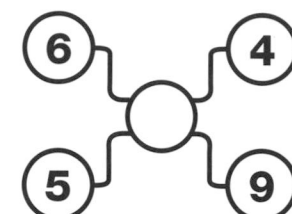

PUZZLE 2

Which card comes next?

PUZZLE 3

Which number is missing from the last grid?

 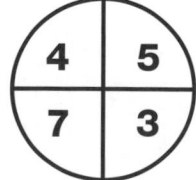 

 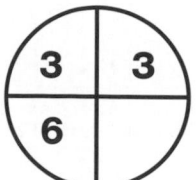

PUZZLE 4

Which number is missing from the empty circle?

PUZZLE 5

Which numbers replace the blanks?

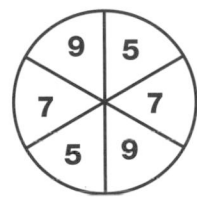

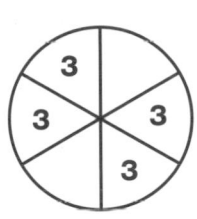

PUZZLE 6

Sisters Janine and Jackie went shopping for new outfits for a wedding. They each bought three items and by coincidence, each spent exactly $222.22. Janine noticed something else – if you look at the price of each item the value in pounds is the square of the pence value.

If one of Janine's items cost $1.01 and one of Jackie's cost $169.13 what are the prices of the other two items?

PUZZLE 7

Which letter is missing from the wheel?

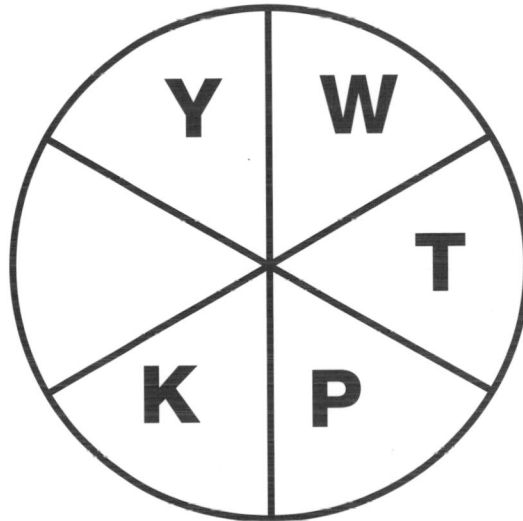

151

PUZZLE 8

Which of the numbered grids fits into the big one?

R	O	Y	G	B	I	V	X	O	I
E	E	A	D	G	B	E	F	A	I
L	O	C	G	D	A	N	A	O	F
T	B	S	O			D	G	T	I
W	F	B				I	C	L	
L	C	I				B	F	W	
I	T	G	D			O	S	B	T
F	O	A	N	A	D	G	C	O	L
I	A	F	E	B	G	D	A	E	E
I	O	X	V	I	B	G	Y	O	R

1

T	B		
C	Y	L	Y
Y	L	Y	C
	B	T	

2

	Q	Q	
S	L	A	A
C	B	L	S
	Q	Q	

3

	X	Y	
B	S	L	E
E	L	S	B
	X	Y	

4

	O	X	
T	V	V	J
J	T	T	V
	X	O	

5

	T	C	
C	Y	L	Y
Y	L	Y	C
	T	C	

PUZZLE 9

Which number completes the wheel?

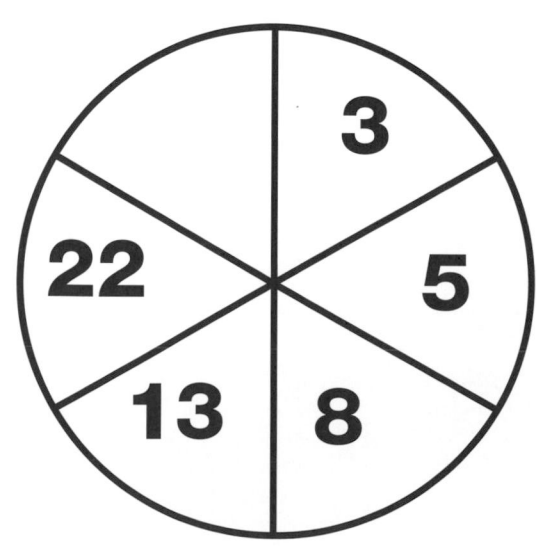

3
5
8
13
22

PUZZLE 10

What is missing from the empty square?

M	1	5
O	1	7

V	2	5
I	1	2

T	2	4
L	1	

Which number completes the bottom grid?

1	3	4
5	2	3

6	2	8
7	1	6

4	7	11
11	2	

Which letter goes in the empty square?

D	R	F	
K	H	V	J
B	O	L	
	F	S	P

Complete the wheel by adding the missing number.

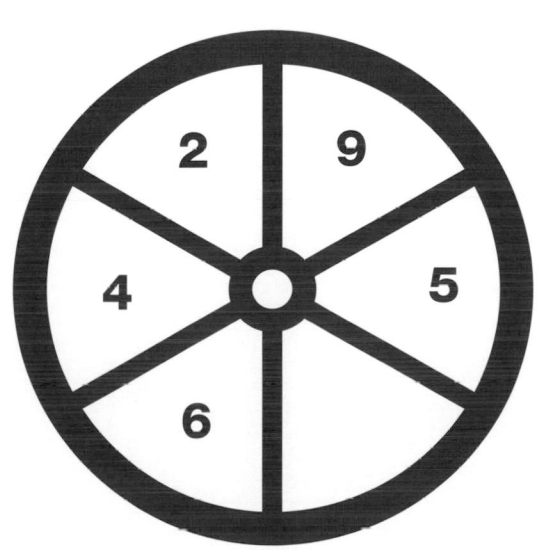

What goes in the empty box to complete the puzzle?

O	V	H
17	10	24

M	E	T
18	26	11

F	N	X
24	16	

LEVEL

16

153

PUZZLE 15

Where is the minute hand pointing to in the bottom clock?

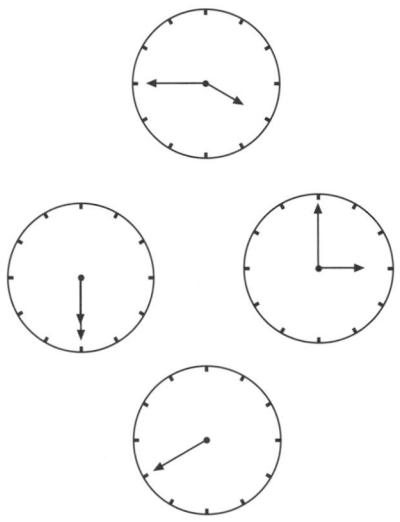

PUZZLE 16

Which number goes in the centre of the bottom right box?

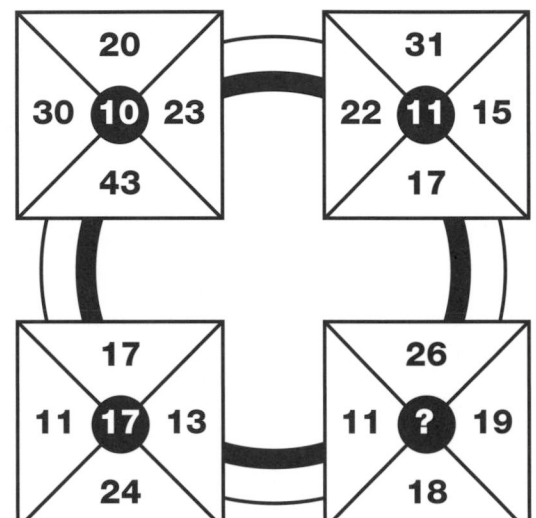

PUZZLE 17

Which of the bottom grids would continue the sequence?

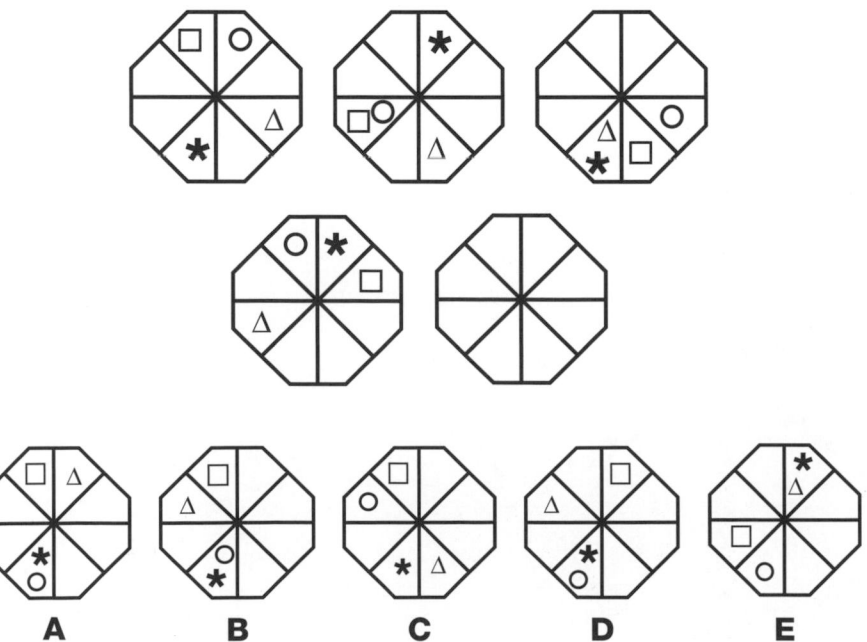

A   B   C   D   E

Which playing cards will fill in the blanks?

PUZZLE 19

Gary writes out a sum for his girlfriend Selina. Although it was wrong he challenged her to change just one symbol to make the sum correct. Can you see how she did it?

$$1 + 2 - 3 = 139$$

PUZZLE 20

Which letter replaces the blank and completes the sequence?

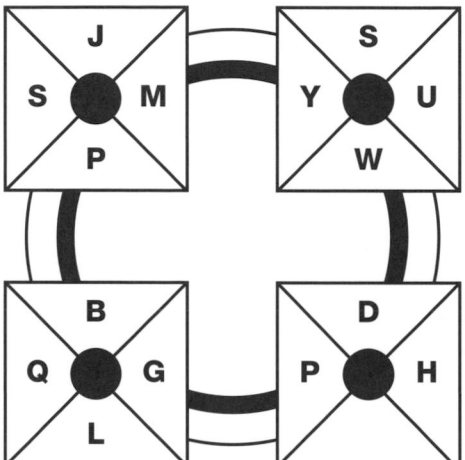

PUZZLE 21

Which figure will come next?

A   B   C

PUZZLE 22

Which number will continue this sequence?

PUZZLE 23

Which number is missing from the last star?

  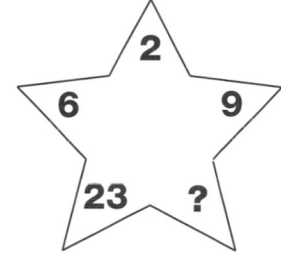

PUZZLE 24

Which shapes are missing?

25 PUZZLE

Move three matches to form a pattern containing 8 equilateral triangles.

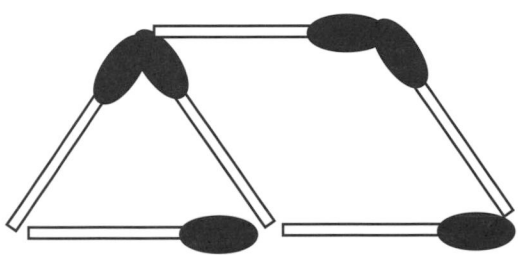

26 PUZZLE

Which number is missing?

5 3 4

60 12

7 6 ☐

42 14

27 PUZZLE

Which numbers are missing from the centre column?

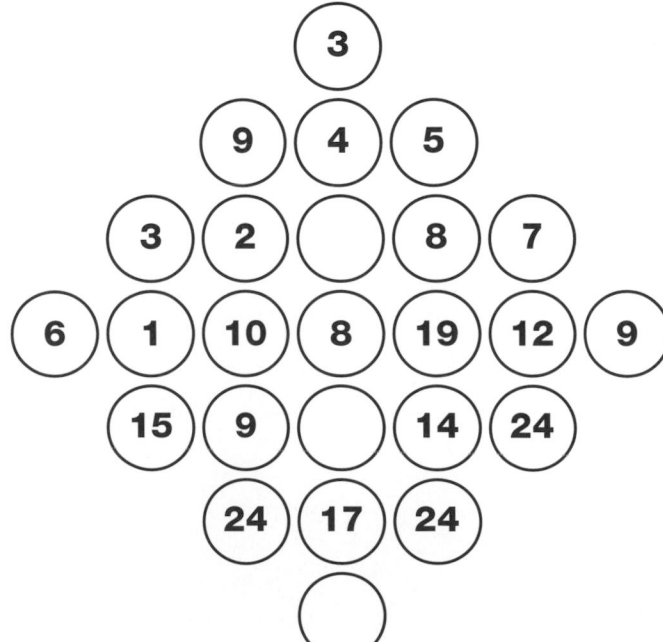

3

9 4 5

3 2 ☐ 8 7

6 1 10 8 19 12 9

15 9 ☐ 14 24

24 17 24

☐

158

PUZZLE 1

Which of the smaller grids goes in the centre of the large one?

1

2

3

4

5

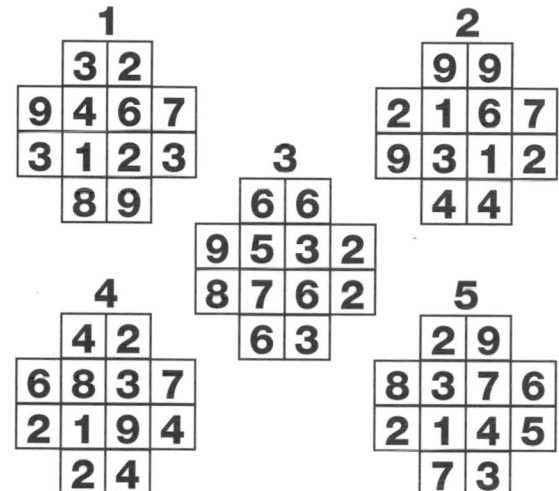

PUZZLE 2

Which number goes in the centre of the third triangle?

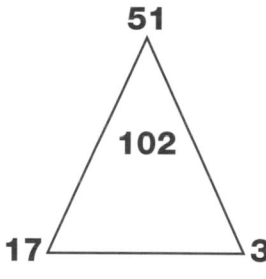 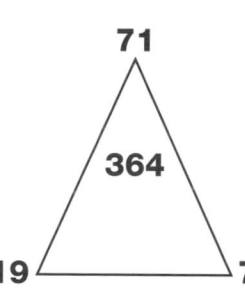 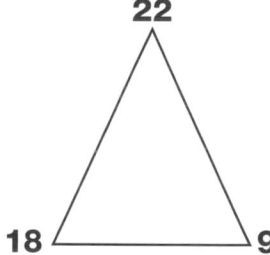

PUZZLE 3

Which number comes next?

   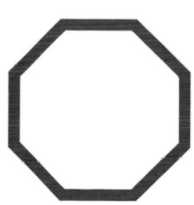

PUZZLE 4

Which number is missing?

18	13	26	21
9	266	261	42
14	133	522	37
7		69	74

PUZZLE 5

Which letter completes the chain?

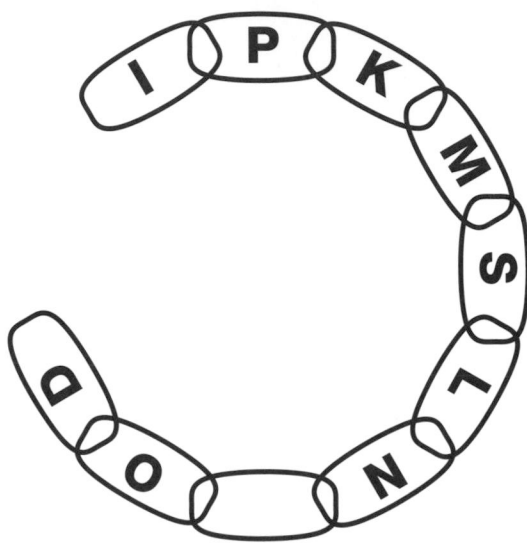

PUZZLE 6

Which letter is missing from the wheel?

PUZZLE 7

Which letter goes in the empty box?

C	I	L
G	M	P

D	Q	S
I	V	X

F	K	R
L	Q	

Which of the smaller pieces will fit into the big grid?

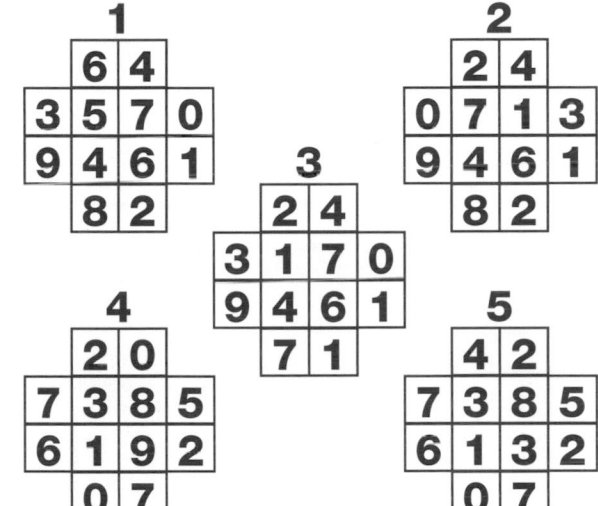

Which number completes the puzzle?

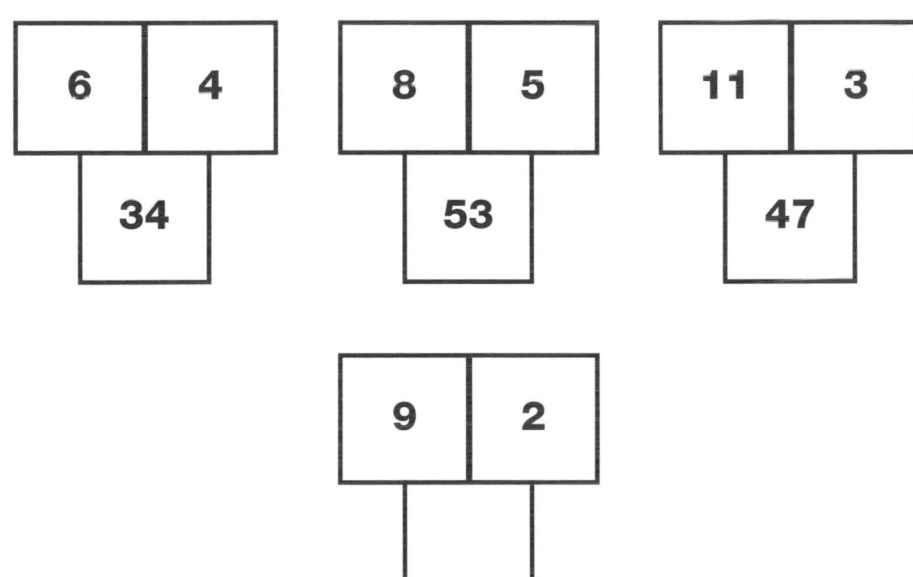

PUZZLE 10

Which letter is missing from the bottom right hand grid?

E	N
T	O

F	L
S	Q

G	J
R	S

H	H
Q	U

I	F
P	

PUZZLE 11

Which of the bottom grids continues the sequence shown on the top line?

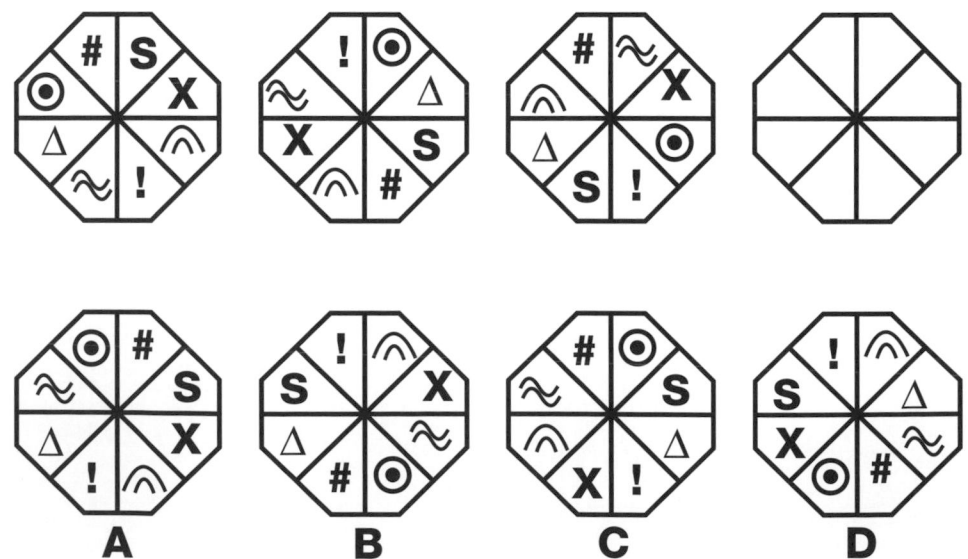

A   B   C   D

PUZZLE 12

Which number goes in the empty circle and completes this puzzle?

1	4	8	4	5	4	6	1	8
5	9	3	9	1	9	3	9	5
2	6	7	6	2	8	7	4	2
8	9	5	9	3	9	5	9	8
3	4	1	8	4	1	6	1	3
8	9	6	9	2	9	7	9	4
2	5	7	3	5	3	8	2	

PUZZLE 13

What goes in the empty box?

C	R	2	1
Q	W	4	0
L	A	1	3
M	T	3	

PUZZLE 14

Which letter replaces the blank and completes the sequence?

B

C

D

G

PUZZLE

Which of the watches on the bottom row continue the sequence shown on the top?

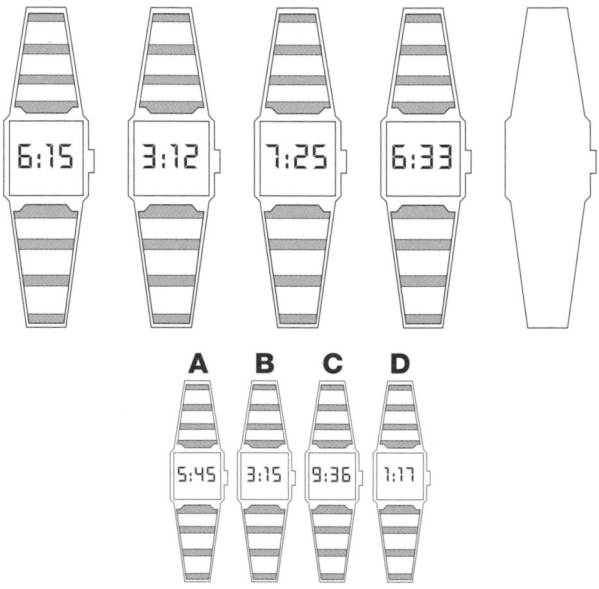

PUZZLE 16

Which of the bottom grids would continue the top sequence?

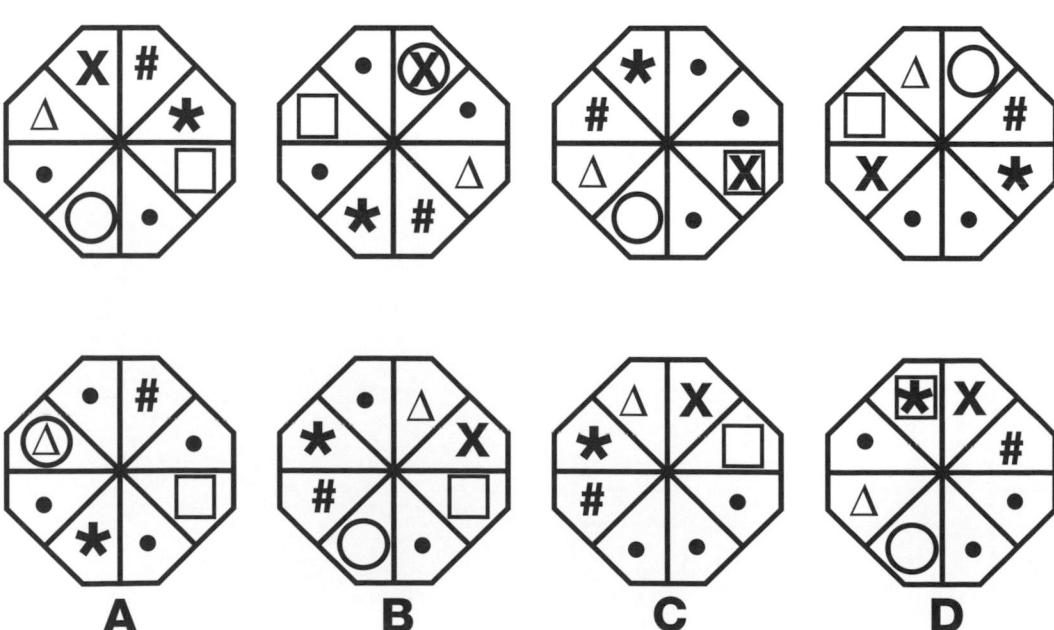

PUZZLE 17

Which numbers are missing?

3	9	1
1		2
7		3
7	2	9

A

1	9	2
3		0
2		6
3	2	

B

2	7	0
5		0
4		5
1	9	

PUZZLE 18

Which letter goes in the blank segment?

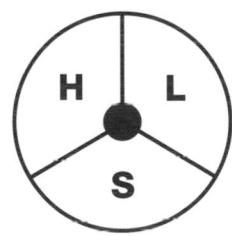
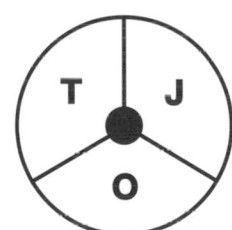
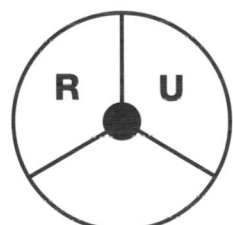

PUZZLE 19

Which number goes in the last circle?

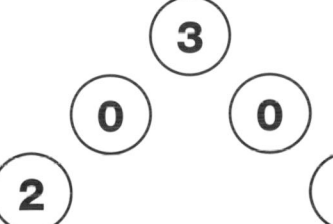
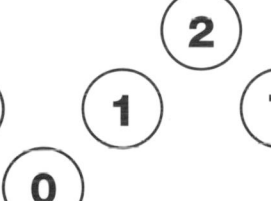

PUZZLE 20

Which number goes at the bottom of the column?

PUZZLE 21

Which number is missing from the empty box?

2	3	5
7	11	13

2	4	8
12	20	24

3	6	12
18	30	

PUZZLE 22

Which number should go in the empty segment of the wheel?

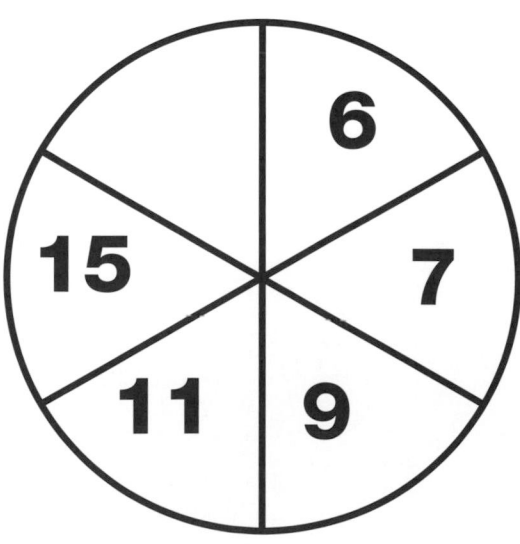

PUZZLE 23

What is missing from the empty ellipse?

Mr Jones, the local greengrocer, has lost the weights from his shop scales. He sells pineapples, grapes and apples by weight, but bananas cost 20 cents each. Mrs Brown wants to buy a pineapple, which Mr Jones will sell to her for the price of the same weight in bananas. He knows that the combinations shown below are correct, so how much will the pineapple cost his customer?

25
PUZZLE

Which number is missing from the top of the last star?

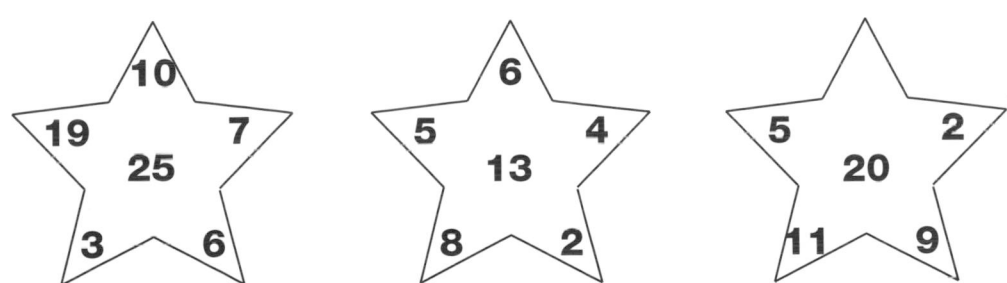

167

PUZZLE 1

Which number is missing from the empty box?

3	6	9
14	8	11

2	4	6
12	8	10

4	8	12
19	11	

PUZZLE 2

What goes in the empty square?

PUZZLE 3

Which number begins this sequence?

121

81

49

25

9

PUZZLE 4

Which letter completes the chain?

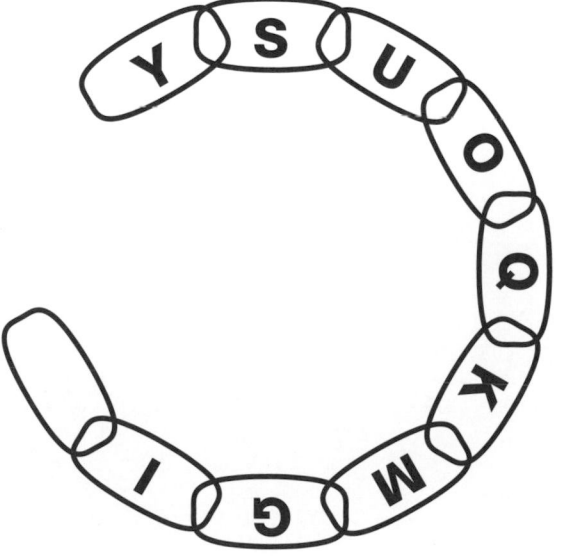

Which number is missing?

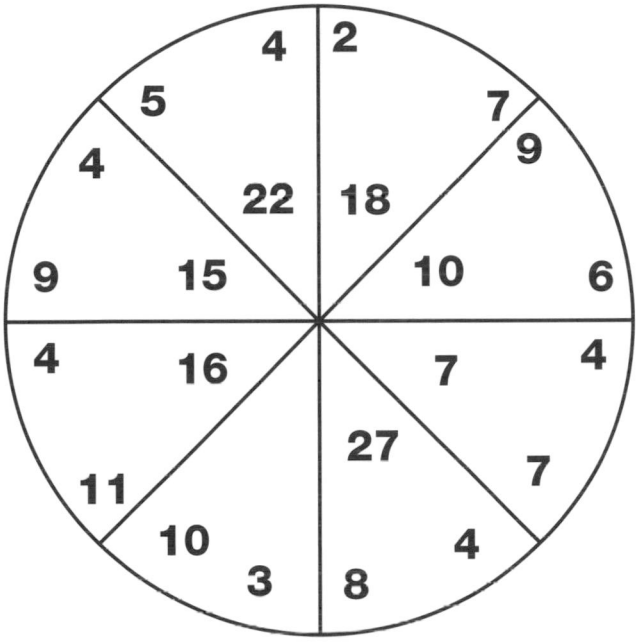

6
PUZZLE

Which two cards from the bottom row continue the sequence shown on the top?

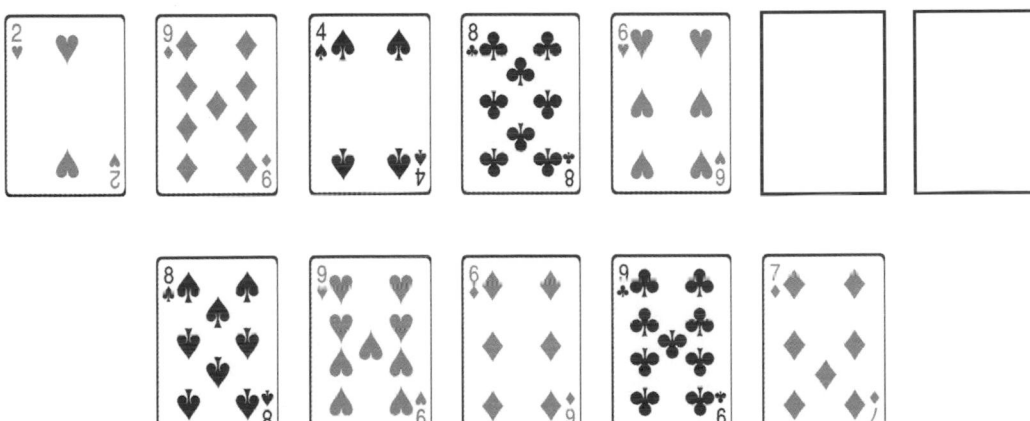

7 PUZZLE

Which two cards complete this sequence?

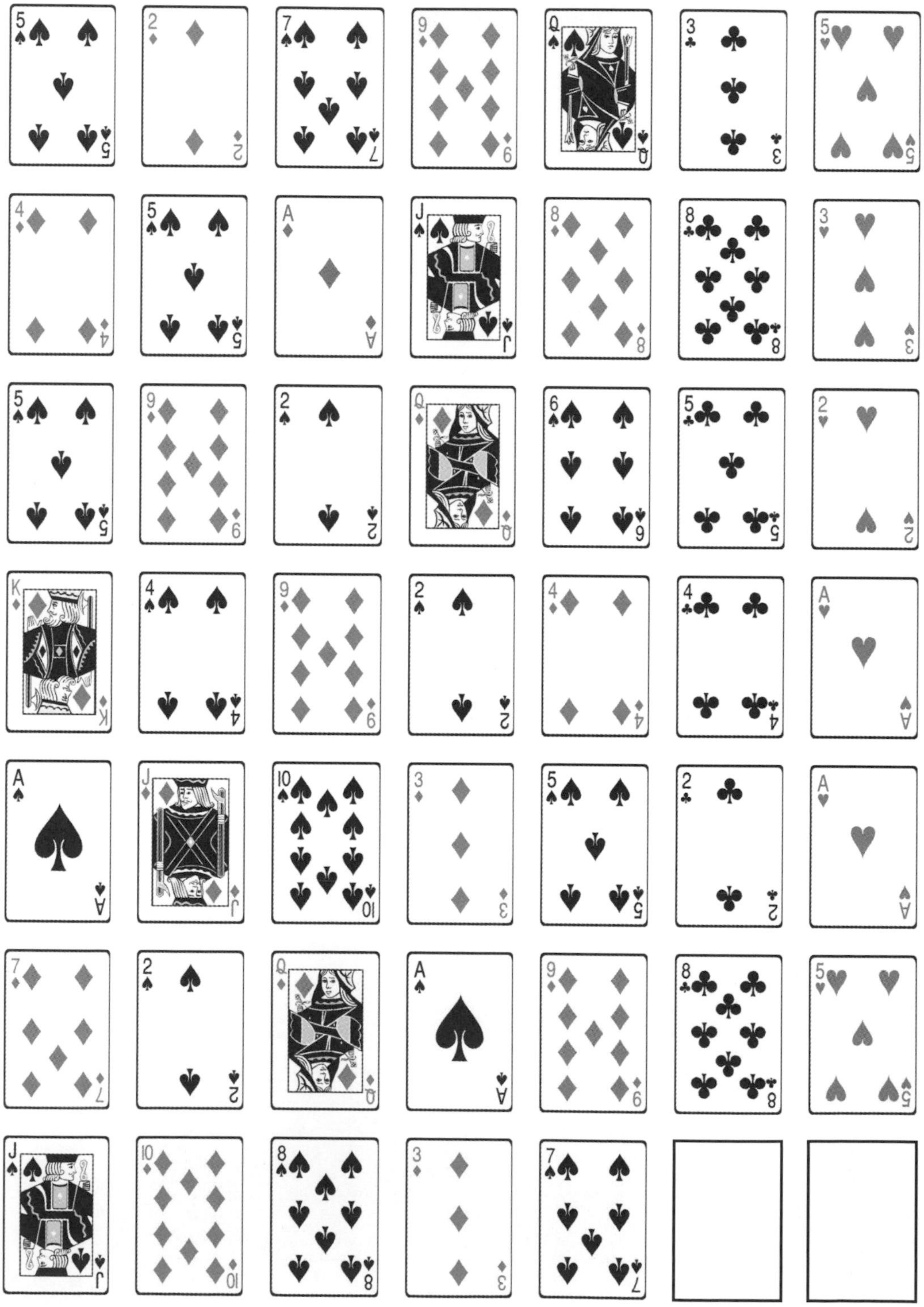

8 PUZZLE

Which number is missing?

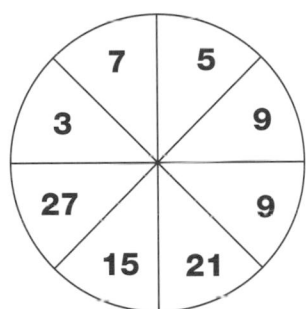

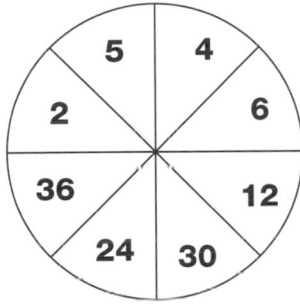

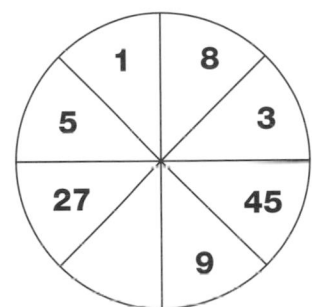

9 PUZZLE

Which of the smaller grids will complete the puzzle?

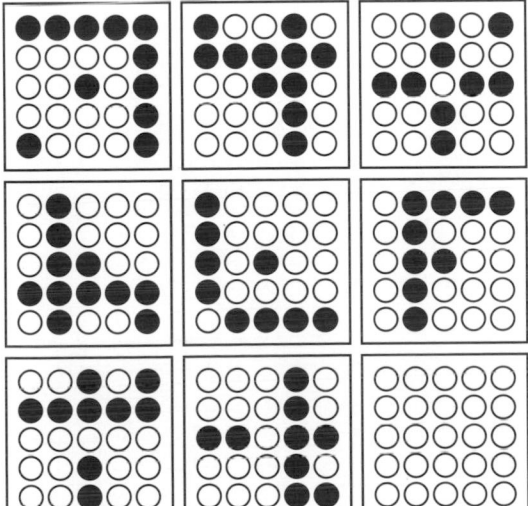

A

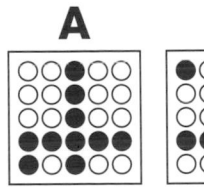

B

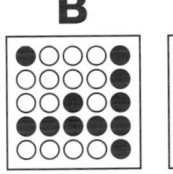

C

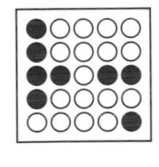

D

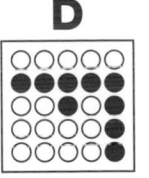

E

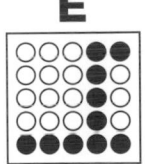

F

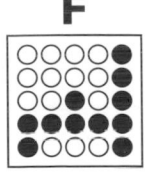

PUZZLE 10

Which number is missing?

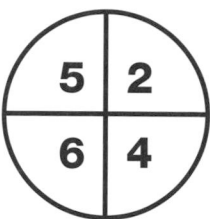

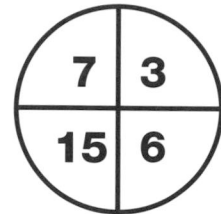

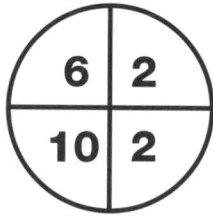

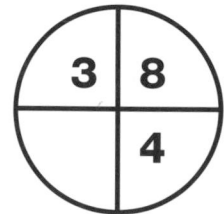

PUZZLE 11

Which number continues the sequence?

5

7

11

19

35

PUZZLE 12

Which of the smaller watches would continue the sequence shown on the top line?

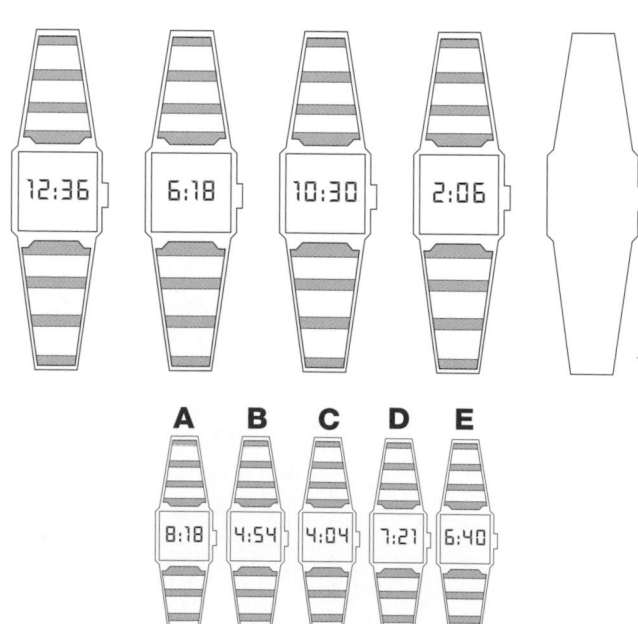

12:36   6:18   10:30   2:06

A   B   C   D   E

8:18   4:54   4:04   7:21   6:40

Which of the smaller grids goes in the middle?

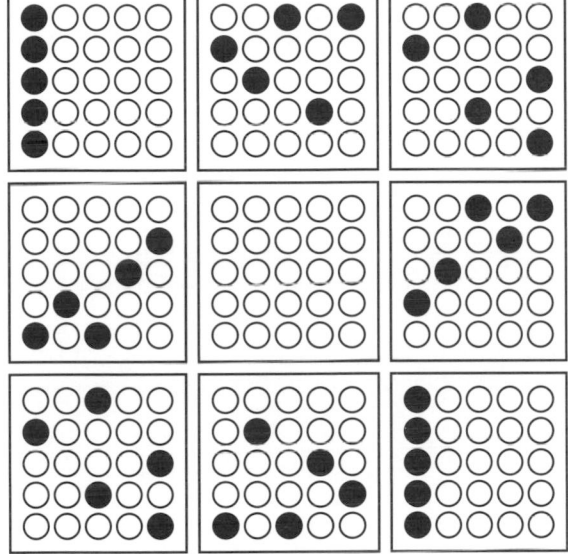

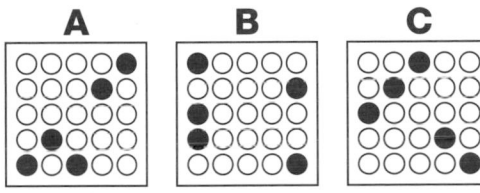

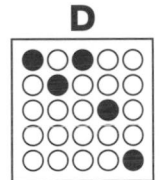 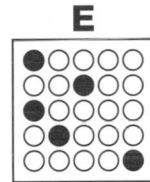 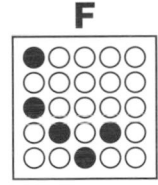

14
PUZZLE

Which number is missing from the empty segment?

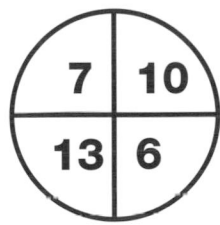

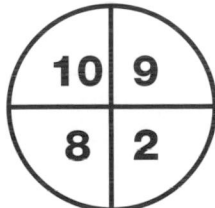

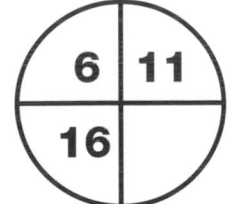

15
PUZZLE

Which letter replaces the blank and completes the sequence?

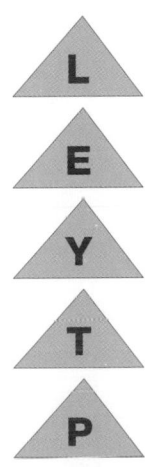

L

E

Y

T

P

16 PUZZLE

Which number is missing from the last circle?

17 PUZZLE

Which watch continues the sequence?

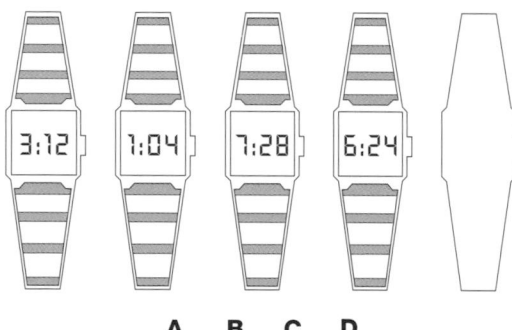

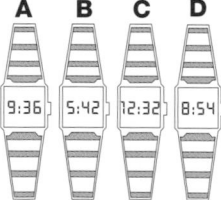

18 PUZZLE

Which number is missing?

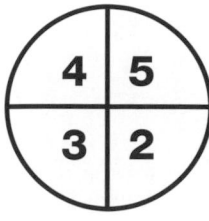

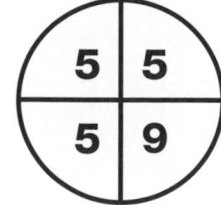

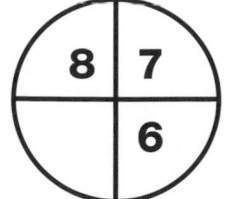

PUZZLE 19

What time will be on the next watch?

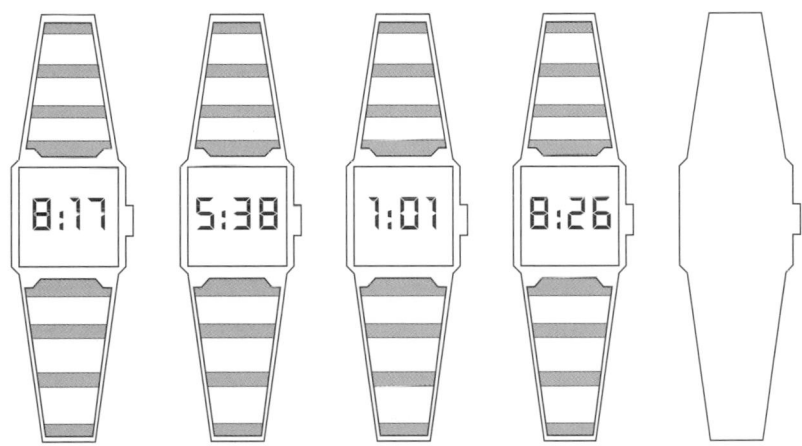

8:17   5:38   1:01   8:26

PUZZLE 20

Which number is missing from the third triangle?

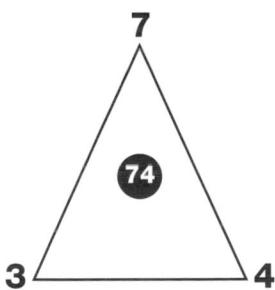

7
74
3   4

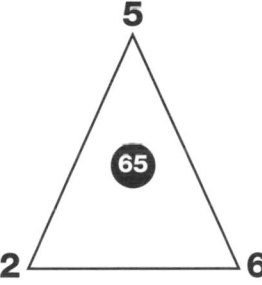

5
65
2   6

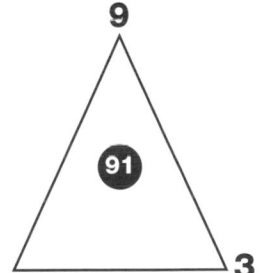

9
91
3

PUZZLE 21

Which number is missing?

7   9
2
5   9

8   5
9
7   5

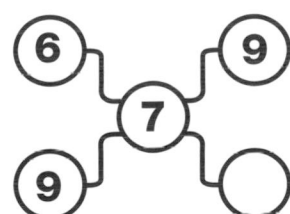

6   9
7
9

LEVEL

18

175

PUZZLE 1

Which number is missing from the web?

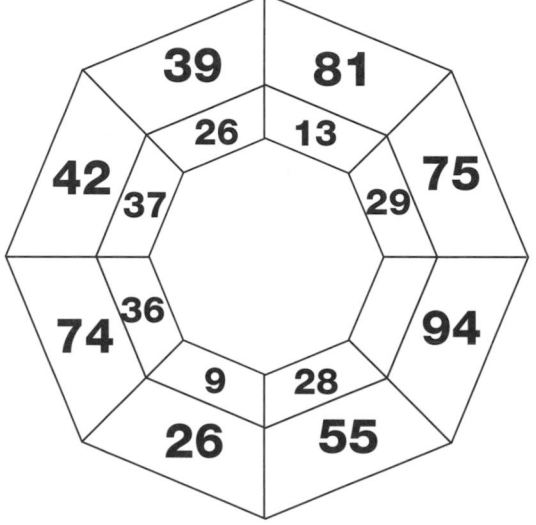

PUZZLE 2

Which number goes in the empty square?

7	3	6
45	5	32

5	8	4
21	60	

PUZZLE 3

Which number goes in the bottom circle?

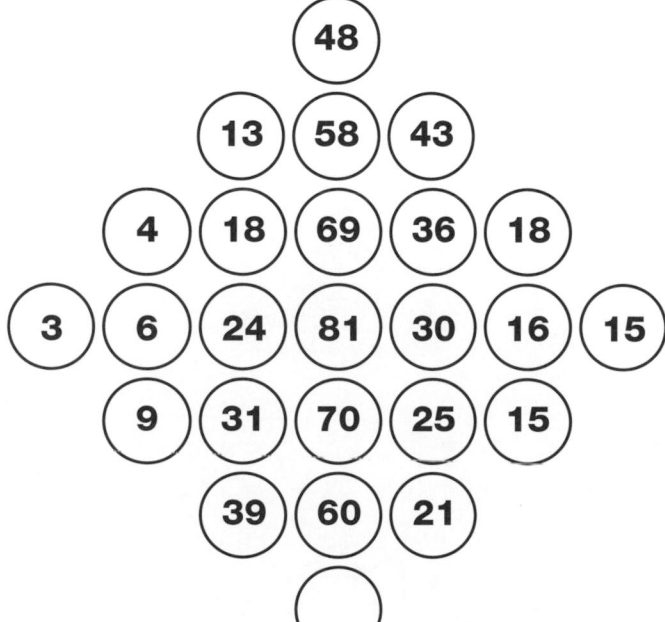

4 PUZZLE

Which number is missing from the bottom grid?

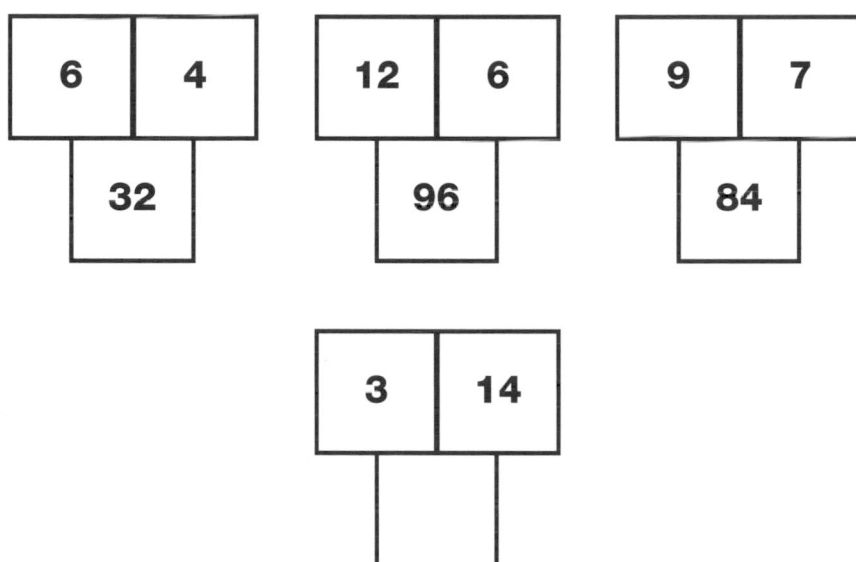

6	4

32

12	6

96

9	7

84

3	14

5 PUZZLE

Draw the correct number of circles in the blank square.

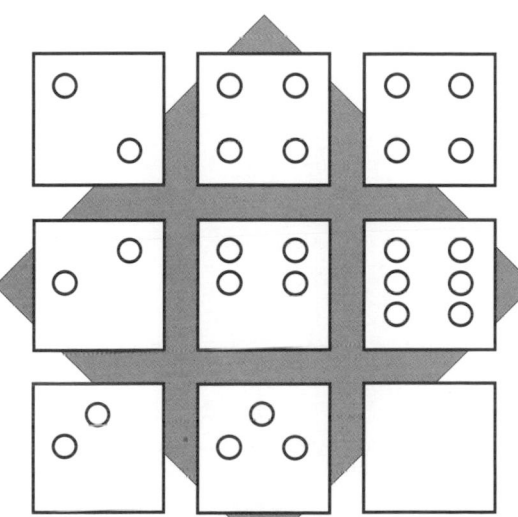

6 PUZZLE

Which number comes next?

10

15

25

35

19

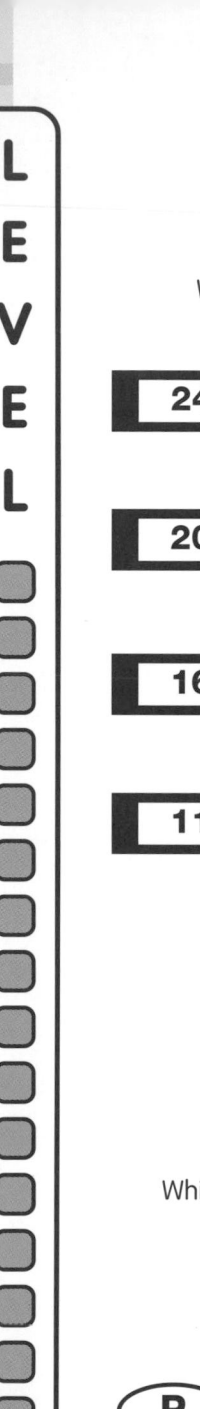

PUZZLE 7

What goes in the empty box?

24	W	5
20	S	9
16	O	13
11		18

PUZZLE 8

Which number is missing from the empty circle?

(4) (10) (28)

(6) (16) (46)

(3) (7) ( )

PUZZLE 9

Which letter replaces the blank and completes the puzzle?

P   C   H

D   L   K

N   (   )   E

PUZZLE 10

Which number comes next?

5

9

17

33

[ ]

11 PUZZLE

Which letter goes in the empty box?

C	B	F
G	G	L
K	L	R
O	Q	

12 PUZZLE

Which number continues this sequence?

3

8

18

38

13 PUZZLE

Which letter goes in the empty circle?

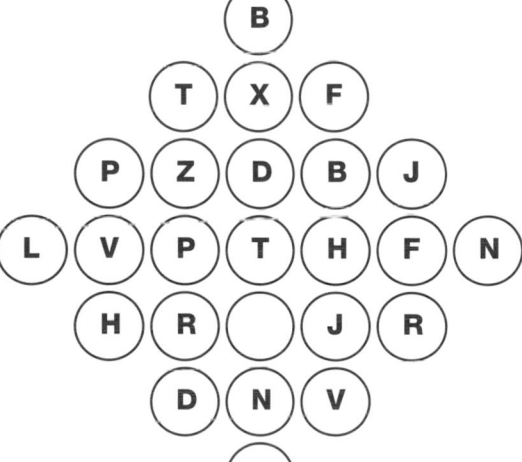

14 PUZZLE

What time should the blank watch be showing?

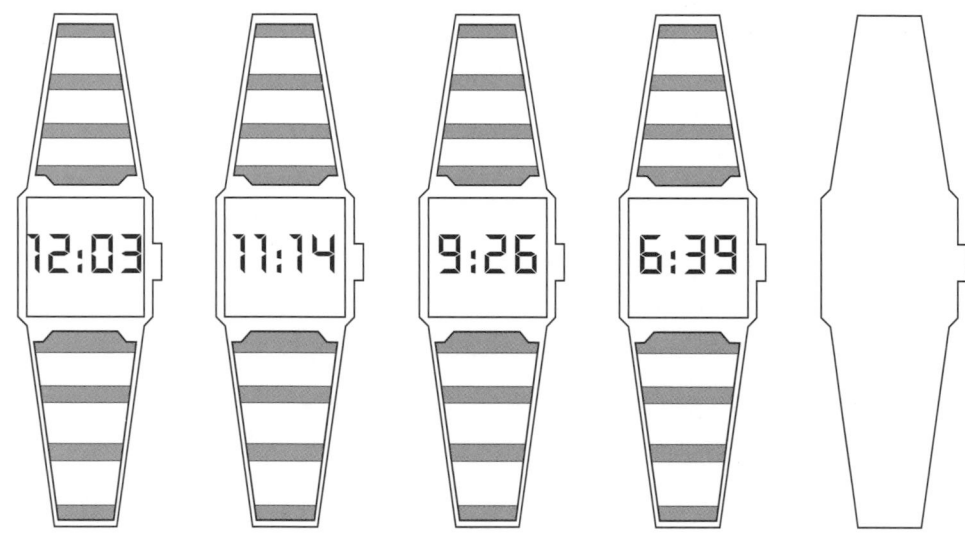

15 PUZZLE

What goes in the empty circle?

16 PUZZLE

Which number is missing?

Four men went to the building supplies centre to buy some tools for the workmen on the building sites they were in charge of. Chris buys 3 screwdrivers, 4 hammers and 5 saws for the men on his building site at a total cost of $9.70. Carl buys 4 screwdrivers, 5 hammers and 3 saws for his carpenters at a total cost of $9. Charlie's $8.90 bought 5 screwdrivers, 3 hammers and 4 saws. Colin, who is in charge of a small building site has less money to spend but still needs 1 screwdriver, 1 hammer and a saw.

How much did he have to spend?

Chris   Charlie   Carl

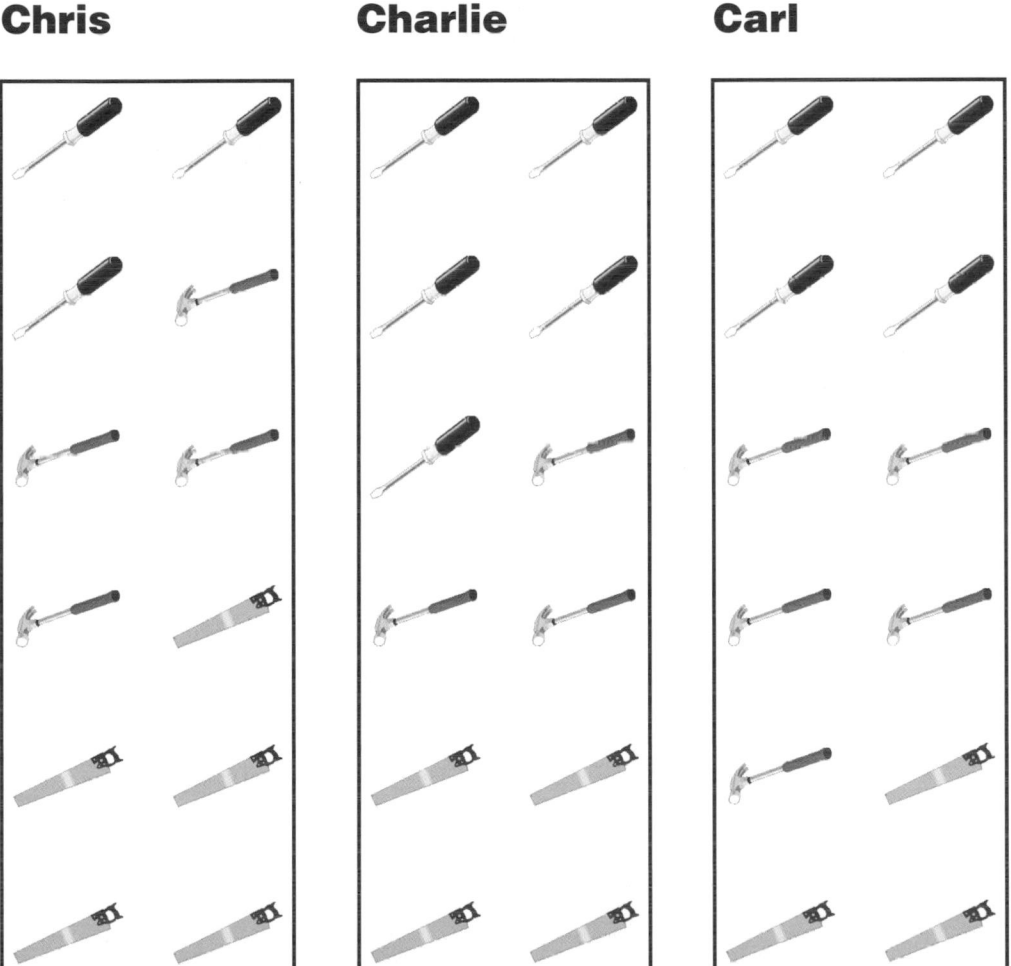

Which of the six smaller boxes finishes this sequence?

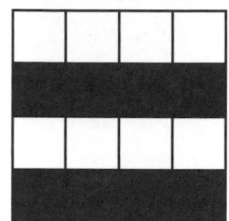

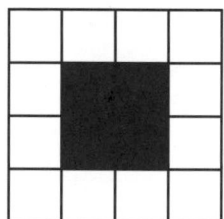

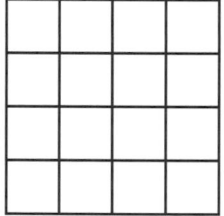

A

B

C

D
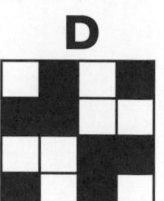

E

F

L
E
V
E
L

19

PUZZLE 1

Which letters replace the blanks and complete the sequence?

Y	O	V	M
K	B	P	A
M	D	R	
Z	P	W	

PUZZLE 2

Which number goes in the empty box?

3	7	9
5	8	11
1	6	7
2	1	

PUZZLE 3

Which letter is missing?

B D G

K T K

C P

PUZZLE 4

Which number is missing from the middle of the circle?

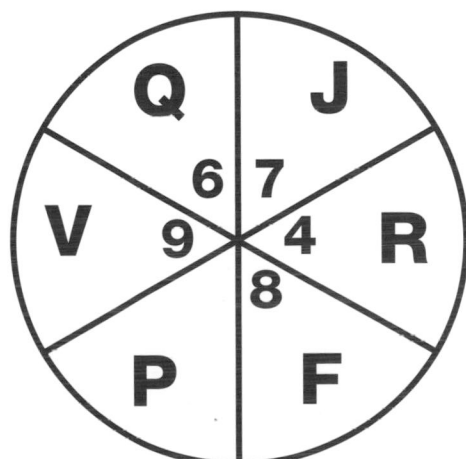

Q J
V 6 7 R
9 4
8
P F

LEVEL

20

183

PUZZLE 5

Which number replaces the question mark?

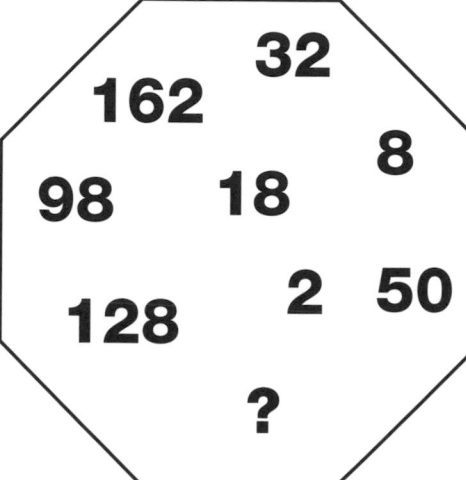

PUZZLE 6

Which number comes next?

199

280

344

360

396

PUZZLE 7

Draw the contents of the empty circle.

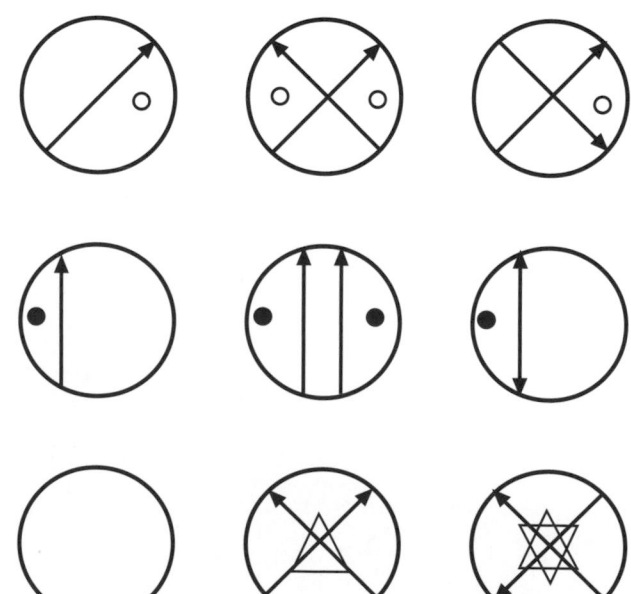

8 PUZZLE

Which number goes in the empty circle and completes the puzzle?

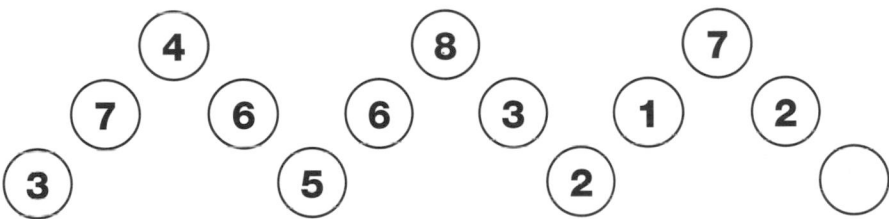

4   8   7

7 6 6 3 1 2

3   5   2   ◯

9 PUZZLE

Which numbers complete the last two grids?

7	8	8
9		0
9		8
4	6	0

A

1	9	2
9		0
7		6
2		9

B

8	8	8
2		1
7		8
6		7

10 PUZZLE

Which number is missing?

3	7	8	6	1	9	1	2	9
5	8	1	3	2	8	3	2	6
4	1	7	2	5	7	4	4	9
7	3	4	9	7	5	2	5	4
6	6	9	1	3	8	8	7	2
1	6	1	8	6	3	7	2	2
6	9	6	3	8	8	3	2	◯

PUZZLE 11

Which domino completes the pattern?

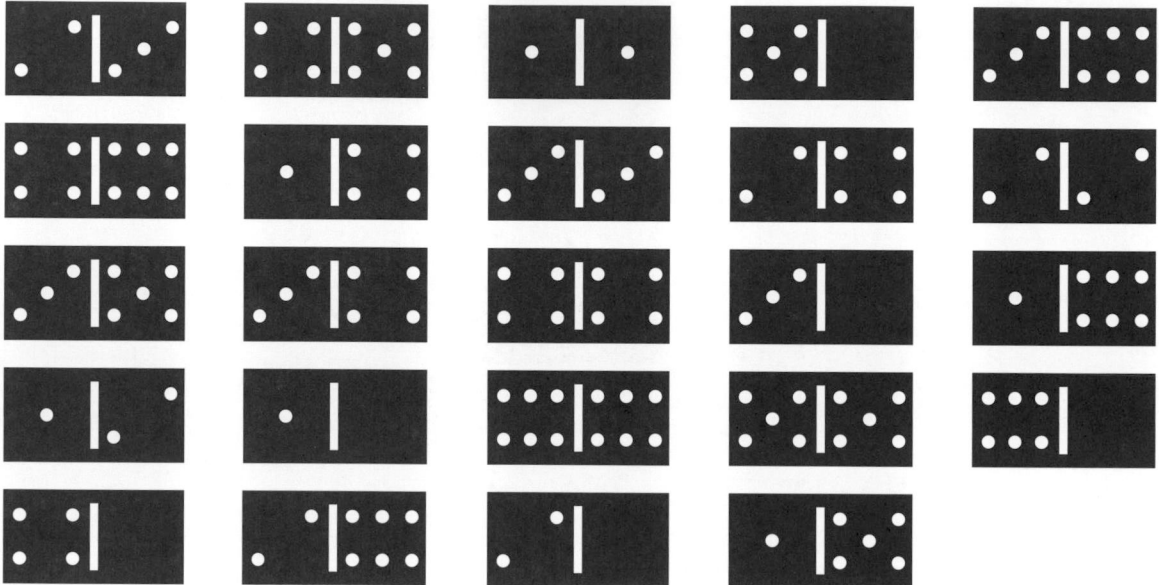

PUZZLE 12

Which of the three letters at the bottom fit into the top grid?

1 G **2** B **3** H

PUZZLE 13

Which letter replaces the blank and completes the sequence?

E	H	L	V	E	M
F	K	T	Z	L	X
I	N	Y	K	W	F
M	X	I	V	E	K
W	H	T	Z	I	M
F	N	Y	H	L	

Which number logically fits into the empty square?

2	9	3	7	6	8
7	1	5	2	0	7
8	5	4	2	9	3

8	8	2	3	9	8
6	5	1	5	4	8
3	5	6	9	5	

Which letter replaces the blank and completes the sequence?

B	D	G	B	A	F
G	D	C	H	H	D
E	F	G	F	E	B

F	D	C	F	H	H
G	D	A	C	C	H
D	C	G	G	F	

Which shape is the odd one out?

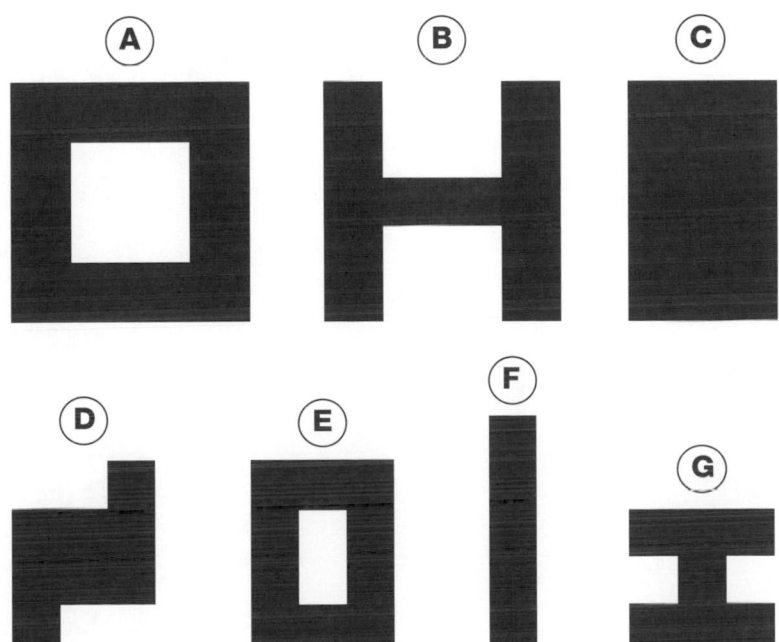

L
E
V
E
L

20

PUZZLE

Complete the last row of the puzzle.

B	J	F	F	L	Z	T	R	F
K	D	G	K	A	S	S	D	I
C	H	J	B	R	T	C	J	Q
I	H	C	Q	U	B	K	P	Z
G	D	P	V	Z	L	N	A	B
E	N	W	Y	M	M	B	Z	Q
M	X	X	N	L	C	Y	R	L
Y	W	O	K	D	X	S	K	J
V	P	J	E	W	T	J	K	S
Q	H	F	V	U	H	L	R	E
G	G	T	V	G	M	Q	F	X
H	S	W	F	N	P	G	W	B
R	X	D	O	N	H	V	C	Z

20

SOLUTIONS

LEVEL

1 - 6
In each square the bottom segment equals the sum of the other 3 segments.

2 - C
In each row, the sum of the centre letter equals the sum of the left and right hand letters.

3 - 71
Add the first two numbers together to get the third, repeating around the grid.

4 - 23
In columns, add the first three numbers together to get the figure in the bottom box.

5 - P
In each circle, letters move clockwise by increasing steps.

6 - 4
Numbers in each column add up to 9.

7 -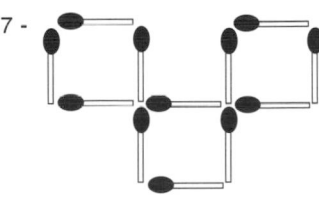

8 - X
Letters advance by 4, 5, 6 and 7.

9 - U
In columns, the value of the bottom letter equals the sum of the values of the other two.

10 - 8
Working in rows, add the left and centre numbers together to give the result on the right.

11 - 9
In rows, add the left and centre figures to get the right hand number.

12 - 3
Working in rows, the figure on the right equals half the difference between the left and central numbers.

13 - 1
Taking the top and bottom lines separately, add the left and centre numbers, then subtract the right hand number to give the figure in the middle.

14 - 4
Numbers in each row add up to 14.

15 -

Working in columns, as you move down, one feature is removed with each step, and the smile alternates with the frown.

16 - 5
In rows, double the left and centre digits and add together to give the right hand figure.

17 - 23
Moving across each row, from top to bottom, the numbers follow the sequence of prime numbers.

18 - 2
In each square, the sum of the 3 outer numbers divided by the central number always equals 6.

19 - 1 = P, 2 = J
All the other letters contain straight lines only.

20 - 36
Segments in the right hand half equal the squares of the diagonally opposing segments on the left.

21 - R
Starting in the top left of each figure and moving clockwise, the letters ascend the alphabet

in steps given in the centre value.

22 - M
Each centre letter is the midpoint between the pairs of letters in the diagonal lines.

23 - 11
Working in rows, halve the first number, double the middle number and add them together to give the right hand number.

24 - 5
Working in rows, the first three numbers add up to the right hand number. In the next line, the three numbers to the right add up to the left hand number, etc. etc.

25 - No.
As the water level rises the pointer moves towards 'Drought'.

26 - X
The letters in the central column come midway in the alphabet between the left and right hand numbers.

27 - P
The numbers between pairs of letters equal the sum of the numerical values of the letters on either side.

28 - Ace (of any suit)
Taking the vertical, horizontal and 2 diagonal lines through the centre of the square, the sum of the values at the ends of the lines equal 12, the value of the centre card.

29 - E & S
Starting on the left and going down, then up the right column, letters advance in steps of two.

30 -

Working in rows from left to

SOLUTIONS

right, the dot moves anticlockwise by one segment, then clockwise by three.

31 - 1
In each circle, the bottom number equals the sum of the squares of the top two numbers.

32 - K
In each star, the letters run clockwise in alphabetical order, in steps of 3 for the left hand star, 4 for the centre and 2 for the right hand star.

33 - W & E
In each circle, add 5 to the value of the top left letter to give the bottom left letter, and then add 2 to the top right to give the bottom right.

34 - 7
Working in rows, the central number equals the sum of the left and right hand numbers.

35 - 17
The chain follows the sequence of prime numbers.

36 - J
In rows, the value of the right hand letter equals the difference between the values of the left and centre letters.

37 - 23
Starting in the top left corner and moving clockwise in a spiral, add 3 to get the next value, then 2, then 1, etc.

LEVEL 2

1 -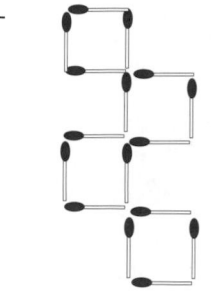

2 - It will rise.

3 - 48
Numbers advance by 2, 4, 8 and 16.

4 - 3
In each row, add the left and the right hand numbers and divide by 2 to get the central value.

5 - U
In each row, add the numerical value of the left and centre letters to give the right hand letter.

6 - 9
Each row, column and diagonal adds up to 15.

7 - 2
Add the numerical values of each pair of letters and write the answer, as two separate digits in the boxes underneath.

8 - G
Working clockwise around each star, letters increase in steps given by the numerical value of the central figure.

9 - Z
Letters advance in steps of 12, returning to the start of the alphabet after Z.

10 - R
In columns, add the numerical value of the top and middle letters to give the bottom letters.

11 - 2
In each triangle, add the lower two digits and multiply by the top digit to give the value in the centre.

12 - 7
In each line, the central number equals the left hand number and double the right hand number.

13 - H
Going clockwise around each square, the letters increase in value in steps presented by the central square.

14 -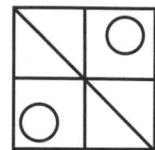

Working in rows, the central figure is made from superimposing the left and right hand figures.

15 - 81
As you go down, subtract the sum of the separate digits in each number from itself to give the next number.

16 - A
In each row, from left to right, the black circle moves clockwise around each corner, the hash moves one place down and the triangle moves anticlockwise around the central 4 squares.

17 - 7
Add the top figures together, then the bottom ones. The central figure is the difference between these two answers.

18 - 4

19 - 14
Starting on the left, double each number and add two to give the value in the corresponding segment in the circle to the right.

20 -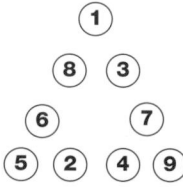

21 - 8
All vertical and diagonal lines through the centre add up to 14.

22 - 8
In each circle, the sum of the odd numbers plus one equals the sum of the even numbers.

190

SOLUTIONS

23 - 34
Starting at 3 and moving clockwise, double the preceding number and subtract 2.

24 - 72cm

25 - 13
Moving clockwise, each segment equals the sum of the previous two segments.

26 - T
Multiply the numerical value of the left hand letter by the right hand letter to give the central figure.

27 - 13
Going down the columns, moving left to right, numbers follow the sequence of prime numbers.

28 - C
Working in rows from left to right, the @ moves 1 place clockwise in the central 4 squares, the △ moves 2 places clockwise around the outside of the square, while the ✻ moves 2 places anticlockwise.

29 - 7
In each circle, the sum of the digits equals 34.

30 - S
The numerical value of the bottom letters equals the sum of the numerical values of the top two letters.

31 - Z
Starting from C and moving clockwise letters advance alternately 5 and 4 places.

32 - M
Working in columns, the bottom letter equals the sum of the top and centre letters.

1 - G
In each triangle the numerical value of the lower left letter

increases by the value of the top letter to give the lower right letter.

2 - 29
The sum of the numerical values of the three letters.

3 - K
Letters in the left hand column move through the alphabet, skipping letters written without curves, letters in the right hand column skip letters with curves.

4 - 6 Painters.

5 - F
In each circle, the sum of the numerical values of opposite segments adds up to the same figure - 16 for the left hand circle, 17 for the top and 18 for the bottom.

6 - 60
Multiply the figures at the opposite ends of the central circle to give the same answer.

7 - 9
The four corners add up to 35, as do the four centre figures on each side of the square.

8 - 6
The numbers in each square, including the middle one, add up to 15.

9 - 3
Working in columns, divide the top value by the centre to give the bottom figure.

10 - 12
As you go down each pair of numbers, the left hand value equals the sum of the numbers above and the right hand value equals the difference of the pair of numbers above.

11 - 2
The figures in each row add up to 11.

12 - W
In rows from left to right each

letter represents the numerical value of the first 9 prime numbers.

13 - Ace of Hearts
In each row the sum of the red cards equals the sum of the black cards, with one card from each suit in every line.

14 - 5
The sum of the numerical values of the letters are written on the bottom two points of each star as a two digit number.

15 - T
Letters are arranged in alphabetical order, skipping any letters written with curved lines.

16 - 8
The centre value equals the difference between the left and right hand numbers.

17 - 5
The product of the numbers in opposite segments always equals 60.

18 - F
Working in columns, subtract the value of the middle letter from the value of the top letter.

19 - 22
The centre number equals the sum of the bottom two digits minus the top digit.

20 - 43
Moving clockwise the numbers increase by 2, 3, 5, 7, 11 etc. – the sequence of prime numbers.

21 - F
Moving clockwise, letters decrease in value from U in steps of 1, 2, 3, 4 and 5.

22 - 2
In each circle subtract the right hand digit from the left hand digit, then subtract a further one to give the lower digit.

23 - 6
The sum of the values around

191

SOLUTIONS

the edge of the puzzle add up to the centre number.

24 - 3
The two digit numbers in alternate boxes represent the sum of the alphabetical value of the left hand letter in the box above and the reverse alphabetical value of the right hand letter.

25 - T
Letters in opposite segments of the circle are the same distance from the start of the alphabet as the other letter is from the end.

26 - 6
Working in rows, add the first and second numbers, then deduct 1 to give the right hand number.

27 - 8
The sequence follows the formula - double the previous number then add 1, etc.

28 - A = 12, B = 25,
They are the only even number or only odd number in each ellipse.

29 - 4
In each column of three the numbers add up to 16.

30 - 5
In each grid numbers move clockwise in steps given by the central number.

31 - E
In each row, subtract the numerical value of the middle letter from the left hand letter to give the right hand letter.

32 - L
Letters at opposite ends of each line come in pairs – one is the same distance from the start of the alphabet as the other is from the end.

33 - 16 years old.

34 - 26

Going clockwise, numbers represent the sequence of prime numbers multiplied by 2.

35 - O
In each box, multiply the numerical values of the letters, and write the three-figure result in the lower half.

36 - 3
Figures in the centre column equal the sum of the numbers in the right and left.

37 - Q
In each circle the letters move clockwise in increments of 7 for the top left circle through to 3 for the bottom right circle.

LEVEL 4

1 - C

2 - 10
In rows, the centre number equals the difference between the left and right hand numbers.

3 - 3
Add the numerical values of the pairs of letters and write the two digit result in the boxes below.

4 -

Working in rows, the figure on the right is formed by superimposing the left hand figure rotated 90° clockwise and the centre figure rotated 90° anti-clockwise.

5 - 4
In each figure, the sum of the left hand digits divided by the sum of the right hand digits gives the central value.

6 - O
Starting bottom left and moving clockwise in a spiral, letters advance by 9 places, then 8, 7, 6, etc.

7 - 25%

8 - 21
Numbers increase down the row by 5, then 4, 3, etc.

9 - 2 & 0
The digits under each group of letters represent the value of the left hand letter and the reverse alphabetical value of the right hand letter, written as a two digit number.

10 - 19
The figures in the central column equal the sum of the numbers in each corresponding row.

11 - O
Working from left to right, letters in corresponding positions on each triangle advance by 7, 6 or 5 places as you move to the right.

12 - 5
Working in rows, multiply the average of the left and right hand numbers by three to give the middle number.

13 - P
In each diagram, the numerical value of each letter plus the numerical value of the letter below it adds up to the same number.

14 - 14
Starting in the top left and moving between circles in a W shape, numbers in corresponding segments increase in value by 2, 3, 4 and 5.

15 - Y
In each circle, starting with the top left letter, move 10 places forward to give the top right figure, and move another 10 places forward to give the bottom letter.

16 - 2
Working in columns, multiply the top and bottom values to get a 2 figure result, written in the 2 central squares.

SOLUTIONS

17 -

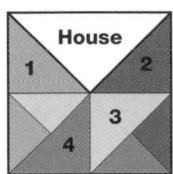

18 - R
Taking rows across each group letters increase by 2, 3, 4, 5 and then 6.

19 - 49
The sum of the digits at corresponding positions on each triangle equals 100.

20 - 54
For each box, the number enclosed by the central box equals the sum of the squares of the other three numbers.

21 - Seven of Hearts
In rows, add the left and central card values to give the value of the right hand card value. The suit of the left card is the same as that of the right hand card.

22 - Q
Starting at the top of each triangle, letters progress clockwise in increments given by the central number plus 2.

23 - 5 mechanics, with a little time left over.

24 - 4

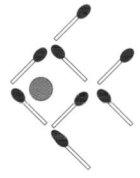

25 - 42
As you go down, double the previous number and subtract 10.

26 - 54 or 6
Segments on the left equal the values in the opposite segments multiplied by three.

27 - 3
In each grid, add the top 6-digit number to the middle number to give the bottom result.

28 -

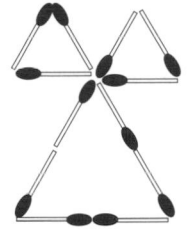

29 - A
Using the numerical values of the letters, each set of four diagonally opposite letters equals 19.

30 - 1 = L, 2 = E
All other letters are written with three lines.

LEVEL 5

1 - 8 biscuits.

2 - 11 & 5
Alternate numbers increase by 2, the others decrease by 1.

3 - 677
Square each value and add 1 to get the next number.

4 - L
Add the numerical values of the bottom two letters and divide by the numerical value of the top letter to give the value of the centre letter.

5 - 66
Working from left to right, double the previous number and subtract 2.

6 - E
Going clockwise letters increase in value by the value of the centre letter.

7 - 13
Starting at the top, add the two numbers together to give the left hand number underneath. The right hand number is the same as the left hand number above.

8 - K
Moving clockwise in alternate sections, letters advance by 6 or 5 places.

9 - 23
Working clockwise, numbers increase by 2, 3 and 4 in a repeating sequence.

10 - 3
The difference in the numbers in each segment equals the numerical value of the letter in the opposite segment.

11 - V
Starting top left and moving clockwise in a spiral, letters advance in steps of 2, 3, 4, 5 etc.

12 - 1/4 of the original amount.

13 - 35
Numbers advance in steps of 7, 8, 9 and 10.

14 - 4
In each figure the middle value equals the difference between the products of the top pair of numbers and the bottom pair.

15 - Yes
The bottom left turns anticlockwise, while all the others turn clockwise.

16 - 14
Working in rows, multiply the left and right hand numbers together and add 2 to give the centre value.

17 - 13
In each circle the lower number equals the average of the top two numbers.

18 - D
Working in columns, one cross is removed at each step, first from one side of the pattern, then the opposite side.

19 - D
On each watch the digits add up to 15.

20 - 2
For each circle multiply the top two numbers together to give a 2 digit value, written in the bottom segments.

193

SOLUTIONS

21 - 4
Starting at the top, the right hand number equals the left hand number plus 6, in the next line add 5, then 4, 3, 2 and 1.

22 - A
Moving from left to right, one dark segment moves 1 place clockwise while the other moves 2 places anticlockwise.

23 - 19
In each circle, going clockwise, alternate even numbers increase in steps of 2, odd numbers increase in steps of 4.

24 - 2
In each row, divide the left hand value by the centre value to get the right hand number.

25 -

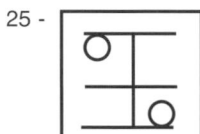

Working in rows from left to right, add the elements of the first two boxes to give the figure on the right.

26 - 8
In each square, multiply the top and bottom numbers then subtract the left and right hand numbers, the result is 40 each time.

27 - 36
In rows, multiply the left and centre numbers then subtract the smaller of the numbers to give the right hand value.

28 - M
Going clockwise move forward 5 places, then back 3, missing out all the vowels.

29 - I
Taking the numerical values of the letters in each figure, subtract the right hand numbers from the left hand numbers on the same line to give the central number.

30 - 15
Each segment in the lower right box equals the sum of the values in the corresponding segments of the other squares.

31 - 2
The numbers in each line of 3 circles, going through the centre, add up to 15.

32 - 10
The values of the points of the central star equal the sums of the values of the corresponding points of the left and right hand stars.

LEVEL 6

1 - 6
In rows the right hand digit equals double the difference between the left and the centre.

2 - J
Letters move clockwise in steps of 10.

3 - 14
Double the numbers in the top left circle to give the values in the lower left circle. Double the numbers in the top right circle to give the values in the lower right circle. The difference between corresponding values are put in the last remaining circle.

4 - 19
The numbers, starting at 2 and going clockwise around each circle, represent the first 9 prime numbers.

5 -

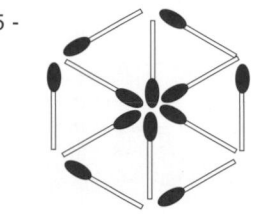

6 - Y
Going clockwise, the letters in alternate segments advance 6.

7 - 6
Numbers in each row add up to 26.

8 - 10
In each circle, add the top 2 numbers and subtract the lower right number to give the lower left number.

9 - 7
Add together the numbers on the outside of each segment and put the result at the centre of the opposite segment.

10 -

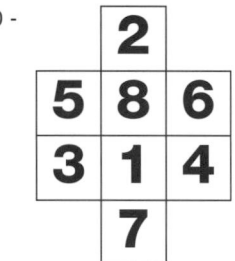

Other answers may also be correct.

11 - W
Letters on the left descend in steps of four. The values of the letters on the right equal the values of the letters on the left plus three, then minus three, etc.

12 - X
In rows letters in the first line increase by steps of 5 from left to right, the second row in steps of 4, the next by three and the bottom line by 2.

13 - 49
Square the values in the segments on the left half, and put the results in the opposite segment on the right.

14 - 24 & 2
Each segment in the lower left circle equals the sum of the corresponding segments in top circles. The numbers in the bottom right circle are the sum of the even numbers in the top circles, minus the odd numbers.

194

SOLUTIONS

15 - 7
In each circle, multiply the upper left number by 2 and subtract 1 to give the upper right number. Then multiply the original number by 3 and subtract 1 to get the bottom number.

16 - A = 127, B = 56
All other numbers are divisible by 9.

17 - 7
Starting at the top left and working down, and bottom right and working up, add the left hand number to the right hand number and put this answer in the centre column reading downwards.

18 - 14
Numbers on corresponding points of each triangle progress by increasing steps, add 6 then 7 for the top, 5 and 6 for the bottom left and then 7 and 8 for the bottom right.

19 - H
In the first box, starting with the top left, letters advance by a decreasing amount, starting with 6, then 5, 4, etc. The second box advances by 7, 6, 5, etc. and the third box by 8, 7, 6, etc.

20 - 29
As you go down each block of two, the right hand number is duplicated in the left hand square below, and the right hand number equals the sum of the two squares above.

21 - 15
In each circle, the lower left value equals the sum of the numerical values of the letters and the top right value equals the difference in the letter values.

22 - 8
In each diagram the central value equals the difference between the product of the top two numbers and bottom two numbers.

23 - 75
Each shape contains the same numbers multiplied by 3, 4 and 5.

24 - W
In each circle add the numerical values of the upper two letters to give the numerical value of the bottom letter.

25 - G
In each circle, going clockwise, alternate letters increase in value by 3 steps for the left hand circle, 4 for the upper and 5 for the lower circle.

26 - D
In each row, divide the numerical value of the left hand letter by the number in the centre column to give the numerical value of the right hand letter.

27 - 152
As you move clockwise multiply the previous number by 2 and add 2, 3, 4, 5 and 6.

28 - 3
Working in rows the central figure equals the difference in the squares of the left and right hand numbers.

29 - B
Moving across each row from left to right, the # appears in alternate boxes, rotating 1/4 turn around the central 4 squares. The O moves to the right on the top row, then down 1 space and to the left. The * moves to each corner up, down to the left, up then down to the right.

LEVEL 7

1 - 42
Divide each circle into left and right halves. The top right value equals the sum of the left hand numbers, the middle right value equals the product of the left hand numbers and the bottom right hand value equals the sum of the squares of the left hand numbers.

2 - 32
Working downwards, square the numbers 0, 1, 2, 3 and 4 and multiply by 2.

3 - M
Starting from A alternate letters increase in steps of 3, the other letters, starting from G increase in steps of 2.

4 - 10
Going clockwise, the values increase equal increments and move 90° clockwise each step.

5 - D
The lines along each half domino add up to the number of dots shown on the right hand side.

6 - A
Add the reverse alphabetical value of the bottom two letters of each triangle and subtract the reverse alphabetical value of the top letter to give the value of the middle letter in alphabetical order.

7 - 236
Working in columns from top to bottom, on the left, multiply each value by 2 then subtract 2 to give the next number. In the centre column by 3 and the right hand column by 4.

8 - 2
Starting with the digits to the top and left move in lines of three digits subtracting the centre digit to give the bottom and right figures.

9 - 2
Add the top 2 digits in each group and multiply the centre, the result is written in the bottom circles.

10 - 6
Starting in the top left of each figure, numbers increase in a clockwise direction by the value given in the central circle.

SOLUTIONS

11 - 4
In each column, the sum of the three smaller figures equals the larger figure.

12 - 6
The centre figure is the product of the left and right numbers, minus 1.

13 - 1 = M, 2 = J
The numerical values of No. 1 are divisible by 3, in No. 2 the numbers are divisible by 4.

14 - 51
Working in rows, invert the digits in the left and right hand numbers and add them together to give the central figure.

15 - Five of Clubs
In rows, add together the values of the first four cards to get a 2 digit number. Add these together to give the value of the right hand card. The suit of this card is the same as the card to the left with the highest value.

16 - 68
In each circle, divide the difference between the top and right hand numbers by 4 to give the left hand value.

17 - 168
Subtract 4 then multiply each number by 3 to give the next number.

18 - M
Taking the numerical value of the letters each row and column adds up to 27.

19 - U
Taking all 3 groups together, letters increase in value in rows from left to right by 3 for the top row, 4 for the middle and 5 for the bottom row.

20 - F
In columns, the central number equals the sum of the numerical value of the top and bottom letters.

21 - 12
Starting from the top, subtract 2 then add 7 and continue this sequence.

22 - Z
In rows, add the numerical value of left and centre letters to give the value of the right hand letter.

23 - 21
In each grid, add up the 4 numbers at the corners and write the result downwards in the centre column.

24 - 30
In each circle, multiply the two upper numbers and subtract 10 to give the lower value.

25 - B
Divide the numerical value of the left hand letter by the numerical value of the right hand letter to give the value of the lower letter.

26 - 25
The larger numbers are the squares of the numbers in the opposite segments of the circle.

27 - 1
The figures in the right hand column equal the difference between the numbers in the left and centre columns.

28 - M
Starting at the bottom left and moving anticlockwise, letters progress through the alphabet in steps of 2, then 3, etc. etc. returning to the beginning of the alphabet whenever Z is reached.

29 -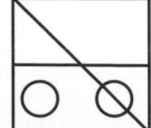

Working in rows, rotate the left hand figure by a 1/4 turn clockwise to give the central figure, and 1/4 turn anticlockwise to give the right hand figure.

30 - 2
In each diagram, add the numerical values of the four letters and write the two digit answer down the right hand column.

31 - O
Starting top left and moving clockwise in a spiral, letters follow the alphabetical sequence, missing out letters written without any curved lines.

LEVEL

1 - 34
Working with the corresponding numbers in each box the numbers decrease by one each move downwards.

2 - P
In each row letters increase in value from left to right in steps of three for the top row, then 4, 5 and 6 for the other rows.

3 - 7
Splitting the diagram into four smaller squares the value in the box towards the centre equals the sum of the other three numbers.

4 - O
In rows, each letter is represented by a 2 digit figure, the first digit being the difference between the left and centre numbers, the second digit equals the sum of the two numbers.

5 - 3
Starting top left and moving clockwise in a spiral, the sequence of letters I, R, T, W, E, D, B, T, F, O, O, S repeats over and over.

6 - 10 metres.

7 - B
In each row, add the black squares from the left hand and centre boxes to give the figure in the right hand box.

196

SOLUTIONS

8 - 6
For the first sequence, double the top numbers separately and enter the answer in the third box down, repeat this for the fifth line. For the next sequence add one to each figure on the second row and put the answer on the fourth row, repeating again for the last row.

9 - 10
Numbers are arranged in columns of 4, with each one increasing downwards in steps of 2.

10 - 17 & M
Numbers on the left descend in prime number order, starting with 3. Values of the right hand letters also follow the prime order sequence, this time starting with 2.

11 - 1600
She likes squared numbers.

12 -

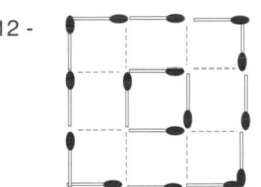

13 - 6
Take the 2 digit number at the centre of each segment putting the sum and the difference of the two digits in the segment opposite.

14 - 37
As you go down, double the previous number and subtract 5.

15 - 6
In each square, add up the outer three numbers, then add the two digits of the result together to give the central number.

16 -

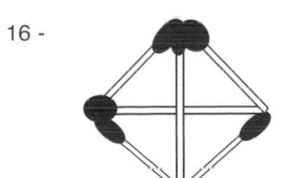

17 - 6
Each row and column contains 4 consecutive numbers in a random order.

18 - F
Starting bottom right and moving in an anticlockwise spiral, letters skip 1 space, then 2 etc. etc. returning to the letter A whenever Z is reached.

19 -

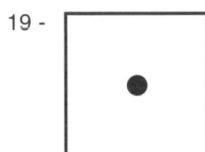

In rows, the right hand box contains only the features common to the two boxes to the left. The columns are calculated the same way, with the bottom box containing only the features common to the boxes above it.

20 - 12
In each triangle, divide the product of the upper and left hand numbers by the right hand number to give the central number.

21 - 3
Working in columns, subtract the middle number from the top number and multiply by 3 to give the bottom value.

22 - 3
In each diagram, add up the 4 outer numbers to give a 2 digit value. Add these 2 digits together to give the central value.

23 - 24
Square the numbers 1, 2, 3, 4 and 5 and subtract 1.

24 - D
The figures in the other three boxes total greater than 100.

25 - O
Moving from left to right, letters on corresponding points of each triangle increase in steps of 4, 5 and 6.

26 - B
In each square take the numerical value of the left and right segments to give the value of the letter in the top segment and the reverse alphabetical value of the letter in the bottom segment.

27 - 8
For each number on the left, starting at the top, double it and subtract 1, then 2, 3, 4 etc. to give the right hand number.

28 - R
Starting on the left in rows, letters ascend in sequence at intervals of 5 for the top row, then 4, then 3.

29 - Jenny is 37, her father is 73.

30 - 14
The numbers in the inner ring are the same as the numbers in the opposite outer ring, divided by 3.

31 - 5
In rows, the sum of the left and centre value equals the right hand value for the first and third rows, in the second and fourth rows the right hand value equals the difference between the left hand and centre numbers.

32 - T
Add the reverse alphabetical values of the three letters around each triangle to give the middle letter in forwards alphabetical order.

33 - 6
In rows, the right hand figure equals the sum of the left and centre numbers plus 2.

LEVEL 9

1 - 29
In each star the central number equals the difference between the sum of the odd and even numbers.

197

SOLUTIONS

2 - 4
The sequence is subtract 2, then add 1, etc.

3 - Z
Going from left to right along the top line then the bottom, letter values increase by three while their positions move 90° clockwise.

4 - 43
In each circle, starting top left and moving clockwise, multiply each number by 3 and subtract 5 to give the next number.

5 - 161
In each circle, going clockwise, double the first number and subtract 1 to give the next number.

6 - E
The sum of the numbers gives the left hand letter, and also the right hand letter in reverse order.

7 - 6
The central number of each triangle equals the difference between the sum of the odd and even numbers.

8 - 3
The numbers in the central column equal the sum of the numbers in the same row to the left, minus the numbers on the right.

9 - 64
Each box represents the cube of numbers 1, 2, 3 and 4.

10 - N
In each square letters in opposite segments hold the same position in the alphabet running forwards as they do going backwards.

11 - 2
In rows multiply the far left number by the far right to give the 2 digit result, written in the central squares.

12 - N
The numerical value of each letter equals the product of the two numbers in the opposite segment.

13 - N Working in rows, letters advance by 4, 2 and 5 places.

14 - P
Starting top left and moving clockwise to end in the centre, the letters increment by a repeating sequence of 1, 2 and 3 places.

15 - 24
Working clockwise, numbers increase by 2, 3, 4, 5 and 6.

16 - B
Working in rows, invert the left and right hand boxes vertically and add the elements together to give the middle box.

17 - 2 and 9 of any suit.
Working in rows the sum of the numerical values of the first five cards equals the 2 digit number represented by the last two cards.

18 - E
Working in columns, top to bottom, one spot is removed in sequence at each step.

19 - 6
In each diagram, the central number equals the difference between the product of the two right hand numbers and the product of the two left hand numbers.

20 - X
Working left to right, starting on the top row, letters increase in value in steps of 2, 3 and 4.

21 - 39

22 -

Break two of the matches in half.

23 - 66
As you move clockwise double the preceding number and subtract 2.

24 - 19
Starting top left and moving clockwise around each square, numbers in corresponding segments advance by 2, 3, 4 and 5.

25 - 23

26 - Z
Going clockwise around each star increase in numerical values by 6, 7 and 8 spaces.

27 - K
The central number in each triangle equals double the sum of the numerical values of the letters on the triangles points.

LEVEL 10

1 - K
Starting at top left and moving clockwise in a spiral, letters move back through the alphabet in steps of 2, 3, 4, etc.

2 - W
Starting at the top, the value of the right hand letter is two ahead of the left hand letter, then 3 ahead, then 4, etc.

3 - 35
In each circle, multiply the two smallest even numbers and put the answer in the opposite segment, do the same for the odd numbers.

4 - 236
Starting at the top, numbers increase in steps of 25, 35, 45, etc.

5 - Y
In each circle opposite segments contain letters the same number of spaces in from the start of the alphabet as they are from the the end of the alphabet.

198

SOLUTIONS

6 - 26
In each square, multiply the three outer values and subtract the number in the centre. Going clockwise the answers are 50, 60, 70 and 80.

7 - 14
Working in column, alternately add 5 then subtract 1 as you move down.

8 - N
Starting at the upper circle and working downwards, letters in corresponding segments increase in value by 2 each time, while their relative positions rotate 1 segment clockwise.

9 - N
Letters are put in alphabetical order, working clockwise around each circle, and from left to right, missing out letters written with any curved lines.

10 - 7
Working from left to right, all digits increase by 2, with their relative positions rotating 1/4 turn clockwise.

11 - 10
In each square, take the sum of the odd numbers and subtract the sum of even numbers to give the number enclosed in the central square.

12 - V
In columns, make a 2 digit number from the numerical values of the top and middle letters to give the numerical value of the bottom letter.

13 - E
Working in rows from left to right, the * moves back and forth along a diagonal line, the ? moves 1/4 turn clockwise, the O moves clockwise by 1 space, then 2, then 3, etc. and the # moves left and right along the second row.

14 - F
In each circle add the reverse alphabetical values of the top two letters to give the reverse alphabetical value of the bottom letter.

15 - 8
In each figure the top left number divided by the centre number gives the top right number, as do the bottom left and right numbers.

16 - 8
Working in rows, the central value equals the product of the left and right hand numbers, minus their sum.

17 - P
The letter in the bottom segment of each square has the numerical value of the sum of the letters in the other three segments.

18 - W
Starting from the top left and going down, then from top right down, letters advance by 5, then back 2 etc.

19 - R
Letters in the right half of the circle are seven places in front of the opposite letters.

20 -

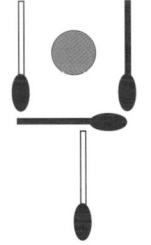

Slide the horizontal match 1/2 length to the right and move the lower left match to the upper right, inverting the glass and enclosing the coin.

21 - 86
Working from top to bottom, double the previous number and subtract 1, 2, 3 and 4.

22 - 1
Multiply the outer 4 numbers together and divide by 2 to give the central figure.

23 - 24
Starting at top left and moving in a uniform pattern, numbers increase by 8, 7, 6, etc.

24 - 11
In each column, numbers increase in steps of 3, 4 and 5.

25 -

The sequence is as follows:

Working from left to right, circles at the top of each triangle move backwards through this sequence, corresponding circles at the bottom move forwards through the sequence.

26 - N
Going clockwise, letters increase in steps of 1, 2, 3 and back to 1 again.

27 - 2
In each diagram divide the top left by bottom right, add bottom left and subtract top right to get the answer in the middle.

28 - 88
Moving downwards, multiply each number by 3 and subtract 14.

29 -

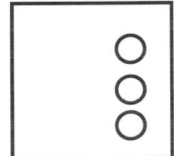

Working in rows starting on the left, one circle is removed in sequence as you move towards the right.

30 - E
The others all cover the same area.

199

SOLUTIONS

1 - 14
In each triangle the centre figure equals the sum of the two lower numbers minus the top number.

2 -

3 - 7
In rows the right hand number equals the difference between the left and centre numbers.

4 - 1
In each box, divide the 3 figure value represented on the upper line by the three figure value on the lower line. The answers are 22, 23 and 24.

5 - 4
Working in rows, the central value equals the sum of the squares of the left and right hand numbers.

6 -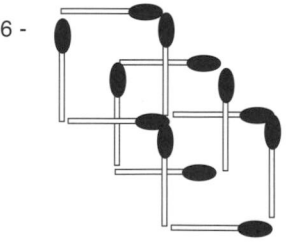

7 - 17
Starting in the top left square and moving clockwise, numbers increase in sequence by 2, 3, 4 and 5, keeping their corresponding positions in each square.

8 - X
Starting at the top, letters increase in value by 5, 4, 3 and 2.

9 - C
From the top, using the first 2 digit figure, the left hand letter below equals the alphabetical value of this figure and the right hand letter below equals the reverse alphabetical value.

10 - 61
Starting at the top, double each number and add three to get the next one.

11 - B
If the watches are inverted, the digits read the same.

12 - D
Starting at the top left of the first figure and moving in a Z shape, letter values increase by 2, then 3, then 4, 5, and 6 to reach the top figure in the next diagram.

13 - 4
The number in the centre of each triangle equals the product of the bottom two digits, plus the top digit.

14 - 1
The grid is symmetrical around the two diagonal axis.

15 - D
Moving left to right along each row, the circle moves 3 places clockwise around the edge of the square, the triangle moves back and forth along the top left, bottom right diagonal and the star moves from the top to the bottom in a zigzag pattern.

16 - 1:02
Three is taken away from each column in turn.

17 - B
In each square, the outer letters advance the same number of spaces indicated by the numerical value of the centre letter.

18 -

21	4	15	24	1
6	8	17	14	20
3	19	13	7	23
10	12	9	18	16
25	22	11	2	5

19 - Five of Spades
Moving from left to right, cards are placed in alternate colours and suits, the red cards increase by two, the black cards decrease by two.

20 - 4
The numbers in the inner ring correspond to the number of lines used to make the letters in the outer ring.

21 - 24
Each number equals the sum of the two numbers above it.

22 - 2 of any suit.
In each row the sum of the even cards, minus the sum of the odd cards, equals 10.

23 - 14
Starting top left and going to the right, alternatively up and down, add 3 to each number.

24 - 3
In each circle the sum of the digits equals 30.

25 - Steve = 270, Simon = 540 and Stewart = 90.

26 - R
Starting at top left and moving clockwise in a spiral, letters increase by four each time.

27 - $6

28 - 22
In each row, add the left and right hand numbers and double the answer to give the central value.

29 - 13, 4, 15 & 9
All rows columns and diagonals add up to 34.

30 -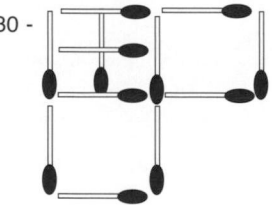

SOLUTIONS

1 - From top to bottom Seven of Clubs and Ace of Hearts.
Each suit has a value, Hearts = 4, Clubs = 3, Diamonds = 2 and Spades = 1, multiply the cards by its suit value and the sum of each row is 100.

2 -

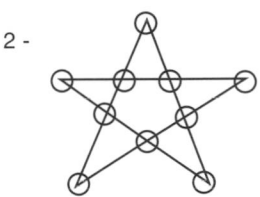

3 - 7
Each row and column contains each digit 0-9 inclusive, sometimes as part of a two digit number, sometimes alone.

4 - A = 92, B = 112
All other numbers are divisible by 3.

5 - 17
Taking the four segments at a time in vertical and horizontal lines, numbers increase by 2, 3, 4 or 5 for each line.

6 - S
Each line and column contains a letter made up of all straight lines, all curved lines or a combination of both.

7 - 6
Multiply the two outer numbers in each segment and divided by 2 then 3, alternately, putting the result at the centre of the opposite segment.

8 - 23
As you go down, numbers increase by 2, 4, 6 and 8.

9 - E
The numerical values of the letters in each column of 3 add up to 26.

10 - From top to bottom, King of Spades, Seven of Spades and Four of Hearts.
The sum of the two court cards equals the sum of the pip cards. There is one pip card of each suit in every row, plus an extra pip card of the same suit as the court cards.

11 - 3
The numbers in each row add up to 21.

12 - 35

13 - F
Starting on the outer left hand circle and going in a clockwise spiral, the letters are written in alphabetical order, missing out the vowels.

14 - 58
The sequence is multiply by 2, then add 3 etc.

15 - 15
In each star the sum of the even numbers, minus the sum of the odd numbers, equals the value of the number in the middle.

16 - Y
In rows, add the numerical values of the left and centre letters to give the value of the right hand letter.

17 - 23

18 - 7
In each diagram, multiply the top two numbers together, then divide by the lower right number and add the lower left number to give the central value.

19 - I
The sum of the numerical values of the left hand letters equals the value of the centre letter, as does the sum of the right hand letters.

20 - 33

21 - L
In each square, the total of the three numbers gives the value of the central letter.

22 - 11
Starting at the top left, and moving alternately right and left as you go down, add 2 to get the next value, then 3, then 4, etc. Follow the same pattern with the top right number but add 1, then 2, then 3, etc.

23 - 3:42am
The watch gains 16 minutes per hour.

24 - 2
In each circle, the letter is converted into its 2 digit numerical value. Add these 2 digits together to give the value in the opposite segment of the circle.

25 - 3
In each row, the sum of the squares of the far left and right numbers is entered in the middle two boxes.

26 - 18
Starting with the left group, the centre figure equals the sum of the left hand digits, the other groups follow suit but the positions of the outer numbers rotate clockwise 90° as you move to the right.

27 - 18
Add 2, 3 or 4 to the numbers in the left hand circle and rotate their positions 1/3 of a turn clockwise as you move along.

28 - 16
In each row, divide the left and right values by 3 and multiply together to give the centre number.

29 - 5
The numbers in the black segments are the difference between the numbers on either side.

SOLUTIONS

LEVEL 13

1 - D
Reading from the left, line by line, the @ moves in a figure of 8 around the corners, the * moves anticlockwise in steps of 2 around the 2 central columns, and the Δ moves to and fro along the third row.

2 - E
The dots form a symmetrical pattern from top left to bottom right.

3 - 17
Moving diagonally downwards from left to right, numbers increase by the same amount each line.

4 - 10
The numbers in the top half of the outer ring are written in reverse order plus 1 in the inner ring and vice versa.

5 - 179
Moving clockwise, double the previous number and add 1, 3, 5, 7 and 9.

6 - E
Add all the digits on each watch together. All the others are square numbers.

7 - From top to bottom, Jack of Hearts, Seven of Clubs, Queen of Clubs and Two of Diamonds. The grid displays rotational symmetry 180° around the central Ace of Hearts, with the cards swapping to the other suit of the same colour.

8 - 3
In each triangle, multiply the bottom numbers to get a 2 digit number, add these together to get the top number.

9 - The figures pointed to by the hands add up to 10, therefore a number of options are available.

10 - 14
In the top pair of boxes the letters are rotated 90° clockwise and the corresponding numerical value is put in the segments on the right. The bottom pair of boxes follows the same rule but the reverse numerical alphabetical value is put on the box on the left.

11 - N
The number in the centre of each triangle equals the sum of the squares of the numerical values around each triangle.

12 - D
In rows, letters increase in numerical value by 3 as you move to the right.

13 - C & Y
Starting at the top of the first 2 columns and working down, each pair of letters is duplicated in the right hand columns from the bottom up with each letter advancing one place alphabetically.

14 - 14
The central value of 15 equals the average of the numbers on opposite sides of the diagram.

15 - L
Letters are arranged in pairs in opposite segments of the circle, the lower value letter is the same distance from the start of the alphabet as the other is from the end.

16 - R & H
Starting top left and working clockwise, move forward 6 places, back 2, then forward 4. etc.

17 - 13
In each row, multiply the first and second numbers, then subtract the third to give the value in the right hand box.

18 - J
Take each letter in the left half of the circle and add 5, put the result in the opposite segment on the right.

19 - 1
In each circle, multiply the top two numbers together to get a 2 digit number, add these together until you get a single figure number which goes in the bottom segment of each circle.

20 - 14
The sum of the left and right numbers equals the sum of the other three numbers.

21 - G
In each circle, going clockwise, letters move back 3 places, then forward 1, etc.

22 - 34 & 36
From top left digit add 2 to get the lower number. Add these together to get the next top number and continue for each column.

23 - 6
In rows, the centre number equals the sum of the left and right hand numbers, plus the central number from above.

24 - 22
Going clockwise, add 1, then 2, then 3 etc.

25 - V
Starting at the top, letters move forward by 2, 3, 4, 5 and 6 places.

26 - 3
The value in each lower box represents the sum of the squares of the two numbers directly above it.

SOLUTIONS

27 - 1 sheep.

28 - K
Add the numerical value of the top left and centre letters to give the lower left letter, similarly with the top right and centre letters to give the lower right letter.

29 - M
Moving down the column, advance 2 letters, then back 5, etc.

LEVEL 14

1 - S
Numerical values of the letters represent the first 10 prime numbers.

2 - 14
Starting top left and moving to the right, then down to the left, and finally down to the right, numbers increase by steps of 2, 3, 4 etc.

3 - 1 = Molly, 2 = Frank, 3 = Ray, 4 = Maude.

4 -
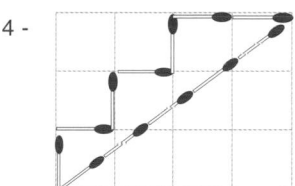

5 -
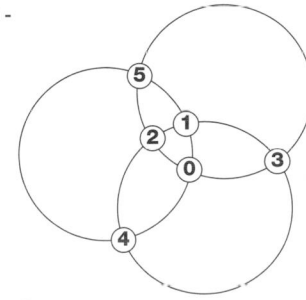

6 - Q
In each circle letters increase in value by 1, while their relative positions move 1/4 turn clockwise as you move to the right.

7 - I
Letters are written in alphabetical order, skipping letters written with curved lines.

8 - 52
Divide each number in the first circle by 2 and enter the new figure one place anticlockwise in the second circle. Multiply the first set of numbers by 2 and enter this figure one place clockwise in the third circle.

9 - Ace of Spades
In each row the value of the right hand card equals the difference between the sums of the red cards and black cards to the left. There is always 1 card of each suit on every row.

10 - A
If the separate digits on each watch are added together, the sum increases by 5 each step.

11 - 21
The numbers in each box equal the numerical values of the five vowels.

12 - 3
Working in rows, reverse the digits in the left and right hand shapes, then divide the new left hand value by the new right hand value to give the number in the centre.

13 - Three (Spades or Clubs)
In each row, add the values of the black cards to get a 2 digit number. Add these digits together to get the value of the red card in the middle.

14 - F
Starting with the letter at the top left, and moving clockwise around each triangle, letters increase in value by 2, 4, 6, 8 etc.

15 - T
In each row, the numerical value of each letter increases by 3 for

the first row, 4 for the middle and 5 for the last.

16 - 5
Add the middle three numbers and write the answer, in reverse, in the first two columns. Multiply the same three numbers and write this answer, again in reverse order, in the last two columns.

17 - 4
Working in alternate rows, from left to right, numbers follow a repeating sequence of 5, 7, 2, 1, 9, 0, 3 and 6. The letters follow the sequence J, Q, L, C, Y, P, R, A, S.

18 - Eight of Clubs
In each row, the numerical value of the answer equals the average of the sum of even cards plus the difference of the odd cards. The suit of the answer equals the suit of the highest odd card in each row.

19 - 21

20 - The bottom line is the product of all the other numbers.

21 - 1
The square is divided into four 5 x 5 squares, each with the same pattern of numbers.

22 - Three of Hearts
In each row the average of the 3 cards to the left equals the value of the card on the right. There is one card from each suit on every row.

23 - 410
In all the other numbers, the first two digits added together give the third.

24 - 9:00pm

25 - From left to right - Four, Nine, Eight and Four (of any suit).

SOLUTIONS

In each column the sum of the top three cards and the sum of the bottom three cards equals the value of the central card.

LEVEL 15

1 - 12
Square each number in the inner ring and take away the original number. Write the answer in the outer ring opposite.

2 - 14
Taking the first two lines as one group starting top left and the bottom two lines as the second group starting bottom right and moving clockwise around each one, the first number in the top group is doubled to give the corresponding value in the second group, the next is halved etc.

3 - C
The sum of the separate digits on each watch add up to 18.

4 - Nine of Spades, Nine of Diamonds, Seven of Spades and Two of Spades.
In each row, spades represent positive numbers and diamonds represent negative numbers. The card on the far right of each row represents the sum of the cards to the left.

5 - 30
In each circle starting top left and going clockwise, double the first number and subtract 2 to give the next value.

6 - A
If viewed from the left edge the boxes show numbers 1-6.

7 - Eight of Clubs.
In each row, as you move to the right, the values increase by 2, 3 and 4 with each suit appearing once in each row.

8 - 41
Opposite sides of a dice add up to 7, giving 21 dots per dice. Multiply this by three and take away the dots you can see.

9 - 13
Going clockwise add 4 to get the next number, then subtract 2, etc.

10 - 37 & 45
In each square the central value equals the sum of the product of the top two numbers and the product of the bottom two.

11 - 27
Starting at the bottom left, move to the right diagonally up, then diagonally down etc. increasing the numerical value by 4 each step. Additionally the two figures remaining in each group add up to the centre figure.

12 - 1
The centre figure is the difference between the product of the top two numbers and the product of the bottom two.

13 - From left to right - Nine of Diamonds, Jack of Hearts, Six of Clubs and Queen of Hearts.
Starting at the top left, cards move clockwise in a spiral in the repeating sequence 2, 9, 5, Q, A, 3, 6, J, K. The suits follow the sequence H,C,H,S,S, D in an anticlockwise formation.

14 - Z
Starting at the top letters increase in steps of three for the left hand column and four for the right hand column whilst missing out all the vowels.

15 - 30
Numbers increase by 7, then 6, 5, 4 and 3.

16 - K
The centre figure equals the sum of the numerical alphabetical value of the left hand letter and the reverse alphabetical value of the right hand letter.

17 - 14
Starting on the left on the first group and moving up and down towards the right, numbers increase by 2 and 3. In the second group by 3 and 4 and in the third group by 4 and 5.

18 - 3
Moving from left to right, letters in the top circles increase in value from one circle to the next by the corresponding numbers in the circles below.

19 - L
Starting at the top of each triangle, letters move forward by three places going clockwise, ending in the centre.

20 - O
Taking the numerical values of the letters in the left hand circle, multiply them by two to give the values of the corresponding letters in the centre circle. Then multiply by three to give the values in the last circle.

21 - Z
In each circle, starting top left and going clockwise multiply the numerical value of each letter by 2 and then subtract 2 to give the next letter.

22 - 13
Going clockwise around the 4 boxes, the values in corresponding segments increase by 1, 2, 3 and 5.

23 - 4
The grid is symmetrical around the bottom axis running from top left to bottom right.

LEVEL 16

1 - 5
Taking the top two numbers to form a 2 digit number, subtract the 2 digit number at the bottom to give the central number.

SOLUTIONS

2 - Eight of Clubs
Moving from left to right, card increase in value by 2, 3, 4, 5 and 6, returning to Ace whenever the King is reached and always following the same suit pattern.

3 - 5
Numbers in the bottom left circle equal the sums of the numbers in corresponding segments in the upper left and centre circles. Numbers in the bottom right circle equal the difference between the numbers in the centre and right top circles.

4 - 14
In rows subtract 1 from the left and centre numbers and multiply together to give the right hand number.

5 - 3 & 3
The values of the segments in the top circle equal the sum of the corresponding opposite segments in the left hand circle. The values in the bottom circle equal the difference between corresponding opposite segments of the left hand circle.

6 -
Janine $1.01, $100.10 & $121.11, Jackie $4.02, $49.07 & $169.13

7 - E
Starting with Y, letter values decrease by 2, 3, 4, 5 and 6.

8 - 1
The grid displays rotational symmetry of 180° around a central point.

9 - 39
Going clockwise, each number is doubled then subtract 1, then 2, then 3 etc.

10 - 6
Starting with each letter on the left, add 2 to give the number in the next two boxes, for the next groups add 3 and 4.

11 - 9
For each group, add first and second figures on the top row to get the final figure, and the difference between the first and second numbers for the bottom right box.

12 - Z
Working in diagonal lines from top left to bottom right, letters move forward by 4 places.

13 - 1
Numbers in the segments on the right hand half of the circle equal double the value of the numbers in the opposite segments, minus 3.

14 - 6
In each diagram the reverse numerical value of each letter is written in the box below plus 5 for the first diagram, 4 for the second and 3 for the third.

15 - 4:30
Multiply the hour value and minute value to give 36.

16 - 14
In each square the centre figure equals the difference between the sum of the left and right segments and the sum of the top and bottom segments.

17 - B
Working from left to right the square moves 2 segments anti-clockwise, the circle 3 segments anticlockwise, the star by 4 segments anticlockwise and the triangle 1 segment clockwise.

18 - From top to bottom, Black Jack, Red King, Red Four and Black Eight.
In the first five rows the sum of the red cards equal the value of the right hand card. In the first 5 columns the sum of the black cards equals the value of the bottom card.

19 - 142 - 3 = 139

20 - L
Going clockwise in each square, letters increase in value by the same amount.

21 - A
The figures are groups of three of the same number squashed and rotated 90°.

22 - 2
Moving from left to right each box contains a decreasing square number, minus the root. (7 x 7 = 49 - 7 = 42 etc.)

23 - 16
Starting with the top value and moving clockwise, numbers move around a 24-hour clock, advancing 5 hours for the left star, 6 for the middle and 7 for the right.

24 - From left to right -

Working in columns add the number of black segments in the first two circles to give the bottom circle. The third circle down is the difference between the first two circles.

25 -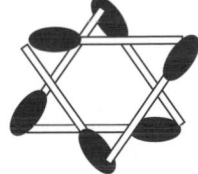

26 - 1
The product of the first row gives the first number in the second row. The sum of the numbers in the top row gives the second number. Repeat this for rows three and four.

27 - From top to bottom, 14, 17 & 33.
Starting at the top and working in diagonal lines from left to right, numbers increase in value by 2, then 4, then 5 etc.

SOLUTIONS

LEVEL

1 - 3
The numbers in each row add up to 52.

2 - 36
The answer in the centre of each triangle equals the difference between the top and left hand values, multiplied by the right hand value.

3 - 63
The sequence follows the cubes of numbers 1, 2, 3 and 4, minus 1.

4 - 138
Starting bottom left and moving in a clockwise spiral, double the last number then subtract 5 etc.

5 - W or E
Moving clockwise, each segment contains an example of a letter written with 1 continuous line, 2 lines, then 3, then 4.

6 - Q
Moving clockwise letters advance in steps of 9, 7 , 5, 3 and 1.

7 - X
Starting top left, add 4 to get the box below, add 5 for the second column and 6 for the third.

8 - 3
Each row contains every digit 0-9 inclusive.

9 - 29
In each diagram multiply the top two values and add their sum to give the bottom value.

10 - W
Moving from left to right, top row then bottom, in each square, letters in the top left corner increase by 1 place, top right letters decrease by 2 spaces, bottom left decrease by 1 place and letters in the bottom right corner increase by 2 spaces.

11 - D
Working from left to right, symbols with curved lines move 2 places clockwise, whilst straight sided symbols move to the segment opposite.

12 - 5
Taking 3 x 3 groups of circles with a 9 in the middle, the figures 1 - 9 appear in every group.

13 - 3
In rows the sum of the numerical values of the two boxes are written as a 2 digit number in the two right hand boxes.

14 - J
The boxes follow the sequence of letters missing out those written with just straight lines.

15 - C
Add the digits in the minutes position to get the hour value.

16 - B
Working from left to right, the X moves clockwise 1 segment, then 2, then 3 etc.the Δ moves clockwise 4 segments, then 3, then 2 etc. The ○ and □ move to opposite segments and back again. A # and * fill the first two consecutive empty segments in a clockwise direction, and the • fills any segments left empty.

17 - A = 4, B = 6. Multiply the numbers on the second and third rows and write this answer along the top row, then multiply together the numbers along the top and write their squares along the bottom row.

18 - L
Moving from left to right, letters advance in steps of 1, 2 and 3 with their relative positions moving 1/3 of a turn clockwise each time.

19 - 2
Add the numbers from the top row to the numbers in the second row to get the third.

20 - 169
A descending sequence of the squares of prime numbers.

21 - 36
The first box shows the sequence of prime numbers. The second box multiplies these numbers by 2 minus 2, the third multiplied by 3 minus 3.

22 - 17
Going clockwise the numbers are the first 6 prime numbers plus 4.

23 - 4
The centre letter has the reverse alphabetical value of the corresponding left and right digits in each row when taken as a 2 digit number.

24 - $1

25 - 7
The sum of the 4 lower points minus the number at the top equals the number in the middle.

LEVEL 18

1 - 15
Top row follows ascending sequence bottom left to top right, plus 5 for the first group, 6 for the second and 7 for the third. Subtract top middle from bottom left to give bottom middle and add top left to give bottom right.

2 - 8
Letters in the top row are the same distance from the front of the alphabet as the corresponding letters in the bottom row are from the end of the alphabet. The figures in the middle row are half the numerical value of the letters in the bottom row.

3 - 1
Each number equals the square of the odd numbers in descending order from 11.

4 - C
Going clockwise letters move back 6 places then forward 2 places, etc.

SOLUTIONS

5 - 14
Multiply the two outer digits in each segment and divide by 2. This result is put at the centre of the segment 2 places clockwise.

6 - Seven of Diamonds & Eight of Spades.
The cards are arranged alternately in two sequences, one increases in steps of two, the other deceases by one. The suits follow the order Hearts, Diamonds, Spades Clubs.

7 - Three of Clubs & Nine of Hearts.
Taking the first five cards in each row, add the values of the odd cards to give a 2 digit answer. Add these 2 digits together to give the value of the club card in that row. Do the same with the even cards to give the value of the Heart in that row.

8 - 72
In the top circle, numbers in the upper half are multiplied by 3 and the result put in the segment opposite, in the left hand circle numbers are multiplied by 6 and by 9 in the bottom circle.

9 - F
Moving in rows from left to right, the row of dots at the top moves down 1 row each time, returning to the top when it reaches the bottom. The left hand column moves back and forth across the box. In addition, one dot starts in the bottom left corner and moves clockwise corner to corner and another dot fills the central space each time, however, should a black dot already fill either of these two places as a result of earlier instructions then the dot is left white.

10 - 20
In each circle, multiply the top two numbers together and subtract the lower right number to give the lower left number.

11 - 67
As numbers go down multiply by 2 and subtract 3.

12 - D
On each watch the minutes value equals the hour value multiplied by three.

13 - B
Starting top left and working to the right in each row, the top and third dot remain stationary, with the dot in between moving to and fro along its line 3 spaces at a time. The lowest dot moves to and fro 1 space at a time and the dot above it 2 spaces. The whole grid rotates 90° clockwise at each step.

14 - 10
In each circle the top right number equals the average of the left hand numbers and the lower right equals the difference between these numbers.

15 - M
Letters descend in reverse alphabetical order in intervals of 7 then 6, 5, 4 and 3.

16 - 21
In each circle, starting top left and moving clockwise, multiply the first number by 3 and subtract 3 to give the next value.

17 - A
Divide the minutes on each watch by 4 to give the hour value.

18 - 13
Starting on the left, values in corresponding segments of each circle increase by 1, 2, 3 and 4. The relative positions of the sequence rotate 1/4 turn clockwise as you move to the right.

19 - 2:53
Taking the hour and minute values separately, the hours decrease by 3, 4, 5 and 6 hours and the minutes increase by 21, 23, 25 and 27.

20 - 1
The figure in the centre of each triangle equals the sum of the squares on the three corners.

21 - 5
Working from left to right in each figure, the numbers add up to 32, 34 and 36.

LEVEL 19

1 - 9
Take each number in the outer ring as a 2 digit number and multiply them together. Write this answer plus 1 in the inner segment opposite.

2 - 12
In each box, square the top numbers and subtract 4 to give the lower number.

3 - 51
Starting from the left hand circle, working top to bottom in columns then to the next column to the right, add 1, then 2, then 3 etc. until the central circle, then subtract 11, 10, 9 etc.

4 - 56
In each diagram, divide the top left value by 3, multiply it by the top right value, then multiply the answer by 4 to give the lower value.

5 -
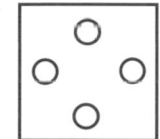

Working in rows, using the left hand figure as a source, reflect around a vertical axis to give the middle figure, and reflect around a horizontal axis to give the right hand figure.

6 - 55
The boxes follow the sequence of prime numbers multiplied by 5.

7 - J
In rows the left hand number equals the numerical value of the centre letter plus 1, the right hand number equals the reverse alphabetical value of the letter plus 1.

207

SOLUTIONS

8 - 19
In each row, starting on the left, multiply the number by 3 and subtract 2 to give the next number on the right.

9 - H
In each row, add the numerical values of the left and right hand letters to give the reverse alphabetical values of the central letter.

10 - 65
Moving downwards, double each number and subtract 1.

11 - X
Letters increase in value down each column by 4 in the first column, 5 in the middle and 6 in the right hand column.

12 - 78
Moving downwards, add 1 to each number and double it to get the next number.

13 - L
Starting at the top and working inwards in a clockwise spiral, letters increase in value by 4 each time.

14 - 2:53
As you move right the hour value decreases by 1, 2, 3, 4 each step and the minutes increase by 11, 12, 13 and 14.

15 - 4
In each row the first and third numbers when read as a 2 digit number give the reverse alphabetical value of the centre letter.

16 - 9
In rows, the centre value equals the product of the left and right hand numbers minus the sum of the left and right numbers.

17 - $2.30
The first three spend a total of $27.60 on 12 of each item, therefore each tool = $2.30.

18 - F
Working in rows, add together the left and central diagrams to make the diagram on the right. If a black square appears in both of these columns it becomes white in the third box.

1 - C & N
Letters in the bottom row are 1 place lower than the corresponding letters in the top row, letters in the third row are 2 places lower than the second row.

2 -2
The sum of the numbers in the top and bottom rows is put in the corresponding position in the second row, the difference between the top and bottom rows is put in the third row.

3 - V
Starting top left and moving clockwise in a spiral, letters move forward by 2 places, then 3, then 4 etc.

4 - 1
The numbers at the centre equal the numerical value of the letter in the opposite segment, if this value exceeds 9 the digits are added together to give a single digit answer.

5 - 72
Moving in a clockwise spiral, numbers are double the square of the first 9 numbers.

6 - 477
Starting with the top 3 digit number, square the central digit and add this to the original number to give the next number.

7 -

Working from left to right and using the left hand circle as a source, the middle circle shows the original and its reflection about a vertical axis, the right hand circle shows the original and its reflection about the horizontal axis.

8 - 6
The sum of the numbers in the lines of three going upwards equal the sum of the numbers in the lines of three going downwards.

9 - A = 7, B = 9
The difference between the first and third columns as a 4 digit number going down is written in the central column going down.

10 - 4
The sum of the odd numbers in each column equals the sum of the even numbers.

11 -

30 dots in each column.

12 - 2
Take the numerical value of each letter and multiply by the opposite to get the answer in the middle.

13 - N
Starting top left and moving diagonally upwards from left to right letters are repeated.

14 - 2
Cube the numbers in each column of the top grid and add the answers together. Write this answer going down the columns of the bottom grid.

15 - B
Cube the numerical values of the letters in the top grid and add the answers together. Write this answer in reverse order in the columns in the bottom box.

16 - D
The others are symmetrical.

17 - Y - C - P - M - I - T - D - Y - A
There are two chains of letters in use. The first goes diagonally upwards from left to right starting in the top left corner and appears on alternate lines. This chain contains every letter of the alphabet except vowels. The second chain starts bottom right and goes diagonally downwards from right to left and contains every letter of the alphabet.

BTEC national

2nd Edition

Information Technology Practitioners

Book 2

Series editor: Jenny Lawson

www.harcourt.co.uk

✓ Free online support
✓ Useful weblinks
✓ 24 hour online ordering

01865 888118

Heinemann

Heinemann is an imprint of Harcourt Education Limited, a company incorporated in England and Wales, having its registered office: Halley Court, Jordan Hill, Oxford OX2 8EJ. Registered company number: 3099304

www.harcourt.co.uk

Heinemann is the registered trademark of Harcourt Education Limited

Text © Karen Anderson, Peter Blundell, Allen Kaye, Jenny Lawson, Richard McGill and Jenny Phillips 2007

First published 2007

12 11 10 09 08 07
10 9 8 7 6 5 4 3 2 1

British Library Cataloguing in Publication Data is available from the British Library on request.

ISBN 978 0 435465 50 6

Typeset by Wearset Ltd
Illustrated by Tek-Art
Original illustrations © Harcourt Education Limited 2007
Picture research by Q2A Media
Cover photo © Alamy Images / 1APix
Printed by Scotprint

Websites
Please note that the examples of websites suggested in this book were up to date at the time of writing. It is essential for tutors to preview each site before using it to ensure that the URL is still accurate and the content is appropriate. We suggest that tutors bookmark useful sites and consider enabling students to access them through the school or college intranet.

Contents

Further resources are available for download from the Heinemann website:

- Go to www.harcourt.co.uk/vocational
- Click on IT & Office Technology
- Click on BTEC and select BTEC National IT Practitioners 2007 (series).

Acknowledgements

The authors and publisher are grateful to all those who have given permission to reproduce material. Every effort has been made to contact copyright holders of material reproduced in this book. Any omissions will be rectified in subsequent printings if notice is given to the publisher.

Photo acknowledgements

Alamy Images / Andy Myatt – pages 2–3
Alamy Images / Eddie Gerald – page 270
Alamy images / Eric Nathan – page 269
Alamy Images / Justin Kase – pages 226–227
Alamy Images / Mary Evans Picture Library – page 264
Commodore Media – page 129
Corbis / Bettmann – page 269
Corbis / Hulton-Deutsch Collection – page 270
Corbis / RCWW Inc – pages 126–127
Corbis / zefa / Auslosser – page 16
Corbis / zefa / Jon Feingersh – page 214
Epson – page 131
Flickr / Thor Muller – page 263
Fotolibra / Gwyn Headley – page 24
Getty Images / Emmanuel Faure – pages 192–193
Kodak Media – page 232
Lalit Dalil Photography – pages 30–31, 60–61
Lonely Planet Images / Richard I'Anson – page 117
Media Pictures – pages 148, 237

Microsoft – page 180
NASA / JPL – page 131
Nikon Media – page 231
Photographers Direct / Caroline Vancoillie – page 202
Photographers Direct / Twisted Photography – page 102
Photolibrary / Mauritius Die Bildagentur GMBH – pages 260–261
Photolibrary / Workbook Inc. / Hill Street Studios – pages 94–95, 156–157
Photoshot – page 132
Samsung – page 133
Science & Society / NMPFT – pages 264, 265 (×2)
Shutterstock / Aga & Rafi – page 131
Shutterstock / Marek Cech – page 231
Shutterstock / Paul Cowan – page 231
Summa, Inc – page 237
Tungsten – page 236
Wacom Technology Corporation – page 235 (×2)

Text and screenshot acknowledgements

Screen shots reprinted by permission from Microsoft Corporation and Borland (UK) Limited (pages 9, 158ff, 239, 240, 241); Adobe (pages 204-207, 241, 277-278); Vizual Impact (page 237); Corel (pages 238, 239, 240, 242, 251); AutoCAD (page 238); Vision Design (page 247); AutoCAD (page 251); DarkBASIC (page 252).

Introduction

Welcome to this BTEC National IT Practitioners course book, specifically designed to support students on the following programmes:

- BTEC National Award in National IT Practitioners
- BTEC National Certificate in National IT Practitioners
- BTEC National Diploma in National IT Practitioners.

The following table shows how each unit covered in this book fits within the different pathways of the BTEC National IT Practitioners qualification at Award, Certificate and Diploma level. Units marked 'M' are mandatory for the pathway; units marked 'O' are optional for the pathway. Please note that some units are optional at Certificate level, but mandatory at Diploma level.

The aim of this book is to provide a comprehensive source of information for your course. It follows the BTEC specification closely, so that you can easily see what you have covered and quickly find the information you need. Every grading criterion for each unit listed above is covered in the tasks, and a grading grid, showing Edexcel's grading criteria mapped against each task, is available from the Harcourt website.

Examples and case studies from IT are used to bring your course to life and make it enjoyable to study. We hope you will be encouraged to find your own examples of current practice too.

Unit	IT & Business	Network	Software Development	Systems Support	Award/Cert/Dip
4: ICT Project	O	O	O	O	C/D
5: Advanced Database Skills	O	O	O	O	A/C/D
6: Advanced Spreadsheet Skills	O	O	O	O	A/C/D
10: Client Side Customisation of Web Pages	O	O	O	O	A/C/D
13: Human Computer Interaction	O	O	O	O	A/C/D
20: Event Driven Programming	O	O	O (Cert) M (Dip)	O	C/D
21: Website Production and Management	O	O	O	O	A/C/D
22: Network Management	N/A	O (Cert) M (Dip)	N/A	O	C/D
24: Digital Graphics and Computers	O	O	O	O	A/C/D
26: Computer Animation	O	O	O	O	C/D

KEY:

M   mandatory unit

O   optional unit

A   award

C   certificate

D   diploma

Guide to learning and assessment features

This book has a number of features to help you relate theory to practice and reinforce your learning. It also aims to help you gather evidence for assessment. You will find the features identified below in each unit.

Your teacher or tutor should check that you have completed enough activities to meet all the assessment criteria for the unit, whether from this book or from other tasks.

Teachers/tutors and students should refer to the BTEC standards for the qualification for the full BTEC grading criteria for each unit (www.edexcel.org.uk).

Assessment features

Activities

Activities are provided throughout each unit. These are linked to real situations and case studies and they can be used for practice before tackling the preparation for assessment. Alternatively, some can contribute to your unit assessment if you choose to do these instead of the preparation for assessment at the end of each unit.

Grading icons

In some activities and case studies throughout the book you will see the **p**, **m** and **d** icons. These show you where the tasks fit in with the grading criteria. If you do these tasks you will be building up your evidence to achieve your desired qualification. If you are aiming for a Merit, make sure you complete all the Pass **p** and Merit **m** tasks. If you are aiming for a Distinction, you will also need to complete all the Distinction **d** tasks.

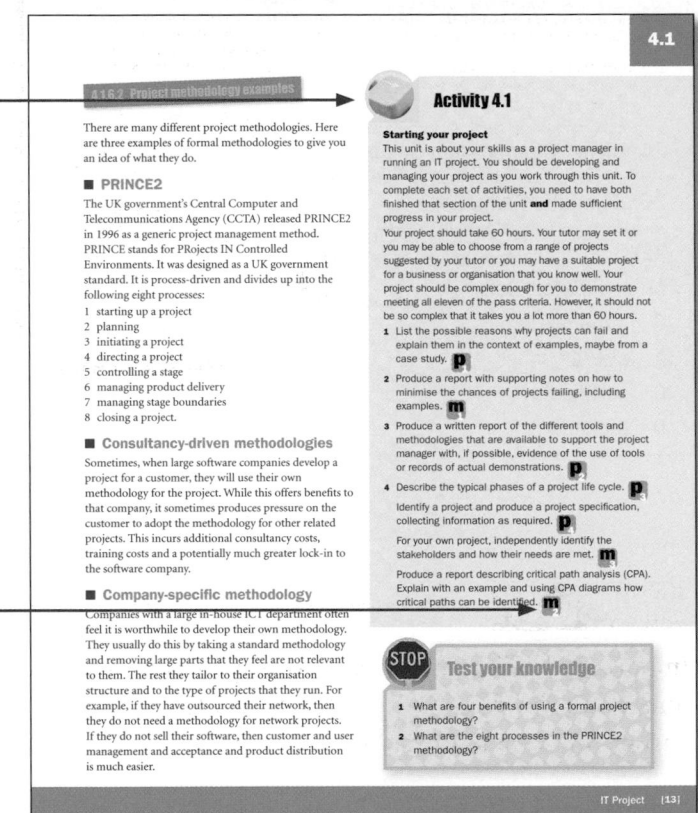

p means the first of the Pass criteria listed in the specification, **m** the first of the Merit criteria, **d** the first of the Distinction criteria, and so on.

Preparation for assessment

Each unit concludes with a full unit assessment, which taken as a whole fulfils the unit requirements from Pass to Distinction. Each task is matched to the relevant criteria in the specification.

Learning features

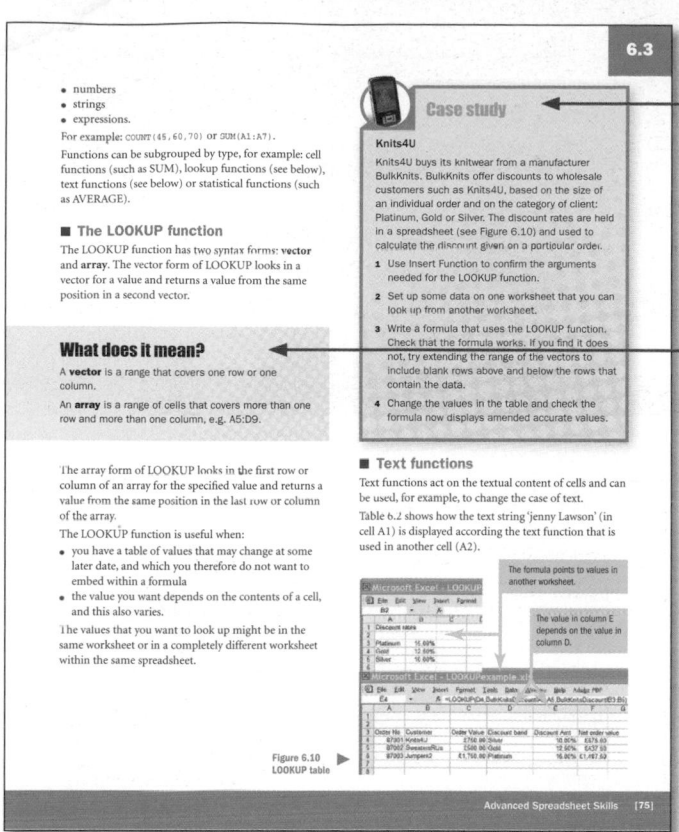

Case studies

Interesting examples of real situations or companies are described in case studies that link theory to practice. They will show you how the topics you are studying affect real people and businesses.

What does it mean?

Terms that you need to be aware of are summarised under these headings. They will help you check your knowledge as you learn, and will prove to be a useful quick-reference tool.

Remember!

Important details that you need to keep in mind are under these headings. They will help identify particularly vital information.

Test your knowledge

At the end of each section is a set of quick questions to test your knowledge of the information you have been studying. Use these to check your progress, and also as a revision tool.

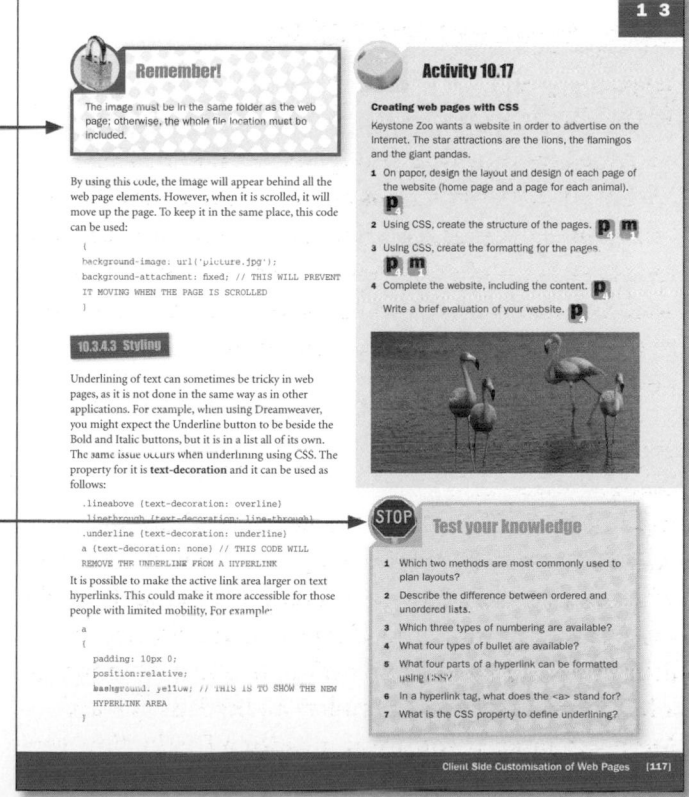

IT Project

Introduction

IT professionals are often involved in projects to introduce new systems or redevelop old ones. It is also very common to hear or read about IT projects that go over their deadline dates, cost more than the estimated cost or do not meet the needs of the clients or users. These problems often arise because of poor project management skills.

To run an IT project, you need more than just IT skills. You should understand the needs of the business, the related systems and procedures, as well as the people and jobs involved for successful deployment.

For this unit, you will plan and manage a complex business IT project, including resources and the time allocated for completion of the project.

After completing this unit, you should be able to achieve these outcomes:

- Understand how projects are specified and managed
- Be able to plan an IT project
- Be able to implement an IT project
- Be able to test, document and review an IT project.

Grading criteria	Activity	Page number
To achieve a pass grade the evidence must show that the learner is able to:		
p₁ Explain, using examples, reasons why projects can fail	4.1, PFA	13, 29
p₂ Describe different tools and methodologies that are available to support the project manager	4.1, PFA	13, 29
p₃ Describe typical phases of a project life cycle	4.1, PFA	13, 29
p₄ Identify a project, collect information as required and produce a project specification	4.1, PFA	13, 29
p₅ Develop and document a project plan M5 meet deadlines and key review dates as identified in the project plan	4.2, PFA	17, 29
p₆ Monitor the project against the project plan	4.2, PFA	17, 29
p₇ Design a product or service based on a project specification	4.3, PFA	22, 29
p₈ Implement an IT project and create a product that meets the specification	4.3, PFA	22, 29
p₉ Test and review the output of a project	4.4, PFA	28, 29
p₁₀ Review the project management process and identify successful and unsuccessful choices made and decisions taken	4.4, PFA	28, 29
p₁₁ Create technical and user documentation	4.4, PFA	28, 29
To achieve a merit grade the evidence must show that, in addition to the pass criteria, the learner is able to:		
m₁ Explain, using examples, how it is possible to minimise the chances of projects failing	4.1, PFA	13, 29
m₂ Describe critical path analysis (CPA) and explain with an example how critical paths can be identified	4.1	13
m₃ Independently produce a project specification that takes into account the needs of all stakeholders	4.1, PFA	13, 29
m₄ Monitor and track the progress of a project using a project plan, adapting the plan as circumstances change	4.2, PFA	17, 29
m₅ Meet deadlines and key review dates as identified in the project plan	4.2, PFA	17, 29
m₆ Undertake an interim review of the project management process and identify any emerging problems	4.3, PFA	22, 29
m₇ Demonstrate effective communications with stakeholders at all stages of the project		
To achieve a distinction grade the evidence must show that, in addition to the pass and merit criteria, the learner is able to:		
d₁ Justify the tools and methodologies used in a project	4.3, PFA	22, 29
d₂ Critically evaluate the effectiveness of a project plan to support the project	4.4, PFA	28, 29
d₃ Identify and accurately assess impact of potential risks to a project	4.4, PFA	28, 29
d₄ Evaluate the potential impact of the introduction of the product or service on wider business systems, people or processes	4.4, PFA	28, 29
Note: 'PFA' stands for 'Preparation for assessment'.		

Before starting the detailed work on a project, there are three areas that you should look at first: how you are going to specify, manage and plan the project.

4.1.1 Project specification

The project specification is a statement, agreed by all **stakeholders**, on *what* the project will do. It does not say *how* it will be done.

What does it mean?

A **stakeholder** is a person or organisation that is actively involved in a project or whose interests the project may affect.

4.1.1.1 Identification of stakeholders

Most business projects will have most of the following stakeholders:

- senior management – in control of the project's overall direction
- customer/client – the person or part of the organisation that benefits most from the project
- users – those people who use or operate the new system
- project manager – runs the project on a day-to-day basis
- team members – those who do the technical work to make the project happen
- peer reviewer – the person who checks the work of the team members
- supplier – the company or person who supplies the necessary equipment.

4.1.1.2 Business case requirements

The **business case** should state what the project should achieve in general terms. It should then state the one-off costs of the project and the ongoing costs of running the delivered system.

Typical cost items are:

- ICT resources to specify, manage, design, build and implement
- customer resources to help specify, manage and implement
- user resources for training and implementation
- equipment costs
- ongoing running costs
- possible costs of moving from an old system to the new one.

The business case should also state the expected benefits. Most projects are an investment, which should repay after the **payback period**.

What does it mean?

A **business case** is a proposal stating the objectives, costs and benefits of a project.

The **payback period** for a project is the length of time taken before the cash benefits exceed the cost.

4.1.1.3 Specific objectives or deliverables

Specific, measurable objectives are very important to the success of a project. Many stakeholders judge the success of a project on how closely it has met its objectives.

One objective is that a project should be delivered *on time*. A specific objective may be that the project produces all its **deliverables** by July. This statement removes all doubt as to what 'on time' means.

Another objective is that a project should be delivered *within budget*. A specific objective could be that, up to the time that a project is delivered to the customers, it will cost less than £200,000. This objective makes it clear

What does it mean?

A **deliverable** is a product or service that a project aims to produce.

▲ **Figure 4.1 Specific objectives are important to the success of a project**

what the budget is. It also makes it clear that the budget does not include any ongoing support costs or any later additional features.

You will learn more about deliverables in section 4.3.3 starting on page 19.

4.1.1.4 Benefits and success factors

At the start of your project, you should define the expected benefits and what success should look like. Success may include any of the factors that are important to the stakeholders (the people involved in the project).

The benefits of a new system could include one or more of the following:

- better customer service
- lower costs
- increased revenue
- greater staff productivity
- better management decision making
- compliance with legislation
- better safety and security.

These benefits may be measurable or it may be possible to put them in cash terms, such as lower costs or higher revenue. A benefit that cannot be measured in cash terms, such as better security, is called an intangible benefit.

Case study

System benefits

A new sales order system has been designed to improve customer service through:

- faster order processing time
- better stock checking
- better features for customers to view the status of their orders.

1 Think of another new computer system.

2 List the benefits that this could bring to its stakeholders.

In order to identify whether a project has been successful, you need to measure the project against pre-defined criteria. Success criteria may be of the following types:

- **Functional.** These state what functions the project must have.
- **Timescale.** This gives the date by which the project must be complete, such as a sales project that must be ready before a Christmas selling peak.
- **Resources.** A project's resources include people, their effort and money. For any project, there may be a limit on how many people can be involved, how much effort they can put in and a fixed cost which the project must not exceed.
- **Ease of use.** Software that full-time, trained users will operate should be full of features; powerful functions should be available with just a few clicks or key presses. Software intended for casual users, perhaps customers of a business using the Internet, should be easy to use; the functions should be very simple and there should be a lot of user guidance.

- **Performance.** Software should meet minimum performance standards that depend upon the user's needs. For example, the functions in a game may need to work in much less than a second, while the time to run a large organisation's monthly payroll could be several hours.

4.1.1.5 Project boundaries or scope

The boundaries or scope of a project are what the project aims to achieve. The project should be no more and no less than what is defined in the scope. If a feature is in the scope, then it should be delivered as part of the project. If it is not in the scope, then it should not be built, as building unnecessary features will incur extra costs. The scope of a project is recorded in the written project specification, which should contain the:

- reason for undertaking the project
- expected benefits
- objectives
- success criteria
- constraints
- risks
- project roadmap
- resource requirements
- stakeholders
- deliverables
- review points
- target completion date.

4.1.1.6 Constraints

These are obstacles that may make the project difficult to achieve. These constraints might be:

- **financial** (e.g. no major investment might be allowed until the next year)
- **ICT staff** (e.g. the skills needed for this project might not be available; the necessary staff would have to be trained or recruited)
- **ICT equipment** (e.g. the project might require specialised hardware or software; this might have to be developed, bought in or installed before the project could proceed very far)

- **business** (e.g. the project might be needed to support the launch of a new product or service; it would therefore need to be complete in some form in time for that launch)
- **legislation** (e.g. the project might be required for the organisation to conform to new laws; work on the project would therefore need to finish in time for these laws)
- **competition** (e.g. the project might provide a competitive advantage or respond to a competitive threat, so a part or phased solution delivered quickly would be preferable to no solution at all)
- **user resources** (e.g. the users might be unavailable for training during the peak business season).

4.1.1.7 Consideration of options

There is usually more than one ICT solution to a business problem. One option may be cheap and quick to produce but will only give limited benefits. Another option may meet every possible need very well; however, this may be very costly and the benefits may never exceed the build and running costs. The chosen option is often somewhere between these two extremes. It is often appropriate to record briefly in the project definition the options that were rejected and why.

4.1.1.8 Issues

The project specification should highlight any issues that the stakeholders need to decide on to make the project a success. Examples of these include the following:

- **Ethical.** Will this project change business terms and conditions to make them unreasonable?
- **Sustainable.** Can the organisation still function effectively once the changes brought in by the project happen?
- **Effect of failure.** What would happen to the organisation if the project failed to hit its deadlines or did not produce a working ICT product?

4.1.1.9 Risks and risk mitigation

All projects face **risks**, which you need to consider. You should also plan for **risk mitigation**; what you might reasonably do both to prevent them happening and if they do happen. There are many types of risk, including business, ICT and implementation risks.

What does it mean?

A **risk** is any event, foreseen or not, that may happen and that puts the success of the project in jeopardy.

Risk mitigation is the actions taken to reduce the effect of a risk if it should happen.

A business risk is that the nature of the business may change during the life of a project. (See section 4.1.5.1 on page 10.)

Typical ICT risks include:

* the reliability of any new hardware or software
* the availability of staff with the right business and technical skills at the right time
* the integration of different technologies.

A project implementation risk is that it is not a good idea to introduce a new system just prior to an expected peak in business activity. This is because relatively minor problems within the project could lead to major risks for the business.

Test your knowledge

1 What is a stakeholder?
2 Who might be the stakeholders in a chosen project?
3 What role would each of these stakeholders play?
4 What is a business case?
5 What is the payback period for a project?
6 What is a deliverable?
7 What is a risk for a project?
8 What is risk mitigation?

4.1.2 Project life cycles

A project may be broken down into stages in a number of different ways. How you break it down is called a project life cycle. This section describes one way to break a project down; there are other ways that are just as valid.

4.1.2.1 Define and produce a specification

This stage is about finding out what the customer wants. It may include recording what the users do now, what the customer wants to happen once the new system is in place and any performance needs. The four main activities of this phase are:

* interview the customer
* analyse the customer's requirements
* produce the specification
* produce a business case.

The end result or deliverables of this phase are usually:

* a specification saying what the new system must do, but not how it will do it
* a business case for going ahead with the new system, giving the potential costs and benefits.

4.1.2.2 Plan and design

The plan for the design stage turns the customer's requirements into a potential computer-based solution. The design stage often has these five major activities:

* produce an overall design
* design an input system
* design an output system
* design a processing system
* produce design documentation.

Alternatively, the plan for design may be based on the proposed system's functions – for example, create, update, delete and display. It could also be based on the system's users – for example, sales, marketing and finance.

4.1.2.3 Collect information

Your plan for a project needs to include a process for you to collect information on how the project is going from others who are working on the project. You will need to review and summarise that information and present it to the stakeholders in your project.

4.1.2.4 Implement

The implementation stage includes:

- build the product
- test that the product meets the need
- provide documentation and possibly training
- hand the product over to the customer.

4.1.2.5 Complete and review

Completion involves the customer and the users using your product. It includes identifying the actual benefits and costs of building and running the product. It also includes a final project review, where the stakeholders review how well you did in managing the project and product delivery.

Test your knowledge

1   What are the four main activities of defining and producing the specification?

2   What are the five main activities of planning and designing?

3   What are the four main activities of implementation?

4.1.3 Project management tools

This section considers a number of project management tools, ranging from simple to complex.

4.1.3.1 General planning and scheduling tools

Project management software helps you to manage the administration, planning and scheduling of your project. You can often use the software charting facilities included in this software to produce graphical versions of your plans.

Project management software has the following features:

- create a task
- store information about a task – e.g. who will do it, how long it will take, how it is to be done, how it depends on other tasks
- update task information as your project changes
- generate plans based on the tasks
- publish charts and reports to help you manage the project and to present information to the stakeholders.

Two common charts are **Gantt charts** (see Figure 4.2) and **PERT charts** (see Figure 4.3).

What does it mean?

A **Gantt chart** is a picture of how long all the tasks should take.

A **PERT (Program Evaluation and Review Technique) chart** shows the dependencies between tasks. It depicts the task, its duration and dependency information.

Task	Minutes							
	1	2	3	4	5	6	7	8
Fill kettle	●	●						
Heat kettle			●	●				
Put tea in pot			●	●				
Pour on water					●			
Get cups						●	●	
Let tea brew						●	●	
Pour tea								●

   Figure 4.2   An example of a Gantt chart

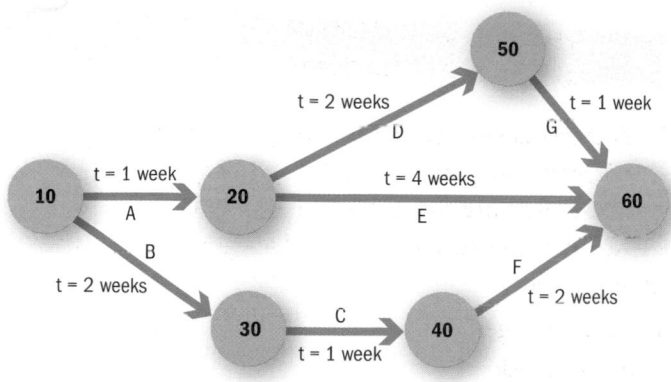

Figure 4.3 An example of a PERT chart

Figure 4.4 Critical path analysis

4.1.3.2 Critical path methods

Critical path methods identify the minimum time needed to complete a project. They show which tasks are on the critical path. This lets you, as project manager, prioritise these tasks to make the project more likely to finish on time.

Critical path analysis (CPA) works on the principle that some tasks cannot start until previous tasks are finished. For example, you cannot test a program until after you have coded it. You must complete these dependent tasks in a sequence. Often, tasks are not dependent on other tasks starting or finishing, so you can do these tasks in parallel.

Consider this series of tasks for a computer system.

1 Specify and design system.
2 Code program 1.
3 Test program 1.
4 Code program 2.
5 Test program 2.
6 Test and implement system.

The project manager works out the dependencies and timescales and draws up the critical path as shown in Figure 4.4. From this you can see that tasks 1, 2, 3 and 6 are on the critical path. A minimum time of 21 days is needed for this project.

4.1.3.3 Specialised software packages

To help manage a project, there are many packages available. At the simplest, there are freeware or shareware packages available from the Internet. Microsoft Project (see Figure 4.5) is a popular middle-of-the-range tool that can help manage a wide variety of projects. For large construction or IT projects involving very many tasks and workers, there is expensive, specialised software available.

▼ Figure 4.5 A screenshot of Microsoft Project

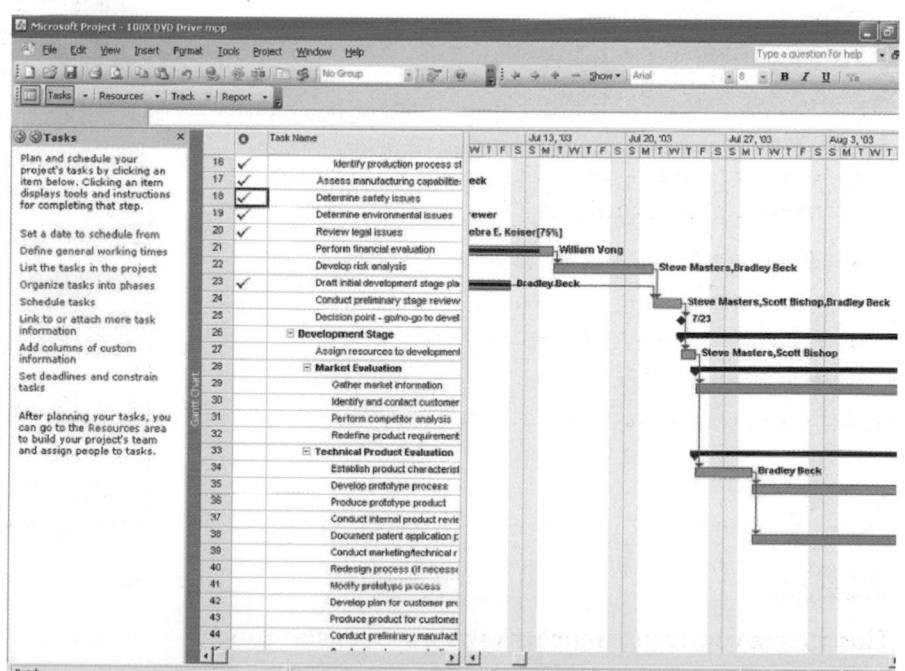

4.1.4 Resources

This section reviews the resources needed for a project: information, people, equipment or facilities, and money.

4.1.4.1 Information

Very few ICT projects could exist without information. Some of the information that your project needs may already exist in other systems. In this case, your project will need to build feeds from these systems. Often your project will need to capture new information or add to or update existing information. Your project will need to include the functions to do this. Finally, your project may need to supply information to other existing systems.

4.1.4.2 People

In your project, there are a number of different ICT skills that contribute towards success. In a small project, one person may possess all these skills. In a larger business project, each of these skills is likely to come from a different specialist. These specialists are likely to include:

- project managers – this unit teaches you all about this skill
- systems analysts – they talk to the customer and the users about their needs and then produce the specification of *what* the project should do
- product developers – either a general term for people who work on an ICT project or, more specifically, the people who turn the specification into a detailed design for the programmer on *how* to build the project
- programmers – the people who write or code the detailed instructions to the computer.

4.1.4.3 Equipment or facilities

Most ICT projects need equipment, such as hardware and software. The developer needs it to build the project. The users need it to run the project. Sometimes the equipment is already in place. Otherwise you must decide on the equipment needs of your project. You must order it and install it early enough in the plan so as not to delay the project. If the equipment is specialised, your plan must allow for designing and building it.

4.1.4.4 Money

In a student project, you may not need to worry about money as a resource. You may have all your equipment for your project already provided for free. Your own time is not chargeable.

In a business project, however, all the resources have a cost. Management expect the project manager to keep the total cost within the overall budget. You have to pay to buy or capture the information your project needs. The people on your project have to be paid. You may have to buy new hardware and software. Even if these exist already, your project is likely to have to pay its share for using them.

4.1.5 Other issues

4.1.5.1 Changing external factors

External factors, such as the nature of the business, may change during the life of a project. (See section 4.1.1.9 on page 7.) While you cannot know about such changes when you write the project specification, they may mean that you need to change the specification once the project is underway. Examples of business changes that could affect a project are:

- the chief executive announces a change in business strategy
- there is a takeover or merger
- there is a radical reorganisation of the structure of the business
- the senior manager who is the driving force behind the project moves on.

4.1.5.2 Monitoring progress

You need to monitor progress on your project. To do this, you should ask for reports from the people doing the work. They will tell you what they have done, what they still have left to do and any problems or delays they have had or are facing. In a formal project, for each task, they may report to you on **man hours** spent, man hours remaining, how much longer they think it will take to finish and percentage of task completed.

What does it mean?

A **man hour** is the amount of work a person can be expected to do in one hour.

These reports may be produced daily, weekly or fortnightly.

The stakeholders will also want to know how things are going. You will learn about this in section 4.3.4.1 on page 21.

4.1.5.3 Taking corrective actions

When you find that things are not going to plan, you should immediately take corrective action to bring the project back towards the plan. Sometimes, the chosen action is within your control, such as changing who will do which task in the future. More often, you may need one or more of the stakeholders to take action or make decisions. You may even need to persuade senior management to accept a delay to the project or to reduce the scope of the project.

4.1.5.4 Communications

One of your responsibilities as project manager is to make sure there is good communication between everyone involved. This does not mean that all communication must go through you. However, you should organise meetings or reports to make sure everyone knows what is going on in those areas of the project that affect them. You should consider your audience when you communicate. (There is more on this in section 4.3.4.1 on page 21.)

4.1.5.5 Internal and external guidelines and legislation

Although this may not be specifically mentioned in the specification, your project should comply with legislation and with the relevant guidelines. The pieces of legislation most likely to affect your project are the Data Protection Act and various Health and Safety laws. Your staff may be subject to laws such as the Offices, Shops and Railway Premises Act.

Most large ICT organisations have internal guidelines stating how they go about developing projects. They may, for example, describe a common look and feel for applications, or say where particular documents should be stored or how files should be named. Smaller organisations without their own guidelines can use external guidelines for good development practice, which are available on the Internet.

4.1.5.6 Dealing with conflict

As project manager, you will need to manage conflict between the stakeholders in order to make the project happen. There may be many causes of conflict – Figure 4.6 shows some of the more common ones.

While, in some cases, you will be able to make an executive decision to resolve the conflict, in others, you will have to use your persuasive skills to get the stakeholders to agree.

Different priorities
A stakeholder is late in delivering his contribution to your project as he has other things to do that he feels have higher priority.

Money
Either the available money has been cut back or your project is overspending. Different stakeholders will have different views on whether to reduce the scope or increase the spend.

Common causes of conflict

Deliverable quality
Stakeholders will have different views about whether or not the quality of some deliverables is good enough for their purposes.

▲ Figure 4.6 Some common causes of conflict

4.1.5.7 Impact on other systems

Few computer systems simply automate existing manual processes. Even fewer new computer systems are just more efficient forms of existing working computer systems. When designing a new system, a good designer takes the opportunity to exploit the strengths of a computer compared with a clerk doing a similar task. The designer should also integrate the new system with other existing computer systems.

The management, therefore, will often take the opportunity to change organisational and existing working practices with the introduction of a new computer system. This could affect staff in these ways:

- the work becomes harder and therefore too difficult
- the work becomes easier and hence there is pressure to reduce pay
- skills built up over the years become redundant
- staff need training to learn how to use the new system.

In extreme cases, the new system may reduce the workload so much that some staff are no longer required. This may mean redundancy, retraining or redeployment.

Test your knowledge

1   What is a man hour?
2   What items might a progress report to the project manager contain?

4.1.6 Project methodologies

Most large organisations use a **project methodology** for their normal projects.

What does it mean?

A **project methodology** is a standard, documented way of tackling a computer project.

4.1.6.1 Benefits and drawbacks of formal methodologies

The benefits, particularly to a large organisation, of a formal methodology (see section 4.1.6.2) lie in the fact that everybody does things in the same way. This means that the organisation can:

- produce a standard set of developer training
- transfer staff more easily between projects
- maintain software more easily
- avoid spending time thinking about how to tackle each project individually.

The drawbacks of a formal methodology are that they:

- are often over-complex for a simple project
- may be inappropriate for an unusual project
- require an investment in training, time and product which might not be repaid.

4.1.6.2 Project methodology examples

There are many different project methodologies. Here are three examples of formal methodologies to give you an idea of what they do.

■ PRINCE2

The UK government's Central Computer and Telecommunications Agency (CCTA) released PRINCE2 in 1996 as a generic project management method. PRINCE stands for PRojects IN Controlled Environments. It was designed as a UK government standard. It is process-driven and divides up into the following eight processes:

1 starting up a project
2 planning
3 initiating a project
4 directing a project
5 controlling a stage
6 managing product delivery
7 managing stage boundaries
8 closing a project.

■ Consultancy-driven methodologies

Sometimes, when large software companies develop a project for a customer, they will use their own methodology for the project. While this offers benefits to that company, it sometimes produces pressure on the customer to adopt the methodology for other related projects. This incurs additional consultancy costs, training costs and a potentially much greater lock-in to the software company.

■ Company-specific methodology

Companies with a large in-house ICT department often feel it is worthwhile to develop their own methodology. They usually do this by taking a standard methodology and removing large parts that they feel are not relevant to them. The rest they tailor to their organisation structure and to the type of projects that they run. For example, if they have outsourced their network, then they do not need a methodology for network projects. If they do not sell their software, then customer and user management and acceptance and product distribution is much easier.

Activity 4.1

Starting your project
This unit is about your skills as a project manager in running an IT project. You should be developing and managing your project as you work through this unit. To complete each set of activities, you need to have both finished that section of the unit **and** made sufficient progress in your project.

Your project should take 60 hours. Your tutor may set it or you may be able to choose from a range of projects suggested by your tutor or you may have a suitable project for a business or organisation that you know well. Your project should be complex enough for you to demonstrate meeting all eleven of the pass criteria. However, it should not be so complex that it takes you a lot more than 60 hours.

1 List the possible reasons why projects can fail and explain them in the context of examples, maybe from a case study. **p₁**

2 Produce a report with supporting notes on how to minimise the chances of projects failing, including examples. **m₁**

3 Produce a written report of the different tools and methodologies that are available to support the project manager with, if possible, evidence of the use of tools or records of actual demonstrations. **p₂**

4 Describe the typical phases of a project life cycle. **p₃**

5 Identify a project and produce a project specification, collecting information as required. **p₄**

6 For your own project, independently identify the stakeholders and how their needs are met. **m₃**

7 Produce a report describing critical path analysis (CPA). Explain with an example and using CPA diagrams how critical paths can be identified. **m₂**

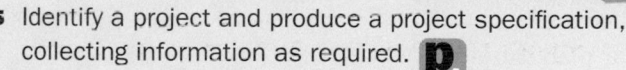

Test your knowledge

1 What are four benefits of using a formal project methodology?

2 What are the eight processes in the PRINCE2 methodology?

This section focuses on the planning aspects of a project: the plan itself and the activities involved.

4.2.1 Project plan

Every computer project should have a plan. A good plan is one that is both easy to read and easy to maintain. For a very simple project you may produce the plan with word processing or spreadsheet software. For larger projects you should use project management software to help you produce detailed plans.

4.2.1.1 Purpose

The project plan has two purposes. For you, it is a tool to monitor progress, manage the project and help you evaluate options and make decisions on how to make the project a success. This means that it should be easy to maintain. For your stakeholders, it is a good way for you to communicate to them how the project is proceeding. This means that for them it should be easy for them to read and understand.

4.2.1.2 Content

Your plan should show:

- phases (in section 4.1.2 you learned ways of splitting up your project into stages or phases; if you are undertaking a different type of project, such as installing or upgrading a PC or a network, you may modify these phases as needed)
- activities (in section 4.1.2 you also learned some of the activities involved in a standard ICT project; you should add activities as you need them; as you work through the project, you should break down the later activities into more detail, but avoid going into unnecessary detail)
- timescales (the start and end date for each activity)
- dependencies
- resources needed for each activity
- dates of key milestones.

4.2.1.3 Review points

Your plan should also show **review points**. The different types of review point are described in section 4.2.2.3 on page 16.

What does it mean?

A **review point** is where the project manager and others meet to review the progress of the project.

4.2.1.4 Use of software

There are several types of software that you can use to help manage and plan your project, including the following:

- **Project management packages** are the most powerful aid and were covered in section 4.1.3.3 on page 9. However, they may be too complex for the simplest of projects.
- **Spreadsheets** can be used to record one activity per row of the spreadsheet. They can help with some of the calculations and also present some of the plan results graphically.
- **Drawing and graphics packages** can present the results of your planning to your stakeholders in ways that are easier for them to understand.
- **Databases** could be used to record and amend the detailed parts of the plan for each activity.
- **Word processors** could be used instead of a database to run simpler projects.

Test your knowledge

1 What is the purpose of the project plan for the project manager?
2 What is the purpose of the project plan for the stakeholders?
3 What six things should your project plan show?
4 What is a review point?
5 Which five types of software might you use to help manage your project?

4.2.2 Detail of activities

You need to record the detail for each activity in your plan. Figure 4.7 shows the details that are recorded in most plans.

4.2.2.1 Potential for parallel or sequential processes

If you had unlimited time to complete a project, the most efficient way to plan it using minimum resources would be to do each activity sequentially. If you had unlimited resources to complete a project, the best way to complete your project in the fastest time would be to do as much as you can in parallel. This would be subject to the dependencies of activities on each other. In practice you are likely to have fixed resources and a fixed timescale. You will be expected to manage your project to finish on time and keep everyone busy.

Case study

How many people do you want?

Your boss, Abdul, estimated your project size as twelve man months and has negotiated with the stakeholders a delivery date four months away. There are no problems to prevent you getting on with the project and no unusual dependencies. He offers you the following three staffing plans. List the advantages and disadvantages of each.

1 3 people for 4 months.
2 4 people for 3 months.
3 1 person now, increasing to 5 or 6 in the 3rd and 4th months.

▼ **Figure 4.7 The details of activities needed for the project plan**

Start and end dates
These should include the original planned dates, the current plan and, after completion of the activity, the actual dates.

Minimum duration of the activity
Many activities, e.g. a weekly progress reviews, cannot be done continuously or are ongoing, but they should still appear in the plan. You may also want someone to do two or more activities at the same time so the minimum duration should also reflect that.

Description
Include both a short description, to uniquely identify this activity and to appear on reports, and a long description, to scope the activity.

Details of activities

Dependencies
Show which activities must complete before this activity can begin and which activities cannot start until this activity is finished.

Resources needed
This should include the number of man hours or man days and the type of skill needed.

People
Include people to whom you have currently assigned the activity.

4.2.2.2 Resources needed for each activity

For each activity, you should record not only the expected man hours needed for completion, but also whether it will require any specialist skills. If, for example, your project needs a specialist database administrator to build your database, it is important to recognise this early on in the life of your project. Otherwise, your project may be delayed while a suitable specialist is recruited or you may need to spend extra resource, have slower delivery and poorer quality while a non-specialist person is trained.

4.2.2.3 Review points

Your project is likely to contain several review points. For these, you should bring your plan up to date and take any decisions needed to bring the project back on track if it has slipped. You may also need to present the progress of the project to the stakeholders. The following terms describe different types of review point, though they are sometimes used interchangeably.

- **Milestones.** For example, a milestone might be that the specification has been agreed or the first part of the project is ready for testing. Milestones are not date related.
- **Checkpoints.** For example, on a project that uses a new coding tool, there might be a checkpoint six weeks after coding starts to see how effective this new tool has been.
- **Deadlines** (for completion of the whole project and for parts of the project). For example, equipment expenditure might need to come in this year's budget, so all equipment orders might have a deadline of 31 December. Holidays and business demands might prevent training during the months of June to September, so there might be a deadline of 31 May for completion of training.
- **Management review.** This looks back on what has recently been done and reviews and approves the plan for the next stage. It is usually done at the end of a phase or stage. It may be done on a timed basis, e.g. every three months.

What does it mean?

A **milestone** is a point where a project achieves an important measurable deliverable.

A **checkpoint** could have any criteria for which stakeholders feel that there should be a review.

A **deadline** is a date by which something must have happened.

A **management review** is a formal review, run on behalf of the customer.

4.2.2.4 Collecting information

You should put in place a process for gathering the input to your plan and how things progress on a regular basis. How you do this depends upon the size, complexity and formality of the project. For a simple project, a regular informal chat is sufficient. For other projects, you may need to run a scheduled formal review or progress meeting or team members may present written progress reports to you.

Once you have collected progress data, then you should update your plan, work out the impact on the remainder of the project and take appropriate decisions.

Test your knowledge

1 What is a milestone?
2 What is a checkpoint?
3 What is a deadline?
4 What is a management review?

Activity 4.2

Planning your project

1 Develop and document your project plan. **p**₅

2 Document how you monitor the project against the project plan. **p**₆

3 While you monitor and track the progress of your project using the project plan, record how you adapt the plan as circumstances change. **m**₄

4 Record how you meet your deadlines and key review dates as identified in the project plan. **m**₅

4.3 How to implement an IT project

This section looks at four aspects of implementation: design, implementation tools, deliverables and monitoring techniques.

4.3.1 Design

The design of an ICT project turns the stakeholders' requirements of *what* a project needs to do as stated in the specification into a technical specification of *how* the programmers should build the project.

4.3.1.1 Design methods

There are many methods for the design of an ICT system. A large organisation, business or software company may have its own method. However, many organisations will use a method that is specified by another organisation and supported through manuals, training and consultancy. A typical design method is Structured Systems Analysis and Design Method (SSADM). This is widely used for UK government computing projects.

SSADM uses three techniques:

- logical data modelling – used to identify the data requirements of the project; data consists of **entities** and **relationships** (see Figure 4.8)
- data flow modelling – used to identify how data moves round a system; it includes **processes**, **data stores**, **external entities** and **data flows**

What does it mean?

An **entity** is a thing about which an organisation wants to record information.

A **relationship** is a link between entities.

A **process** is what changes data from one form to another.

A **data store** is a holding area within a system for data.

An **external entity** sends data into or gets data from a system.

A **data flow** is movement of data from one area to another, often through a process.

- entity behaviour modelling – used to identify the events that affect each entity and the sequence in which they occur.

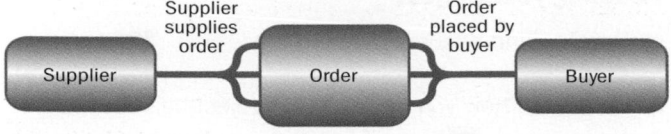

Figure 4.8 Logical data model

The two SSADM design modules are:
- logical system specification – this produces the technical systems options, as well as the logical design of update, enquiry and system screens
- physical design – this creates the physical database design and a set of program specifications (see Figure 4.9).

For a simple piece of application design, there are likely to be four pieces of design documentation:
- logical data model (see section 4.3.1.1)
- physical database design (see section 4.3.1.1)

▼ **Figure 4.9 Physical database design (equivalent to the logical data model in Figure 4.8)**

Physical database design

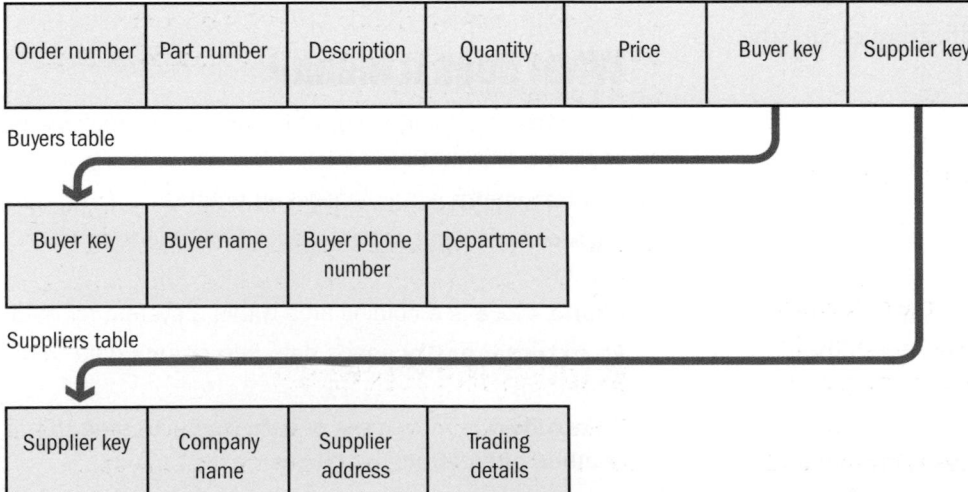

Order table

Order number	Part number	Description	Quantity	Price	Buyer key	Supplier key

Buyers table

Buyer key	Buyer name	Buyer phone number	Department

Suppliers table

Supplier key	Company name	Supplier address	Trading details

- user interface (documents all the screens in a system)
- program specifications (instructions to the programmers on what each program or module in a system should do and how it should do it).

STOP

Test your knowledge

1 What is an entity?
2 What is a relationship?
3 What is a process?
4 What is a data store?
5 What is an external entity?
6 What is a data flow?
7 What documentation is needed for the design of a simple application?

4.3.2 Implementation tools

There are many hundreds of design, programming and testing tools available to you. It is a similar choice to what PC tool you might use to write a letter. To write a long, formal letter you would probably choose your favourite or standard full-featured word processor, while for a quick note you might choose your favourite or standard text editor.

Do not attempt to choose an implementation tool until the specification is complete. The business requirements may rule out certain technical solutions. The larger and more complex a project is, the more likely it is that you will choose powerful, but perhaps more difficult-to-use tools. This may mean that you need to allow some time for developer training in your project plan.

In the business world you may have little choice. Your organisation may state that for your type of project you must use a particular set of tools. You may have a development team that has skills in only one set of relevant tools. You may not have the time or the budget to retrain them even if there is a better tool available.

It is often fun to evaluate new tools. However, it is best to choose the set of tools that you and your team have used effectively before and with which you are confident that you can successfully complete the project.

4.3.2.2 Use of software or hardware

It is best that any tools that you plan to use do not require new software or hardware – this will simplify your project, as you do not need to spend any money or manage the installation of new equipment or software. If there is a choice between a software and a hardware tool, choose the software tool, as this will be much easier to upgrade.

4.3.3 Deliverables

The output of a project is a set of deliverables. Examples of **customer deliverables** are the final version of the developed software or installed equipment. **Interim deliverables** often have an IT focus, such as specifications. Many activities involved in the project such as 'interview customers' or 'evaluate possible design solutions' do not directly produce a deliverable.

What does it mean?

Customer deliverables are those that are useful to the customer.

Interim deliverables are those that appear part way through the project.

Early in the project you will need to be able to identify the project's customer deliverables. These are typically software products, documentation, user training and equipment.

You need to manage these from both the customer and ICT perspective. For example, the customer will want to

know when a complete new system can be introduced into their Kingston shop and their Slough factory. They will not be concerned about exactly which software modules Kingston will use or which ICT equipment Slough needs. However, these will be very important issues for the development team.

▲ Figure 4.10 It is important to use language that your customer will understand

4.3.3.1 Product

Your project may involve delivery of a software application, a service or a system. You should be clear what product you are delivering.

■ Plans

The initial plan may just indicate the functions of the new system. However, the **baseline plan** at the start of the build phase should show all the modules in the project.

What does it mean?

A **baseline plan** is a plan that is fixed and agreed at a key point in a project, often the start of a phase.

The customer does not want to know all the details of the plan, with possibly hundreds of IT module names that are meaningless to them. You should summarise this information into functions or groups of functions that the customer understands. So for the Kingston shop, you might have a till or point of sale system, a stock control function and a shop management reporting function.

■ Prototyping

In the development of an IT product, it is usual to build a **prototype**. This is usually done so that the user can have an idea of what the system will look like and what it will do. The idea for prototyping comes from engineering, where a prototype is often built before construction of an assembly line to produce many copies.

What does it mean?

A **prototype** is a quickly and cheaply built version of a product that contains the main features and is close to the real thing.

A prototype does not usually have the robustness and validity checking features that are built into the final system. It is often thrown away, as it can be more costly to add in the necessary robustness than to start again.

■ Equipment

Your project may require more equipment to be bought for the users. This equipment also needs to be installed and tested. If it is specialised equipment, then you may need to manage software or hardware development by its supplier.

■ Schedule

You should produce from your plan a schedule for the customers of what will be delivered when and to whom. You should write this in terms the customer can understand. So you should write, for example, 'Point of sale hardware delivered to Kingston shop' rather than '5 model 684B-3 and 1 model 8500 server to site KIN02'.

4.3.3.2 User training

Most ICT projects are complex enough to need user training before the system can be used fully. The development team may have to train the users. Even if the user takes responsibility for training, the development team needs to produce training materials or train the trainers. Your plan should show these activities, even if you do not have direct responsibility for delivery of training. Probably the most important user training aid is the user guide (see section 4.4.6 on page 27).

4.3.3.3 Technical and user documentation

Each project phase is likely to have documentation recording the output of that phase. The analysis phase has a document that analyses the business problem. It may also have a business case document. The build and test phases have lots of documents describing what is built.

The final phase delivers most or all of the documentation that the user needs to learn, run and support the system. You should make sure that your project plan has activities to produce and review all this documentation. Do not underestimate how long this takes to produce. (See also section 4.4.1.2 on page 23.)

STOP Test your knowledge

1. What is a customer deliverable?
2. What is an interim deliverable?
3. Give four examples of customer deliverables.

4.3.4 Monitoring techniques

4.3.4.1 Routine communications with stakeholders

Another of your responsibilities as project manager is to make sure there are good communications between everyone on the project. This does not mean all communication goes through you. However, you should put in place meetings or reports to make sure that everyone knows enough about what is going on in the areas that affect them. This does not mean that every email about the project should be copied to everyone involved.

You should consider your audience when you communicate. The customers will mainly want to know what the project will do for them. The technical people building the project may only be interested in technical aspects of their part of the project.

You are involved in two sorts of report. You will receive reports from those doing the work. This is covered in section 4.1.5.2 on page 11.

You will also send reports to the stakeholders. One of your major tasks is to put together all the information that you receive from the project team members. From this, you can then report to the project stakeholders on how well the project as a whole is going, any major problems that it faces and how likely it is to be ready when expected. This reporting will take place weekly, fortnightly or monthly.

4.3.4.2 Interim reviews

You will need to call and run an interim project review meeting at key points in the project. The aim of the review could be to let everyone in the team know what is going on and what is expected of each of them. The review meeting might also be used to consider the problems that the project needs to overcome before it can move forward. These reviews (see section 4.2.2.3 on page 16) are often held:

- at the start of a project phase
- at the end of a project phase

- when there is a major change to the project scope
- when there is a major delay
- a few months after project implementation.

This last type of review is called a post implementation review. Its aim is to learn from the project. At this review you will record what things went well and what went badly. For any problems identified you will consider how things could be done better next time (see section 4.4.4 on page 26).

4.3.4.3 Use of logbooks

You should keep a **logbook** or project history for you and others to understand how well your current project is going. It is also a way for you to improve your planning skills for future projects. You should keep a set of baseline plans (see section 4.3.3.1) from the start of each phase and from other key events. You can then build up over the life of the project a complete detailed project history.

What does it mean?

A **logbook** is a record of every important thing that happens on a project.

These two documents form a valuable input into the post implementation review at the end of the project (see section 4.4.4 on page 26).

4.3.4.4 Routine updating of plan

Far from being fixed in time, the project plan is a dynamic document. It is likely to change many times during the course of a project. You should check progress against the plan at regular intervals. After each progress review, you should modify and update the plan, so that it is always current. Your plan should accurately show:

- what work has been done
- what still needs to be done
- what potential problems need to be addressed.

The plan provides a snapshot of the project at a particular point in time. You or anyone looking at it should see at a glance the current state of the project.

4.3.4.5 Other monitoring

You should monitor your plan more often than is necessary just to satisfy the needs of the stakeholders. This is so that you get an early warning of any shortage of resources, so you may access additional resources where necessary. You may also need to react quickly to unforeseen circumstances.

Test your knowledge

1 When are interim reviews carried out?
2 What is a log book?
3 What is a baseline plan?

Activity 4.3

Implementing your project

For the project you began in Activity 4.1:

1 Design a product or service based on the project specification. **p**₇

2 Implement your project and create a product that meets the specification. **p**₈

3 Run an interim review of the project management process and identify any emerging problems. **m**₆

4 Produce a document justifying the tools and methodologies used in your project. **d**₁

4.4 How to test, document and review an IT project

This section covers the final parts of your IT project. It includes completion of the build of your project, as well as other important supporting activities.

4.4.1 Completion process

During the completion process you will finish all the activities needed to hand over a working product to your customer.

4.4.1.1 Testing

This phase may also be known as build and test.

■ Program or formative testing

The aim of program or formative testing is to find the errors in the program code while the program is under test.

The main activities involved in testing for each part of the design are:

1 build the code
2 produce test data

then repeatedly:

3 test the program
4 get user feedback
5 fix the problems.

In this phase there are often lots of dependencies. You may want to use the programs in your system that input data to create the test data for your update, report or delete programs. This means that you must build and test the data input programs first. There may be people dependencies: one developer cannot start full-time on the project until they have finished a previous one.

This phase of testing is often the easiest phase to plan. Although you have a lot of activities, for each one it is easier to estimate the time from the expected size and complexity of the module. It is easier for you to track how this phase is progressing as you can add up the progress on many small activities.

■ System or summative testing

The aim of system or summative testing is to make sure that all parts of the system fit together as they should. System testing is different from program testing in that it is done at the end of the development phase rather than as you go through it.

The activities are:

1 produce system test data

then repeatedly:

2 run test
3 produce error reports
4 analyse reports
5 fix errors.

You might find that this is the most difficult testing phase to plan. The time taken for this phase depends upon the quality of the system delivered for testing and how good the developers are at finding and fixing errors. There are often a lot of implicit dependencies. If there has been an error in the first part of a test, then this may cause a later part of a test to give unexpected results. For example, suppose the first part of a test is to create a new record and the second part is to update that record. If the first part fails to create the new record, then the second part will fail, with a 'record not found' error.

4.4.1.2 Documentation

The software methodology that your project uses may specify the documentation your project should produce. If a document is specified as optional and you decide not to produce it, you should record why not.

If your project does not use a specific methodology with laid down documentation, then your project definition should say what documents you and your team will produce.

Typically, you should document:

1 the business and technical requirements
2 the design of each of the functions of the system: *what* each piece does
3 the logical and physical data design
4 *how* each piece of the system does its function.

You should plan to write most of the documentation before, during or immediately after building the part of the system to which it refers. However, towards the end of the project, you should plan for the important activity of producing the final copy of each piece of documentation. Each document should include all the changes that have taken place during development. All these pieces of documentation should be consistent. They should also accurately reflect what the delivered system does.

Once these final versions are complete, you should put in place a change control process. This means that any requested changes to the project need to be agreed, documented and planned before any work takes place on them.

4.4.1.3 Review

A good way for you to check that your project is going well and is likely to succeed is to arrange for an independent review to be carried out. Someone who has no day-to-day involvement with your project is best to carry out this review. This reviewer usually feeds back to you as the project manager and also to senior management.

You need to identify suitable people and persuade them to act as reviewers for your project. Here are some characteristics that they should have:

- credibility with senior management
- knowledge of similar types of project to yours
- project management experience.

You should make full use of their knowledge and expertise.

Formal management reviews also take place from time to time during the life of a project. The dates for these are usually agreed at the start of the project. You should list them in the project definition. In the business world, you should not forget that senior management have the power to order work on a project to stop or change direction at any time.

At a formal management review, you need to prepare and present the following information:

1 a summary of the project's aims and objectives
2 the purpose of the review – perhaps to mark the end of a phase or a special review called because of problems or because things have changed
3 what you have achieved since the last review
4 the current state of the project
5 the plans for the rest of the project, with an emphasis on the next phase
6 the issues faced by the project
7 the decisions that you want the management review to make
8 their commitment for support and the resources for the rest of the project.

You should also prepare answers for the questions that you think management may ask. Management will expect you to have a view on any issues faced by the project, even if they might not expect you to make a decision on them.

4.4.1.4 Handover and sign off

Once the system has been thoroughly tested and all the documentation is complete, you will hand over the system to the client and users for acceptance. This means that you believe the project is finished. However, the client may have a different view. They should check the documentation to see if it is complete and to an acceptable quality. The users should also test that the system does what they expect it to do. Often you will have to make changes to the system or documentation at this stage before the client is satisfied.

When the client is satisfied, they will sign off the system as fit for purpose.

Once sign off happens, you should put in place a change control process as mentioned in section 4.4.1.2. This

means that any requested changes to the project need to be agreed, documented and planned before any work takes place on them.

4.4.1.5 Arranging support

Most ICT projects need some form of post-implementation support. For a packaged PC product, this may be as simple as a website with a list of frequently asked questions and their answers. In addition, the developer may offer email or telephone support, usually paid for by the client. Where a software company has run a major project to develop software for a client company, it may be very important to decide if ongoing support comes from the developer, the client or another software company that specialises in this sort of work.

Test your knowledge

1 For each part of the system, what four things should you document?

2 What are handover and sign off?

4.4.2 Functional testing of product

Before developers release any product to the client, they need to test the product to make sure that it does what it should. They also test to make sure that it doesn't break or behave in an unexpected way.

4.4.2.1 Test data

The tester designs test data to meet four sorts of conditions. These are:

- normal – valid data that the program should handle correctly
- extreme – also valid data, but at the limit in terms of size, range or other constraint that the program should handle
- just wrong – invalid data that is just beyond the limit that the program should handle
- wrong – invalid data that is clearly wrong.

An example is given in Table 4.1.

Test data type	Typical value of a date
Normal	15th January
Extreme	29th February 2008 (in a leap year)
Just wrong	29th February 2009 (not a leap year)
Wrong	38th Septober

Table 4.1 Examples of the four types of value that need to be tested

4.4.2.2 Structured walkthroughs

The first part of testing might be a **structured walkthrough**. Its main benefit is to pick up any major logic flaws in the design or coding of a program or

What does it mean?

A **structured walkthrough** is a review by one or more developers who manually go through the main paths of a program or system simulating how the computer executes them.

system. It is also sometimes used where an important bug is particularly difficult to find and fix. Structured walkthroughs can be expensive in terms of time and resources and so are not often used.

4.4.2.3 Test plan or schedule

The first step in preparing a test plan is for the tester to specify what tests they want to do on which functions. The tests will involve a mixture of valid and invalid input. This reflects how the product will be used, with all users making some errors at some point. The next step is for the tester to generate the right test data to cause each test to happen. Finally all the tests are put together in the right sequence to test all aspects of the program and capture what happens to each test.

The tester then runs this test plan on the software. The results are captured. The tester compares the actual results against the expected results. Often on early tests there are big differences. These differences may be caused by wrong test data, but more usually they are caused by bugs in the program.

The tester records all the bugs found and gives these to the developer to be fixed. When a significant number have apparently been fixed, the tester reruns the test plan and compares results. They record where bugs have actually been fixed and also any new bugs that are found. Testing is complete when either all the actual results match the expected results, or only a few insignificant bugs remain that are hard to find and fix.

STOP

Test your knowledge

1 Describe the four different conditions that a tester tests for.

2 What is a structured walkthrough?

4.4.3 Review of product

This section explains how you should review a software product.

4.4.3.1 Against specification

The specification agreed before the development of a project normally states *what* the software does. It does not say *how* it does it. It is therefore important to review the software and compare it against the specification. It is unusual for developers not to deliver major pieces of functionality as set out in the specification – these are referred to as quantitative aspects of the project and it should be clear to everyone what is meant by them. However, a specification might also refer to qualitative features such as ease of use, high security or fast response time – these are more open to personal opinion, so a developer and a user might have different views on what they mean.

4.4.3.2 Identification of potential additional development

Often when the customer or the user sees the finished product, they see further opportunities for improvement. They may even have expected these features to be in the delivered product, but did not spell this out in the specification. A functional review identifies and records these features. This will provide the input to any future product developments.

4.4.4 Review of project management

This type of review may be called a post implementation review. Its purpose is to identify and document the successes of the project. It also records those things that did not go so well, in order to help you make sure that they do not happen on your next project. Either you or an independent reviewer may set up and run this meeting.

The organiser of this meeting should make sure that:

- all stakeholders or their representatives come to the meeting so there is a balance of views

- all attendees voice their opinions
- the meeting covers all aspects of the project
- someone takes accurate notes of the discussion
- there is a written summary of the main points.

You should use this opportunity to gather information about your own performance and identify further development needs. You should make a list of the lessons learned.

This meeting usually covers the topics of dates, resources, external factors and tools.

4.4.4.1 Actual dates versus planned dates

The most common cause of project failure is missing the planned dates. The reviewer often starts by finding out which parts of the project were on time or late. If parts were late, then the reviewer may try to identify why they were late and what impact the delays had on project success. They may also consider whether the project manager could have done anything about the delays.

4.4.4.2 Actual use of resources versus planned resources needed

This part of the review is similar in principle to the review of dates. The reviewer will identify which parts of the project used much more or less resources than planned. If more resources were used than planned, the reviewer may try to identify why and what the impact on project success was. They may also consider whether the project manager could have done anything about the overspend.

4.4.4.3 External factors

Sometimes unanticipated external factors will affect the project. For example, the customer's priorities may change; expected resources may not appear on time or at all; there may be major changes to the specification. The reviewer should consider what impact this had on the project and how well the project manager managed the change to the project.

4.4.4.4 Validity of the tools used

The choice of tools may have a major impact on the success of a project. For example, was the project management tool powerful enough to help the project manager manage the project effectively? Was it too powerful and was time wasted in learning and using unnecessary features?

The review scope may also include the validity of tools used to design, build and test the project. These again may have either been too simple or too powerful and complex for use on the project.

Test your knowledge

1 What five things should the organiser make sure happen at a post implementation review?

2 What four aspects of the project will be covered in the post implementation review?

4.4.5 Technical documentation

All projects should deliver some documentation to the customer, appropriate to the customer's needs.

For a PC game, the customer would expect a user guide (see section 4.4.6). However, the only technical documentation is likely to be an installation guide, as the customers would not expect to support or modify the game themselves.

At the other end of the scale, if a software company writes an application especially for one of its customers, and the customer expects to maintain the application themselves, then the customer would expect a large amount of technical documentation. This may consist of all the specifications used to produce the software. These should be completely up to date with the delivered version of the software. The documentation may also include a listing of all the program code, with suitable comments on what each piece of code does.

4.4.6 User guide

The primary aim of the user guide is to instruct the user on how to use the product or service.

4.4.6.1 Instructions on how to use the product or service

The user guide may take several forms. There may be a 'Getting Started' section, which contains just enough information to let the user start using the product. As well as the main guide, there may be an 'Advanced Features' section, which only very experienced users would need to read.

Most user guides deliver advice to the user's computer screen. They may reside on the user's computer, a local server or on the Internet. Sometimes they are available as a printed book or manual.

4.4.6.2 Getting help

Most software has help available by pressing one key or clicking a menu. Function key F1 is a common source of help. Many top-level menu toolbars have 'Help' as one of the options. Access to help often presents either sets of menus or a search function for the user to find the piece of help they want. Sometimes there is **context-sensitive help**.

What does it mean?

Context-sensitive help means that the help system provides appropriate and different help information depending on where the user was when they asked for help.

4.4.6.3 Known bugs

Sometimes when software is delivered, it contains known bugs that the developers have not yet been able to fix. One way to tell this to the users is to have a 'read me' file as part of the help system. This lists the effects of the known bugs and sometimes possible work-arounds.

4.4.6.4 Gaining and using feedback

Most developers are keen to gain feedback on how users get on with their products. They often like suggestions for improvements. Originally this was done through a postcard or form in a printed user guide that a user mailed in. Today an email or web form is more likely to be the way for a developer to gain feedback. Where the feedback is about a bug in a program, the developer will fix this with an appropriate priority. Often feedback will be about an improvement. Many software companies have a process that considers all potential improvements. They then decide which ones are worthwhile and the order in which they will do them.

4.4.6.5 Hardware and software requirements

For off-the-shelf software, it is important that the developer specifies what hardware and other software the software needs to run. This is often divided into minimum requirements, which is what the software needs just to be tested, and typical requirements, which is what is needed to run the software with typical data volumes and reasonable performance.

For hardware, the requirements may specify the processor type and power, the amount of memory and the amount of free disk storage needed. For software, the requirements may specify the operating systems. For a game add-on, for example, they would state the minimum version of the game required.

Test your knowledge

1 What is context-sensitive help?

2 What are the requirements for software likely to specify?

3 What are the requirements for hardware likely to specify?

Activity 4.4

Finalising your project

For the project you began in Activity 4.1:

1 Test and review the output (product or service) of your project. **p₉**

2 Review the project management process and identify and document the successful and unsuccessful choices that you made and decisions that you took. **p₁₀**

3 Create technical and user documentation for your project. **p₁₁**

4 Write a document that critically evaluates the effectiveness of the project plan you used to support your project. **d₂**

5 Identify, accurately assess and document the impact of the potential and actual risks to your project. **d₃**

6 Evaluate and document the potential impact of the introduction of your product or service on wider business systems, people or processes. **d₄**

Preparation for assessment

In this unit you have run a project and produced a product or service. In the four assessment activities at the end of the sections of this unit you have produced much of the supporting material for your assessment. As well as this, you will need to produce evidence of three sorts. Your assessor may want to see all of your project management documentation, such as plans and records of meetings, the product or service documentation and the final working product or service.

Task 1 (P1, P2, P3, P4, P5, P6, P10, M1, M3, M4, M5, M6, D1, D2, D3)

■ Project management documentation

- List the possible reasons why projects can fail and provide an explanation of them in the content of an example. **p**₁
- Report, with supporting notes, on how to minimise the chances of projects failing. **m**₁
- Prepare a report of the different tools and methodologies that are available to support the project manager with, if possible, evidence of the use of tools or records of actual demonstrations. **p**₂
- Write a description of typical phases of a project life cycle. **p**₃
- Write a description of your project specification. **p**₄
- Identify the stakeholders and how their needs are met. **m**₃
- Create a documented project plan. **p**₅
- Prepare a document describing how you monitor the project against the project plan. **p**₆

- Create a record of how you adapted the plan as circumstances changed while you monitored and tracked the progress of your project using a project plan. **m**₄
- Create a record of how you met deadlines and key review dates as identified in the project plan. **m**₅
- Create an interim review of the project management process with any identified emerging problems. **m**₆
- Prepare a document justifying the tools and methodologies used in your project. **d**₁
- Review the project management process, identifying and documenting successful and unsuccessful choices made and decisions taken. **p**₁₀
- Prepare a document that critically evaluates the effectiveness of a project plan to support the project. **d**₂
- Prepare a document that identifies, accurately assesses and records impact of potential risks to a project. **d**₃

Task 2 (P7, P11)

■ Product or service documentation

- Develop a design of a product or service based on the project specification. **p**₇
- Supply technical and user documentation to accompany it. **p**₁₁

Task 3 (P8, P9, D4)

■ Working product or service

- Implement your project and create a product that meets the specification. **p**₈
- Test and review the output (product or service) of your project. **p**₉
- Create a document on the potential impact of the introduction of your product or service on wider business systems, people or processes. **d**₄

Advanced Database Skills

Introduction

Most people who use computers as part of their work will routinely use one or more databases. In most situations, users will be interacting with an existing database – perhaps adding or amending records, searching for information or producing reports. Some users, however, will need to be able to design and create databases – this unit covers the knowledge and skills required to do this.

After completing this unit, you should be able to achieve these outcomes:

- Understand the purpose and features of relational databases

- Be able to create, populate and test a multiple database

- Be able to use advanced features of a database and test functionality.

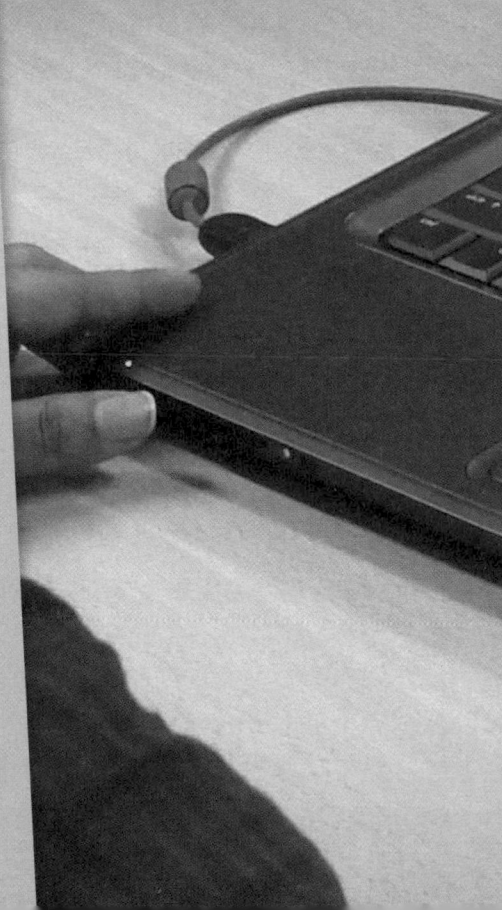

Grading criteria	Activity	Page number
To achieve a pass grade the evidence must show that the learner is able to:		
p₁ Describe the purpose and features of a relational database	5.7, PFA	39, 58
p₂ Design and implement a working relational database with five tables and set up relationships according to the user need	PFA	58
p₃ Design and implement features in data entry forms to ensure validity and integrity of data	PFA	58
p₄ Import data from an external source and export query or report results to another application	PFA	58
p₅ Carry out modifications to an implemented database with the addition of another table according to user need	PFA	59
p₆ Devise and test queries using multiple tables and multiple criteria	PFA	58
To achieve a merit grade the evidence must show that, in addition to the pass criteria, the learner is able to:		
m₁ Explain referential integrity and the purpose of primary keys in building the relationships between tables	PFA	59
m₂ Implement consistent and appropriate styling in the design and construction of a database	PFA	58
m₃ Implement an automated function	PFA	58
m₄ Explain how records and related records are deleted to ensure the integrity and consistency of the database is maintained	PFA	59
To achieve a distinction grade the evidence must show that, in addition to the pass and merit criteria, the learner is able to:		
d₁ Analyse potential errors in the design and construction of a database and how these can be avoided	PFA	58
d₂ Evaluate a database against the required user need	PFA	58
d₃ Customise the user interface to meet the needs of a defined user type		

Note: 'PFA' stands for 'Preparation for assessment'.

The purpose of any database is to store information efficiently and reliably so that the information can then be retrieved on demand in the form and structure required. A key theme of this unit is the need to ensure that users can rely on the information contained in a database – the mechanisms that are used to ensure this are covered in some detail. If there is insufficient control over the input of data into the database, then it is possible that the information held is not reliable and this will have serious implications for the people who use the output from the database.

5.1.1 Relationships

The main feature of **relational databases** that distinguishes them from other types of databases is the use of simple named tables to store the information. These tables are created separately and then linked.

What does it mean?

A **relational database** contains a set of tables which are held together by the relationships between the tables. It is for this reason such a database is called relational.

Two such tables are shown in Table 5.1. The two tables are called Stock and Orders; only the names of the fields are shown.

STOCK	ORDERS
Stock reference	Order reference
Stock name	Stock reference
Stock level	Customer reference
Minimum stock level	Order date
Supplier reference	Order quantity
Price	

Table 5.1 Two examples of tables

The field that will enable the linking to take place is Stock reference. It is usual to use exactly the same field name when the same field is included in different tables,

though not essential. It is essential that the properties of the Stock reference field in the Stock table are identical to the properties of the Stock reference field in the Order table.

There are some special characteristics of tables that are used in relational databases.

■ Ordering of records and fields

The ordering of records or fields is not significant. When data is added to tables, it should be possible to interchange records and fields without changing the information content.

Order reference	Stock reference	Order quantity	Order date
HN56	JKY34	367	3/7/2006
HN57	KNL13	234	14/6/2006
HN87	JRD01	78	5/9/2006

Order reference	Stock reference	Order date	Order quantity
HN56	JKY34	3/7/2006	367
HN57	KNL13	14/6/2006	234
HN87	JRD01	5/9/2006	78

Table 5.2 Two identical Order tables with example data – the ordering of records and fields does not matter

■ Field content

Each entry in the table contains a single field (or attribute) value only. Multiple values are not allowed. This is often described by saying that each entry is **atomic**.

What does it mean?

An **atomic** item is a single item of information. For example, someone's name is non-atomic because it should be broken down into at least three fields – title, first name and last name. Breaking fields down in this way gives more flexibility as to how the data can be used.

Order reference	Stock reference	Order date	Order quantity
HN56	JKY34, JKL46	3/7/2006	4 of each stock item
HN57	KNL13, KNM78	14/6/2006	234 of KLL13 and 45 of KNM78
HN87	JRD01	5/9/2006	78

Table 5.3 Table with unacceptable example of field entries

Activity 5.2

Key fields

1 Identify the two key fields of the tables shown in Table 5.1 (on page 32).

2 Identify the key field of the table shown in Table 5.3 and also the new key field (or combination key field) after you have amended the table in Activity 5.1.

Activity 5.1

Making fields atomic

1 Fix the entries in the order table shown in Table 5.3 to make sure that each entry represents a single item.

Hint: You will need to add two more rows.

■ Key field

Each record (row) must be distinct; no two rows can be the same. Quoting an appropriate combination of field values, called the primary key, will always uniquely identify each record. Sometimes the **primary key** is a single field.

5.1.1.1 Creating and modifying relationships

In Table 5.4, two tables are shown with their primary keys highlighted.

The relationship between the two tables can be formed by a link between the two Stock reference fields. In most situations, one of the linking fields is the primary key

field of a table. In this example, the primary key field concerned is the Stock reference field in the Stock table. If an equivalent Stock reference field in the other table is missing, the relationship cannot be built.

Where the primary key of one table appears in another table, this field is called a **foreign key** and links are very often made between the primary key of one table and the equivalent foreign key in another table.

Modifying relationships can be done once a database has been constructed but this should only be undertaken with care. Once information has been added to tables, and a variety of other forms, queries and reports have been designed and created, changing one of the relationships can cause significant problems and it may be necessary to first delete a relationship and then create all of them again.

Remember!

Make sure the design and the relationships are correct before you begin to further develop the database. It may be necessary to confirm the relationships with some test data.

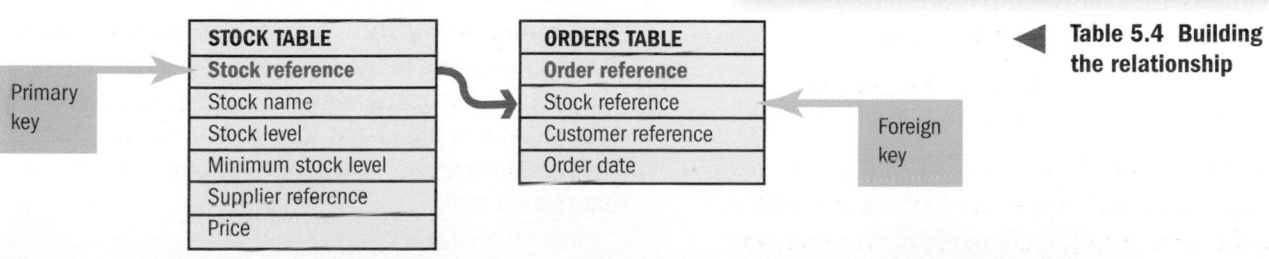

► **Table 5.4 Building the relationship**

Table 5.4 shows a relationship between the Stock table and the Orders table but it only shows which fields are involved, not everything we need to know about the nature of the relationship.

Each item in the Stock table can be ordered by many customers, so for every record in the Stock table, there may be more than one record in the Orders table. For this reason it is described as a **one-to-many** relationship.

The tables actually relate to **entities** (for more on this, see Unit 7 in Book 1). The relationship can be shown using an **entity relationship diagram** (**ERD**) as in Figure 5.1a.

What does it mean?

Entities are the real world things that are represented in the database. Examples are products, customers and orders information.

▲ Figure 5.1a ERD showing a one-to-many relationship

In many situations, however, the relationship is **many-to-many**. For example, if a number of products could be ordered in any one order, then the relationship becomes a many-to-many relationship. Many-to-many relationships are difficult to implement in a database and so, to deal with this type of relationship, another intermediate table is created that breaks the many-to-many relationship into two one-to-many relationships (see also Unit 7 in Book 1, page 117).

In some situations, the relationship is one-to-one – for example, between the Patient Details table and the Patient Medical Details table shown in Tables 5.5 and 5.6. However, one-to-one relationships are not good practice and can be terribly inefficient.

PATIENT DETAILS
Patient reference
Patient first name
Patient address
Patient phone number
Patient next of kin
Patient data of birth

Table 5.5 Patient table

PATIENT MEDICAL DETAILS
Patient reference
Blood group
GP
Gender

Table 5.6 Patient medical details table

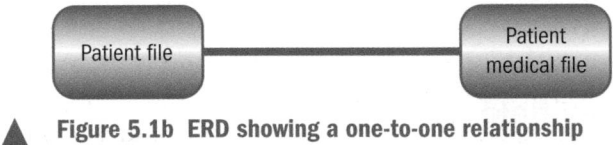

▲ Figure 5.1b ERD showing a one-to-one relationship

It is very important to ensure that the relationships between the tables are correct. The database designer must also ensure that, as changes are made to the content of the tables during routine use, the integrity of the database is not compromised. **Referential integrity** is needed in order to achieve this.

What does it mean?

Referential integrity is a system of rules to ensure that relationships between records in related tables are valid, and that users do not accidentally delete or change related data. That means making sure that a 'foreign key' has a 'primary key' with the same value in the related table.

In Microsoft Access, with a relationship in which referential integrity is enforced you can specify whether you want to automatically **cascade** update or cascade delete related records. If you set these options, delete and update operations that would normally be prevented by referential integrity rules are allowed. When you delete records or change primary key values in a primary table, Access will make the necessary changes to related tables to preserve referential integrity.

What does it mean?

Cascade means following up any changes in one table by making the changes to all other related tables.

If you select the **Cascade Update Related Fields** check box when you define a relationship, any time that you change the primary key of a record in the primary table, Microsoft Access automatically updates the primary key to the new value in all related records. For example, if you change the Supplier reference field in a table called Suppliers, the Supplier reference field in the Products table will update automatically for every one of the products supplied by that supplier – this ensures that the relationship is not broken. (See Figure 5.2.)

▼ **Figure 5.2 Defining the referential integrity rules between two tables**

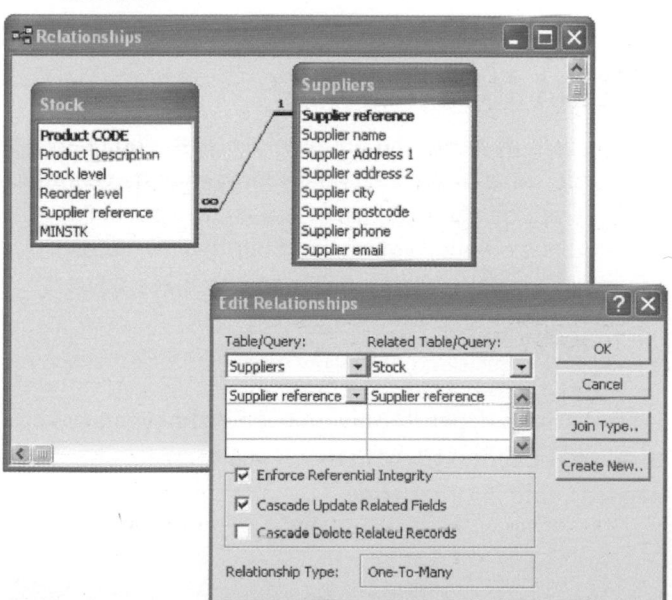

If you select the **Cascade Delete Related Records** check box when you define a relationship, any time that you delete records in one table, Access will automatically delete related records in the related table. For example, if you delete a Supplier record from the Suppliers table, all the products produced by that Supplier would be deleted in the Products table.

As shown in Figure 5.2, the relationship between the two tables using the Supplier reference field is defined as one in which referential integrity is enforced. The system will 'cascade update' related fields but not 'cascade delete' related records.

In practical terms, this means that if the Supplier reference is changed from, say, S2 to S002 in the Supplier table, then all S2 supplier references of the records in the Stock table will automatically change to S002. So this would be a useful setting to make.

Not checking the cascade delete option means that if the Supplier table record for S2 was deleted because the company went out of business, the related records in the Stock table would not be deleted. This is also a useful setting.

STOP Test your knowledge

1 Explain why, in the above example, it would be sensible not to check the Cascade Delete Related Records option.

2 What is a relational database?

3 What is an atomic entry?

4 What is a primary key and a foreign key?

5 Define one-to-many relationships and many-to-many relationships. Can you give an example of each?

6 What does referential integrity mean?

There are a number of benefits of the relational model for databases:

- efficiency of storage – minimising unnecessary **data redundancy**

What does it mean?

Data redundancy describes a situation where information (such as a supplier address) is duplicated in more than one table. It wastes space and can cause problems if all copies of the duplicated data are not updated at the same time, resulting in inconsistency within the database. In some cases, however, duplication can be acceptable if it speeds up processing.

- simplicity of design
- ease of modification – new tables can be added without putting the whole database out of action
- can represent complex relationships between objects in the real world (often called **entities** – see page 34)
- different 'views' of the database can be created for different users according to their need.

Activity 5.3

Alternatives to the relational model

1 Find out what other database models exist and why they might be used.

An outline of one **normalisation** process is presented here, so that you can recognise when sets

What does it mean?

Normalisation is the process by which complex real world information used by an organisation is analysed and represented in a number of simple tables that can then be implemented using relational database software such as Microsoft Access.

of tables in a database have not been normalised acceptably.

■ First normal form

The first series of checks involves three tasks:

- to identify and remove **calculated fields**
- to make sure each item of data is **atomic** (see page 32)
- to identify and remove repeating items and show them in a separate table – make a link so as not to lose the relationship.

What does it mean?

A **calculated field** is one that can be derived from other fields. For example, if age and date of birth are two fields, then age is a calculated field because you can always work out someone's age given today's date.

■ Second normal form

Problems with second normal form will only occur if there is a combination primary key field.

A table can only be in second normal form if it is already in first normal form. In order for a table to be in second normal form, every field that is not part of the composite primary key (i.e. non-primary key fields) must **depend on** the whole of the primary key rather than just a part of it.

What does it mean?

One field **depends on** another if you can find out the unique value of the second field knowing the value of the first one. For example, if you know a patient's reference number, you can find out their name or address or telephone number and so these fields depend on the reference number.

If an attribute depends only on part of the primary key, it should be removed, with its key field (create one if needed), into another table.

Activity 5.4

Converting to first normal form

1 Make appropriate changes to the Orders table shown in Table 5.7 to turn it into first normal form. Create new table(s) as needed.

2 Make appropriate changes to the Suppliers table shown in Table 5.8 to turn it into first normal form. Create new table(s) as needed.

ORDERS

Order reference

Customer reference

Customer telephone

Products and quantities ordered

Date of order

Estimated date of delivery

Number of days to delivery date

Table 5.7 An un-normalised Orders table

Suppliers

Supplier reference

Supplier name

Supplier address

Supplier telephone

Product name

Qty in stock

Price

Price + VAT

Table 5.8 An un-normalised Suppliers table

Activity 5.5

Converting to second normal form

1 Look at the list of fields in the Appointments table shown in Table 5.9. Make appropriate changes to turn it into second normal form. The primary key is a combination primary key (shown in bold). Create new table(s) as needed.

APPOINTMENTS

Patient ref

Date of appointment

Patient name

Patient address

Patient tel

Doctor

Table 5.9 Appointments table

Test your knowledge

1 What would be the impact on your answer to Activity 5.5 if you considered that people often have two phone numbers?

■ Third normal form

To be in third normal form, the table must already be in first and second normal forms and none of the non-primary fields must depend on any other non-primary fields.

If a non-primary field does depend on another non-primary field, remove it to a separate table, leaving one of the fields (the primary key of the new table) behind in the original table.

Activity 5.6

Converting to third normal form

1 Look at the list of field names in the Holidays table shown in Table 5.10. Make appropriate changes to the table to turn it into third normal form. The Holiday type field will store such things as whether it is an activity holiday, a cruise, etc.

HOLIDAYS TABLE
Holiday reference
Destination
Holiday type
Hotel reference
Hotel name
Hotel address

Table 5.10 Field names of a Holiday table

Notes

- Every time you regroup a set of field names and create additional (often smaller) tables, you have to start again and test for first normal form, then second and then third.

- Once you are sure that the design of the tables are in first, second and third normal forms, you can start to actually create the tables. Don't start until you are sure!

Test your knowledge

1 Summarise what is meant by first normal, second normal and third normal forms.

2 How would you check that a table is fully normalised?

5.1.2 Fields and field properties

Each record is divided into fields and each field has **properties** that define it. The two most important properties are the **data type** of the field and the **field size**.

What does it mean?

The **properties** of a field are the characteristics that are set by the database designer.

The **data type** of a field determines how the data will be stored in that field.

The **field size** determines how much space should be set aside for that field.

As a table is created, it is also possible to define additional properties, many of which serve to control the accuracy of data entered later or how the data appears when displayed on screen or printed in a report.

5.1.2.1 Data types

The data types available in Microsoft Access are shown in Table 5.11 opposite.

5.1.2.2 Other field properties

The screenshot shown in Figure 5.3 shows some of the additional properties that can be set in Microsoft Access. The exact set shown will depend upon the particular data type of the current field selected.

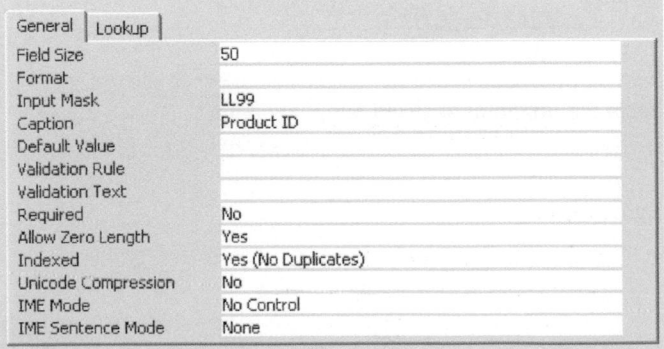

 Figure 5.3 Field properties

Data type	Description	Comment
Text	Text or combinations of text and numbers	Up to 255 characters. Microsoft Access only stores the characters entered in a field. Examples are names or addresses. You can control the maximum number of characters that can be entered using the FieldSize property.
Memo	Large amount of text and/or numbers	Used for potentially large volumes of text and numbers, such as notes or descriptions. Maximum length is 64,000 characters.
Number	Numeric data	Can be used for calculations, but calculations involving money normally use Currency type.
Date/Time	Dates and times	Uses 8 bytes only. Different formats can be chosen.
Currency	Currency values	Use the Currency data type to prevent rounding off during calculations. Accurate to 15 digits to the left of the decimal point and 4 digits to the right.
AutoNumber	Unique, incrementing by 1 each time	Automatically inserted when a record is added. Uses 4 bytes only. Can also choose random numbering instead of sequential.
Yes/No	Field to contain only one of two values	Appropriate for fields storing Yes/No, True/False or On/Off. Only uses 1 bit.
OLE Object	Objects	Examples include documents, spreadsheets, pictures or sounds. Can use up to 1 gigabyte but may be limited by disk space.
Hyperlink	Field that will store a hyperlink	Can store up to 64,000 characters.
Lookup Wizard	A field that allows you to choose from another table or from a list of values	The same size as the field that is also the Lookup field. Choosing this option in the data type list starts a wizard to define the lookup table for you.

Table 5.11 Descriptions of data types available in Access

A particularly useful pair of additional properties are the Validation Rule and Validation Text. The Validation Rule property allows the table designer to set rules that control the data to be input. These rules provide additional controls beyond those defined by the data type itself and the other properties set.

Test your knowledge

1   Define the terms properties, data type and field size.

2   Give at least five examples of commonly used data types.

Activity 5.7

Data types

1 Explore and document the potential of the other properties of different data types for helping to validate data entry. **P₁**

5.1.3 Creating and modifying databases

An ideal table:

- has a field (or pair of fields) that uniquely identifies each row (the primary key)
- does not contain unnecessary duplicate fields
- has no repetition of the same type of value
- has no fields that belong in other tables.

An ideal field:

- represents a characteristic of a table subject
- contains a single value
- is atomic (i.e. not multi-part)
- is not calculated or **concatenated**
- is unique throughout the database structure
- has an appropriate name.

What does it mean?

A **concatenated** field is one that is formed by combining the contents of two or more other fields, e.g. Full name might be a concatenation of First name and Last name.

Remember!

Use field naming conventions. Fields must be carefully and uniquely named. One convention when referring to fields in a number of tables is to prefix the field name with the table name. This means that the Stock reference fields shown in Table 5.1 (on page 32) would be more completely named as Stock. Stock reference (in the Stock table) and Orders. Stock reference (in the Orders table).

■ How to create a database

1 Choose an appropriate name and place to store your database.
2 Select New from the File menu. The dialogue box shown in Figure 5.4 will display, offering three options. Select Create table in Design view.

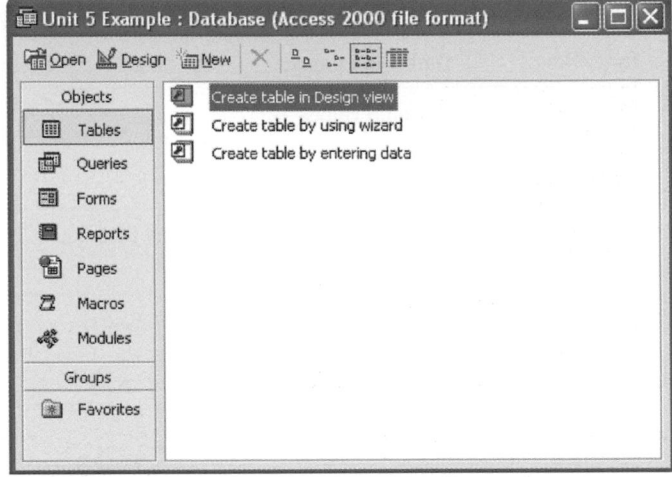

▲ **Figure 5.4 Creating a database – opening screen**

3 Enter the field names and data types. You can also enter a description if you think that it is not obvious. Set any necessary properties for each field in the bottom half of the screen. Note that the properties details at the bottom of the screen relate to the particular field that is selected in the top half. See Figures 5.5 and 5.6.

It is important to put as much control on to key fields and foreign keys as possible.

The Product CODE is the primary key shown in Figures 5.5. and 5.6 – note the key icon to the left of the field name. All fields set to be a primary key will automatically have the 'No duplicates' flag set in the indexed property.

4 Create other tables as necessary. Check in particular that any fields that are used to link the tables have the same properties in both tables.
5 Build the relationships. This must be done before data can be entered into the tables to ensure that the relationships work. Select **Relationships** from the drop-down menu and bring in the two tables using the Add table facility.

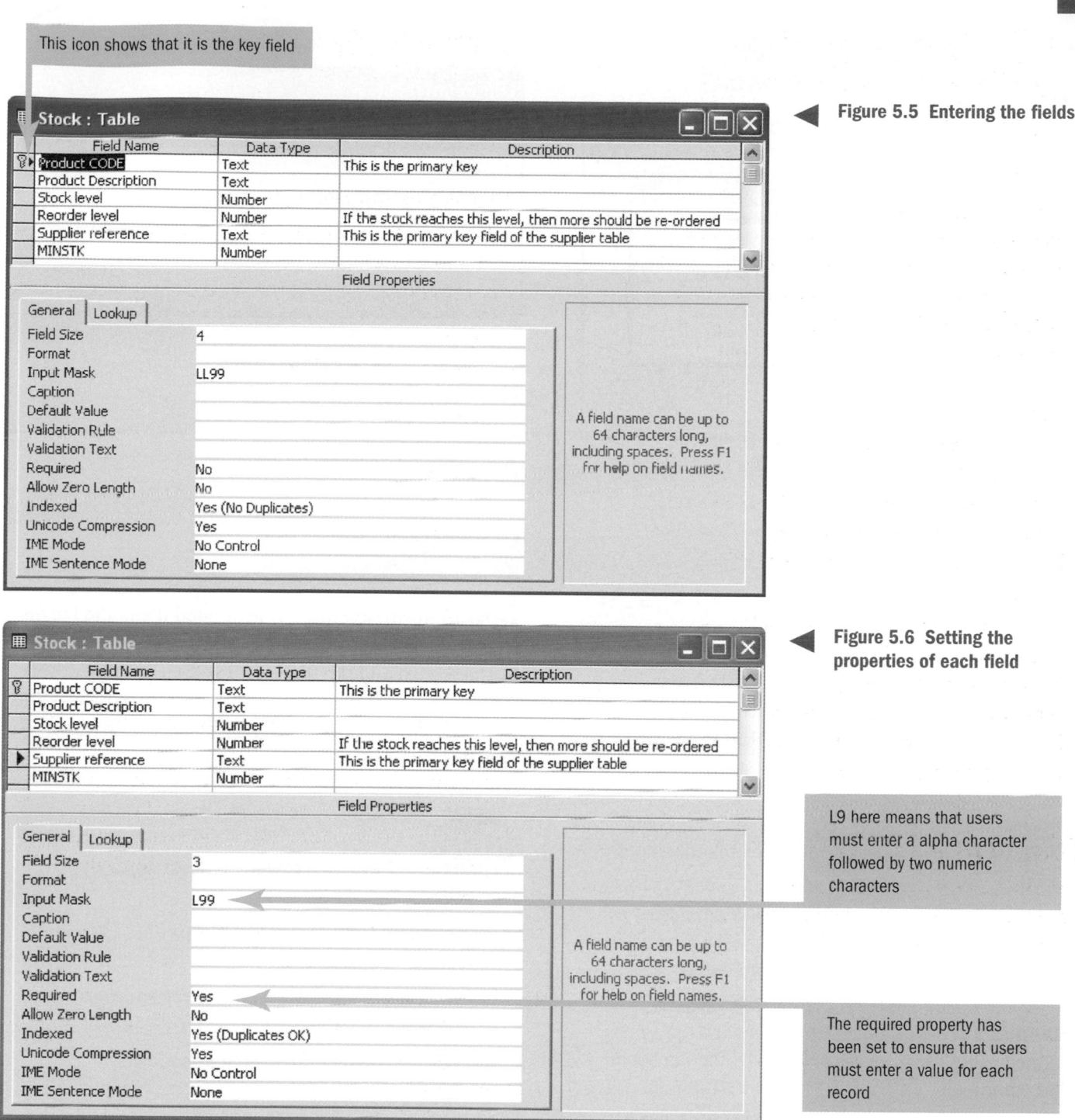

This icon shows that it is the key field

Figure 5.5 Entering the fields

Figure 5.6 Setting the properties of each field

L9 here means that users must enter a alpha character followed by two numeric characters

A field name can be up to 64 characters long, including spaces. Press F1 for help on field names.

The required property has been set to ensure that users must enter a value for each record

In the example shown in Figure 5.7, two tables have been created. They are to be linked by the Supplier reference field.

There are a few ways that you can link the tables and make the relationship. When the screen shown in Figure 5.7 is open you can drag one field over the other. A line

is created showing the link and a dialogue box opens as shown in Figure 5.8.

It would be usual to enforce referential integrity to ensure that the various data in the database are always kept consistent. It is less obvious whether to cascade updates or cascade deletes (see section 5.1.1.3 on page 34).

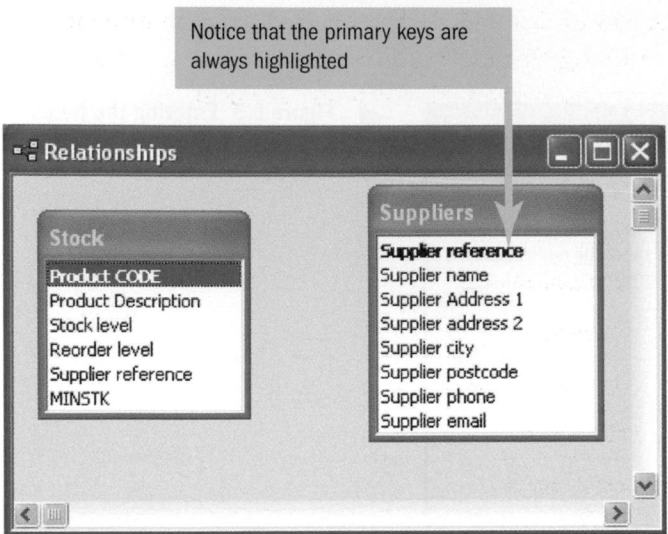

Notice that the primary keys are always highlighted

Figure 5.7 The Relationships window

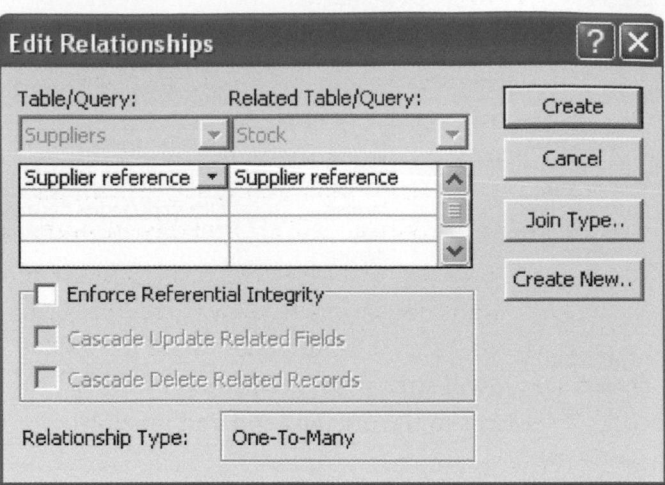

Figure 5.8 Defining the relationship

Activity 5.8

Confirming relationships

Create the two tables as shown in Figure 5.7 and define the relationship as shown in Figure 5.8. Experiment with different combinations of the relationship options.

For example:

1 Remove the relationship and add a record into the Stock table with a Supplier reference that does not exist.

2 Attempt to recreate the relationship and enforce referential integrity. Consider what message you get and why. Delete the new stock record and try again.

3 Establish a relationship with **Cascade Update Related Records** selected. Then change the values of the linked fields in one table to see the impact in the other table.

4 Make a backup copy of your database. Establish a relationship with **Cascade Delete Related Records** selected. Then delete a Suppliers record and see the impact in the Stock table.

5.1.3.2 Creating Forms

Typically, forms are initially generated using the Forms wizard. A number of basic design choices are provided by the wizard and the final form is then produced automatically. The forms produced can then be modified using the toolbox if necessary. See section 5.3.1.2 on page 52.

Test your knowledge

1 Write a checklist of four criteria for an ideal database table.

2 Write a checklist of six criteria for an ideal database field.

3 What does the term concatenated mean?

4 Write a list of instructions for how to create a new database.

5.1.4 Key fields

To uniquely identify each record in a table, a primary key field is necessary. In some situations, there are naturally occurring primary key fields (such as car registration plates or national insurance numbers). In other situations, database applications will provide an 'autonumber' field type that will achieve this purpose.

If the organisation already uses a particular combination of letters or numbers to uniquely identify records, such as a product code, then it makes sense to use this as the primary key. It will already be understood by other people or systems in the organisation and possibly outside the organisation.

In Figure 5.9, the primary key fields are marked in bold. Note that relationships are usually built using a primary key field of one of the tables.

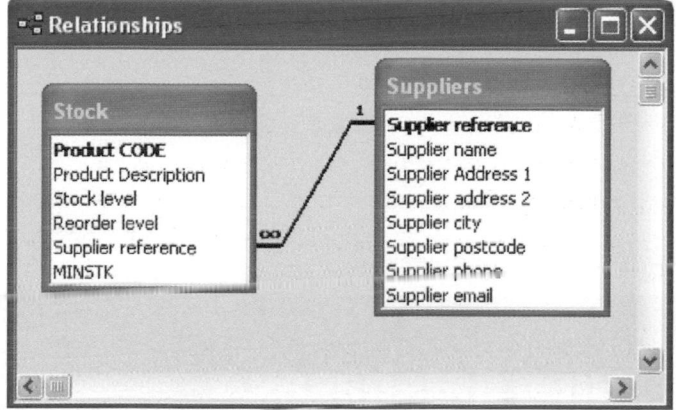

Figure 5.9 Two tables shown as linked

As described in section 5.1.1.1 on page 33, where the primary key of one table appears in another table to enable the linking, it is called a foreign key. In the example shown in Figure 5.9, the supplier reference in the Stock table is the foreign key.

■ Combination primary keys

In some circumstances, one field is not enough to uniquely identify each record. In the example shown in Table 5.12, an Appointments table stores the details of appointments in a doctor's surgery. The patient reference looks like it might work as a primary key field – however, the patient may have many appointments and so it cannot be a primary key field on its own.

A pair of fields (Patient reference and Appointment date) together create a unique combination and so provide a combination primary key field.

APPOINTMENTS
Patient reference
Appointment date
Telephone
Appointment time
Patient name
Doctor reference

Table 5.12 Fields of an Appointments table

Activity 5.9

Problems with combination keys

1 Explain in what circumstances the combination primary key proposed for the table shown in Table 5.12 will still not be appropriate. What might be a better combination primary key field?  (partial evidence)

Test your knowledge

1 What is a combination primary key?

2 What problems might occur with using a combination primary key?

5.1.5 Errors

It is common for problems to arise in the use of databases. Some are caused by the underpinning design, while others are caused by insufficient control of the entry of information into the records. Organisations come to rely on the detail and the reports they obtain from databases, so it can be crucial that these reports are based on reliable information.

Symptom	Possible error	Solution
Tables will not link at all.	The properties of the two fields that create the relationship are different.	Check that the data type of each of the two fields is the same. Fix as necessary and check the implications on other objects such as forms, queries and reports.
Tables appear to link but the information in the related table does not appear.	The range of values in the tables are not consistent, e.g. G010 and GO10.	Add validation controls to stop alpha letters being entered instead of numbers.
Information relating to the same thing in different tables is different.	The database has not been normalised properly, resulting in data redundancy.	Back up the data. Redesign, reconstruct and repopulate the database.
It is not possible to enforce referential integrity rules when a relationship is being created.	There are some values of one of the linked fields for which there are no equivalent values in the other table.	Inspect the data in the tables and add or amend as necessary.

Table 5.13 Some typical database errors and their solutions

Test your knowledge

1 Describe one problem not mentioned in Table 5.13 that might occur in a database.

2 Suggest a possible solution for this problem.

5.2 Creating, populating and testing databases

It is possible for data to be entered directly into tables but it is strongly recommended that data entry forms are used, as they provide additional possibilities for verification and validation of data input. They also allow you to produce more visually appealing input screens that can reflect an organisation's style.

5.2.1 Data entry forms

5.2.1.1 Verification and validation

Microsoft Access offers a number of techniques to enable verification. One technique used is shown in

Figure 5.10. A simple form is used for entering order details over the phone. To avoid an incorrect Stock reference being entered, a query (new virtual table)

What does it mean?

Verification is a method of checking that the data entered on to the system is correct and the same as that on the original source.

Validation is the process of checking that data entered into a system is reasonable and in the correct format.

Figure 5.10 Order entry form

has been created that uses the relationship between the Orders table and the Stock table. This allows the Stock description to be displayed as the Stock reference is entered in order to confirm that the correct product is being ordered.

The data entry clerk can then confirm this by looking at the source document and checking that it matches. If the clerk has miskeyed the code, they will notice their mistake during this verification check, and can re-enter the code.

5.2.1.2 Input masking

One very useful validation technique is to set up an **input mask** for a particular field, as shown in Table 5.14.

Input mask character	Description of control
0	Number (0 to 9, entry required; plus [+] and minus [-] signs not allowed).
0	Number or space (entry not required; plus and minus signs not allowed).
#	Number or space (entry not required; blank positions converted to spaces, plus and minus signs allowed).
L	Letter (A to Z, entry required).
?	Letter (A to Z, entry optional).
A	Letter or number (entry required).
a	Letter or number (entry optional).
&	Any character or a space (entry required).
C	Any character or a space (entry optional).
. , : ; - /	Decimal placeholder and thousands, date and time separators. (The actual character used depends on the regional settings specified in Microsoft Windows Control Panel.)
<	Causes all characters that follow to be converted to lower case.
>	Causes all characters that follow to be converted to upper case.
\	Causes the character that follows to be displayed as a literal character. Used to display any of the characters listed in this table as literal characters (for example, \A is displayed as just A).
Password	Setting the InputMask property to the word Password creates a password entry text box. Any character typed in the text box is stored as the character but is displayed as an asterisk (*).

Table 5.14 Input mask characters

Activity 5.10

Input masks

1 Create the following input masks and test them in appropriate fields.

a) Two letters followed by one or two numeric characters, e.g. HG45 or NK7

b) Three numeric characters always enclosed in brackets, e.g. (044).

c) An ISBN number of the form ISBN 6-343444455-4. Assume that the structure is always:

"ISBN"+space+single numeric character+ hyphen+9 numeric characters+hyphen+single numeric character

Activity 5.11

Exploring postcodes

1 Find out what variations there are in postcode structures and consider how an input mask could be used to validate the input of postcodes.

Test your knowledge

1 Explain the difference between verification and validation of data.

2 How can the use of forms help with the validation of data?

3 What is input masking? Give an example.

5.2.2 Importing data

If data that is to be used in a database is already available in another form, it makes sense to import that data electronically, thus avoiding the possibility of errors made when re-entering the data.

If the data is already stored electronically, it should be possible to import it in some way. However, it may be complex to do so. Indeed, importing can be a dangerous and sometimes time-consuming job. Things can go wrong and, if the file is large, then it will not be possible to check the accuracy of every single entry. It is recommended that small tests are done on a limited number of records to make sure that the technique chosen is working.

Some common formats of files that can be imported are explained in this section.

5.2.2.1 Delimited files

Some files are stored as text but with a **delimiter** to separate the fields and a 'hard return' to separate records. In the example shown in Figure 5.11, the delimiter is a comma.

What does it mean?

A **delimiter** is a character used to separate fields when data is stored as plain text. The delimiter most often used is the comma, hence the term **comma-delimited file**.

```
"AS01","Psion Finance Pack",3.00,25.00,"S1",10.00
"BH61","Usernet Software/86",7.00,25.00,"S3",10.00
"BR45","LAN ROM kit (Diskless PC)",27.00,25.00,"S1",50.00
"BR51","Usernet2 LAN Board u",75.00,25.00,"S2",75.00
"BV22","AST Prem.Workst. 203 1.44,EGA",3.00,25.00,"S1",10.00
"CS03","Mouse Adapter (25way-9)",90.00,25.00,"S1",90.00
"CX31","AST Premium 286 FastRAM 2000",5.00,25.00,"S1",10.00
"DF61","Psion Oxford Dictionary",8.00,25.00,"S2",10.00
"DS12","AST Premium 286 Model 90",53.00,25.00,"S1",50.00
"DW01","Floor stand (800)",9.00,25.00,"S1",10.00
"EW22","AST Premium White Monitor",53.00,25.00,"S1",60.00
"FD03","AST Premium 286 Model 85",90.00,25.00,"S1",50.00
"FD31","AST Premium/386 390 90MB",0.00,25.00,"S2",10.00
```

Figure 5.11 A comma-delimited file
Note that text fields are always contained within inverted commas.

■ How to import data into Access

1 Select Get External Data and Import from the File menu – the screen shown in Figure 5.12 is then displayed.

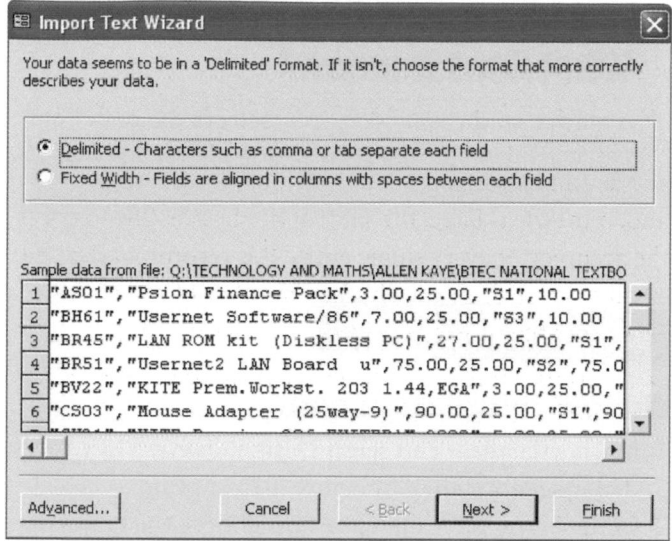

▲ **Figure 5.12 Importing text files**

2 The wizard should automatically detect that the file is delimited. After selecting Next, you can check any settings such as the exact nature of the delimiter and change them if necessary prior to actually importing the data.

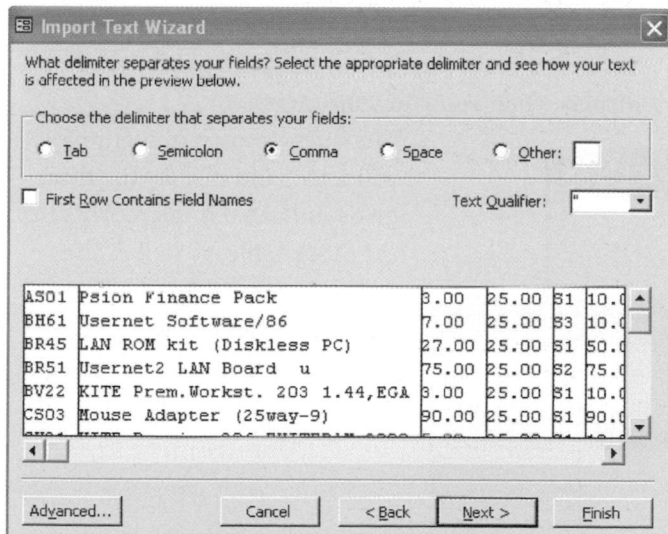

▲ **Figure 5.13 Importing comma-delimited files**

Note that in Figure 5.13, the field names are not contained in the file and so that box is left unchecked. The wizard has correctly detected that a comma separates the fields.

3 On the next screens of the wizard, enter the field names.

4 On the final screen, make a choice as to whether the data is added as a new table or into an existing one. If you plan to add new data into an existing table, then you must make sure that the existing fields and properties match the new data coming in.

Delimited format can often be an intermediary format between the database and any other formats not recognised by Access or the database package you are using. As long as the target application can export its data into a delimited format, then you can import it into Microsoft Access or other equivalent database application packages.

5.2.2.2 Spreadsheet input

If data is already held in spreadsheet format you can import the data directly into the database. When you make the choice to import a file, change the file filter to see spreadsheet files and navigate to the appropriate directory – this will allow you to select the appropriate file.

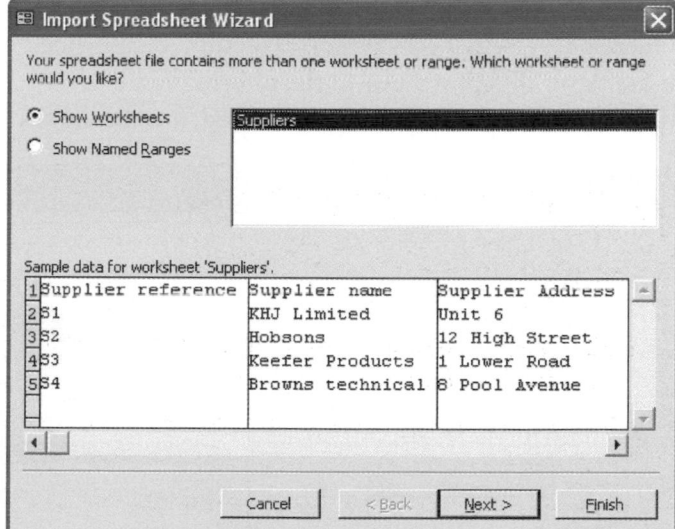

▲ **Figure 5.14 Importing spreadsheets**

If the spreadsheet has named ranges, then you can select from these. This is particularly useful if the spreadsheet layout is complex and the data you wish to import is only in part of a sheet.

It is important that the spreadsheet is in a simple format, without additional rows or columns of cells that do not form part of the actual data to be imported. The top row is normally interpreted as a heading line with field names in each column.

Subsequent screens in the wizard allow you to add a new auto primary key field as needed and decide whether the imported data should go into a new table or an existing one.

As an alternative to importing the data, it is possible to link tables in appropriate formats to an existing database. This has the advantage that the data is stored only once if another application also needs to use the data in its original format.

Test your knowledge

1   What is a comma-delimited file?

2   What other file type can easily be imported into a database?

5.2.3 Query design

Queries represent a very powerful method of allowing users to see different views of the information in a database. Once a query has been created, it acts as if it is a real table – however, the underlying information is not duplicated. Queries can be created based on a number of tables that are linked together. The default type of query is the **select query**.

What does it mean?

A **select query** is a query that selects the data from the fields that you specify and with the criteria that you set for those fields.

5.2.3.1 Creating a query

■ How to create a query

1   Open a database and select Design Query. The dialogue box shown in Figure 5.15 appears.

2   In the Show Table dialogue box, choose the tables that you wish to work with. Note that it is possible to select existing queries as well as tables.

3   The selected tables from your database will be displayed at the top of the screen (see Figure 5.16) – note that the one-to-many relationship between the tables is displayed visually as 1-∞.

4   You create the query in the lower part of this screen. Drag field names down as needed. Make sure that the Show box is checked for all the fields you wish to display when you run your query.

The query shown in Figure 5.17 will select and display the three fields indicated of all records in the Stock table, as well as the Supplier name field of all records in the Suppliers table.

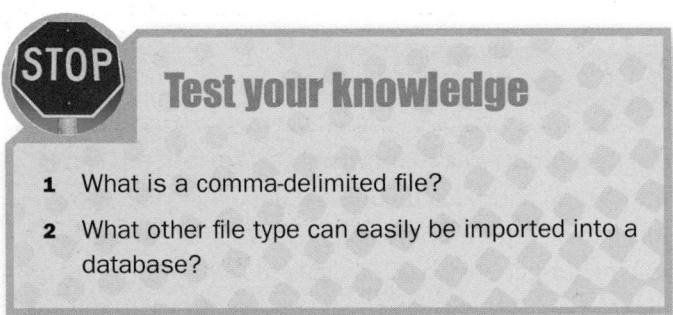

Figure 5.15 Select queries

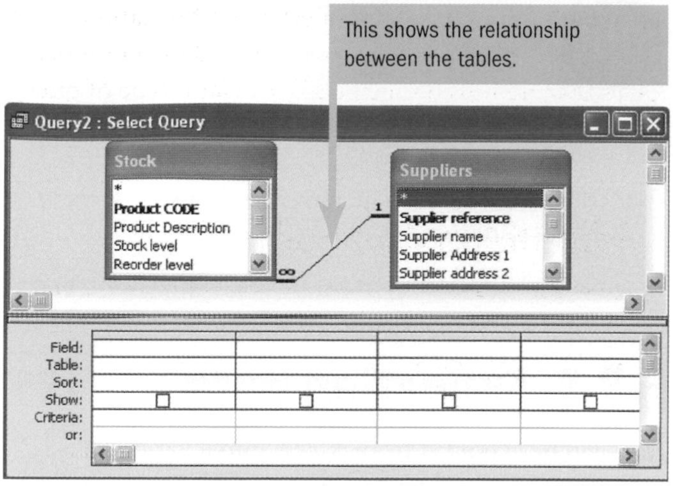

This shows the relationship between the tables.

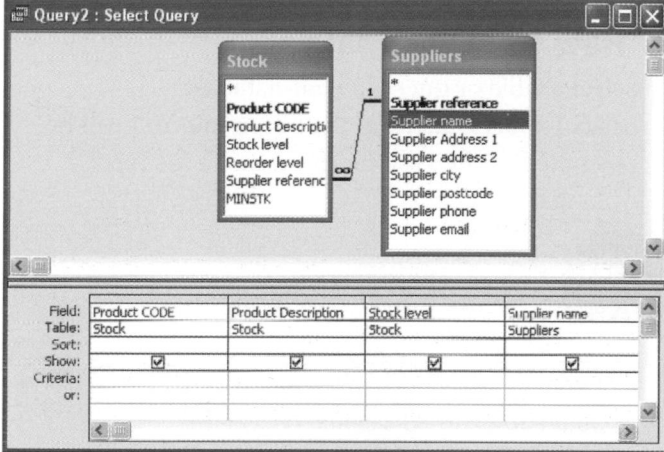

Figure 5.16 Adding the tables to be used in the query

Figure 5.17 A simple select query

5 You can also set criteria for your query. For example, the query shown in Figure 5.18 (bottom half of screen only in the screenshot) will select the three fields indicated from the Stock record, but only for those records which have a Stock level less than 20. Additionally, the records will be sorted by Product Description instead of by the default primary key field.

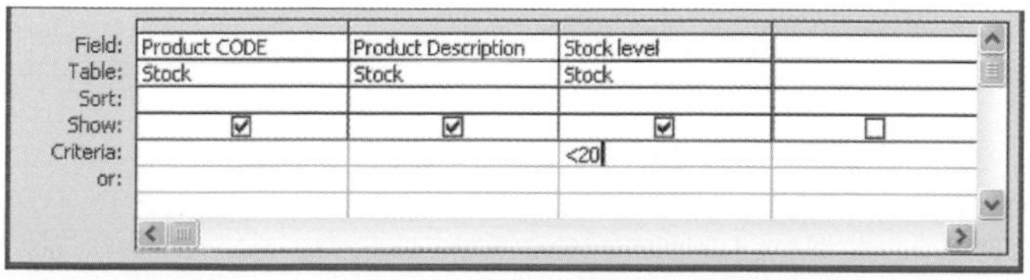

Figure 5.18 A select query with one criterion set

6 You can set multiple criteria for your query. For example: the query shown in Figure 5.19 will select the fields indicated, but only for those records which have a Stock level less than 20 and that are supplied by supplier "S2".

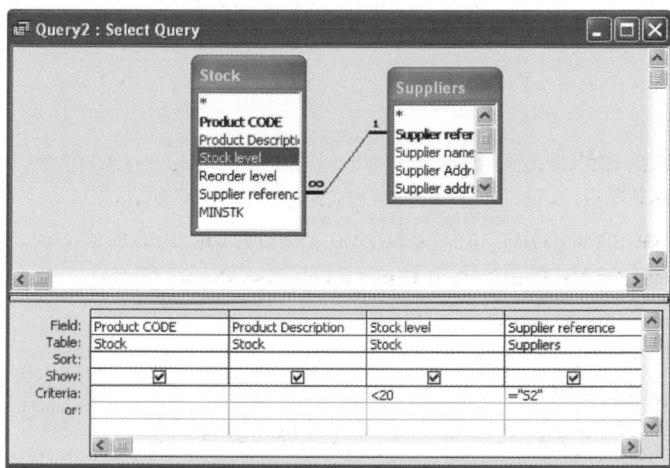

Figure 5.19 A select query with multiple criteria

7 Click on the Run button on the toolbar (with the red exclamation mark) to run the query and check that it selects the correct fields.

Activity 5.12

Designing queries

1 Design a query to show all details of the products in the Stock table except for the Supplier reference.

2 Design a query to show the Product Description and Product Code of all products supplied by suppliers based in Bristol.

5.2.3.2 Use of logical operators

The method used by Microsoft Access to create queries is called **Query by Example**. In this method, an example is given of what the output will be (e.g. the query shown in Figure 5.20 specifies that the Supplier reference must be "S2" and the Stock level must be less than 20). The system uses the normal set of operators as given in Table 5.15.

Operator	Meaning
=	Equal to
<>	Not equal to
<	Less than
<=	Less than or equal to
>	Greater than
>=	Greater than or equal to
Like	Matches a prescribed character pattern. The * symbol is used as a wildcard.

Table 5.15 Operators that can be used in query criteria

In other systems, other logical operators such as AND and OR are also employed to develop complex queries. However, in Query by Example systems AND and OR are implemented through the design of the query itself – there is no need for the user to enter them.

For example, the query shown in Figure 5.20 has both the criteria on the same line. So, the query means:

(Stock level <20) AND (Supplier reference ="S2")

If the criteria are on separate lines, the meaning will be:

(Stock level <20) OR (Supplier reference ="S2")

Test your knowledge

1   What is a select query?

2   Give five examples of operators that can be used in query design.

5.2.4 Exporting data

Data can be exported from Access into a variety of formats quickly and easily. It is very easy, for example, to export the data from a table or query from Access into a spreadsheet.

■ How to export data

1   Select a table or query in your database.
2   Select Export Data from the File menu. You will be prompted to choose a file name and a file type.

Test your knowledge

1   Find out which file types can be exported from your database application package.

As with all application packages, database software has a range of advanced features that are available to the user. The particular features that are needed will depend upon the purpose of the database being built. Some examples of advanced features are given in this section.

5.3.1 Advanced features

Many of the advanced features available are particularly related to ensuring and maintaining integrity within the database.

5.3.1.1 Special queries

■ Parameter queries

What does it mean?

A **parameter query** prompts the user of a database to set the specific criteria for the field(s) selected for that query by the database designer.

For example, a query on a Suppliers table could be written to select the suppliers based in London only. Users might also want queries to select suppliers from other cities too. To create a set of such queries – one for each possible city – would be time-consuming and tedious to do.

A parameter query overcomes this problem by allowing the user to choose the city when they run the query – this makes the query a lot more flexible. The query is set up in the same way as usual, but instead of putting a specific city into the Criteria row, you enter a question inside square brackets, as shown in Figure 5.20.

When the query is opened or run, the question given in square brackets is displayed in a dialogue box (see Figure 5.21) and the user enters the city that is required. Once the city is entered, the query runs as normal.

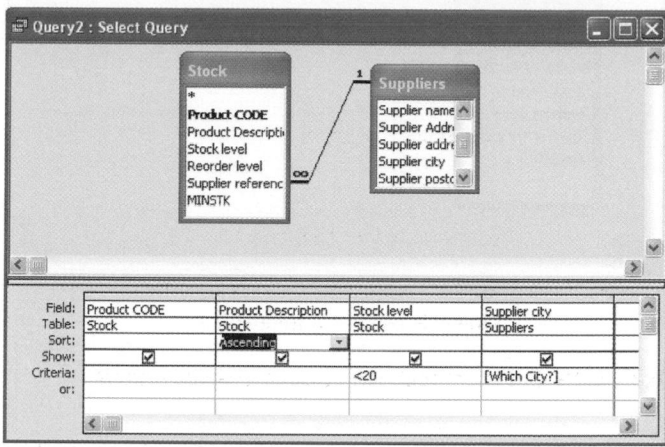

▲ Figure 5.20 Example of a parameter query

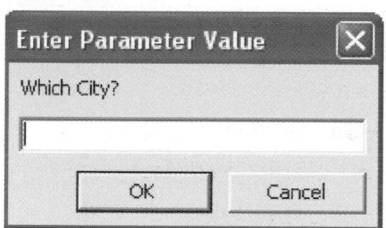

▲ Figure 5.21 Dialogue box for parameter query

■ Delete queries

The default type of query already described is a **select query** (see section 5.2.3 on page 48). Another type of query that can prove useful is the **delete query** – as shown in Figure 5.22.

What does it mean?

Instead of selecting all the records that fit the criteria of a query, a **delete query** will delete the records. So use with care!

The query is built in the usual way, but the type of query is changed to **Delete** using the options in the **Query** drop-down menu.

The query shown in Figure 5.22 uses the criteria option "Like" (see Table 5.15 on page 50). When the query is run, it will delete all records with a Product Code that starts with the letters "FD".

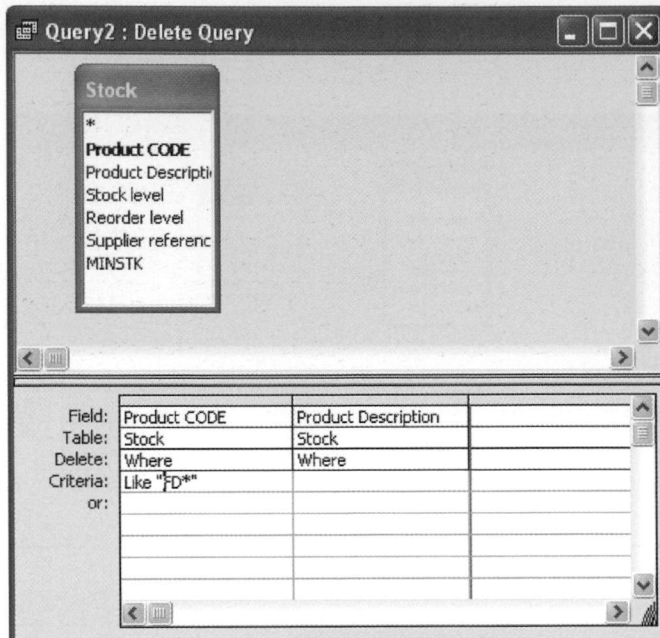

Figure 5.22 **Example of a delete query**

It is a good idea to create your query as a select query first, to test that it selects the correct records, before changing to a delete query and running.

■ Other special queries

Other special queries such as **update** or **append** can be created in the same way as the delete query.

Activity 5.13

Special queries

1 Find out how the other types of queries operate and experiment with them to be sure you understand how they operate.

Tip: Experiment on a backup copy of your database.

Test your knowledge

1 Name four different types of special queries.

2 Explain what each of these queries does and give an example of each.

5.3.1.2 Creating special forms and reports using the Toolbox

A form is designed to be viewed on-screen and a report is designed to provide a printed output. Wizards can be used to design basic forms and reports in a limited number of styles and can be modified to suit particular needs. It is possible to create forms and reports from scratch, but database designers often choose to let the wizard create a basic object and then use the Toolbox to modify it.

The Access Toolbox is a toolbar. Choosing one of the buttons that appear in the Toolbox adds or influences a control, represented by that tool's symbol.

It is useful to understand about the different objects that are found on forms and reports. For example, tools that require user input, such as combo boxes, are often used in forms but very rarely in reports.

■ Control object categories

There are three types of **control objects** in forms and reports:

What does it mean?

A **control object** is an object on a form. It can have a variety of purposes, including, for example, displaying titles or descriptions, accepting data, or performing an action.

- **Bound controls** are associated with a field in the table or query for the form or subform. Text boxes are the most common bound control. You can also show the content of graphic objects or play a waveform audio file with a bound OLE object. You can bind toggles, check boxes, and option buttons to Yes/No fields.

All bound controls have associated labels that display the Caption property of the field; you can edit or delete these labels without affecting the bound control.

- **Unbound controls** display data you provide that is independent of any data in the database. You can use the unbound OLE object to add a drawing or bitmap image to a form. You can use lines and rectangles to divide a form into logical groups, or to simulate boxes used on a paper form. Unbound text boxes are used to enter data that is not intended to update a field.

- **Calculated controls** use expressions derived from normal mathematical operations. Usually, the expression includes the value of a field.

Figure 5.23 shows the Access Toolbox and the name of each control. Table 5.16 gives details of what each of the controls is and what it does.

Select objects	Control Wizard	
Label	Text Box	Option Group
Toggle Button	Option Button	Check Box
Combo Box	List Box	Command Button
Image	Unbound Object	Bound Object
Page Break	Tab Control	Subform/Subreport
Line	Rectangle	Advanced controls

▲ **Figure 5.23 The toolbox in outline**

Control Wizard	Activates wizards for all controls. It is normally left on.
Label	Control that displays descriptive text, such as a title, a caption or instructions.
Text Box	Use to display, enter or amend data in a record. A text box can also be used to display the results of a calculation or to accept input from a user.
Option Group	Use along with check boxes, option buttons or toggle buttons to display a set of alternative values – valuable to help control user input.
Toggle Button	Use as a standalone control bound to a Yes/No field in a Microsoft Access database.
Option Button	Use as a standalone control bound to a Yes/No field in a Microsoft Access database.
Check Box	Use as a standalone control bound to a Yes/No field in a Microsoft Access database.
Combo Box	Used for controlling data entry. You can type in the text box or select an entry in the list box to add a value to a field.
List Box	Displays a scrollable list of values.
Command Button	Use to create buttons with actions attached, such as via macros.
Image	Use to display a static picture on a form.
Unbound Object Frame	Use to display an unbound OLE object, such as a Microsoft Excel spreadsheet, on a form.
Bound Object Frame	Use to display OLE objects, such as a series of pictures, on a form. This control is for objects stored in a field in the form's or report's underlying record source.
Page Break	Starts a new screen on a form or a new page in a printed form.
Tab Control	Creates a tabbed form with several pages or a tabbed dialogue box.
Subform/Subreport	Use to display data from more than one form or table.
Line	Adds a graphic line to help visual layout.
Rectangle	Adds a graphic box to help visual layout.

Table 5.16 The parts of the Access Toolbox explained

■ Examples of the use of the Toolbox with forms

The Command Button can be used to create bespoke systems that provide more limited options to the end user. Navigation buttons on blank forms can be used to create friendly front ends to systems (see Figure 5.24).

In the form shown in Figure 5.25, text entry in the Supplier name field is controlled by a drop-down combo box.

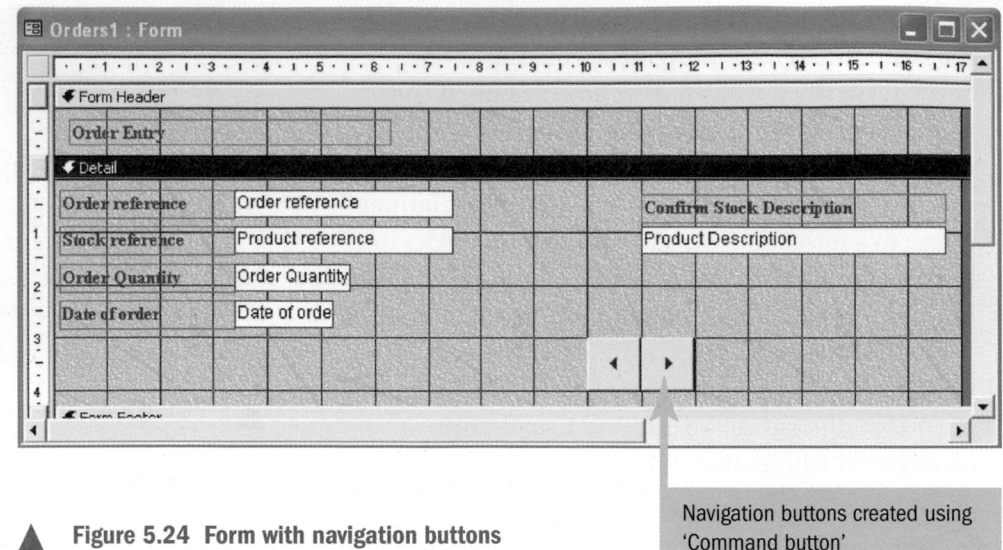

Navigation buttons created using 'Command button'

▲ **Figure 5.24 Form with navigation buttons produced using the Toolbox**

Remember!

Make sure the wizard button is activated in the Toolbox before you add the combo box, then the wizard will take you through the options.

■ Use of the Toolbox with reports

Only a limited number of the tools available in the Toolbox are normally used when generating reports.

Particularly useful are the Page Break and Unbound Object Frame, the latter allowing a graphic image to be added to the report layout.

5.3.2 Creating styles

As with all applications, there are a number of advantages in imposing particular styles on various aspects of the finished product.

- A style can help to provide or reflect an image of the organisation or company.
- Users will find it easier to navigate the system if they interact with all screens in a similar way, and if there is consistency in where items are placed on the screen

▼ **Figure 5.25 Form with controlled data entry combo box produced using the Toolbox**

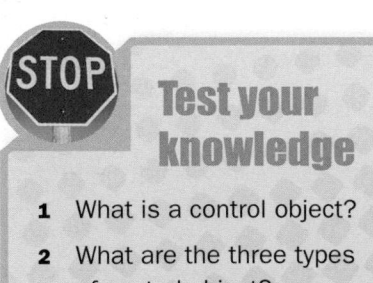

Test your knowledge

1 What is a control object?

2 What are the three types of control object?

3 Give at least one example of each type of control object.

and how they are named. This may reduce errors and also increase the speed of interaction.

- Whole systems are easier and quicker to develop if styles are reused.

As database application packages are opened, it is usual for the designer to be given choices as to which overall style or template should be used.

5.3.3 Customising

Most database application packages are generic and are designed to be used in any and all situations. When a particular application is designed for a specific purpose, it can be very useful to customise it in order to remove unnecessary options or provide specific front ends to support the intended users.

Customising a database will probably involve only providing the user with those tools that are appropriate to their work. It can also be useful to remove tools that could be used, deliberately or accidentally, to carry out unacceptable actions, e.g. deleting table fields or changing relationships.

5.3.3.1 Customising toolbars

In general, all of the options available on toolbars are also available within the menu choices, and the sets of options on a particular toolbar are grouped because they relate to a similar area or function. It is possible, however, to build a new toolbar.

■ How to customise a toolbar

1 Select the Tools menu and then Customise. Ensure that the Toolbars tab is chosen.
2 A dialogue box is displayed as shown in Figure 5.26. Select New and enter an appropriate name for your new toolbar.
3 When the new toolbar is initially created, it is empty. Switch to the Commands tab – this gives you access to all of the commands on all of the toolbars. Highlight and drag the commands you want onto the new toolbar.
4 In the examples shown, a very limited toolbar is created with, for example, no access to the New command. You can still select the New command using Toolbars within the View drop-down menu.
5 The final result is shown in Figure 5.27: a new toolbar has been created called Unit 5 Example.

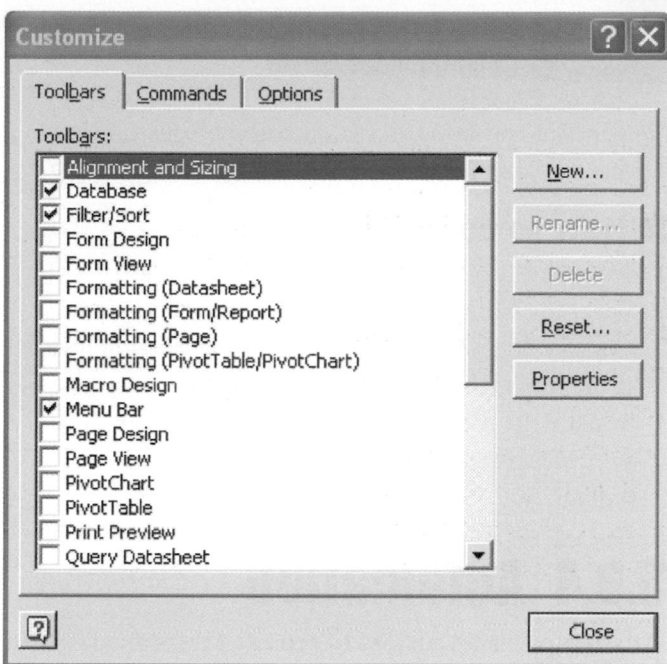

Figure 5.26 Creating and customising a new toolbar

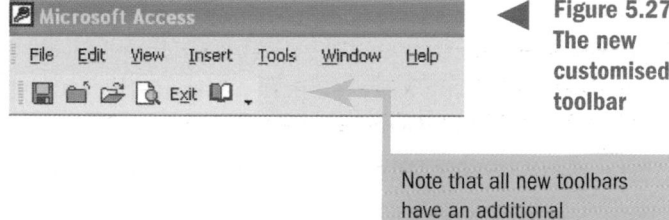

Figure 5.27 The new customised toolbar

Note that all new toolbars have an additional command, which allows further customisation.

Figure 5.28 A new toolbar has been created called Unit 5 Example

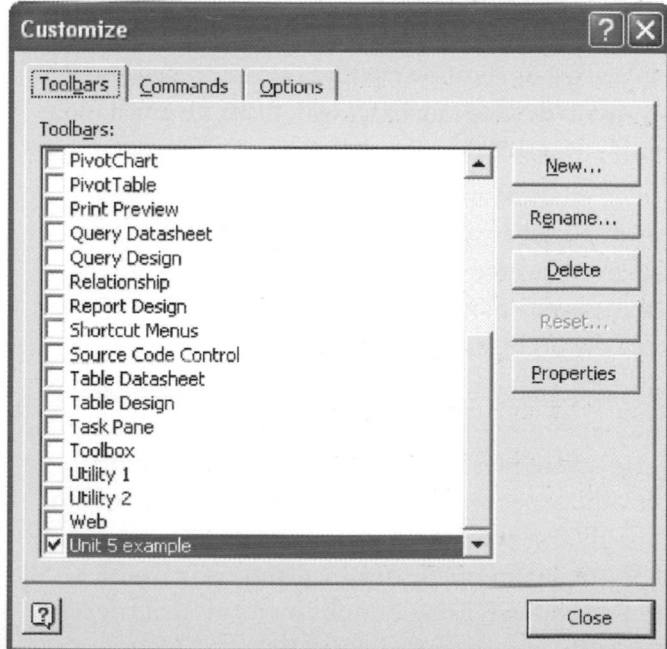

New menus can also be created and then customised in a similar way and for similar reasons.

■ How to customise a Menu

1 Select the Tools menu and then Customise.
2 Select the Commands tab and choose New Menu.
3 You can drag the new menu up to the existing menus at the top of the screen.
4 Initially the menu will be empty, but you can drag commands onto the menu in the same way as for a toolbar.

5.3.4 Automation

Database packages such as Microsoft Access are designed to be used in the widest variety of situations – they are application packages rather than bespoke solutions. This makes them very powerful. Database systems created using these application packages are generally relatively easy, quick and cheap to develop. In addition, the final solution tends to be more reliable as it is built using a tried and tested underpinning application package.

Building a database solution from scratch using a programming language in some respects allows for the production of a very specially focused product, but it would be unusual for companies to adopt this approach unless it was really necessary. Apart from the advantages of database application packages already noted, the skills needed to develop databases with them are much more readily available than the skills of specialist programmers.

However, there are some disadvantages to using a generic database package. Many of the options and features available will not be used in any one given database and allowing users access to all of them could generate problems.

In addition, there may be some actions or complex combinations of keystrokes that are used time and time again – designers of systems need to find ways of providing special interfaces or automated routines to simplify these complex entries for users. An apparently bespoke system can be designed and created with a generic package, using buttons on forms that trigger macros to carry out predefined tasks.

Automated routines can be created using:

- macros
- scripts
- a programming language such as Visual Basic for Applications.

5.3.5 Evaluation criteria and testing

The primary criterion that should be used when evaluating a finished database system is whether it meets the user need. In Unit 7 (Book 1, page 104) and Unit 4 (Book 2, page 10) there was an emphasis on capturing the requirements of a system fully and formally – without such a requirements specification, it is impossible to test and evaluate properly.

Other units, particularly Units 4 and 20, detail the test strategies that should be used. To summarise:

- the detailed functionality of the components of the system can tested using **white box testing** (see Unit 20, page 187) – this is typically undertaken by someone who understands the detail of the system
- the less detailed check on user requirements is typically done using **black box testing** (see Unit 20, page 187), perhaps using a formal requirements specification that was produced during the design phase.

Finally, it is necessary to confirm that the system is fit for purpose by asking the client to formally 'sign off' the finished system. The act of asking a client to sign off typically encourages a more detailed check than would otherwise be made. Once the client has signed off the system, it means that they accept it as it is.

 **Test your knowledge**

1 What are white box testing and black box testing?
2 What does 'sign off' mean?

Preparation for assessment

The assessment tasks in this unit are based on the following scenario.

A large department store wishes to improve its customer service. It decides that it needs a database to capture and store information relating to customer complaints in order to be better informed about the problems. The database must be easily available to staff in different locations within the same store and also at different stores. You will be working on the project as a database designer.

A systems analyst has been asked to undertake a feasibility study – this resulted in the following specification requirements for the database.

■ Data stores

Complaints details – This should include an open text box to allow the customer the opportunity to describe the complaint, but there should also be some yes/no fields that relate to different categories of complaints (e.g. product malfunction, rude staff, late delivery, overcharging, etc.). The customer contact details will be needed as well as information about the product/department that the complaint related to, the date of the complaint and the store where the complaint was made. It must be possible to add progress details – this might involve an additional table.

Store details – This should include at least the contact details and store manager's name.

Product details – This data store is likely to have already been developed for stock control purposes. However, in the development of this system, a limited product database should be developed.

Manufacturer details – This stores the manufacturers of the products. Again, this is likely to be already available in the company, but a limited version should be developed for use in the development stages.

Customer details – The company already holds a database of all customers who use a store card; however, the system must be able to cope with customers who do not and perhaps have bought from the store by cash purchase.

■ Input requirements

These are limited to the need for the customer service department to take the details of the complaint and subsequent actions and log them onto their system. A one-page data entry screen will be sufficient. It is very important that the details are captured accurately and that good use is made of validation and verification. The screen must also be able to capture ongoing progress comments as the investigation into the complaints is undertaken. It must be able to store the date the complaint was finally resolved so that analysis of the time taken can be made.

■ Output requirements

A variety of on-screen and printed reports will be necessary. As an on-screen minimum, anyone should be able to view the records and query the complaints by category of complaint or by store or by product. There should be a facility for outputting appropriate fields for mail merging letters to customers.

■ Processing

Some processing of the data held will be required, but it is probable that the inbuilt routines for searching, sorting, etc. will be sufficient. No additional routines will be required, except for ones that might be used to automate some of the tasks involved.

A consistency of styling must be employed – both to provide a professional image and also to help users interact with the system effectively. This consistency of styling should extend to the layout, use of logos, etc. of the forms and reports, as well as such things as naming conventions for the tables and fields.

Task 1 (P1)

As part of the initial information gathering, the systems analyst encounters a number of staff who are negative about the project and feel that a complex computerised database is an inappropriate solution.

- You are asked to prepare a presentation that can be used to both describe the purpose and features of a relational database.
- Alternatively, by negotiation, you could be asked to describe the purpose verbally and demonstrate practically the features using an example.

Task 2 (P2)

- Consider the information provided and **normalise** the information required into five related tables.
- Decide on and document the relationships, table structures, fields and properties.

Check with your tutor or client and get this signed off before proceeding to the next task.

- Modify as necessary and implement your design.

Task 3 (P3)

Using the information provided, design and implement a suitable data entry form for the capturing of the complaint itself which incorporates features to ensure the validity and integrity of data.

You must include at least three of the following techniques:

- validation routine
- verification routine
- input masking
- check for completeness
- visual prompts
- data consistency
- check for data redundancy
- drop-down/combo boxes.

Task 4 (M3)

- Create a further two on-screen and two printed reports that would be useful.
- Create a form and objects with associated macros that acts as a menu, allowing the objects to be easily chosen by the user.

Note: M2 can also be assessed at this point.

Task 5 (P4)

- Populate the tables, ensuring that at least one of the tables is populated by importing data from an external source. (Your tutor may provide this data – e.g. for the products, manufacturers or customers.)
- By agreement with your tutor, export the output of a query to a spreadsheet.

Task 6 (D1)

Analyse potential errors in the design and construction of your database and explain how you have ensured that these have been avoided.

Task 7 (P6)

Devise and test queries that respond to the requirements identified using multiple tables and multiple criteria.

Task 8 (D2)

Check whether your database has met the various user requirements and use this to evaluate the database, identifying strengths and weaknesses.

Task 9 (P5)

During the process of testing and evaluation, the company decides that it needs to store further details about the customer service employee who is handling each complaint. Only brief details of the customer scrvice employee is needed – such as employee reference number, name and internal telephone number.

- Design and add this table to the database and relate it to the appropriate existing table. This may require changes to the other table as well.

Task 10 (M1, M4)

The store manager has appointed one of the existing staff to be a 'local expert' who will help to advise staff and maintain the database. Although this person is technically competent, they have little experience in using a relational database.

- You are asked to prepare some guidance on the following topics that can be used by this person. The guidance can be in the form of a word processed document, a web page or a presentation with supporting notes.

  a) The characteristics of a primary key and how primary keys are used to build relationships.

  b) An explanation of referential integrity.

  c) How to ensure integrity of the database when records are deleted.

Advanced Spreadsheet Skills

Introduction

Spreadsheets can be used in a variety of ways.

- They can support organisational activities such as credit control, sales forecasting and stock analysis.

- They can be set up as reusable templates which produce immediate results when data is input, such as payroll or invoice templates.

As an IT practitioner, you need to be able both to use spreadsheet software competently and to support users as part of a technical or help desk role.

You should already be familiar with setting up and using spreadsheets. In this unit, you will learn the more advanced features and functions of spreadsheets.

After completing this unit, you should be able to achieve these outcomes:

- Understand how spreadsheets can be used to solve complex problems

- Be able to create technically complex spreadsheets that are well structured and fit for purpose

- Be able to use functions and formulae to solve complex problems

- Be able to create efficient automated and customisable spreadsheets that enable easy analysis and interpretation.

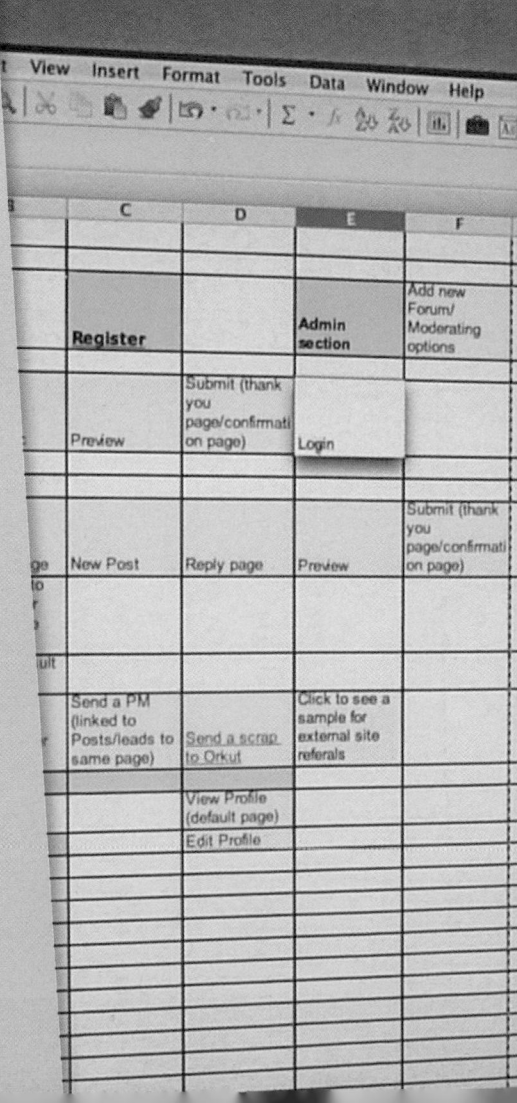

Grading criteria	Activity	Page number
To achieve a pass grade the evidence must show that the learner is able to:		
p₁ Create a complex spreadsheet that is fit for purpose and check accuracy	6.11, 6.13, 6.20, 6.23, 6.25, PFA	73, 74, 84, 87, 89, 92
p₂ Use formulae and functions to solve a complex problem	6.14, 6.16, PFA	76, 79, 92
p₃ Use sorting and summarising techniques to interpret a complex spreadsheet	PFA	92
p₄ Use charts or graphs to present data graphically and to meet a defined user need	6.21, PFA	85, 92
p₅ Use conversion facilities to export the contents of a spreadsheet to an alternative format	6.26, PFA	91, 93
p₆ Customise or automate an aspect of the spreadsheet	6.24, 6.26, PFA	88, 91, 93
To achieve a merit grade the evidence must show that, in addition to the pass criteria, the learner is able to:		
m₁ Check accuracy of a spreadsheet using a range of appropriate techniques and explain the choice of techniques used	6.23, 6.25, PFA	87, 89, 93
m₂ Explain with the use of examples how data can be manipulated to aid interpretation	6.22, PFA	86, 93
m₃ Use and compare two customisation and two automation techniques	6.26, PFA	91, 93
To achieve a distinction grade the evidence must show that, in addition to the pass and merit criteria, the learner is able to:		
d₁ Evaluate a spreadsheet	PFA	93
d₂ Justify the structure of their spreadsheet	6.22, PFA	86, 92

Note: 'PFA' stands for 'Preparation for assessment'.

The basic design of a spreadsheet is a two-dimensional table of rows and columns.

- The **rows** of a spreadsheet are numbered 1, 2, 3, . . .
- The **columns** of a spreadsheet are lettered A, B, C, . . .

Each cell has a **cell reference** based on its row number and column letter: A7, B2, etc. In its simplest form, each cell can then contain one of four types of data:

- **text** – including titles, headings and labels, as well as names, addresses and telephone numbers
- **numeric data** – any type of number – can be formatted as currency, percentage or date, for example
- **formulae** – involving single operators, relative cell references and simple functions.
- left **blank** – useful for creating white space on a spreadsheet, which makes the rest of the data easier to read and understand.

A spreadsheet can increase in complexity in a number of ways:

- additional worksheets may be created and links formed between them
- complex formulae may be set up to perform more sophisticated calculations such as statistical analysis.

This section considers how spreadsheets may be used and the problems they might be used to solve, before looking at how they might be created.

6.1.1 Uses of spreadsheets

It is commonplace for the accounting and finance departments of an organisation to use spreadsheets to record the transactions made by that organisation. Spreadsheets have replaced manual pages in ledgers, where income and expenditure were organised into rows and columns.

Any problem involving a lot of calculations and analysis of numerical data is ideally suited to being solved using a spreadsheet.

In the past, you needed special training to understand the accounts. Nowadays, users can benefit from the inbuilt functionality of spreadsheets; it helps them to understand the data without needing specialist mathematical skills. Data can also be presented in graphical form at the press of a button.

Activity 6.1

Keeping a diary of time spent

1 For one week, keep a diary of how you spend your personal time, e.g. sleeping, washing/dressing, travelling, studying, watching TV, socialising. Collect relevant data.

2 Think about how you might set up a simple spreadsheet model to record how you spend your time each day for one week. Design the spreadsheet using appropriate column and row titles.

3 Decide what statistics would be useful, and consider what formulae you might use to calculate totals and averages.

6.1.1.1 Manipulation of data

The data in a spreadsheet is mostly numeric. Spreadsheets are ideally suited to process numeric data, just as word processors are ideal for writing reports and presentation packages for creating slide shows.

Having designed a spreadsheet so that you know what you plan to put in and where, you can physically create the spreadsheet model. This involves entering a title, column headings and row labels. You then enter text, numeric data, formulae involving single operators and relative cell references and simple functions, and format all these cells appropriately.

If the spreadsheet does not quite fit the purpose intended, you may need to edit it. When editing a spreadsheet, there are two options.

- You can change the 'shape' – or design – of the spreadsheet, by inserting or deleting rows and columns.
- You can change the data within particular cells, including the formulae in those cells.

To change the contents of a cell, the cell has to be selected first to make it the **active cell** (as specified in the Name Box) before you can overwrite its contents. If you only want to make a minor change, you can do so in the Formula Bar.

Activity 6.2

Using a spreadsheet for time sheet analysis

1 Following on from the work you did in Assessment activity 6.1, create a simple spreadsheet model to record how you spend your time each day for one week. Include appropriate column and row titles.

2 Generate formulae to calculate totals and averages.

6.1.1.2 Presentation of data

The spreadsheet data will be visible on-screen, but may also be needed in hard copy form. With a spreadsheet, the pagination is not as straightforward as in some other applications. If there are too many columns to fit across a single page, even in landscape orientation, your printout will present only a range of cells on each page, and it might prove difficult to see how it all fits together (see Figure 6.1).

To control exactly what is printed, you need to set the Print Area.

■ **How to set a print area on a spreadsheet**

1 Select the range of cells that you want to print, so that they are highlighted.
2 Select File/Print Area/Set Print Area.
3 Dotted lines will indicate the edges of the pages. You can change the width of columns to fit more (or less) onto any page.

When you print out your spreadsheet, you can choose to have the row numbers and column letters printed too – or they can be omitted (see Figure 6.2).

Activity 6.3

Time sheet analysis: print options

1 Preview the spreadsheet you created in Activity 6.2. Make sure it will fit sensibly on to a page, setting the print area as necessary.

2 Print out your spreadsheet, once with the row numbers and columns letters and once without.

Numeric data is harder to interpret than graphical representations of the same data. To create output that suits the requirements of the user and the audience, you may generate line graphs, bar/column charts and/or pie charts.

▼ **Figure 6.1 How a large spreadsheet is split into separate pages for printing**

You can choose to turn on/off the page break review option.

The dotted lines show where the pages will start and end.

Figure 6.2 Option to print/omit
row numbers and column letters ▶

Microsoft Excel - PiningForYou.xls

	A	B	C	D	E	F	G	H
1	Pining for You Furniture							
2								
3	ITEM	PRICES	North	South	East	West	Total	Value
4	Book case	£35.00	13	10	11	12	46	£1,610.00
5	Coffee table	£60.00	5	5	2	1	13	£780.00
6	Chess board	£15.00	6	0	1	7	14	£210.00
7	Kitchen bench	£75.00	21	2	15	5	43	£3,225.00
8	Magazine rack	£30.00	4	10	15	3	32	£960.00
9	Lamp standard	£40.00	5	5	22	3	35	£1,400.00
10	Totals							£8,185.00

Preview: Page 1 of 2

You have several options when
trying to represent a single data
series.

- **Pie charts** are best for
  categorical data, such as
  colour of front door or make
  of car.
- **Bar/column charts** are best
  for **discrete ordinal** data,
  such as shoe sizes. For discrete
  data, the bars should not
  touch. If a bar chart is used
  for continuous data, the bars
  should touch, and the chart
  is then called a **histogram**.
- **Line graphs** are useful to display trends in
  continuous data. If a graph is used for discrete data
  (such as shoe sizes), the points should not really be
  joined, because the values between the discrete values
  are unachievable – but often the points are joined to
  show some trend.

During the development
stage of a spreadsheet it
may help you to print out
the row numbers and
column letters.

You might opt for grid
lines too.

Microsoft Excel - PiningForYou.xls

File Edit View Insert Format Tools Data Window Help Adobe PDF

A1 ▾ Pining for You Furniture

Page Setup

Page | Margins | Header/Footer | Sheet

Print area:

Print titles
Rows to repeat at top:
Columns to repeat at left:

Print
☐ Gridlines   ☑ Row and column headings
☐ Black and white   Comments: (None)
☐ Draft quality   Cell errors as: displayed

Page order
◉ Down, then over
○ Over, then down

Print... | Print Preview | Options...

OK | Cancel

Spreadsheet software provides a wizard to generate
graphical representations (see Figure 6.3). It makes sense
to use the wizard to set up a chart or graph and then fine
tune it so it shows exactly what you want.

What does it mean?

Categorical data has separate categories, and there
is no natural ordering.

Ordinal data may be discrete or continuous, but has a
definite ordering, e.g. from smallest to largest, or
oldest to newest.

Discrete data takes values, but not the values
between them. For example: shoes sizes are 4, 4½, 5,
5½, 6, 6½, 7 and so on. There is no shoe size
between a 4 and a 4½.

Continuous data can take a value anywhere on a
number line. For example, time is a continuous
variable, as are height, length and weight.

Note that to create
a conversion graph
between two
variables, choose
XY (scatter).
The line graph
option creates
separate lines, one
per variable.

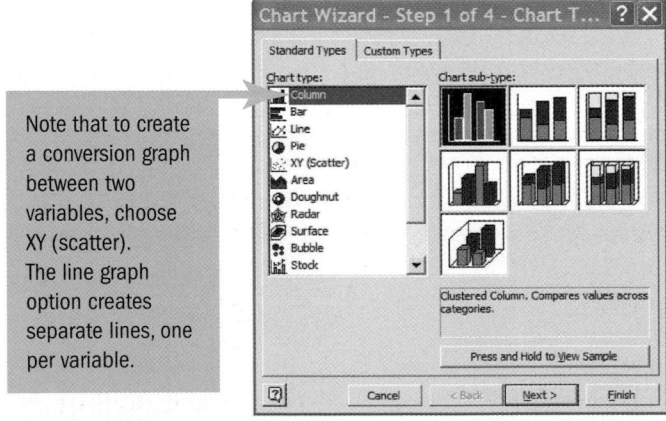

Chart Wizard - Step 1 of 4 - Chart T...

Standard Types | Custom Types

Chart type:
Column
Bar
Line
Pie
XY (Scatter)
Area
Doughnut
Radar
Surface
Bubble
Stock

Chart sub-type:

Clustered Column. Compares values across
categories.

Press and Hold to View Sample

Cancel | < Back | Next > | Finish

▲ Figure 6.3 Graphical options available in Excel

Activity 6.4

Time sheet analysis: print options

1 For the spreadsheet you created in Assessment activity 6.2, decide what data would be better presented graphically rather than numerically. Explain why.

2 Create charts and graphs to illustrate your data.

3 Look at the charts and graphs produced by others in your group. Do they help you to compare how you spend your time with how they spend theirs?

4 Consider refinements to your spreadsheet. What extra information might be usefully included?

5 Keep a diary for one more week. Collect relevant data. Enter the data into your amended spreadsheet and complete the analysis and presentation of your statistics.

6.1.1.3 Supporting decision making

Spreadsheets can be used to support decision making. They can be used to provide timely and accurate information in a variety of situations, including: analysis of data, goal seeking, scenarios, regression and **data mining**.

What does it mean?

Data mining involves the automatic collection of large amounts of data and then analysing the data for trends and patterns. For example, all credit card transactions might be stored and then the data analysed to spot possible fraudulent activity.

The power of spreadsheet software lies in its ability to recalculate the contents of cells that hold formulae and to display the revised contents almost instantly. This means you can answer 'what if?' questions using a spreadsheet model.

■ How to answer a 'what if?' question

1 Set up the data in a spreadsheet to create a model of some real-life situation.

2 Identify which cells hold the data that you are trying to maximise or minimise or that you want to meet some criteria. Identify which cells hold data that you might change.

3 Change the input data in some way and note any changes in the displayed output.

4 If the new value made the situation better, can you make it better still? If it made it worse, undo the change and consider changing the data in the other direction.

5 Repeat steps 3 and 4 until you feel you are as close to a solution as you want to be.

Activity 6.5

What if?

1 Using your spreadsheet from Assessment activity 6.2, carry out a 'what if?' exercise to solve the following problem:
  - You want to find an extra six hours per week in order to join a club, start driving lessons or take up some other activity.

2 Compare your spreadsheet with others in your group. What other 'what if?' questions could be answered using these spreadsheets.

Test your knowledge

1 Check that you are happy with how to set up a spreadsheet: setting up a model; editing the content and formatting the cells; printing individual pages; creating charts and graphs to represent your data; and answering 'what if?' questions.

2 Explain the four main types of content that you may place in any one cell. What other content options does your spreadsheet software offer?

3 What is an active cell?

4 Explain these terms: categorical data, ordinal data, histogram, discrete, continuous.

6.1.2 Problems

Essentially, spreadsheets are models that simulate a real-life situation. Spreadsheet models can be used to solve a number of problems, such as cash flow forecasting, budget control, sales forecasting, payroll projections, statistical analysis and trend analysis.

For example, in one spreadsheet model, the rows could be used to list the variables that relate to a situation, and the columns could reflect the passing of time. The cells will be allocated to contain relevant data and to show the results of any calculations. Some values are fixed, whereas others will change. Some values will depend on other values within the spreadsheet.

The formulae that are used reflect current thinking on the 'rules' that apply in real life. For some formulae, there is no debate. For example, the cost of a product including VAT can be calculated with a degree of certainty. However, the effect on future sales of a price increase might be based on past experience but is, at best, an educated guess.

Having set up a model, it can then be used to simulate a situation and to forecast what might happen, given certain circumstances.

6.1.2.1 Forecasting

Forecasting is inherently difficult. How can you possibly tell what is going to happen in the future? The answer is: you can't. But you can make an educated guess if you have sufficient information about how things have worked out in the past, and you have the tools to process this data. You can take measurements today and, if you have a formula that you think will work, you can calculate the values for tomorrow, the day after and so on. Then, as time passes, you can check the accuracy of your forecasts, and amend your model – the formulae that you used – until they more accurately forecast the future.

A spreadsheet is particularly useful for forecasting because it will do all the calculations for you. Each new row (or column) can be used to represent the next day (or whatever time interval you choose for your model).

6.1.2.2 Statistical analysis

To make sense of a lot of numeric data, statistical analysis can provide insights into trends and arrive at **representative values**.

What does it mean?

Representative values are single values that represent many items of data. Representative values include mean, mode and median, as well as other statistical values.

To design spreadsheets for statistical analysis requires considerable knowledge of statistics, and the formulae can be complex. However, using them once the model has been set up should be easy if the user interface has been well designed.

6.1.2.3 Cost-benefit analysis

Cost-benefit analysis is a relatively simple and widely used technique for deciding whether to make a change. You add up the value of the benefits of a course of action and subtract the costs associated with it. If the benefits outweigh the costs, you go ahead. Simple!

Costs may be one off or they may be ongoing. Benefits, however, are most often received over a period of time. It is important to build the effect of time into any analysis by calculating a **payback period**. Many companies look for payback over a specified period of time, say, five years.

What does it mean?

The **payback period** is the time it takes for the benefits of a change to repay its costs.

In its simplest form, cost-benefit analysis is carried out using only financial costs and financial benefits. For example, a simple cost-benefit analysis of a road scheme would measure the cost of building the road and subtract this from the economic benefit of improving transport links. It would not measure either the cost of environmental damage or the benefit of quicker and easier travel to work.

A more sophisticated approach to cost-benefit analysis is to try to put a financial value on these intangible costs and benefits. This can be highly subjective.

- How do you put a price on the environmental importance of a copse that is home to butterflies but lies in the way of a planned motorway?
- For the motorist, what value can be put on stress-free travel to work in the morning?
- For those that live near the proposed route, what price do you put on air and noise pollution?

Test your knowledge

1 Give two examples of spreadsheet models that forecast the future.

2 Why are spreadsheets useful for statistical analysis?

3 What is a representative value?

4 Explain the terms cost-benefit analysis and payback period.

Activity 6.6

Problem solving using spreadsheets

For this unit, you have to produce evidence that demonstrates your proficiency in the use of advanced spreadsheet features and functions.

1 Identify an end user with a problem to be solved.
- Read the specification for this unit. What is expected of you?
- Can the problem you have chosen be solved by creating a sufficiently complex spreadsheet? If not, try to extend the problem so that it needs a more complex spreadsheet or think of another problem.

2 Start to develop ideas for the solution to your end user's problem.
- What data is involved? What input forms might you need to develop? What validation might you need to include?
- What processing will you have to do? What functions and formulae might be needed?
- What charts and diagrams might you create for output?
- How will you design the interface for your user?

Write notes on all your findings and your decisions.

3 Discuss your plans with your teacher to check that you are attempting a project that is within your capabilities and yet sufficiently complex to meet the requirements of the qualification.

Your aim in creating a spreadsheet for your portfolio is to show that you can create a complex spreadsheet that is well structured and fit for purpose. But what is complex? And how is this demonstrated through the structure of your design?

6.2.1 Complexity

Complexity can come from a combination of factors.

- **Multiple worksheets.** Rather than having a single worksheet, you may design a spreadsheet to have several separate worksheets. Depending on the purpose of your spreadsheet, you may have one worksheet per month, one per employee or one per event.
- **Complex formulae.** Complex calculations can be carried out using library functions or users can choose to create their own formulae.
- **Large data set.** Processing a large data set might involve using large and cumbersome worksheets. Using named ranges is one way of coping with this complication (see section 6.3.1.1 on page 70).
- **Cells linked between worksheet pages.** Changes on one worksheet will have an effect on the data on another worksheet.

6.2.2 Accuracy

Accuracy of data is clearly important, but who checks the data?

Two ways of checking data are as follows.

- During the design stage, you can build in a **cross-cast check** (see Figure 6.4). For example, to calculate the

total sales for a team of salespeople over twelve months, you can do one calculation by month and another by salesperson. The two totals should tally.
- You can also display intermediate values of a calculation, which makes it easier to check the logic of your formulae.

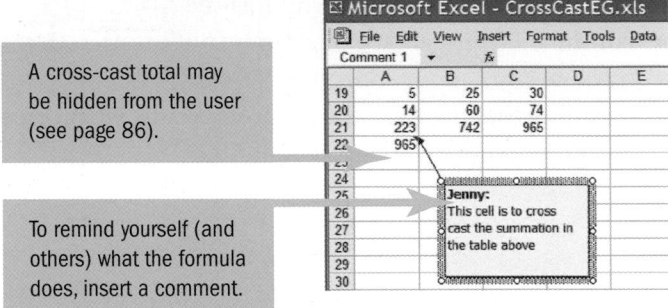

A cross-cast total may be hidden from the user (see page 86).

To remind yourself (and others) what the formula does, insert a comment.

▲ **Figure 6.4 A cross-cast check**

Data needs also to be displayed at the appropriate level of detail: for example, to the nearest penny for currency or to the nearest £1000 for larger amounts of money.

6.2.3 Structure and fitness for purpose

A worksheet is essentially a set of cells arranged in rows and columns but, within that format, you can create a structure. You can also set up a number of worksheets and link these.

To make it crystal clear what the data in your spreadsheet represents, you should include a title (to describe the whole spreadsheet and individual worksheets), column headings (to describe the data in each column) and row labels (to describe the data in each row). To make these cells stand out, it is a good idea to format them differently.

As well as formatting the headings and labels, you should format all the cells in your spreadsheet. The format that you apply should depend on the contents – the type of data the cell holds (see Figure 6.5).

What does it mean?

A **cross-cast check** involves doing a calculation in two different ways and checking that the two totals are the same.

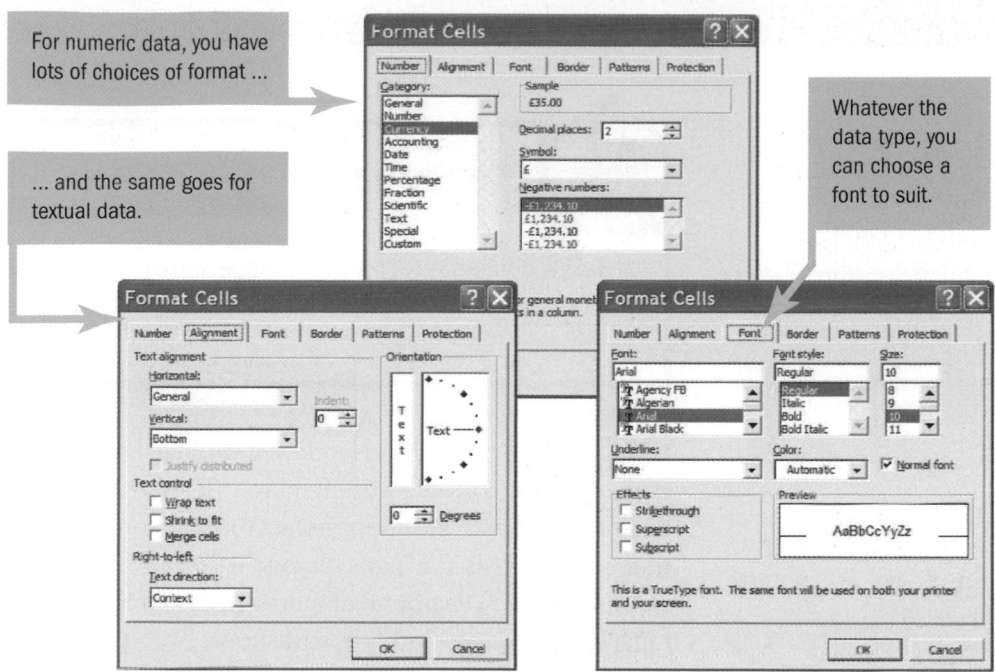

For numeric data, you have lots of choices of format ...

... and the same goes for textual data.

Whatever the data type, you can choose a font to suit.

▲ Figure 6.5 Formatting options

- For cells that contain **text**, you can set the font, style, size and alignment. You should aim for consistency, using a minimal number of different fonts, and sparing use of colour and shading, and italics and bold.
- For cells that contain **numeric data**, you need to specify the type of number: integer (i.e. whole number), the number of decimal places, percentage, currency or date/time.
- For cells that contain a **formula**, the format will depend on the type of data that the formula creates – for formulae that display a number, you can set the format of the cell as for numeric data; for formulae that display text, you can set the format of the cell as for text data.

You might also decide to create borders around groups of cells to make them stand out even more, or use patterns.

Your overall aim should be to create an organised spreadsheet that is fit for purpose. This means making sure the size of font is legible enough for the intended audience, and that the layout of the data is as straightforward as possible.

6.2.4 Alternative formats

Spreadsheets can be saved in a number of different formats, such as:

- xls (Excel spreadsheet)
- txt (text)
- xms (eXtended Memory Specification)
- html (Hypertext Markup Language, as used for web pages)
- csv (Comma-Separated Variable).

CSV is one of the most useful formats – it can be read by many applications, so data created in one type of spreadsheet software can easily be exported to other programs.

Activity 6.7

Complex spreadsheets

1 Review your plans for your spreadsheet project. In what ways will your spreadsheet solution be complex? List the features that it will include.

2 Decide whether you need to plan to incorporate more complexity into your solution and discuss this with your teacher.

What does it mean?

A **formula** is an expression written in terms of cell references and operators, which specifies a calculation that is to be done. The result of the calculation appears in the cell in which the formula is stored.

A **function** is a command that results in a value being returned.

The main benefit of a spreadsheet is that the software can do the calculations for you. This is especially useful when you are facing complex problems.

6.3.1 Features and functions

This section looks at a range of features and functions that will prove useful when you are faced with complex problems to solve using a spreadsheet. The focus is on features that will be of particular use if more than one user is involved in the creation and/or editing of a workbook.

6.3.1.1 Named ranges

Each cell can be referred to by its column letter and row number: e.g. A7 or B9. A range of cells can also be referred to by the cell references, separated by a colon: e.g. A3:B7.

▼ Figure 6.6 Named ranges in Excel

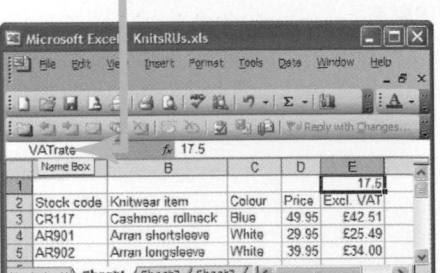

Using names for cells allows for more meaningful formulae.

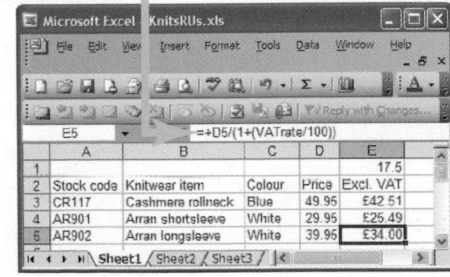

Remember!

A **range** defines a rectangular shape within a worksheet, so the range A3:B7 includes columns A and B, and rows 3 to 7.

Cell references are fine and work well enough, but named ranges provide a more meaningful way of referring to cells and ranges of cells within formulae. You can even name non-adjacent cells as a 'named range' if you wish, and you can also create 3D names that represent the same cell or range of cells across multiple worksheets.

Using named ranges is particularly important when a team of users are developing a complex spreadsheet, as it serves as documentation of the data.

■ How to name cells

1 Select the cell, range of cells or non-adjacent selections that you want to name.
2 Click the Name Box at the left end of the formula bar (see Figure 6.6).
3 In the Name Box, type the name for the cells.
4 Press Enter.

Activity 6.8

Features of Excel: named ranges

1 You can also name ranges of cells using Insert/Name/Define (see Figure 6.7). How might this option help you to check what range of cells a given name refers to?

2 Identify cell ranges within your spreadsheet project that you ought to name. Think about how you will document your decisions about the structure of your spreadsheet solution.

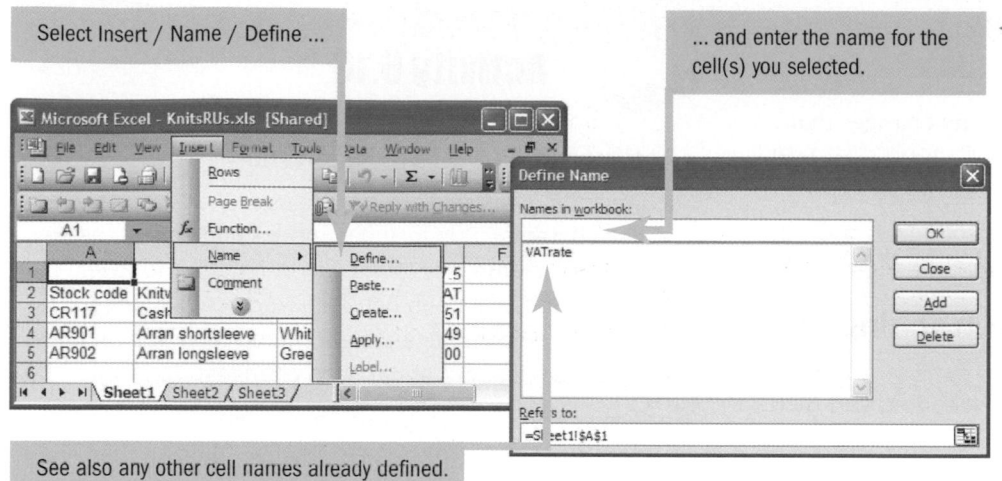

Select Insert / Name / Define ...

... and enter the name for the cell(s) you selected.

Figure 6.7 Insert / Name / Define

See also any other cell names already defined.

6.3.1.2 Sharing files and data

The more complex a spreadsheet becomes, the more likely it is that more than one user will need to have access to it – during development and/or during use.

Sharing of files and data is possible, with restrictions. Having created a workbook that you want to make available for multi-user editing, you can enter any data that you want to provide. Some features (such as merged cells, conditional formats and data validation) need to be incorporated prior to sharing because you cannot make changes to these features after you share the workbook.

■ How to share a workbook

1 On the Tools menu, click Share Workbook, then click the Editing tab.
2 Select 'Allow changes by more than one user at the same time' and click OK.
3 When prompted, save the workbook.
4 On the File menu, click Save As. Save the workbook on a network location that is accessible to the intended users, using a shared network folder.
5 Check any links to other workbooks or documents, and fix any that are broken.

Once you have set up the workbook for sharing, all users with access to the network will then have full access to the shared workbook, unless you use the Protect Sheet command (Tools/Protection/Protect Sheet) to restrict access.

Remember!

Any users who want to edit a shared workbook need up-to-date software which supports this feature: Microsoft Excel 97 or later for Microsoft Windows users or Excel 98 or later for Macintosh users.

Activity 6.9

Features of Excel: sharing workbooks

1 Check what features will *not* be available once a workbook has been set up for sharing.

2 How could you and others in your group collate the information in your spreadsheets about how you spend your time? Set up a shared workbook to show how two or more of you spend your time. Include analyses that compare your leisure time versus studying time.

Track Changes is an option that logs any changes that are made to a workbook. Each user who has access to the file can view these changes. They can see when the change was made and who made the change. A user can then accept or reject the changes made (see Figure 6.8).

■ How to turn on change tracking for a workbook

1 On the Tools menu, click Share Workbook, and then click the Editing tab.
2 Select 'Allow changes by more than one user at the same time'.
3 Click the Advanced tab.
4 Under Track changes, click 'Keep change history for:' and key in the number of days of change history that you want to keep.
5 Click OK and, if prompted to save the file, click OK.

Remember!

You must choose a large enough number of days because Microsoft Excel permanently erases any change history older than this number of days.

Activity 6.10

Features of Excel: tracking changes

1 Track Changes records any changes that you make to cell contents. This includes moves and copies, as well as row/column insertions and deletions. However, Microsoft Excel does not keep track of all changes. Find out what changes might not be recorded and how you might find out about such changes.

2 Activate Track Changes on your shared workbook from Activity 6.9 to give yourself practice in using this feature.

3 Use Track Changes on your spreadsheet project to record the changes that you have made and to document your use of this feature.

6.3.1.4 Security issues

Giving access to a workbook to other users introduces security issues. Who should have access? And what level of access should they be given?

Excel offers a wide range of protection options. You can protect or unprotect individual elements of the spreadsheet using the Protect Sheet dialogue box (Tools/Protection/Protect Sheet) by selecting or clearing the check box for each element.

- You could protect the worksheet and the contents of locked cells to prevent users from making changes to these cells. Before protecting the worksheet, unlock

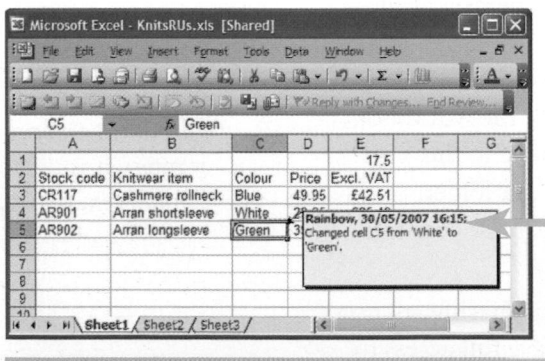

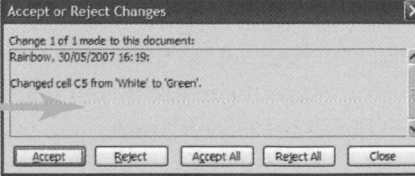

Changed cells are highlighted. An explanation of any change appears for the current active cell.

Selecting on Tool / Track Changes / Accept or Reject Changes opens a dialogue box, and you can then decide what to accept/reject.

Figure 6.8 Using Track Changes in Excel ▶

any cells that you want users to be able to change. You can give a specific user permission to edit locked cells using the Allow Users to Edit Ranges dialogue box (Tools/Protection/Allow Users to Edit Ranges).

- You could prevent users from viewing certain rows or columns or certain formulae. To do this, hide the rows/columns (Format/Row (or Column)/Hide) or the formulae (Format/Cells/Protection, then check Hidden) before you protect the worksheet.

Within the chart sheet elements, you can prevent users from making changes to items that are part of the chart, such as the data series, axes and legends. However, if you have allowed the user access to change the source data, the chart continues to reflect any changes made to this data.

You can even control the size and position of the windows and prevent users from moving, resizing or closing the windows. However, they can still hide and unhide windows.

Activity 6.11

Features of Excel: security issues

1 Explore the Protection menu to discover the range of controls available to you to prevent users from making changes to your spreadsheet design and/or to the data.

2 Working in a group, set up your time analysis spreadsheet so that some individuals within the group can view different aspects of the spreadsheet (such as hidden columns and formulae) and others cannot. Experiment with locking cells and password control.

3 Introduce appropriate security controls on your own spreadsheet project. Ask a friend to test it for you. How much of the design of the spreadsheet can your friend view and/or alter. How well protected is your spreadsheet?  **(partial evidence)**

4 Given a spreadsheet that has a level of protection on it, find out how much of the design of the spreadsheet you can view and/or alter. How well protected is the spreadsheet?

The design of the user interface must take into account the needs of your intended user(s) and include appropriate user interface features such as data entry forms, prompts and error messages.

- **Data entry forms:** You may choose to design a user-friendly interface that requires the user to enter all data using data entry forms. In Excel, the controls you need to create your own form are available on the Forms toolbar (see Figure 6.9).

▲ **Figure 6.9 Forms toolbar**

- **Prompts:** The form will guide the user through the correct order of entry, but you may also provide prompts to remind the user what is expected.
- **Error messages:** You will need to build some level of validation into your design – at least sufficient to prevent the user from entering invalid data. Create error messages that display if the user inadvertently enters invalid data.

Activity 6.12

Features of Excel: data entry forms

1 Explore the Excel Forms and Control Toolbox toolbars to discover the variety of controls on offer.

2 For your spreadsheet project, identify what data you might need to input via a data entry form. Design and test your input form. Include sufficient validation of data to prevent the user entering invalid data. Include prompts and error messages to make your form as user-friendly as possible.

3 Try out someone else's data input form to test how well the form has been designed. Is the data entry straightforward? Have prompts been included to help the person entering data? What happens if you enter invalid data?

Add-ins are programs that add optional commands and features to a software application such as Excel. For example, the Analysis ToolPak add-in program provides a set of data analysis tools.

Excel offers three types of add-in programs: Excel add-ins, custom (**COM**) add-ins, and automation add-ins.

What does it mean?

COM stands for **component object model**.

Some Excel add-ins are available when you install Excel and others are available from the Microsoft Office website. The add-in is installed on your computer (as a .xla file) and then loaded into Excel. Once loaded into Excel, it becomes a feature and can be used like any other feature. Any commands that are associated with the add-in appear automatically on appropriate toolbars and menus.

Why not have all available add-ins present all the time? The reason is that they take up space. So, to conserve memory and improve performance, it is wise to unload add-ins that you don't use or use only rarely. Unloading an add-in removes its features and commands from Excel (although the add-in program remains on your computer so you can easily reload it when you next need it).

Remember!

When you unload an add-in program, it remains in memory until you restart Excel.

Activity 6.13

Features of Excel: add-ins

1 Find out what add-ins have already been installed on your version of Excel.

2 Install additional add-ins, selecting ones that would be useful to you in creating a complex spreadsheet solution. **P** (partial evidence)

3 Find out about alternative add-ins, such as COM add-ins and automation add-ins. What are these used for? How are they installed?

Functions provide the mathematical or logical rules to perform calculations or make decisions. Excel provides many inbuilt functions such as those shown in Table 6.1.

Within the definitions for a function, triangular brackets (<>) are used to indicate the **arguments** (shown in italics) of the function.

What does it mean?

An **argument** is a value or expression used within a function. It specifies what data is to be acted upon, the criteria that are to be applied or the resulting value that is required.

You need to complete the arguments within a function using the following as appropriate:

*   cell references (such as A5 and Overview!B7 or a named range)

Function	Description
COUNT(<value1>, <value2>, . . .)	Counts the number of cells that contain the value(s) listed
SUM(<cellref1>:<cellref2>)	Adds up the cells within the stated range
AVERAGE(<cellref1>,<cellref2>, . . .)	Adds up the contents of the cells and divides by the number of cells listed

Table 6.1 Functions

- numbers
- strings
- expressions.

For example: COUNT(45,60,70) or SUM(A1:A7).

Functions can be subgrouped by type, for example: cell functions (such as SUM), lookup functions (see below), text functions (see below) or statistical functions (such as AVERAGE).

■ The LOOKUP function

The LOOKUP function has two syntax forms: **vector** and **array**. The vector form of LOOKUP looks in a vector for a value and returns a value from the same position in a second vector.

What does it mean?

A **vector** is a range that covers one row or one column.

An **array** is a range of cells that covers more than one row and more than one column, e.g. A5:D9.

The array form of LOOKUP looks in the first row or column of an array for the specified value and returns a value from the same position in the last row or column of the array.

The LOOKUP function is useful when:

- you have a table of values that may change at some later date, and which you therefore do not want to embed within a formula
- the value you want depends on the contents of a cell, and this also varies.

The values that you want to look up might be in the same worksheet or in a completely different worksheet within the same spreadsheet.

Case study

Knits4U

Knits4U buys its knitwear from a manufacturer BulkKnits. BulkKnits offer discounts to wholesale customers such as Knits4U, based on the size of an individual order and on the category of client: Platinum, Gold or Silver. The discount rates are held in a spreadsheet (see Figure 6.10) and used to calculate the discount given on a particular order.

1. Use Insert Function to confirm the arguments needed for the LOOKUP function.

2. Set up some data on one worksheet that you can look up from another worksheet.

3. Write a formula that uses the LOOKUP function. Check that the formula works. If you find it does not, try extending the range of the vectors to include blank rows above and below the rows that contain the data.

4. Change the values in the table and check the formula now displays amended accurate values.

■ Text functions

Text functions act on the textual content of cells and can be used, for example, to change the case of text.

Table 6.2 shows how the text string 'jenny Lawson' (in cell A1) is displayed according the text function that is used in another cell (A2).

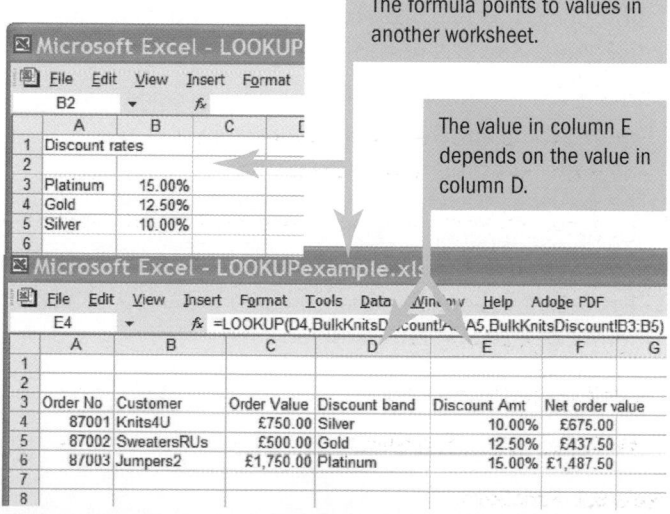

The formula points to values in another worksheet.

The value in column E depends on the value in column D.

Figure 6.10 ▶
LOOKUP table

In A1	Text function in A2	Result displayed in A2
jenny Lawson	=UPPER(A1)	JENNY LAWSON
	=LOWER(A1)	jenny lawson
	=PROPER(A1)	Jenny Lawson

Table 6.2 Example text functions

If you are not sure which function you need, Excel provides help. Select Insert Function (see Figure 6.11) and type a brief description or look through the lists of functions available.

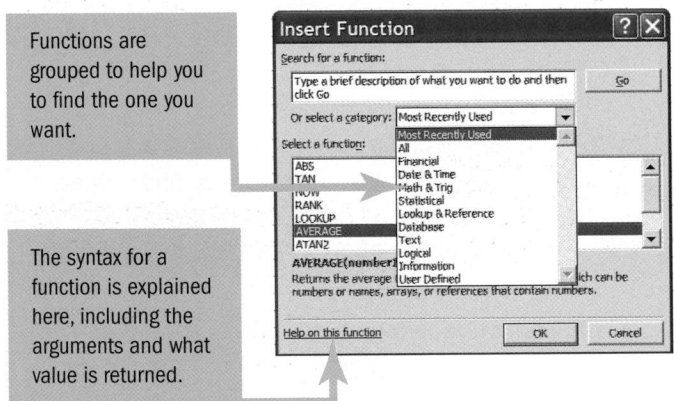

Functions are grouped to help you to find the one you want.

The syntax for a function is explained here, including the arguments and what value is returned.

▲ **Figure 6.11 Inserting a function**

Activity 6.14

Features of Excel: built-in functions

1 Use Microsoft help to identify a variety of built-in functions, including cell functions, lookup functions, text functions and statistical functions.

2 Using sample data that you invent, incorporate a range of functions into formulae within your spreadsheet project. Include examples of cell functions, lookup functions, text functions and statistical functions. **P₂ (partial evidence)**

3 Document your examples to explain the effect of the formulae that you have created

6.3.2 Formulae

Formulae are the 'equations' that perform calculations on values in your worksheet. A formula starts with an equals sign (=) and is followed by the expression that describes the calculation you want to perform.

Within the expression, you can use:

- numerical values, including decimal numbers with a decimal point and negative values indicated by a minus sign
- operators, + for addition, − for subtraction, * for multiplication, / for division
- brackets, to indicate the order in which you want the calculation to be done
- functions, e.g. SUM
- cell references, to indicate what data is to be used in the calculation.

■ When are existing formulae recalculated?

When you change the contents of one cell, Excel automatically recalculates any cells that are dependent on the cell that you changed. Excel also calculates workbooks each time they are opened.

While these calculations are happening in the background, you may be choosing commands or performing actions such as entering numbers or formulae. Excel temporarily interrupts the background calculation to carry out these commands or actions and then resumes calculation.

Completion of the background calculation process takes more time if the workbook contains lots of formulae, or if you have included lots of data tables or functions. Also, the calculation process may take more time if you have linked the worksheet to other worksheets or workbooks. However, you can change the calculation process control to manual calculation (see Figure 6.12). This will free up the processor to do the actions you want done now, and delay the recalculation to a later time.

To stop automatic calculation, turn on the Manual radio button.

Figure 6.12 Manual calculation

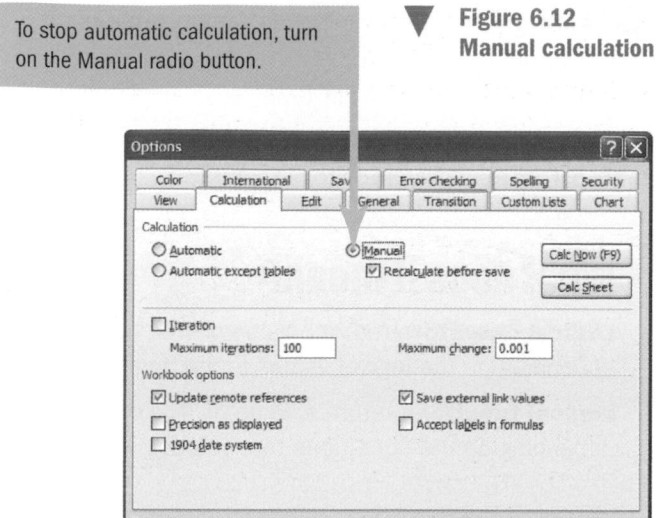

What does it mean?

A **relative cell reference** in a formula is based on the relative positions of the cell that contains the formula and the cell the formula refers to. If the position of the cell that contains the formula changes (because you copy it or move it), the cell reference in the formula changes automatically. So, if you copy the formula across rows (or down columns), the reference automatically adjusts for you.

Absolute cell referencing allows you to copy or move a formula without the cell reference changing. You can make all or part of a cell reference absolute.

Activity 6.15

Recalculation of formulae

1 Use Excel help to find out how to change when and how formulae are calculated.

2 Incorporate manual calculation into your spreadsheet project. What effect does this have during development when you make changes to data that is used in calculations?

If you don't used named ranges (page 70), the formula in cell E3 has to include absolute referencing to cell E1.

The dollar symbol before the row number means that the row number for E1 will remain the same when E2 is copied to E3 and F4, and so on. The reference to D3 will change relative to the row. So the formula in E4 is =+D4/(1+(E$1/100)).

▲ **Figure 6.13 Absolute addressing**

6.3.2.1 Relative and absolute cell references

When setting up a formula that includes a reference to another cell, you have two options: **relative** or **absolute cell referencing**. By default, new formulae use relative references.

Case study

Knits4U

Knits4U sells high-quality knitwear. Tourists may buy the jumpers without paying the VAT, provided the purchase is for export.

A stock list shows the price without VAT and, in a separate column, the price including VAT. The VAT rate is currently 17.5% but may change, and so absolute

addressing (see Figure 6.13) is used for the VAT rate, rather than embed the value in the formulae.

1 Experiment with the inclusion of the dollar symbol to check how necessary each one is, according to whether you replicate across rows or across columns.

2 Identify situations where you will need to use absolute addressing in your spreadsheet solution.

The usual mathematical functions (+, -, *, /) and many others, such as the percent sign (%) and the caret (^) for exponentiation, can be used within any expression for a formula to perform an arithmetical calculation.

For decision-making purposes, there are also **logical operators** (see Table 6.3).

The arguments should evaluate to logical values such as TRUE or FALSE, or the arguments could be arrays or references that contain logical values. If the array or reference argument contains text or empty cells, those values are ignored. If the specified range contains no logical values, the operator returns the error value: #VALUE!

You can also incorporate **logical functions** (see Table 6.4) into expressions for formulae.

What does it mean?

Logical operators return a value of True or False, depending on the logical values in the argument.

Logical functions return a value of True or False, depending on the conditions that you set up.

Logical operator	What it does	Syntax	Notes
AND	Returns TRUE if all arguments are TRUE. Returns FALSE if one or more argument is FALSE.	`AND(<logical1>,<logical2>,...)`	
OR	Returns TRUE if any argument is TRUE. Returns FALSE if all arguments are FALSE.	`OR(<logical1>,<logical2>,...)`	You can use an OR array formula to see if a value occurs in an array. (To enter an array formula, press CTRL+SHIFT+ENTER.)
NOT	Reverses the value of the argument.	`NOT(<logical>)`	If logical is FALSE, NOT returns TRUE; if logical is TRUE, NOT returns FALSE. NOT can be used when you want to make sure a value is not equal to one particular value.

Table 6.3 Logical operators

Logical function	What it does	Syntax
IF	Checks the condition of the logical test and returns one of the two values accordingly.	`IF (<logical_test>,<value_if_true>,<value_if_false>`
SUMIF	Tests the cells in cellrange1 against the criteria, and sums the corresponding cells within cellrange2.	`SUMIF(<cellrange1>, "<criteria>",<cellrange2>`

IS	Checks the type of value and returns TRUE or FALSE depending on the outcome. For example, the ISBLANK function returns the logical value TRUE if value is a reference to an empty cell; otherwise it returns FALSE.	`ISBLANK(<value>)`
		`ISERR(<value>)`
		`ISERROR(<value>)`
		`ISLOGICAL(<value>)`
		`ISNA(<value>)`
		`ISNONTEXT(<value>)`
		`ISNUMBER(<value>)`
		`ISREF(<value>)`
		`ISTEXT(<value>)`

Table 6.4 Logical functions

Activity 6.16

Formulae

1 It is possible to nest functions within a formula. Find out what **nesting** means and how much nesting is possible in Excel formulae.

2 Array formulae: use Excel Help to find out ways of using array formulae. Experiment with using array formulae and then write notes explaining how you might incorporate array formulae into a spreadsheet solution.

3 Look at the formulae that you have used in your spreadsheet project. Use a wide range of formulae to demonstrate the complexity of your spreadsheet solution. **p**₂ **(partial evidence)**

6.4 Creating efficient automated and customisable spreadsheets

One of the main advantages of spreadsheet software is that it can be customised to meet the needs of the intended user as closely as possible. Section 6.4.5 looks at how buttons and macros can be used to good effect to create a user-friendly interface. There are also many features that can be used to restrict user access to whole workbooks, spreadsheets or parts of a spreadsheet – these features are also considered in section 6.4.5.

This section first looks at the features that enable easy analysis and interpretation of the data within a spreadsheet: sorting and summarising, how to interpret numerical data, how to present data graphically and how to present combined information to support an argument.

6.4.1 Sorting and summarising data

Utilities such as ordering, sorting and filtering will show the same data in different ways.

- **Ordering** of actions can affect the outcome. For example, sorting data on three different fields will produce different results depending on which field is sorted first, second and third.
- **Sorting** rearranges the data (e.g. in one column of a spreadsheet) into a sequence (such as alphabetical or numerical, ascending or descending). It allows you to identify the smallest and largest items (at the start and end). Provided some sensible ordering has been used, when it is graphed sorted data may indicate a trend.
- **Filtering** extracts data according to some criteria, e.g. all the data relating to one particular sales person or product. It focuses on one aspect of the data.

6.4.1.1 Subtotals and pivot tables

Faced with a lot of data, statisticians tend to try to find representative data, such as an average, which can be used to describe all the data using just one representative item of data. Such single numbers can give a lot of information to the reader.

This section considers another type of single number that can inform the reader: **subtotals**.

What does it mean?

A **subtotal** is the sum of some data, which together with other subtotals makes a **grand total**.

■ Pivoting

A **pivot** table report is an interactive table that combines and compares data.

What does it mean?

To **pivot** mean to rotate about a point. In a spreadsheet, the point is a cell and the rows and columns become interchanged.

You can rotate the rows and columns to view different summaries of the source data, and display the details for areas of interest.

You might use a pivot table report when you want to analyse related totals – for example, if you have a list of figures to sum and you want to compare several facts about each figure (see Figure 6.14).

Because a pivot table report is interactive, you can change the view of the data to see more details or calculate different summaries, such as counts or averages.

Each column (or field) in your source data becomes a pivot table field that summarises multiple rows of information. For example, the Project column becomes the Project field, and each record for one value in that column, such as 'Project A', is summarised in a single 'Project A' item.

■ How to create a pivot table

1 From the main menu, select Data/PivotTable and PivotChart Report. This opens the wizard (see Figure 6.15).
2 Select the source data from your worksheet list, or you might choose an external database source.
3 In the area that is provided for the report, drag the fields offered in the list window to the outlined areas. (Excel automatically summarises the data and calculates the report for you.)
4 Customise the report by amending the layout and the format.
5 Drill down if you want to have more detailed data on display.

Activity 6.17

Pivoting

1 Experiment with pivoting so that you understand how it is done, and the effect on the data.

2 Identify options for including pivoting in your spreadsheet project. Consider whether this will be one of the techniques you demonstrate in your spreadsheet solution.

Figure 6.14 Pivoting ▶

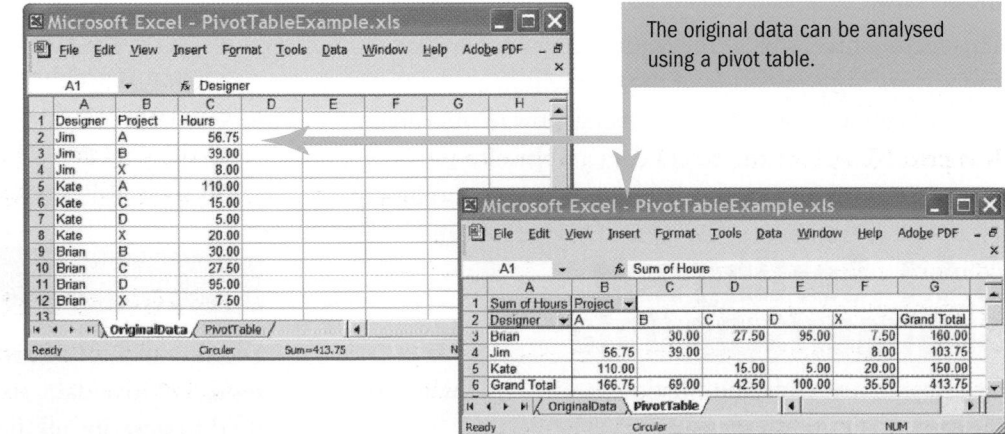

The original data can be analysed using a pivot table.

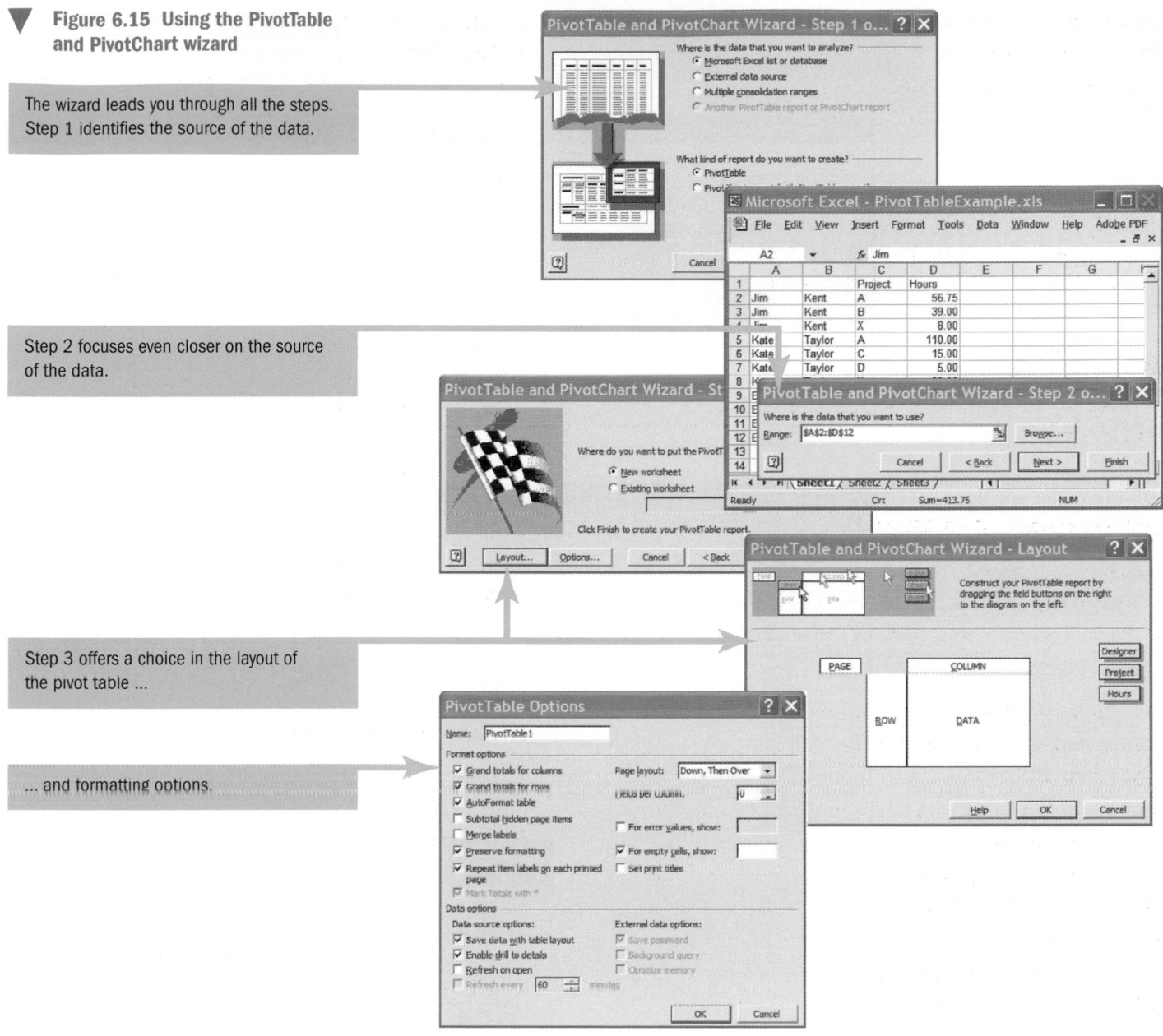

▼ **Figure 6.15 Using the PivotTable and PivotChart wizard**

The wizard leads you through all the steps. Step 1 identifies the source of the data.

Step 2 focuses even closer on the source of the data.

Step 3 offers a choice in the layout of the pivot table ...

... and formatting options.

6.4.1.2 Sorting

It is possible to sort the data in one column of a spreadsheet, while leaving the rest of the data in place. However, if each row represents a record and each column a field, then sorting in this way destroys the **integrity** of the data (see Figure 6.16).

So, if the cells contain material that needs to be kept together in rows (or columns, depending on your design), it is important to expand the selection.

It is also possible to sort on multiple fields. The order of sorting results in different groupings of the data.

What does it mean?

Maintaining **data integrity** means keeping the data accurate.

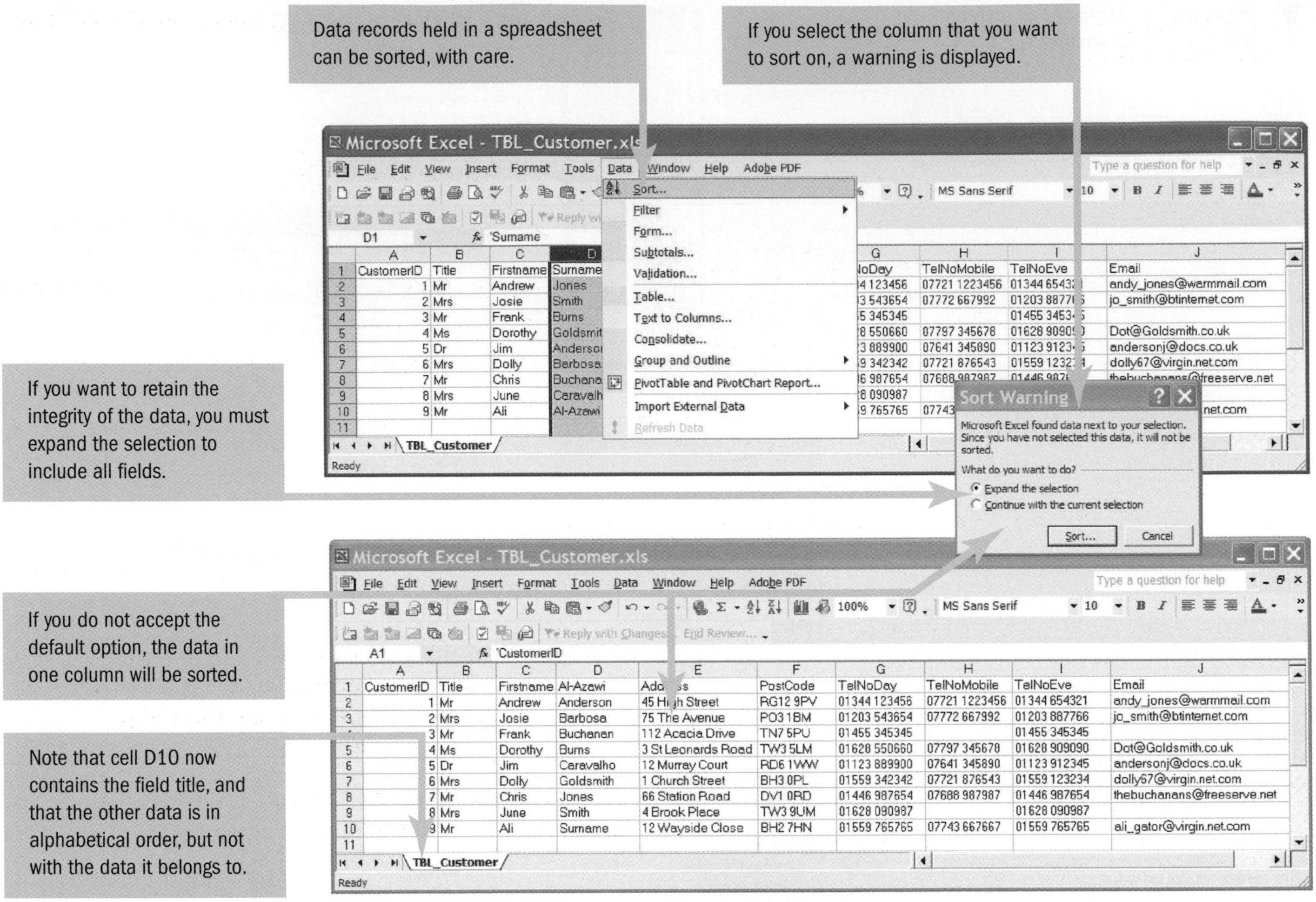

Data records held in a spreadsheet can be sorted, with care.

If you select the column that you want to sort on, a warning is displayed.

If you want to retain the integrity of the data, you must expand the selection to include all fields.

If you do not accept the default option, the data in one column will be sorted.

Note that cell D10 now contains the field title, and that the other data is in alphabetical order, but not with the data it belongs to.

Figure 6.16 Sorting data in a spreadsheet

Activity 6.18

Sorting

1 Use the Sort command (in the Data menu) to sort data in both ascending and descending order.

2 Check that you can sort on more than one field.

3 Explore other features available, such as case sensitive sorting.

4 How would you sort on a field that contains the days of the week (Mon, Tues, Wed, ...) or the months of the year (January, February, ...)?

5 Identify options for using sorting in your spreadsheet project.

6.4.1.3 Filtering

Filtering is one way of finding a subset of data from a **list**.

What does it mean?

A **list** is a series of worksheet rows that contain related data. The first row contains labels for the columns.

The filter can be used to extract information to meet a specific user need.

There are two filtering options available from the Data/Filter menu.

- The AutoFilter creates drop-down menus for each column heading and you can click on the item you want (see Figure 6.17).
- For more complex criteria, you need to use the Advanced Filter option (see Figure 6.18).

Choose AutoFilter from the Data drop-down menu, and drop-down lists are created for every column.

Clicking on a choice from the drop-down menu will result in only those rows that match the criteria being displayed.

Figure 6.17
AutoFilter

The filtered list displays only those rows of the list that match the criteria that you specify for a particular column. None of the data is lost – it is just hidden from view while the filter is on.

Remember!

Filtering does not sort the data; it just displays relevant rows according to your criteria.

To remove the effect of filtering, select Data/Filter/Show All.

Activity 6.19

Filtering

1 Experiment with filtering using both the AutoFilter option and the Advanced Filter facility.

2 Identify any filtering requirements of your spreadsheet solution.

6.4.2 Interpretation methods

Having presented the data in a more meaningful way (in a sensible order, with subtotals as appropriate), you can help your readers if you go one step further in interpreting the data for them.

You could use formatting to highlight particular data, so that the comparison of totals is made easy.

Having set up the criteria rows, select the list range of cells and then select Advanced Filter from the Data menu.

Figure 6.18
Advanced Filter

To turn the filtering off, click on Show All.

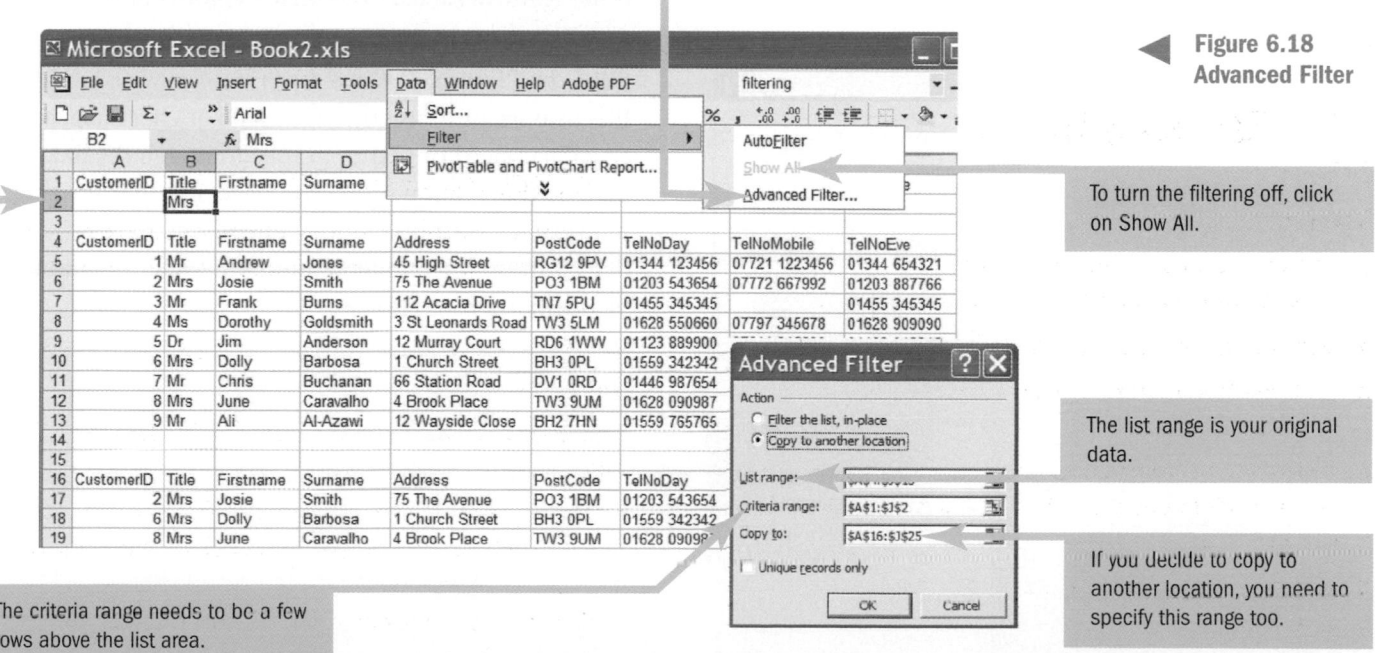

The list range is your original data.

If you decide to copy to another location, you need to specify this range too.

The criteria range needs to be a few rows above the list area.

For example, to draw attention to the data in particular cells and to create interest in your layouts, you can use colour (see Figure 6.19) for the font and/or background shading.

Choose colours that tone in together.

▲ **Figure 6.19 Using colour**

You might also outline a cell or range of cells – a border (see Figure 6.20) draws the eye to the cells and creates a focal point of the screen. Similarly, shading can be used to make some cells (such as headings) stand out.

Select Format, Format Cells and click on the Border tab.

▼ **Figure 6.20 Using borders and shading**

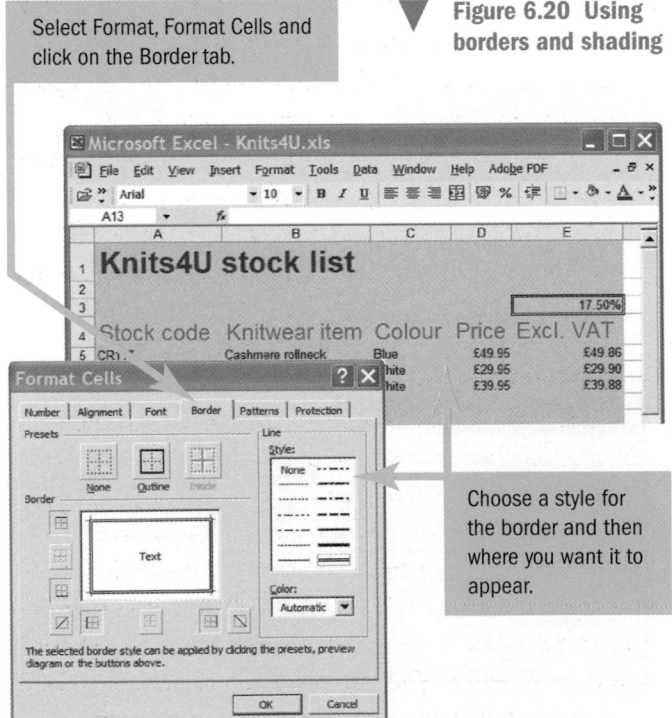

Choose a style for the border and then where you want it to appear.

You might also use trend analysis in an attempt to predict future events or to show a particular pattern in the data – this would be best displayed using charts and graphs, as explained in the next section.

Activity 6.20

Colour

1 For your spreadsheet project, review your use of colour and other techniques that can be used to improve the presentation of information in a spreadsheet.

2 Incorporate appropriate presentation techniques in your spreadsheet solution and print out examples to go in your portfolio. **p** (partial evidence)

6.4.3 Charts and graphs

Charts and graphs display information visually rather than as lists of numerical data. Statisticians rely on graphical representation of data because the shape of a graph can say a lot about the general trend of the data.

Excel offers facilities to create a range of charts and graphs. With appropriate choice of titles, labels and other features such as axis scales, colours and annotation, a chart or graph can provide a lot of the information needed at a glance.

It is important to use the right type of chart (e.g. pie chart, bar chart or scatter graph) to match the data (as discussed in section 6.1.1.2 on page 63). In preparing material for your portfolio, you will also have to demonstrate your understanding of the different options by justifying your choices.

Activity 6.21

Charts and graphs

1 Check that you are proficient in creating a range of different charts and graphs: pie charts, bar charts and line graphs.

2 Identify options for using charts and graphs in your spreadsheet project.

3 Incorporate appropriate charts and graphs in your spreadsheet solution and print out examples to go in your portfolio. **P**₄

6.4.4 Presentation

A spreadsheet full of rows or columns of numeric data soon becomes too difficult to read.

You will be designing a spreadsheet solution that will handle complex data, so it must be easy to understand, not just for you, but for anyone else reading it.

6.4.4.1 Using combined information

Often, a single source of data is not sufficient to inform the reader or to support an argument. Instead, you may need to bring together two sources, or the original data and a diagram of it, to present the reader with the full picture. For example, you may show the results of a survey presented as the numerical data and totals, together with a pic chart of relevant results.

6.4.4.2 Linking worksheets and workbooks

Sometimes, it is not practical to keep large worksheet models together in the same workbook. Instead, you can set up several worksheets and **link** them.

What does it mean?

A **link** is a reference to another workbook; it is sometimes called an **external reference**.

For example: in a spreadsheet, one worksheet contains the current selling prices of products and another worksheet shows a forecast of turnover based on those prices. Unless suitable links are set up between the two worksheets, a change in the prices of products would mean that someone has to make a change to the data in the turnover worksheet too.

Two sets of changes double the risk of input error, and the time delay between the two entries means that the data is inconsistent for that period of time.

Remember!

When you want the information in a file to be updated when the data in another file changes, use linked objects (rather than embedding). This is because the link just points to the address of the original data and will refer to that whenever the data has to be displayed or used in a calculation.

If, however, the data is held in a number of worksheets (or workbooks or software packages) that have been linked, any changes to one sheet will automatically impact on the data on other sheets. This will maintain the currency of all the data so you can be sure of an accurate and up-to-date forecast of turnover.

Although it requires greater skill when setting up formulae, there are a number of benefits to using linked worksheets.

- You can streamline the development of large, complex models by breaking them down into a series of interdependent workbooks. You can then work on the model without opening all of the related sheets. Smaller workbooks are easier to change, they don't require as much memory and they are faster to open, save and calculate.

- You can link workbooks from several users or departments and then integrate relevant data into a summary workbook. When any of the data in the source workbooks is changed, the summary workbook changes automatically.

- You can enter all the data into one or more source workbooks and then create different views of this data by setting up a report workbook that contains links to only the relevant data. For security purposes, you may restrict access to the source data but provide open access to the reports for those who need to see this information.

Formulae with links to other workbooks are displayed in two ways, depending on whether the source workbook (the workbook that supplies data to a formula) is open or closed:

- when the source is open, the link will appear as e.g.: `=SUM([Turnover.xls]Annual!C12:C23)`

Remember!

The workbook name (Turnover.xls) is shown in square brackets, followed by the worksheet name (Annual), an exclamation mark and then the relevant cell references (or named range) within that worksheet.

- when the source is not open, the link includes the entire path, e.g.: `=SUM('C:\Accounts\[Turnover.xls] Annual'!C12:C23)`.

Excel provides options for controlling the updating of the links. All linked objects are updated automatically every time you open a file and at any time that the original data file changes while your file is open. When you open a workbook, a start-up prompt automatically asks if you want to update the links – it makes sense to do so at this time. You can also manually update the links if you wish.

Activity 6.22

Presenting combined information

1 For your spreadsheet project, check that you have combined data with relevant charts and graphs in a way that suits your user. **m**₂ (partial evidence)

2 Review your use of linked data in your spreadsheet solution. Check that your structure of linked worksheets is as simple and straightforward as possible. **d**₂ (partial evidence)

6.4.5 Customisation

Some cells on a worksheet – and perhaps entire worksheets – may contain material that you do not want the end user to access and/or change.

6.4.5.1 Restricting data entry

In some circumstances you might want to restrict data entry. There are two main methods open to you:

- you can hide cells so that the user is not even aware they are there
- you can lock cells so the user can view them but not change the contents of them.

■ Hiding cells

If a user cannot see a cell, so long as there is no option to unhide it, the cell is protected. You can hide entire spreadsheets from the user.

■ How to hide/unhide a spreadsheet

1 Open a spreadsheet.
2 Select Window/Hide. The whole spreadsheet disappears.
3 If you select Window/Unhide you will be presented with a list of all hidden spreadsheets and can choose the one(s) you wish to unhide (see Figure 6.21).

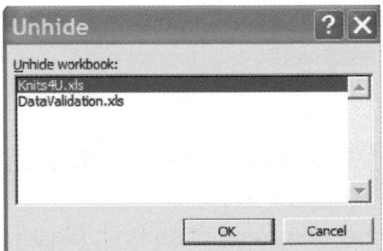

 Figure 6.21 Hiding a spreadsheet

You can also hide rows and columns within a worksheet (see Figure 6.22) so that the end user is unaware of their existence (and is therefore not tempted to change them).

■ How to hide/unhide a row/column

1 Select the row(s) or column(s).
2 Select Format/Row (or Column).
3 Click on Hide. The row/column will disappear from view.

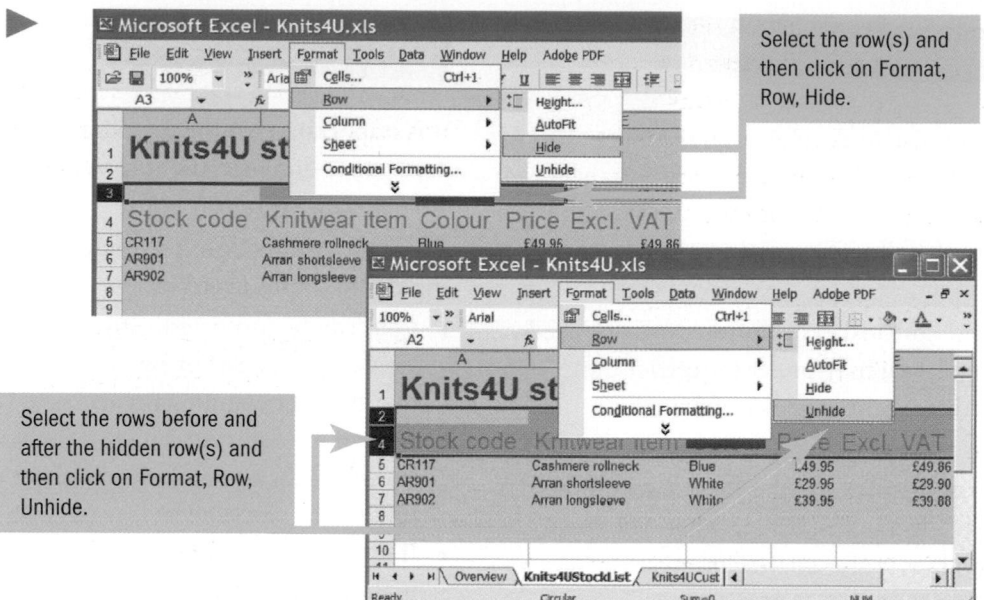

Figure 6.22 Hiding a row

Select the row(s) and then click on Format, Row, Hide.

Select the rows before and after the hidden row(s) and then click on Format, Row, Unhide.

4 The row numbers (or column letters) are no longer consecutive so you can see where the hidden rows (or columns) are.

5 To unhide a row (or column), select the rows (or columns) immediately before and after. Then click on Format/Row (or Column) and choose Unhide.

■ Locking cells

If you want the user to see the contents of a cell but not be able to change them, you need to lock the cell. The method involves unlocking the cells that you want them to be able to change and then protecting the whole sheet using a password.

■ How to lock cells

1 Switch to the worksheet that you plan to protect.

2 Select the cells that you want the user to be able to change (e.g. data entry cells) then select Format/Cells.

3 On the Protection tab, clear the Locked check box (see Figure 6.23) and click OK.

4 At the same time, hide any formulae that you do not want the user to see by choosing Format/Cells/Protection/Hidden for each one.

5 Then on the Tools menu, choose Protection/Protect Sheet. Enter a password for this sheet. (Make sure you do not forget this!)

6 In the same dialogue box, tick what you want to allow in the 'Allow all users of this worksheet to ...' list.

7 Confirm the password and click OK.

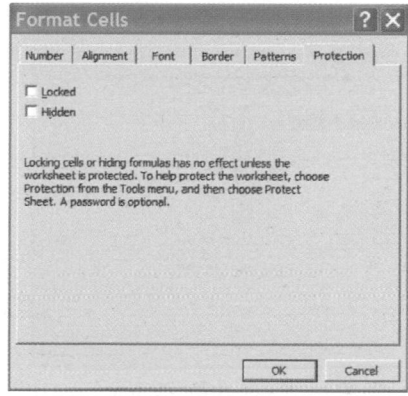

▲ Figure 6.23 Protecting cells

Activity 6.23

Hide and lock

1 Explore the options to lock or hide data in your spreadsheet project. Consider which of your cells ought to be protected from users and which ought to be hidden from view.

2 Document your decisions and implement them. Test your spreadsheet solution to make sure that your changes have worked correctly.

The software that you use to develop a spreadsheet solution provides all the tools that you need to change the structure of the worksheet, to format the data and to present the data graphically. These features appear in toolbars and menus.

The end user of your spreadsheet solution does not need all these tools. Indeed, you may prefer to restrict the user's actions by reducing the number of features available within the software.

As with other Microsoft software, the Tools/Customize option (see Figure 6.24) lets you decide what will appear on any standard toolbar. It also allows you to set up a custom toolbar.

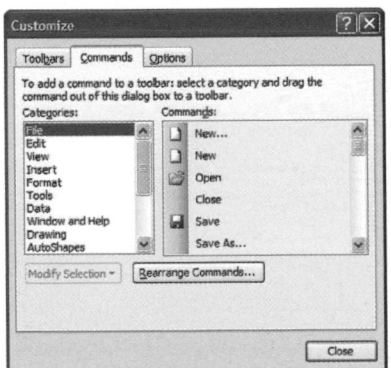

▲ **Figure 6.24 Tools/Customize option**

Activity 6.24

Customising a spreadsheet using toolbars

1 Check that you are familiar with which commands appear on which toolbars within Excel. Customise your Excel workspace to include only those commands that you use frequently during spreadsheet development.

2 For your spreadsheet project, which commands would your user need?

3 Set up one or more custom toolbars to present all these commands to your user. **p**₆

It is important that the data that goes into a worksheet is accurate. Otherwise, the information gleaned from that worksheet is compromised.

There are a number of techniques for validating data input and trapping errors.

● Cells can be protected, either by hiding them from view (see page 86) or by locking them (see page 87) so that the user cannot gain access to them.

● Instead of requiring data to be entered twice, you can transfer data from one spreadsheet to another by linking the worksheets (see page 85).

● If data has to be entered, it is possible to restrict data input so that only acceptable data values can be input.

Data validation begins when you first design your spreadsheet and decide what goes where. The user interface design can include data entry forms with form controls such as list boxes and drop-down menus which force users to enter valid data. Excel also provides a wide range of validation options that can be applied to a cell or range of cells. You can:

● set upper and lower limits for numeric data entries (e.g. so a month number must be between 1 and 12)

● compare the entry against items in a list

● specify a time range and/or a data range

● limit the number of characters accepted in a text string to prevent strings that are too long ruining a layout elsewhere on your spreadsheet

● calculate what is allowed according to the contents of another cell – for example, if the cell contains an amount of credit available, then a loan for anything higher than that would be rejected

● use a formula to calculate what is allowed – in the Formula box (see Figure 6.25), the formula will have a TRUE (valid) or FALSE (invalid) value according to the data that is entered.

For some data, it may be necessary to insist that an entry is made before the entire form is accepted. For example, if an entry is zero, you may insist that the user enters the number 0, rather than just leave the entry blank.

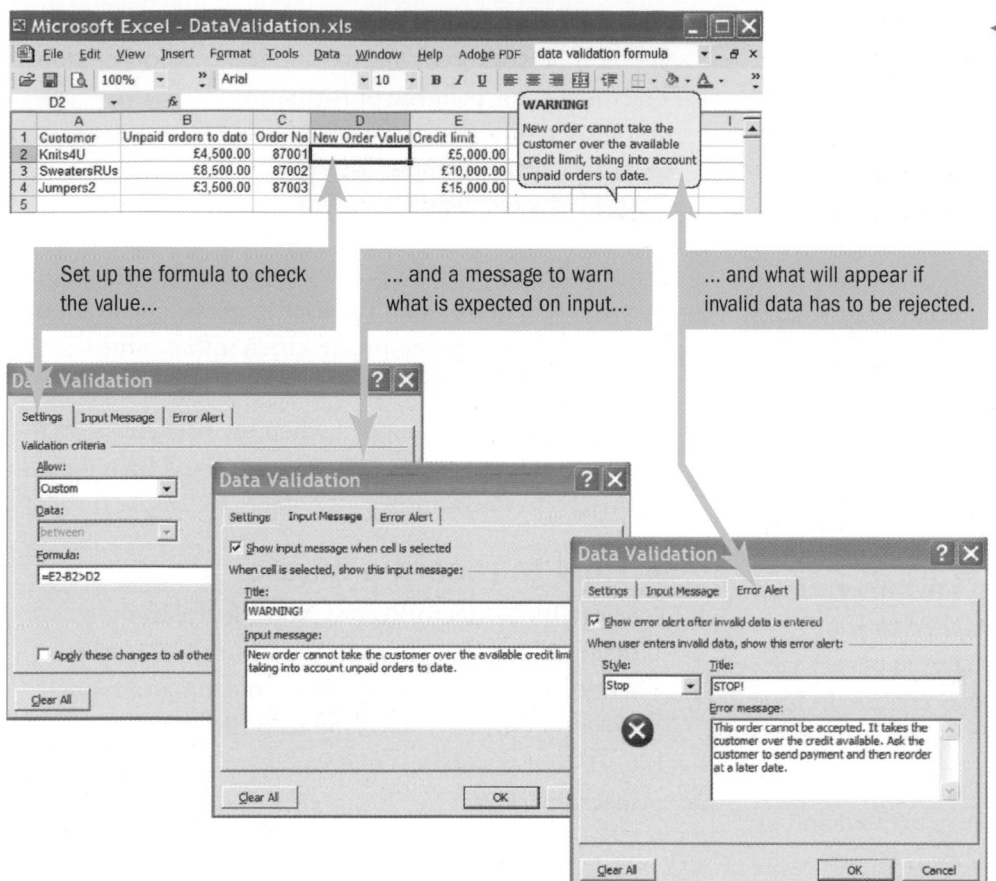

◀ Figure 6.25 Using a formula to validate data entry

Set up the formula to check the value...

... and a message to warn what is expected on input...

... and what will appear if invalid data has to be rejected.

■ How to restrict data input

1 Select the cell(s) for which you want to restrict data input.
2 Select Data/Validation and, on the Settings tab, set what you will allow.
3 According to your entry in the Allow: box, you then need to give further information as guided by the dialogue box (see Figure 6.26).

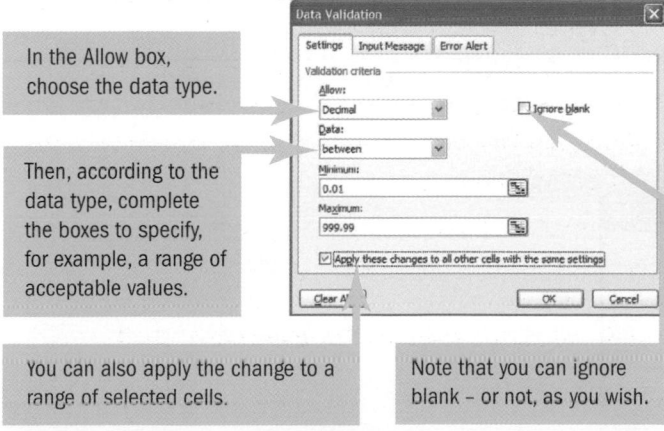

In the Allow box, choose the data type.

Then, according to the data type, complete the boxes to specify, for example, a range of acceptable values.

You can also apply the change to a range of selected cells.

Note that you can ignore blank – or not, as you wish.

▲ Figure 6.26 Decimal validation

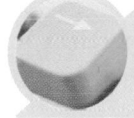

Activity 6.25

Data validation

1 Explore the Data Validation dialogue boxes to see what options are available to you.

2 For your spreadsheet project, consider which data entries require validation and which would benefit from having restrictions set.

3 Implement your validation decisions, document them and test that your validation works. **p** (partial evidence) **m** (partial evidence)

6.4.6 Automation

The end user of a spreadsheet may be proficient in using the software, but the more that you automate processes, the easier it should be for the user. If a task is to be repeated, it can be automated with a **macro**.

What does it mean?

A **macro** is a series of commands and functions that are stored in a Microsoft Visual Basic module and can be run whenever the user needs to perform the task.

When you record a macro, Excel remembers data about each step you take (what menu options you choose, what values you select, and so on) and stores this information about the macro in a new module attached to your workbook. When you run the macro later, it plays back the commands – including any mistakes you might have made when recording it!

After you have recorded a macro, you can use the Visual Basic Editor to view the code you have generated and to correct errors or change what the macro does. The Visual Basic Editor is designed to make writing and editing macro code easy – plenty of online help is provided, so it is not necessary to learn how to program or use the Visual Basic language to make simple changes to your macros.

This section considers two types of automation: the creation of workbook macros and the creation of global macros, e.g. for printing or formatting.

6.4.6.1 Workbook macros

Within the user interface, you can automate procedures by providing buttons for the user to press. The event of a particular button being pressed then initiates the appropriate procedure.

For the procedure to happen when the user clicks on the button, you first have to create a macro and then assign the macro to the button.

■ How to record a macro

1 Select Tools/Macro/Record New Macro. In the dialogue box that appears (see Figure 6.27), enter a name for your macro. Choose a meaningful name!
2 Click on OK. This starts the recording process.
3 Carry out the actions that you want to make the macro perform.
4 When you have completed the actions, click on Tools/Macro/Stop Recording.
5 Test the macro by running it: select Tools/Macro/Macros, then from the list offered, select your new macro and click on Run.
6 When you are sure your macro works as required, you can assign it to a button.

The same macro could be assigned to more than one button in your spreadsheet solution, so if there are actions that are used frequently, plan your macros carefully.

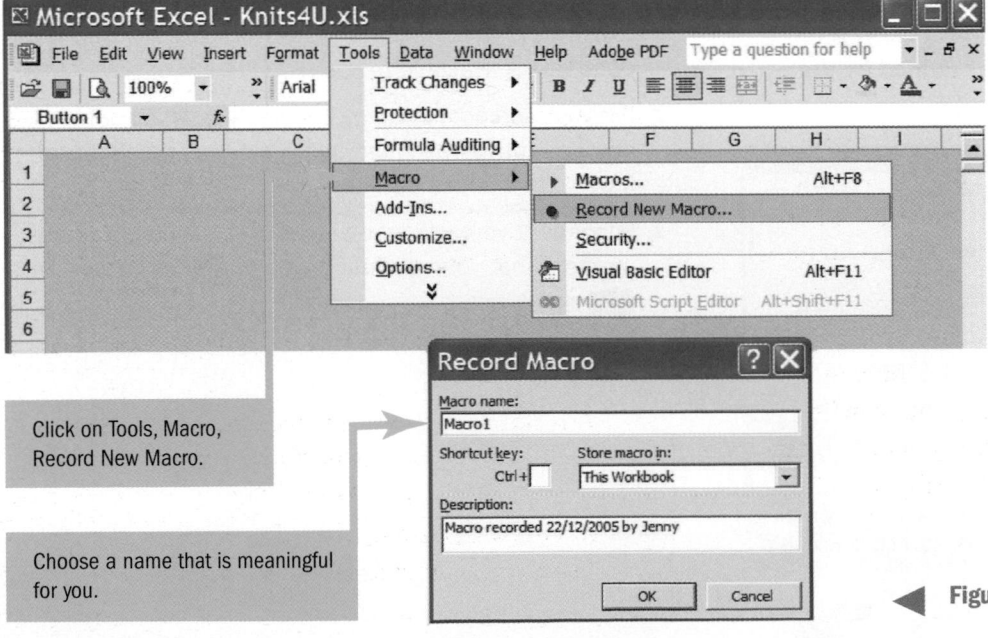

Click on Tools, Macro, Record New Macro.

Choose a name that is meaningful for you.

Figure 6.27 Recording a macro

■ How to assign a macro to a button

1 Click on the Button icon on the Forms toolbar.
2 Drag the cursor to draw the button where you want it.
3 When you release the mouse, the Assign Macro dialogue box appears (see Figure 6.28).
4 Select the macro you have already created and tested.
5 Relabel the button so that the name clearly indicates what the macro does (e.g. Top of Page for a macro that takes you to the top of the page).
6 Test the button.

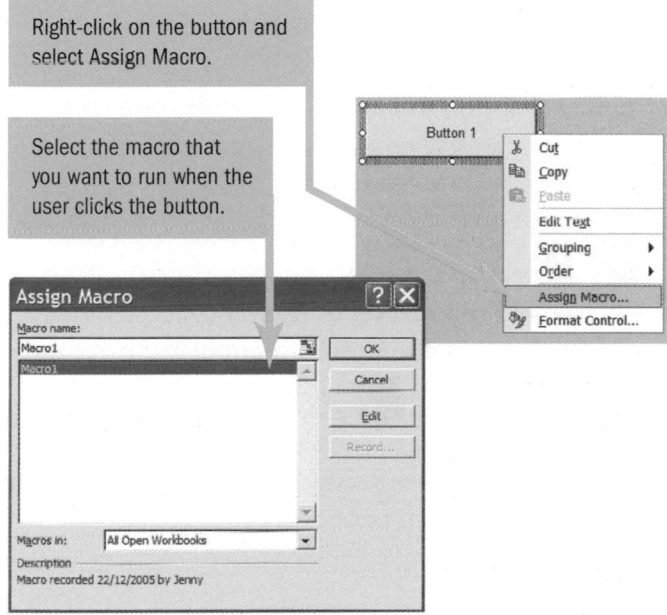

Right-click on the button and select Assign Macro.

Select the macro that you want to run when the user clicks the button.

Figure 6.28 Assigning a macro to a button

6.4.6.2 Global macros

As well as editing the macro code, the Visual Basic Editor also allows you to copy a macro from one module to another. You could even copy macros between different workbooks. If you need to, you can rename the modules that store the macros or rename your macros.

Microsoft Excel provides safeguards that help to protect your computer against viruses that can be transmitted by macros. If you need to share macros, they can be certified with a digital signature so that other users can verify that each macro is from a trustworthy source.

WATCH OUT!

Whenever you open a workbook that contains macros, you should verify their source before you enable them.

Activity 6.26

Macros

1 Using the **How to record a macro** steps on the previous page, experiment with setting up macros in Excel. Identify how you might use macros within your spreadsheet project to introduce an element of automation. Discuss this with your teacher.

2 Customise your spreadsheet solution to automate some aspect of the processing for the end user. Choose two customisation techniques and two automation techniques that you have used, and write notes comparing them.

3 To demonstrate your skills in converting from Excel format to another format, export part of your spreadsheet solution into another software package, such as Word. **p**₅

STOP Test your knowledge

1 Explain these terms: ordering, sorting, filtering, hide, lock.

2 What is a pivot table? What does it mean to pivot a table?

3 Explain how you can protect the integrity of data during a sort.

4 What kind of data is best presented using a pie chart? Under what circumstances might you display data as a scatter graph?

5 What is a macro? How can macros be used to customise a spreadsheet solution?

Preparation for assessment

The assessment tasks in this unit are based on the following scenario.

Ridgeway is a large college offering a full range of academic courses, together with vocational courses such as plumbing, carpentry and so on. It also offers evening and weekend courses as part of its adult education programme.

There are more than 60 members of staff, working full- or part-time, together with 1600 students. The administration team at Ridgeway want to use spreadsheet software to keep track of student enrolments, class sizes and attendance. They also want to keep track of staff timetables and workloads.

Each department has a budget for purchasing essential materials such as equipment and books. Each head of department is responsible for keeping within budget on an annual basis, but the bursar would like to use a spreadsheet to check the cash flow implications of any spending on a monthly basis.

Task 1 (P1, P2, P3, P4, D2)

Design a spreadsheet to meet the needs of the staff at Ridgeway.

- Your spreadsheet should be sufficiently complex to need: complex formulae, including a range of functions; the processing of large data sets; a design that involves multiple pages and linked data. **p₁ p₂**

- Format your spreadsheet using bold, italic, borders and shading. Use appropriate column alignment and a consistent design. **p₁**

- Include, as appropriate, at least one of the following features to help make decisions and judgements about data: subtotals; pivot tables; data sorting; data comparison. **p₁**

- Incorporate sorting and summarising techniques to interpret the data within your spreadsheet. **p₃**

- Create relevant graphical output from your spreadsheet. Choose a chart or graph type that is appropriate for your data. Choose appropriate titles, labels, axis scales and colours. **p₄**

- Write a report justifying the structure of your spreadsheet, including your formatting decisions, and the choices you made in the production of charts and graphs. **d₂**

Task 2 (P5, M2)

Use conversion facilities to export the contents of your spreadsheet to an alternative format. Incorporate this material in one or more of the reports that you are preparing for these tasks. **p**5

Explain, with the use of examples, how data can be manipulated to aid interpretation. **m**2

Task 3 (P6, M3)

Customise or automate one aspect of your spreadsheet and provide full documentation of what you achieved. Select one of the techniques from section 6.4 to evidence this objective. Choose from: hiding and protecting; data validation; a macro. **p**6

Use and compare two customisation and two automation techniques and write brief notes on what you discovered. **m**3

Task 4 (M1, D1)

Check the accuracy of your spreadsheet using a range of appropriate techniques and explain the choice of techniques used. **m**1

Evaluate your spreadsheet, its fitness for purpose and its effectiveness in providing information to meet a particular user need. **d**1

Client Side Customisation of Web Pages

Introduction

Increasingly, websites consist of sophisticated, interactive web pages. A key feature is that the code is stored on the user's computer rather than on the web server.

In this unit, you will learn about web page layout using cascading style sheets (CSS) and interactivity using a scripting language, such as JavaScript or VBScript.

After completing this unit, you should be able to achieve these outcomes:

- Understand the fundamentals of CSS

- Understand the fundamentals of a scripting language

- Be able to control the layout of a web page using CSS

- Be able to create an interactive web page

- Be able to test and review a web page which uses CSS and JavaScript.

The examples for a scripting language given throughout this unit are in JavaScript.

Grading criteria	Activity	Page number
To achieve a pass grade the evidence must show that the learner is able to:		
p₁ Describe three implementation styles of CSS, showing how they are called from HTML	10.1, PFA	97, 125
p₂ Describe the features of the box model for CSS and describe the selectors and how they are used	10.2, PFA	99, 125
p₃ Describe the main features of the chosen scripting language and outline some typical uses	PFA	125
p₄ Design, create and test web pages using CSS to control layout	10.3, 10.11, 10.12, 10.13, 10.14, 10.15, 10.16, 10.17, 10.25, PFA	101, 112, 113, 114, 116, 117, 124, 125
p₅ Design, create and test web pages using scripts to implement interactivity	10.18, 10.19, 10.20, 10.21, 10.22, 10.23, 10.24, 10.25, PFA	119, 120, 121, 122, 123, 124, 125
To achieve a merit grade the evidence must show that, in addition to the pass criteria, the learner is able to:		
m₁ Compare two methods of accessing external CSS script	10.1, 10.17, PFA	97, 117, 125
m₂ Clarify, with examples, the differences in implementation of two aspects of CSS	PFA	125
m₃ Explain how web pages using scripts are implemented in two different browsers	10.26, PFA	124, 125
To achieve a distinction grade the evidence must show that, in addition to the pass and merit criteria, the learner is able to:		
d₁ Change the layout of a web page by changing the external CSS	10.12, 10.13, PFA	112, 113, 125
d₂ Show how existing interactivity could be extended or additional interactivity introduced into a web page	10.20, 10.21, 10.22, 10.23, 10.24, PFA	119, 120, 121, 122, 123, 125
d₃ Evaluate the impact of using CSS to control layout	10.24, PFA	123, 125

Note: 'PFA' stands for 'Preparation for assessment'.

It is good practice to use the same layout and styling throughout a website. This is known as the **house style**.

CSS allows you to create a standard layout and style which can be easily used on each web page in the site. Due to this standardisation, it is also easier to alter and maintain the site. For example, in HTML, to change the font colour of all the titles to white would involve changing each one individually. When using CSS, only one value would need to be changed, and the change would be immediately applied throughout the whole site for every title.

What does it mean?

House style is a standard design that is carried throughout an organisation's website. It can also be extended throughout the business, e.g. on promotional brochures, letterheads, etc.

CSS stands for **cascading style sheets**. This is a form of web language which can be used to standardise the layout throughout a website.

10.1.1 Characteristics of CSS

CSS is made up of a series of **styles**, each of which is given a name so that it can be recognised throughout the code.

The style is defined in the CSS, and then used in the HTML. The style **tags** are placed around the content which is to be affected (see Figure 10.1).

What does it mean?

A **style** is a group of formatting decisions to be applied together as defined in the CSS. For example, to have text display as red and centred could be a style.

What does it mean?

Tags are elements of web page code, either in HTML or CSS. Usually they are written between angle brackets < and > to indicate that they are code words.

```
<html>
<head>
<link rel=stylesheet type="text/css" href="styles.css">
</head>

<body>
<h1>Example of h1</h1>
<h2>Example of h2</h2>

</body>
</html>
```

▲ **Figure 10.1 CSS tags used around text in HTML code**

10.1.1.1 Implementation styles

CSS can be written into the HTML in three ways: inline, header and external.

- **Inline:** the CSS is defined in the same area of the code as that to which it is to be applied:

```
<p style="background: red; color: white;
font-family: Times New Roman;">An example
of inline CSS</p>
```

This code will produce:

> An example of inline CSS

- **Header:** the CSS is defined in the **head** section of each web page and applied throughout the **body**:

```
<head>
<style>
h1 {
background: red;
color: white;
font-family: Times New Roman;
}
</style>
</head>
```

```
<body>
<h1>An example of header CSS</h1>
</body>
```
This code will produce:

> An example of header CSS

What does it mean?

The **head** of the web page is the part of the code where all the styling and other invisible parts are written.

The **body** is where all the elements that are visible on the web page are coded.

- **External:** the CSS is defined in a separate file, which all web pages can reference (see Figure 10.2). This is a .css file, rather than an .html file. There are two lines which can be put in the head of the HTML to link to external CSS pages:

```
<link rel="stylesheet" type="text/css"
href="styles.css" />
```
or
```
<style type="text/css" title="currentStyle"
media="screen">
@import "styles.css";
</style>
```

Both the header and external methods can also be called **block** methods. This is because the CSS is grouped together in a block, rather than distributed throughout the code.

Activity 10.1

Implementation of CSS

1 Create an example of each method of using CSS in HTML.

2 Print each example and annotate them to show how the CSS links to the HTML.

3 Compare the two methods of accessing external CSS.

10.1.1.2 Box model

CSS is used to create layouts on web pages. Using this method, the pages can be viewed in any browser or at any screen resolution and the integrity of the design should remain. This is because the layout is recalculated on each opening. The resulting web page can therefore be designed very accurately; in fact, it can be **pixel perfect**.

What does it mean?

Pixel perfect is a term used in the design field to describe graphics that are accurate down to the very last pixel.

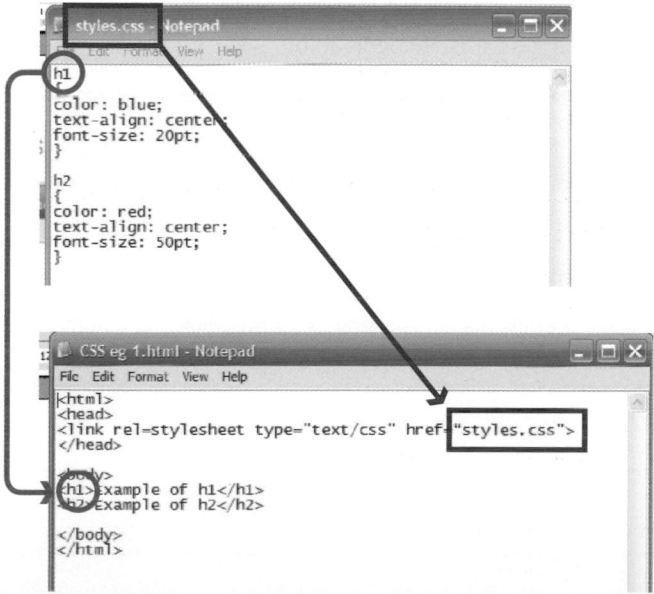

◄ Figure 10.2 A .css file applied to an .html file

The CSS **box model** structures the web page in a similar way to a table. Margins, borders, padding and content are each defined (see Figure 10.3).

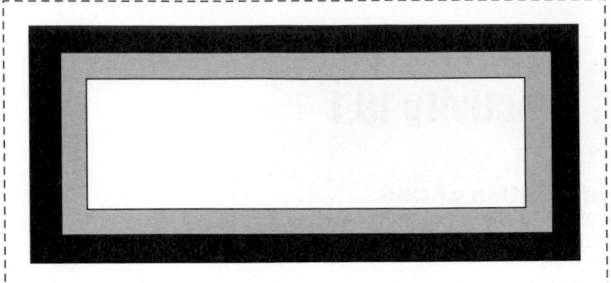

▲ Figure 10.3 Layout of box model elements

Four elements can be defined in the box model:

- The **content area** is where the text and images which will be displayed on the web page should be placed. There can be more than one content area.
- The **padding** is the blank space around the content area, so that the content is not displayed right up to the edges of the border.
- The **border** is the design surrounding the padding and content area.
- The **margin** is the blank space around everything so that the box does not display right up to the edges of the screen.

The padding, border and margin are optional and, if not defined, are set at a default value of zero. At this value they would be invisible.

The height and width can be defined for each area. Different widths and heights can be set for top, bottom, left and right. It is even possible for margins to have negative values.

Setting the dimensions can be done using a variety of measurements, the most popular being pixels and percentages. Defining the layout by percentage of the screen is the most effective for maintaining layout consistency.

As with formatting statements, layout statements can be written inline or using a block method (header or external).

10.1.1.3 Selectors

Each style that is defined in CSS consists of a **selector**, a **property** and a **value**.

What does it mean?

A **selector** is similar to the title of the style. The **property** is what is being changed. The **value** is the amount by which it is being changed.

For example, h1 {color:red} will create the rule that wherever h1 is used, the colour will be red.

Table 10.1 shows some of the selectors available and how they would be implemented in a web page.

Remember!

For class and id selectors, any label can be applied after the dot or hash. It is advisable to use sensible naming so it is recognisable.

Type of selector	CSS	HTML
Headings	h1 {color:red}	`<h1>A red heading</h1>`
Paragraph	p{color:red}	`<p>Some red text.</p>`
Anchor (as in "a href")	a:hover{color:red}	This should overrule the default settings for hyperlinks, so that the hyperlinks turn red when the cursor hovers over them.
Class	.alert{color:red}	`<p class=alert>Some red text.</p>` `<span class=alert>Some red text.</span>`
ID	#alert{color:red}	`<p id=alert>Some red text.</p>` `<span id=alert>Some red text.</span>`

Table 10.1 CSS selectors

A class can be used for formatting that needs to be used several times, whereas an id is used for individual instances of formatting only.

Activity 10.2

Box model and selectors

1 Describe the four parts of the box model and how they are used.

2 Describe the three parts of each style and how they are used.

10.1.1.4 Accessing CSS from HTML

External CSS needs to be accessed from every web page in which it is to be used. There are two methods of connecting to it:

```
<link rel="stylesheet" type="text/css"
href="styles.css" />
```

or:

```
<style type="text/css" title="currentStyle"
media="screen">
@import "styles.css";
</style>
```

The appropriate line needs to be inserted into the head section of each web page.

10.1.2 Uses of CSS

CSS can be used to alter the layout and formatting of any web page. Here are some examples of the hundreds of properties than can be changed (using the header method).

- Background colour:
```
<head>
<style>
body {background-color: yellow}
</style>
</head>
```

- Background images:
```
<head>
<style>
body {background-image: url('picture.jpg')}
</style>
</head>
```

Remember!

The image must be in the same folder as the web page; otherwise the whole file location must be included.

- Formatting text:
```
<html>
<head>
<style>
h1{
font-family: serif;
font-style: italic;
font-weight: bold;
font-size: 200px;
color: green;
}
</style>
</head>

<body>
<h1>Formatted example text</h1>
</body>
</html>
```

- Applying borders:
```
<html>
<head>
<style>
.border1 {border-style: groove}
.border2 {border-style: double solid}
.border3 {border-style: double solid groove}
</style>
</head>
```

```
<body>
<p class="border1">Border 1 example text</p>
<p class="border2">Border 2 example text</p>
<p class="border3">Border 3 example text</p>
</body>
</html>
```

- Applying padding:

```
<html>
<head>
<style>
.padding1 {padding: 1cm}
.padding2 {padding: 0.5cm 1.5cm}
</style>
</head>

<body>
<table border="1">
<tr>
<td class="padding1">
Padding 1 example text
</td>
</tr>
</table>
<br>
<table border="1">
<tr>
<td class="padding2">
Padding 2 example text
</td>
</tr>
</table>
</body>
</html>
```

- Heading styles:

```
<html>
<head>
<style>
h1 {
background: red;
color: white;
font-family: times new roman;
font-style: italic;
}
h2 {
```

```
text-align: center;
text-decoration: underline;
font-size: xx-large;
font-weight: bold;
}
</style>
</head>

<body>
<h1>Heading level 1</h1>
<br>
<h2>Heading level 2</h2>
</body>
</html>
```

- Positioning elements:

```
<html>
<head>
<style>
.position_relative
{
position:relative;
left:20px;
}
.position_absolute
{
position:absolute;
left:200px;
top:200px;
}
</style>
</head>

<body>
Not positioned example text
<p class="position_relative">Relatively
positioned example text</p>
<p class="position_absolute">Absolutely
positioned example text</p>
</body>
</html>
```

- Creating columns:

```
<html>
<head>
<style>
.nav {
```

```
    width: 220px;
    padding: 10px;
    float:left;
    }
.content {
    padding: 10px;
    margin-left: 230px;
    border-left: 1px solid #006;
    }
.footer {
    border-top: 1px solid #006;
    text-align: right;
    }
```

```
</style>
</head>

<body>
Example text unformatted
<div class="nav">Example text in nav div</div>
<div class="content">Example text in content
div</div>
    <div class="footer">Example text in footer
div</div>
    </body>
    </html>
```

Test your knowledge

1 What does CSS stand for?

2 Describe the three methods of using CSS with HTML.

3 What are the two methods of linking HTML with CSS in another file?

4 Describe the structure of the box model.

5 Name five types of CSS selector.

Activity 10.3

Uses of CSS

1 Design and create each of the examples of the uses of CSS given above and make notes on how they affect the formatting.

2 Try altering the values and make notes on how this alters the formatting.

This Activity should be completed in conjunction with Activities 10.12, 10.13, 10.14 and 10.15 (see pages 112–114).

10.2 The fundamentals of a scripting language

Scripting languages create **interactivity** on a web page. For example, you might want to create a form for users to fill in and then send them a message saying thank you once they have submitted the form. Another example could be a user typing a product name into a search bar and the computer displaying the relevant product from its catalogue. Essentially, interactivity involves data being sent from user to computer and vice versa.

Interactivity is not only useful but is now expected by customers. **Static** sites are seen as old-fashioned and useless.

What does it mean?

Interactivity is two-way communication between user and computer.

A **static** website has only fixed information on it. If it is to be altered, the designer needs to change the code and then upload the amended page to the web server; a laborious task.

▲ **Interactivity is expected by visitors to websites**

Users on the whole prefer using **dynamic** websites, and they are also easier to maintain once they are **live** on the Internet.

What does it mean?

A **dynamic** website is one that is updated live online and including interactivity. Usually, there are scripting languages and/or databases involved.

A website goes **live** when it is uploaded to be viewed on the Internet.

There is a wide variety of scripting languages available. In order to provide consistency, all examples of scripting code given in this unit are in JavaScript.

10.2.1 Characteristics of scripting languages

Scripting languages are inserted into HTML between `<script>` and `</script>` tags. They usually occur in the head of the HTML.

```
<head>
<script>
SCRIPTING LANGUAGE WOULD BE INSERTED HERE
</script>
</head>
```

The scripting language is put into the head section because an HTML page is **interpreted** as it is loaded into the browser – the browser loads each line as it encounters it. If the scripting language is below the visible elements of the web page, it will run after all the elements have been loaded into the browser.

What does it mean?

HTML is **interpreted** to convert the language the developer can understand to a language the computer understands.

10.2.1.1 Nature of language

Scripting languages can be object-oriented and event driven.

With object-oriented languages, the code is broken into **objects** (see Figure 10.4). Each object knows about itself and what it can do. Each object is a self-contained module. By knowing what it can do, an object knows what it can interact with.

With languages that are event driven, the code is broken into **events** (see Figure 10.5). An event is any action.

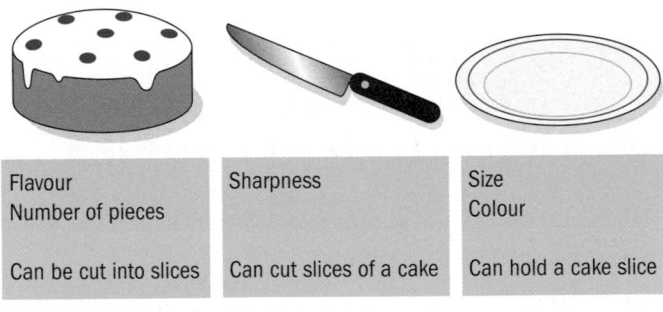

Flavour Number of pieces	Sharpness	Size Colour
Can be cut into slices	Can cut slices of a cake	Can hold a cake slice

▲ **Figure 10.4** In object-oriented languages, the code is broken into objects

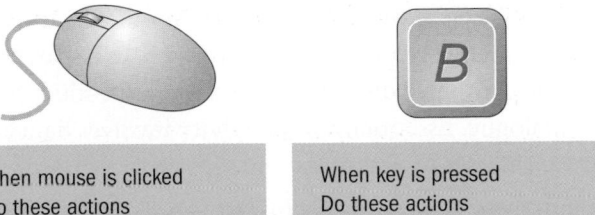

When mouse is clicked Do these actions	When key is pressed Do these actions

▲ **Figure 10.5** In event driven languages, the code is broken into events

It could be a click of a mouse, a press of a key, a movement or the transmission of data. The code is triggered into running when a particular action happens.

10.2.1.2 Objects

An **object** is a type of data that knows things about itself (its properties) and it knows how to do things (methods). There are many objects that already exist in scripting languages and it is also possible to create new ones.

What does it mean?

An **object** is a special type of data that has properties and methods.

This is an example in JavaScript of the String object:

```
<script>
hw="Hello world"
document.write(hw.length)
</script>
```

The output on the screen would be **11**, as 10 characters plus the space make up the length of the string called hw. For more detail see section 10.2.3.7 on page 110.

10.2.1.3 Methods

Each object knows which **methods** it can carry out.

What does it mean?

A **method** is an action that can be performed by an object.

This is an example in JavaScript of the String object:

```
<script>
hw="Hello world"
document.write(hw.toUpperCase())
</script>
```

The output on the screen would be **HELLO WORLD**, as the method UpperCase has forced the whole word to be in upper case.

10.2.1.4 Handling events

Events are actions that are sensed by the script and that cause a reaction. Events can include a mouse button being clicked or a keyboard button being pressed. For more detail see section 10.2.3.5 on page 108.

What does it mean?

An **event** is an action that can cause a reaction in the code.

10.2.1.5 Hiding scripts from older browsers

Some older browsers do not support scripting languages or the activities that they create. Therefore, to prevent confusion, it is best to hide the scripting language from older browsers. This can be done by putting the script within HTML comments (see section 10.4.4.1 on page 122). For example:

```
<script>
<!--
INSERT SCRIPT HERE
//--!>
</script>
```

Browsers that can interpret script will see the <script> tags and interpret the code between them. Browsers that cannot interpret script will ignore the script tags and also the HTML comments, therefore preventing the browsers becoming confused when trying to interpret script as HTML.

10.2.1.6 Security issues

When using client side scripting, there is an inevitable security implication. As code is being executed on the user's computer, a possible entry point for hackers is opened up. Reading from and writing to client files make both the website and the client's computer vulnerable. In addition, by using client side scripting, it is possible for unscrupulous website owners to read the content of the client's computer. They can perform operations on the computer such as data mining, opening applications and reading other browser windows.

10.2.1.7 Including scripts inside HTML

Script can be placed anywhere within a web page, depending on what result is desired. Because HTML is interpreted, it is executed line by line. Script in the body is run at the point it occurs in the code. Functions can be placed anywhere, as they are not run until they are called. Script needs to be placed between <script> </script> tags for the browser to know it is no longer interpreting HTML, but a scripting language.

Activity 10.4

Features of scripting languages

1 Describe how scripting languages can be embedded into HTML.

2 JavaScript is an object-oriented scripting language. Explain what that means.

3 VBScript is an event driven scripting language. Explain what that means.

10.2.2 Uses of a scripting language

Scripting languages provide interactivity, which is a vital part of modern web design. Table 10.2 shows some of the actions that can be performed using scripting languages.

Alerts	Pop-ups to alert the user to something.
Confirming choices	Feedback to ensure the user has made the choices wanted.
Prompting the user	A message to help the user or to ask for an action.
Redirecting the user	To move the user to another page.
Browser detection	When a user loads a website, it can detect which browser they are using and load the optimum viewing settings.
Creating rollovers	To add more visual interactivity, a web page can use **rollover buttons**.
Checking/validating input	Examines what a user has entered – e.g. if they have entered words in a search box, the script can read it and search the website's databases.
Handling forms	Allows users to fill in forms and submit them, either for the website to process or by email to an inbox.
Maintaining **cookies**	Deposits cookies on a user's computer, then reads them when the user returns to the site. It also can ensure that the user has the latest cookies for that site.

Table 10.2   Scripting language uses

What does it mean?

Rollover buttons work as normal buttons on a web page, but when the mouse hovers over them, the image or text changes.

Cookies are packets of data exchanged between the client computer and the web server for authentication or personalisation of a website.

10.2.3 Scripting language constructs

As with any code, scripting languages need to use the correct construction for them to work. This includes the **syntax**.

What does it mean?

Syntax is the grammar of a programming language – it sets out the order in which words must appear within the code.

10.2.3.1 Syntax

It is important for any programming language that the syntax is correct.

The dot operator is used to allow an object to use a method. For example, for the object String to use the method replace, you need to use the dot as follows:

```
<script>
str="First message"
document.write(str.replace(/First/,"Second"))
</script>
```

Programming languages use **variables** to store a variety of data including text and numbers.

What does it mean?

A **variable** is used to store data and is given a name, e.g. the data "Fred" might be stored in the variable "firstname".

Each variable must have a unique name within that script. Variable names cannot contain spaces or begin with a number. It is good practice for them to be meaningful, both to the initial developer and also to any others who may work on the code in the future.

Variables can be assigned values – these will be the initial data stored by the variable. For example:

```
<script>
product_name="turnip"
quantity=50
</script>
```

A collection of variables can be stored in an **array**, where each variable can be called by its position in the list (see Figure 10.6). The array has a name, e.g. vegetables, and the items within it are numbered from 0 onwards.

Vegetables	turnip	carrot	spinach	celery	cabbage
	0	1	2	3	4

▲ Figure 10.6 Variables in an array

Quite often, within a script, a mathematical calculation will need to be performed, especially on e-commerce sites. An **operator** is used to carry out this task, e.g. + (plus), – (minus), * (multiply), / (divide), ++ (increment by 1), – – (decrement by 1).

What does it mean?

An **array** is a collection of indexed variables that each have a single value.

An **operator** is a mathematical symbol used in a calculation or comparison.

For example:

```
<script>
order=200
quantity=50
total= order + quantity
</script>
```

Operators are used to assign values to variables. For example:

```
<script>

order=quantity
```
puts the value of quantity into order

```
order+=quantity
```
puts the value of order plus quantity into order (order=order + quantity)

```
order-=quantity
```
puts the value of order minus quantity into order (order=order – quantity)

```
</script>
```

Also, operators can perform comparisons between values. For example:

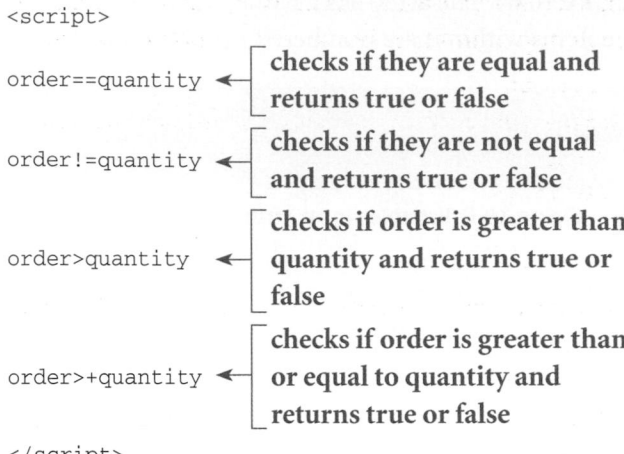

```
<script>

order==quantity        checks if they are equal and
                       returns true or false

order!=quantity        checks if they are not equal
                       and returns true or false

order>quantity         checks if order is greater than
                       quantity and returns true or
                       false

order>+quantity        checks if order is greater than
                       or equal to quantity and
                       returns true or false

</script>
```

Activity 10.5

Syntax of a scripting language

1 Describe how a variable is defined and obtains an initial value.

2 Create syntactically correct scripts to:
   a) add two numbers together
   b) multiply two numbers together
   c) check if an amount is greater than the other
   d) check if two amounts are equal.

10.2.3.2 Loops

A **loop** (also known as an iteration) is a piece of code that is executed over and over again until it fulfils a preset criterion. There are different types of loop which each produce different effects. The criterion for exiting the loop is defined either at the beginning or end of it, and the actions to be performed during the loop are placed within curly brackets { }.

What does it mean?

A **loop** (or iteration) is a piece of code that is executed over and over again until it fulfils a preset criterion.

The following FOR loop will be executed while count is less than or equal to five. Once count is equal to six the loop will be exited. This means the loop will run six times.

```
<script>
for (count = 0; count <= 5; count++)
{
document.write("The number is " + count)
document.write("<br>") // THIS USES HTML WITHIN
THE SCRIPT TO PUT IN A LINE BREAK
}
</script>
```

The following FOR/IN loop will be executed through an array. This array will run through for each of the three elements.

```
<script>
numbers = new Array()
numbers [0] = "zero"
numbers [1] = "one"
numbers [2] = "two"
for (x in numbers)
{
document.write("The number is " + numbers[x])
document.write("<br>")
}
</script>
```

The following WHILE loop will be executed while count is less than or equal to five. Once count equals six the loop will be exited. This means the loop will run six times.

```
<script>
count = 0
while (count <= 5)
{
document.write("The number is " + count)
document.write("<br>")
count++
}
</script>
```

The following DO/WHILE loop will be executed while count is less than or equal to five. Once count equals six the loop will be exited. This means the loop will run six times.

```
<script>
count = 0
```

```
do
{
document.write("The number is " + count)
document.write("<br>")
count++
}
while (count <= 5)
</script>
```

Activity 10.6

Loops in a scripting language

1 Create each of the examples of loops given above.

2 Print each script and annotate it to explain how it works.

10.2.3.3 Decision making

Decision making code has a criterion defined and different actions to be executed if it is met and if it is not met (also known as a selection).

An IF/ELSE loop can take three forms: IF, IF/ELSE or IF/ELSE/IF. The latter version is where there are several conditions to be met with several different actions, so IF statements are nested inside each other. An example of an IF/ELSE loop:

```
<script>
name=prompt("Please enter your name","")
if (name!="")
{
document.write("Hello " + name + "! How are you today?")
}
else
{
document.write("Hello anonymous! How are you today?")
}
</script>
```

A SWITCH/CASE loop allows there to be a variety of conditions, each with an action. The same can be achieved with nested IF statements, but SWITCH/CASE is much neater and so is less likely to contain mistakes.

```
<script>
colour=prompt("Please enter a colour for your T-shirt","")
switch (colour)
{
case "blue":
document.write("Good choice. Blue is brilliant.")
break
case "red":
document.write("Nice! A bright, vibrant colour.")
break
case "green":
document.write("Fabulous! A wonderful colour.")
break
default:
document.write("Sorry, we don't stock that colour.")
}
</script>
```

Activity 10.7

Decision making in a scripting language

1 Create each of the decision making examples given above.

2 Print each script and annotate it to explain how it works.

10.2.3.4 Functions

A function is a piece of code, written separately, which can be **called** and executed whenever needed.

What does it mean?

Calling a function means accessing it from wherever it is stored and executing it.

A function will not be executed until it is called. Functions can be written anywhere in the web page or even in a different page, such as a .js file. Below is an example of a function (could go in head section or in a different page or even in the body section) and the function being called (within the body section of the page):

```
<script>
function hello() // THIS IS WHERE THE FUNCTION IS
NAMED
{
alert("Hello!")
}
</script>
…
<body>
<input type="button"
onclick="hello()" // THIS IS WHERE THE FUNCTION
IS CALLED
value="Click me!">
</body>
```

Notice the brackets beside the name of the function. This is so a **parameter** can be passed. This means either a value that is passed to the function and that the function uses while running, or a value that is passed back to the main code once the function has run.

```
<script>
function topping()
{
topp=prompt("Enter your favourite topping.", "")
alert(topp + " " + food)
}
</script>
…
<body>
<script>
food="pizza"
topping(food)
</script>
</body>
```

What does it mean?

A **parameter** is a value passed to or from a function to use in its execution.

Activity 10.8

Functions in a scripting language

A prompt box can take an input from a user and has this syntax: x=prompt("message","")

1 Create the pizza topping example of a function given above.

2 Adapt the code to allow the user to enter their favourite food type. If it is pizza, it should call the topping function.

10.2.3.5 Handling events

Remember!

An **event** is an action that can cause a reaction in the code.

Events can be triggered by something gaining focus (**onfocus**), something losing focus (**onblur**), when a page is loaded (**onload**) and when the cursor moves over something (**onmouseover**). They are used within the HTML tags in the body.

The syntax for the onfocus event could be:

```
<form>
<input type="text" onfocus=" alert('An onFocus
event')">
</form>
```

Here is an example of the onmouseover event (NB: image1.gif must be in the same folder as the code file):

```
<img src="image1.gif" onmouseover="alert('An
onMouseOver event')">
```

The syntax for the onload event could be:

```
<body onload=alert("loaded")>
```

The text of the alert cannot contain spaces when it is part part of the onload command. To be able to do more, a function should be called from the onload, e.g. `<body onload="functionname()">`

Activity 10.9

Handling events with a scripting language

1 Create a page that has a rollover button using the onmouseover event.

2 Create a page that displays a message using the onload event.

3 Research on the Internet for other events and make notes on what effect they might have.

10.2.3.6 Methods

Remember!

A **method** is an action that can be performed by an object.

Methods can be applied to objects to create actions. There are several preset objects with predefined methods.

The method `.write` can be used to display information on screen. It can be fixed text, e.g. `document.write ("Hello")`, or it could be the value of a variable, e.g. `document.write(x)`.

The method `.click` will simulate a click, such as a button being clicked or a check box being checked. In the following example clicking the button automatically clicks the check box:

```
<script>
function autoclick()
{
myform.box.click();
}
</script>
...
<body>
<form name="myform">
<input type="check box" name="box">check box
<input type=button value="button"
onclick="autoclick()">
</form>
</body>
```

The method `.value()` will extract the value from an input, using the format `formname.inputname.value`. For example, on a form called "student" there is a text box called "firstname". The user enters "Fred" into the text box. The method `student.firstname.value` will extract the value "Fred" from this text box.

The method `.open` will load a page in a new browser window. The format of the command would be `window. open("index.html")`.

The method `.selectedIndex` will show which option in a drop-down list has been selected, allocating the entry a number starting with 0. In the following example, clicking the button will find which entry has been selected.

```
<script>
function selected()
{
opt=document.getElementById("mylist")
alert(opt.selectedIndex);
}
</script>
...
<body>
<form name="myform">
<select id=mylist>
<option>option 0</option>
<option>option 1</option>
</select>
<input type=button value="button"
onclick="selected()">
</form>
</body>
```

Activity 10.10

Methods in a scripting language

1 Enter this code into a text editor such as Notepad:

```html
<html>
<head>
<title>Methods Example Page</title>
<script>
function details()
{
// INSERT YOUR NEW CODE HERE
}
</script>
</head>

<body>
<b>Methods Example Page</b>
<br><br>
<form name="DetailsForm">
Enter full name  <input type="text"
name="fullname">
<br>
Gender:
<select id=gender>
<option>male</option>
<option>female</option>
</select>
<br>
<input type="button" value="Click Me"
onClick="details()">
</form>
</body>
</html>
```

2 Save the file as **methodexample.html**.

3 Amend the function using methods so the following things happen:
   a) find out the value of **name**
   b) find out which **gender** has been selected
   c) write both to the page so they are displayed on-screen.

Properties are characteristics of objects in code. For example, an input object has a type, name and value. For example:

```html
<input type="radio" name="gender" value="male">
```

The type shows that it is a radio button; the name is how to refer to that radio button; the value is what that radio button means – the method `form.gender.value` would result in male if it had been selected.

Instead of the name property, id can also be used in the same way. Whereas there can be more than one element with the same name, the id must always be unique. The methods `getElementById(AnId)` will always return an individual element, whereas `getElementByName(AName)` can return a collection of elements.

The properties width and height can be used with visible items such as tables and images, to define their dimensions. For example: `<table width=200 height=200>`. It is also possible to define the size of new pages or pop-up windows with JavaScript. For example, `window.open("index.html", ","width=200, height=200")` will open index.html in a new window that is 200 pixels square. Notice the extra set of quotes between the page and the sizes – these can be used if a name is to be allocated to the window.

Test your knowledge

1 What is the main purpose of a scripting language?

2 Where is client side scripting processed?

3 HTML is interpreted. What does that mean?

4 What is the difference between object-orientated (like JavaScript) and event driven (like VBScript)?

5 Name three uses of a scripting language.

6 What is an operator?

7 Name the four types of loop (iteration) available.

8 Name the two types of decision (selection) available.

9 What is the purpose of a function?

By using CSS, the website can more easily use a house style; it is also easier to maintain. This section explains practical ways to implement CSS in a web page to control layout.

10.3.1 Design

When the design of a website is created in CSS, all the formatting is done in the CSS file and so the HTML web page itself only holds the content. Without the CSS, the HTML page would just read like a normal text document.

Changes only need to be made to one entry in the CSS, rather than throughout the HTML – this saves a lot of time and helps prevent errors from occurring. CSS promotes standardised design throughout a website, which is good practice and helps maintain **house style**.

What does it mean?

House style is a standard design carried throughout a website. It can also be extended throughout the business. It can include logos, colour combinations and layouts.

There are several methods which can be used to design the layout of a website in a graphical way. It is useful to do this to ensure that when coding begins there is a clear idea of how the website should look and therefore the code which needs to be created.

A **screen design** should clearly show the precise layout of each page including the fonts, sizes, colours, images and other elements to be included in the page (see Figure 10.7).

The screen designs show each individual page, whereas the **navigation diagram** shows how all these separate pages will be linked together (see Figure 10.8).

What does it mean?

A **screen design** depicts the layout of a web page and should be drawn before starting to build it.

A **navigation diagram** shows how the different parts of a project will be arranged. In web design, it shows how different pages will interrelate.

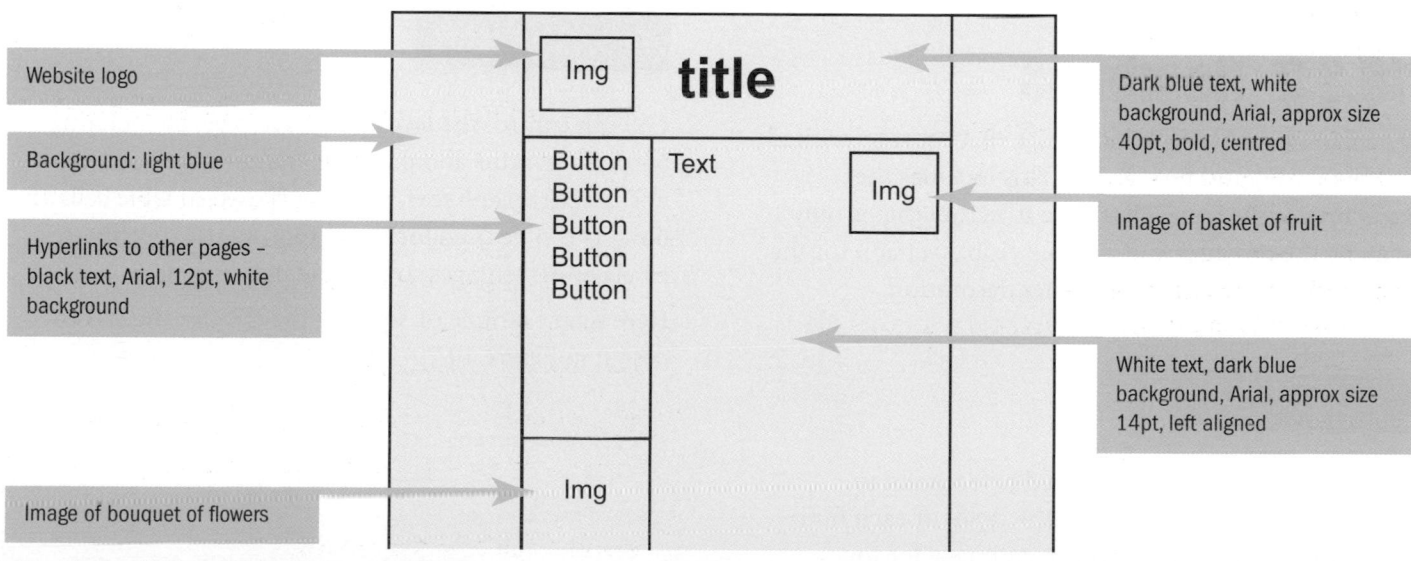

▲   **Figure 10.7 Example of a screen design**

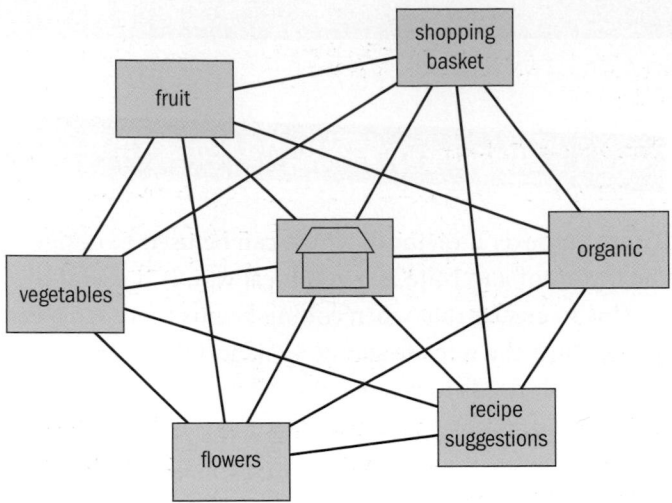

Figure 10.8 Example of a navigation diagram

Here is an example of some of the CSS for the screen design in Figure 10.7.

```
body {background-color: #DDDDFF}
.title
{
color: #0000FF;
font-family: Arial;
font-size: 40pt;
font-weight: bold;
text-align: center;
}
```

Activity 10.11

Design with CSS
Choose an existing website with which you are familiar, such as your school or college site.

1 Create a screen design for the home page.

2 Create a navigation diagram for the whole website.

Activity 10.12

Styling with CSS

1 Using the screen design in Figure 10.7, create the CSS for the background and fonts in the web page. (For now, don't worry about the layout.) **p**₄

2 Test it works by creating a prototype of the page in HTML. **p**₄

3 The business has decided to change its house style to a red theme. Alter your prototype web page accordingly. **d**₁

10.3.2 Headings

The first elements of the web page that must be created are the layout and formatting. This includes the structure of the page – both the structure that is only seen by the designer and also the visible version for the user, including borders and other decoration.

10.3.2.1 Styling

To implement the design defined beforehand in screen designs, CSS can create the styles of each font to be used. Also, it can establish an image for the background.

10.3.2.2 Spacing

CSS can control the layout of a web page by dictating the borders, margins and padding. Margins are used for normal paragraph text, padding is used in table cells and borders can be used for both. You can use centimetres, pixels or percentages to indicate dimensions.

Here is an example of some of the CSS for the screen design in Figure 10.7.

```
<style>
.titleparagraph
{
border: red solid thin;
margin: 30%;
}
```

```
.titlecell
{
border: blue groove;
padding: 3cm 6cm; // THE FIRST NUMBER IS TOP AND
BOTTOM, THE SECOND NUMBER IS LEFT AND RIGHT
}
</style>
```

This is how these would be implemented in the HTML:

```
<body>
<span class="titleparagraph">Title</span>
<br>
<table border="0">
<tr>
<td class="titlecell">Title</td>
</tr>
</table>
</body>
```

10.3.3 Lists

Most users prefer not to have to read huge paragraphs of text, so a developer should try to lay out the content in the easiest format for reading. By using lists, the content can be put in an orderly format which is easy for the user to read and so makes the website usable by more people.

10.3.3.1 Ordered and unordered lists

There are two types of list which can be created with CSS: ordered lists are numbered and unordered lists are bulleted. The style is defined in the CSS, then within the HTML using the `<li>` tag to identify each item in the list.

Ordered lists can be created with numbers, roman numerals or alphabetical letters:

```
<style>
.numbers {list-style-type: decimal}
.numerals {list-style-type: lower-roman}
.letters {list-style-type: lower-alpha}
</style>
```

This is how it would be implemented in the HTML:

```
<body>
<ol class="numbers">
<li>Pumpkin</li>
```

Activity 10.13

Spacing with CSS

1   Using the screen design shown in Figure 10.7 on page 111 and the prototype web page you created in Activity 10.12, create the CSS for the layout of the web page.

2   Test it works in the HTML page.

3   The business has decided to change the design (see screen design below). Alter your prototype web page accordingly.

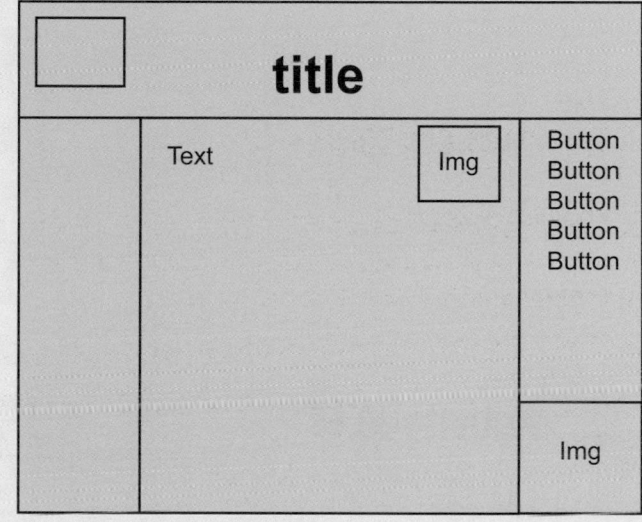

```
<li>Aubergine</li>
</ol>
<ol class="numerals">
<li>Pumpkin</li>
<li>Aubergine</li>
</ol>
<ol class="letters">
<li>Pumpkin</li>
<li>Aubergine</li>
</ol>
</body>
```

Unordered lists can be created with round filled bullets, round empty bullets, square bullets or invisible bullets:

```
<style>
.round_full {list-style-type: disc}
```

```
.round_empty {list-style-type: circle}
.square {list-style-type: square}
.invisible {list-style-type: none}
</style>
```

This is how it would be implemented in the HTML:

```
<body>
<ul class="round_full">
<li>Daffodil</li>
<li>Sunflower</li>
</ul>
<ul class="round_empty">
<li>Daffodil</li>
<li>Sunflower</li>
</ul>
<ul class="square">
<li>Daffodil</li>
<li>Sunflower</li>
</ul>
<ul class="invisible">
<li>Daffodil</li>
<li>Sunflower</li>
</ul>
</body>
```

The anchor links must be written in the order shown in Table 10.3 for them to work. Other formatting can be used instead of colour using the same syntax.

`a:link {color: red}`	the original colour of the link, before it has been clicked
`a:visited {color: blue}`	the colour of the link once it has been visited
`a:hover {color: green}`	the colour of the link when the mouse hovers over it
`a:active {color: yellow}`	the colour of the link when it has been clicked and is active

Table 10.3 Examples of settings for hyperlinks – they must be written in this order

Activity 10.14

Styling with CSS

Using the prototype web page you created in Activity 10.13:

1 Add an ordered list of your favourite five fruit and vegetables to the main body of text. ![P4]

2 Add an unordered list of your three favourite flowers below the first list. Make sure there is at least one line break `<br/>` between them. ![P4]

Activity 10.15

Hovering with CSS

1 Using the prototype web page you created in Activity 10.14, create the buttons in the navigation bar, based on the navigation diagram in Figure 10.8 on page 112. ![P4]

2 Using CSS, create the following:

○ for the unclicked link, the text should be black
○ when the user hovers over the link, it should become a larger font size
○ when the link is visited, it should become a different font
○ when the link is active, the background colour of the link should become yellow. ![P4]

10.3.3.2 Styling hyperlinks

There are default settings for hyperlinks, such as blue and underlined turning to purple and underlined once clicked. These can be overridden by CSS so they can fit in with a design.

10.3.3.3 Use for navigation

Using CSS, it is possible to create menus which simulate drop-down menus – these can look very impressive when implemented correctly. Opposite is an example of how this can be done.

```
<style>
  ul {
  margin: 0;
  padding: 0;
  width: 150px;
  list-style: none;
  }
ul li {
  position: relative;
  float: left;
  }
li ul {
  position: absolute;
  top: 0;
  left: 149px;
  display: none;
  }
ul li a {
  display: block;
  padding: 5px;
  border: 1px solid red;
  height: 1%;
  text-decoration: none;
  color: black;
  }
li:hover ul, li.over ul {display: block;}
</style>
```

The ul style formats the whole list, which is surrounded by a <ul> tag.

The ul li style formats the main list headers as they exist between both <ul> and <li> tags.

The li ul style formats the list subheaders as they exist between both <li> and <ul> tags.

The ul li a style formats the actual list elements as they exist between <ul>, <li> and <a> tags.

The hover and over commands control the appearing and disappearing of the list items.

This is implemented in the HTML as follows.

```
<script>
ie_patch = function() {
if (document.all&&document.getElementById) {
  listitem = document.getElementById("nav");
  for (i=0; i<listitem.childNodes.length; i++) {
    ie_element= listitem.childNodes[i];
      if (ie_element.nodeName=="LI") {
        ie_element.onmouseover=function() {
        this.className+=" over";
      }
      ie_element.onmouseout=function() {
        this.className=this.className.replace(" over", "");
      }
    }
  }
}
}
```

Some browsers, including Internet Explorer, do not support the hover command, so this script will allow it to work.

```
window.onload=ie_patch;
</script>
…

<body>
<ul id="nav">
  <li><a href="#">FRUIT</a></li>
    <ul>
      <li><a href="#">cherry</a></li>
      <li><a href="#">tangerine</a></li>
      <li><a href="#">peach</a></li>
    </ul>
  </li>
  <li><a href="#">VEGETABLES</a></li>
    <ul>
      <li><a href="#">celery</a></li>
      <li><a href="#">cucumber</a></li>
      <li><a href="#">lettuce</a></li>
    </ul>
  </li>
</ul>
</body>
```

This is the HTML where the content of the list is written. Notice the only formatting in this is the structure of the <ul> and <li> tags.

Activity 10.16

Navigation with CSS

1 Using the prototype web page you created in Activity 10.15, add the menus given in the code above.

2 Add three more menus for: flowers, nuts and herbs.

10.3.4 Links and pseudoclasses

Hyperlinks are controlled by the <a> tag, which stands for anchor. They are one of the **pseudoclasses** which can be controlled by CSS. There are others; however, they are

What does it mean?

Pseudoclasses are the states of a hyperlink that can be set in CSS: link, visited, hover and active.

not supported by all browsers so it is better not to use them. By ensuring a website is accessible by all browsers, a developer can increase traffic to their site.

10.3.4.1 Setting pseudoclass order

The default settings for hyperlinks can be overridden by CSS, as shown in Table 10.3 on page 114.

Hover must follow link and visited. Active must follow hover.

10.3.4.2 Adding background images

The background colour of a web page can be changed by using the code:

```
body {background-color: #DDDDFF}
```

Alternatively, an image can be used as the background instead of a colour, using the following code:

```
body
{
background-image: url('picture.jpg');
background-position: center; // THIS WILL CENTRE
THE IMAGE ON THE WEB PAGE
}
```

Remember!

The image must be in the same folder as the web page; otherwise, the whole file location must be included.

By using this code, the image will appear behind all the web page elements. However, when it is scrolled, it will move up the page. To keep it in the same place, this code can be used:

```
{
background-image: url('picture.jpg');
background-attachment: fixed; // THIS WILL PREVENT
IT MOVING WHEN THE PAGE IS SCROLLED
}
```

10.3.4.3 Styling

Underlining of text can sometimes be tricky in web pages, as it is not done in the same way as in other applications. For example, when using Dreamweaver, you might expect the Underline button to be beside the Bold and Italic buttons, but it is in a list all of its own. The same issue occurs when underlining using CSS. The property for it is **text-decoration** and it can be used as follows:

```
.lineabove {text-decoration: overline}
.linethrough {text-decoration: line-through}
.underline {text-decoration: underline}
a {text-decoration: none} // THIS CODE WILL
REMOVE THE UNDERLINE FROM A HYPERLINK
```

It is possible to make the active link area larger on text hyperlinks. This could make it more accessible for those people with limited mobility. For example:

```
a
{
  padding: 10px 0;
  position:relative;
  background: yellow; // THIS IS TO SHOW THE NEW
  HYPERLINK AREA
}
```

Activity 10.17

Creating web pages with CSS

Keystone Zoo wants a website in order to advertise on the Internet. The star attractions are the lions, the flamingos and the giant pandas.

1 On paper, design the layout and design of each page of the website (home page and a page for each animal).

2 Using CSS, create the structure of the pages.

3 Using CSS, create the formatting for the pages.

4 Complete the website, including the content.

5 Write a brief evaluation of your website.

STOP Test your knowledge

1 Which two methods are most commonly used to plan layouts?

2 Describe the difference between ordered and unordered lists.

3 Which three types of numbering are available?

4 What four types of bullet are available?

5 What four parts of a hyperlink can be formatted using CSS?

6 In a hyperlink tag, what does the `<a>` stand for?

7 What is the CSS property to define underlining?

Scripting languages can provide a wide range of interactivity for a website. This section will look at some of the more commonly used types of interactivity. As with all programming languages, it is important to have a clear design of the script before beginning to code it.

10.4.1 Script requirements

It is important to define the inputs, processes and outputs of a script so that you understand exactly what is happening in the code.

10.4.1.1 Inputs

Inputs are the data entering the system. They could be from the user or another application. By defining the inputs before creating the code, a programmer can ensure that they make provision for the appearance of the data.

10.4.1.2 Processes

By identifying all the processes to be carried out in the script, the programmer can write the code more efficiently. For example, the programmer can decide if the processes are to be performed straight from the bulk of the code or in separate functions.

10.4.1.3 Outputs

Outputs are the information that is produced by the processes. The output could be yielded in a variety of ways, such as on-screen or as a printout. The customary aim is to convert input data to output information that is meaningful and useful.

10.4.2 Design script

It is important to plan the script before beginning to implement it. There are several methods available – the most popular methods are flowcharts and pseudocode. Using both of these methods will provide the full picture of how the script should function and in what order.

10.4.2.1 Flowchart

A flowchart shows the order in which actions should be executed and can also model selections and loops (see Figure 10.9). Symbols are used to represent certain activities, which means that any flowchart can be understood by all system designers (see Table 10.4).

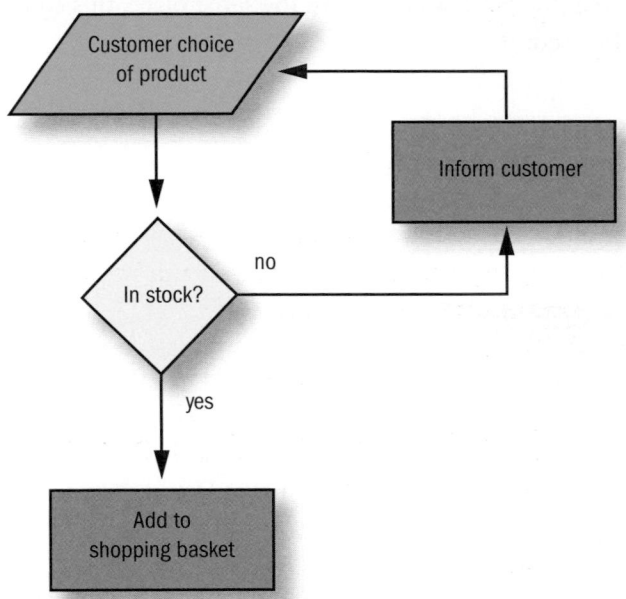

▲ Figure 10.9 An example of a flowchart – this one models purchasing from an e-commerce site

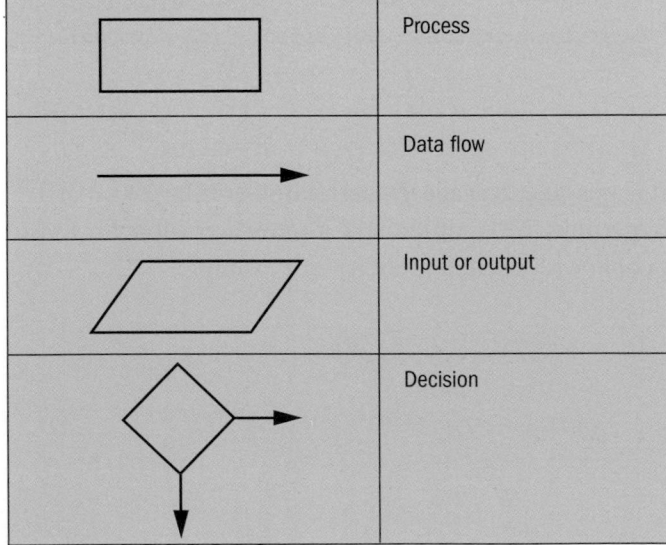

	Process
	Data flow
	Input or output
	Decision

Table 10.4 Flowchart symbols

Activity 10.18

Flowcharts

1 Draw a systems flowchart for a user filling in a feedback form which is then emailed to the administrator. If any fields are left blank, it should loop back to allow the user to fill it in again. **p**₅

2 Research to find what other symbols can be used in a systems flowchart and make notes for future reference. **p**₅

10.4.2.2 Pseudocode

Pseudocode is a method of designing code, forming an intermediary step between an explanation in English and the coding language – see Table 10.5.

Pseudocode	JavaScript
age = input from user	`age=prompt("Enter age","");`
if age >= 18 then	`if (age>=18)`
print onscreen "i am an adult"	`{document.write("I am an adult");}`
else	`else`
print onscreen "i am x years old"	`{document.write("I am " + age + " years old");}`

Table 10.5 Example of Pseudocode used to plan JavaScript

By using pseudocode, a designer can plan what the code will do, without having to worry about ensuring the correct words and syntax are used. It is also easier to convert from a flowchart into the full programming language by using this transitional step.

Activity 10.19

Pseudocode

1 Design the pseudocode for a feedback form on a website. **p**₅

10.4.3 Implement script

Once you have designed the script, you can implement it into the web page. This section shows a few features that can be created with client side scripting.

10.4.3.1 Rollovers

A rollover is where a button displays a different image or formatting when the mouse hovers over it. Two separate images would need to be prepared first to be used for both parts of the rollover.

The following script can produce a rollover:

```
<script>
function over()
{
document.button1.src ="red.gif"
}
function out()
{
document.button1.src ="blue.gif"
}
</script>
…
<body>
<a href="index.html">
<img src="blue.gif" name="button1"
onmouseover="over()" onmouseout="out()" /></a>
</body>
```

Activity 10.20

Rollovers

1 Create an example rollover button. **p**₅ **d**₂

Time can be used in JavaScript with the `setTimeout` object. For example:

```
<script>
function timer()
{
setTimeout("alert('3 seconds')",3000)
}
</script>

…

<body>
<script>
setTimeout("alert('3 seconds')",3000)
</script>
</body>
```

This will display an alert saying "3 seconds" once three seconds have elapsed. The measurement 3000 is in milliseconds.

In programming, it is usual to try to avoid infinite loops (loops that repeat forever). However, using an infinite loop is a way of creating a counter in JavaScript. The following code is an example of how to create a timer with two buttons, one to start and one to stop the timer:

```
<script>
count=0
function startCount()
{
document.getElementById("txt").value=count
count=count+1
t=setTimeout("startCount()",1000)
}
function stopCount()
{
clearTimeout(t)
}
</script>

…

<body>
<form>
<input type="button" value="Start"
onClick="startCount()">
<input type="text" id="txt">
<input type="button" value="Stop"
onClick="stopCount()">
</form>
</body>
```

It is possible to pull the time and date from the computer's system clock. This allows calculations to be done, such as calculating the age of a person from their date of birth. The following code will write today's date and time to the screen:

```
<script>
document.write(Date())
</script>
```

The next example will calculate the separate parts of a date from the current date on the system clock:

```
It is now
<script>
now = new Date()
day = now.getDate()
month = now.getMonth() + 1
year = now.getFullYear()
document.write(day + "/" + month + "/" + year)
</script>
```

Activity 10.21

Clocks and calendars

1 Create a counter that counts even seconds: 2, 4, 6, etc.

2 Write the code to calculate the user's age when they input their date of birth. Use today's date to calculate their age.

Calculations can be carried out with variables using **operators** (see section 10.2.3.1 on page 105).

Remember!

An **operator** is a mathematical symbol used in a calculation or comparison.

The following example will output 25 to the screen:

```
<script>
x=10
y=15
total=x+y
document.write(total)
</script>
```

There are also other mathematical objects available. The next example shows the use of max() and min():

```
<script>
document.write(Math.max(5,7) + "<br />")
document.write(Math.min(7,5))
</script>
```

Both commands will also work for negative and decimal numbers.

Activity 10.22

Calculations

1 Using mathematical operators, find the min, max and total of 10, 837, 267, 94, 293, 2, 112, 398, 62, 928, 737, 918. **P**₅ **d**₂

When users are inputting data into a form, there is a risk of them filling it in incorrectly, which can cause problems later on. It is therefore useful to check their input as it is entered. This example will check that the name field is not null:

```
<html>
<head>
<script>
function validate()
{
   namefield=myform.yourname.value;
   if (namefield=="'')
   {
      alert('You must enter your name.');
      event.returnValue=false;
   }
}
</script>
</head>
<body>
<form name="myform" onsubmit="validate();">
<input type="text" name="yourname" > Please enter
your name (required).
<br>
<input type="submit" value="enter name">
</form>
</body>
</html>
```

This example will check that a radio button has been selected:

```
<html>
<head>
<script>
function validate()
{
   if (!(myform.mood[0].checked))
   {
      if (!(myform.mood[1].checked))
      {
         alert('You must choose a mood.');
         event.returnValue=false;
```

The [0] checks the first radio button (happy) and the [1] checks the second radio button (sad).
The ! (exclamation mark) denotes a NOT, so this checks if it is not checked.

```
      }
    }
  }
</script>
</head>
<body>
<form name="myform" onsubmit="validate();">
<input type="radio" name="mood"
value="happy">happy
<input type="radio" name="mood" value="sad">sad
<br>
<input type="submit" value="enter mood">
</form>
</body>
</html>
```

Activity 10.23

Forms validation

1 Create your own form to enter the title of a film and a set of check boxes to choose its genre (horror, sci-fi, comedy, etc). **p**₅ **d**₂

2 Validate the form to check that the film title has been entered. **p**₅ **d**₂

3 Validate the form to check that at least one check box has been selected. **p**₅ **d**₂

10.4.3.5 Mouse movement followers

A mouse movement follower creates an image trail behind a cursor. This can add fun to website and can attract users, but use carefully as it can also annoy users and may turn them away.

▲ **Figure 10.10 What a mouse trail looks likes**

10.4.4 Good practice

The original writer of the code may not be the person who maintains or updates it. Therefore, it is essential that a developer follows good practice in their programming. Good code should be understood by any programmer, even if they are not familiar with that specific language.

10.4.4.1 Comments in the script

Code needs to be converted from a language the programmer understands to one the computer understands. In HTML and client side scripting, code is interpreted one line at a time in the order in which it is stored. A **comment** is a line of code which is ignored by the interpreting software; comments can be used to explain what action each piece of code performs.

What does it mean?

A **comment** is an uninterpreted line of code which describes what is happening and helps developers understand how the code works.

- To comment in HTML and CSS, use `<!-- Comment -->`.
- To comment in JavaScript, use `//Comment`. (Notice that comments have been added in this way to provide explanations in the example code provided throughout this unit.)
- To comment in VBScript, use `'Comment`.

10.4.4.2 Indentation

To ensure that code can be clearly understood, sections can be indented to show which tags affect it. For example:

```
<body>
  <script>
  if (time < 10)
    <b>document.write("Good morning</b>")
  else
    <b>document.write("Good day</b>")
  </script>
</body>
```

10.4.4.3 Naming of variables

Variables should have meaningful names so that wherever they are used in the code, their purpose is clear. Their aim is to store some data so it can be used later. The name should clearly reflect what the variable does and be easily understandable.

Variable names must begin with a letter, which can be followed by either letters or numbers. Spaces are not allowed but it is acceptable to use an underscore (_) as part of the name to make it more meaningful: e.g. **product_ quantity**.

Care must be taken not to use a **reserved word** as a variable.

What does it mean?

A **reserved word** is a word that is already used in the programming language and therefore cannot be used as a variable name.

Short, simple names are easier to work with. If variable names are long, complicated or easy to spell incorrectly, it becomes tiresome to have to rekey them throughout and can cause problems if they are not keyed consistently.

Activity 10.24

Creating web pages with a scripting language

1 Keystone Zoo wants to add more interactivity to its website. Using the site you made in Activity 10.17, add the following features using a scripting language:
   a) rollover buttons
   b) a button which, when clicked, displays the current date and time
   c) a calculation to multiply the cost of entry into the zoo by the number of visitors. **p**₅ **d**₂

2 Create a form so customers can enter their details to book tickets. Validate the form to ensure all required fields are entered. **p**₅ **d**₂

3 Comment and indent your code to make it easy to read by other developers. **p**₅ **d**₂

4 Briefly evaluate each function you have created with regard to user needs. **d**₃

Test your knowledge

1 Draw and name four symbols used in flowcharts.
2 What is the purpose of pseudocode?
3 Why is code commented and indented?

Once the website is built, it must be tested to ensure there are no errors in the pages before they are uploaded to the web server and go live worldwide. It can be harmful to an organisation's reputation if its website contains errors, especially if it is an e-commerce site, as potential customers may lose faith in the business.

10.5.1 Testing and reviewing

All the elements of the website should be tested, including the HTML, CSS and scripting language.

A test plan such as the one shown in Table 10.6 can be used:

Activity 10.25

Testing web pages with CSS and a scripting language

1 Using a test plan like the one shown in Table 10.6, test the website you built in CSS (in Activity 10.17 on page 117) and JavaScript (in Activity 10.24).

10.5.2 Checking different platforms

It is important to test whether the website also functions correctly in the variety of browsers available. The more browsers on which it runs successfully, the more potential users are available. The test will involve loading the web pages into different browsers such as Microsoft Internet Explorer, Mozilla Firefox and others.

Activity 10.26

Scripts in different browsers

1 Explain how scripts are implemented differently in two browsers, such as Internet Explorer and Firefox. m₃

Test your knowledge

1 What is the purpose of testing?

2 Briefly, why do browsers read script in different ways?

Test number	Test element	On page	Test data	Expected result	Actual result	Success or failure	Screenshot reference
1	Title	Index.html	Load page	Font should be green	Font is green	Success	S1
2	Home rollover	Index.html	Hover	Should turn purple	Doesn't change	Failure	S2

Table 10.6 Example test plan

Preparation for assessment

The assessment tasks in this unit are based on the following scenario:

oink is a business selling piggy banks. They want to create a website which is easy to maintain and interesting and interactive for their users. They hope to sell their products online in the future.

To work towards a Distinction you will need to achieve all the Pass, Merit and Distinction criteria in the unit and provide evidence to show that you have achieved each one.

You are advised to research wherever possible and use correctly referenced sources.

Task 1 (P1, P2, M1)

oink have heard that it is best to have the website's structure and design built in CSS. Write a short report that describes three implementation styles of CSS, showing how they are called from HTML.

What are the box model and selectors? Describe how they are used.

Compare two methods of accessing external CSS script.

Task 2 (P3, M3)

oink have also heard that a scripting language can add extra functionality and interactivity. Write a short report describing the following:

- What are scripting languages?
- How do they work in a web page?
- What types are available?

Select a scripting language and describe its main features. What are the typical uses of this scripting language?

Explain how a website with scripts would be implemented in two different browsers.

Task 3 (P4, P5, D2)

Design a website for *oink* using CSS and a scripting language. It must include at least five pages and at least three examples of interactivity. For the whole site:

- state ten user requirements.

To create the design for the CSS, include:

- a navigation diagram
- a description of the house style
- screen designs for each page.

To create the design for the scripting language, include:

- inputs, processes, outputs
- a flowchart
- pseudocode.

Task 4 (P4, M2, D1)

Implement the CSS for the website, building the structure and formatting.

Task 5 (P5, D2)

Implement the scripting language for the website, building the functionality and interactivity.

Task 6 (P4, P5)

Complete the website, making sure that you include good content.

Task 7 (P4, P5, D3)

Test the website thoroughly and evaluate it, comparing it to the user requirements.

Human Computer Interaction

Introduction

In the last 20 years, the introduction of the **graphical user interface (GUI)** has revolutionised the ways in which users interact with computers, known as **human computer interaction (HCI)**. Although there is no single definition of HCI, this truly fascinating subject will lead you to explore, not only the engineering of GUIs but, probably more importantly, the philosophy that lies behind them. The topic is so huge that, in this unit, you will only experience some elements of HCI theory with practical aspects of designing and producing interfaces.

After completing this unit, you should be able to achieve these outcomes:

- Know about the impact of HCI on society, economy and culture

- Understand the fundamental principles of interface design

- Be able to design and produce simple interactive computer input and output based on HCI principles

- Be able to compare and contrast, using HCI principles, the effectiveness of different designs of input and output.

Grading criteria	Activity	Page number
To achieve a pass grade the evidence must show that the learner is able to:		
p₁ Describe one impact of HCI in recent years on each of society, economy and culture	PFA	154
p₂ Explain two fundamental principles of HCI design	PFA	154
p₃ Design and create three input HCI to meet given specifications, using a variety of techniques	PFA	154
p₄ Design and create three output HCI to meet given specifications, using a variety of techniques	PFA	155
p₅ Briefly describe how each of the input and output HCI they have created meet the specifications provided	PFA	155
To achieve a merit grade the evidence must show that, in addition to the pass criteria, the learner is able to:		
m₁ Explain how modern advances in HCI design, have contributed to the impact of computers on society, economy and culture	PFA	154
m₂ Design one HCI dedicated to specialist needs indicating how some of the fundamental principles have been applied and how the needs are met	PFA	154
m₃ Describe how effectiveness of HCI may be measured	PFA	155
To achieve a distinction grade the evidence must show that, in addition to the pass and merit criteria, the learner is able to:		
d₁ Evaluate the HCI developments over recent years	PFA	154
d₂ Compare the HCI they have developed with those commercially produced for similar products	PFA	155

Note: 'PFA' stands for 'Preparation for assessment'.

This section will help you to identify and understand the impact that HCI has on society, economy and culture.

13.1.1 Development

This subsection investigates developments to HCI that have taken place over the last 20 years. Probably the most widely recognised graphical user interface (GUI – pronounced 'gooey') is that used on PCs (personal computers). The most commonly used GUI is Microsoft Windows, which was based on the earlier Macintosh model. Windows version 1.0 (see Figure 13.1) was introduced in the mid-1980s, although this was by no means the first of its kind and did not go unchallenged. Almost all software introduced today uses GUIs, through which users (humans) interact with their computers: hence HCI.

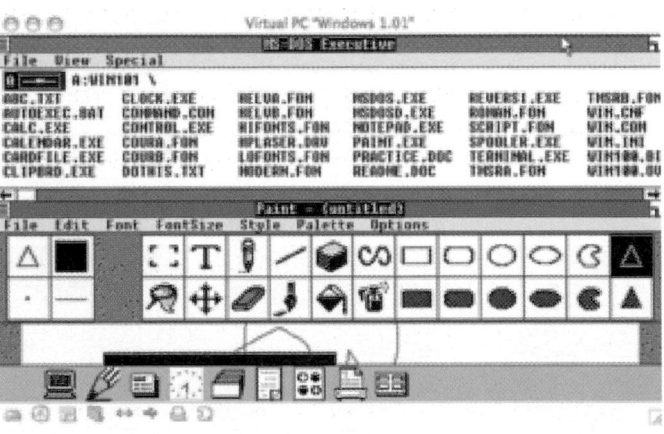

▲ Figure 13.1 Windows 1.0

▲ Figure 13.2 Human computer interaction

Activity 13.1

Microsoft versus Macintosh

1 Investigate the tension between Macintosh and Microsoft regarding the development of their GUIs. Produce a short account of why the tension arose, when and what happened as a result.

2 Prepare a presentation to give to your peers, which should take no less than five and no more than ten minutes.

3 Include all your references.

Remember!

Include references and a bibliography in any reports and presentations that you produce.

13.1.1.1 Early designs

One early GUI design was developed in the early 1960s by a US graduate student called Ivan Sutherland. He developed a computer graphics program called Sketchpad, which was inspired by research into how humans learn. This led to developments at Xerox during the 1970s which were based on the **WIMP** model – the concept became available in the early 1980s.

What does it mean?

WIMP stands for windows, icons, menus and pointers.

Meanwhile, Apple computers continued to develop the WIMP concept and, in 1984, the Macintosh computer appeared. These machines successfully made use of GUIs in the form of a computerised desktop with icons that were images of paper, desktops, files and a rubbish bin. This concept, with the addition of a mouse, enabled the user to easily locate documents and click to open them, as well as pick up documents and put them in the bin. This early Apple desktop design has truly influenced how users interact with computers today and has provided access to the world of computerised technology to millions of people.

Historically, early HCI designs were restricted by the hardware available. Users were required to type lengthy code into the computer just to log in. The highly popular Commodore 64 in the mid 1980s is one such example; at that time no GUI requesting a username and password existed. Other examples included the BBC B Micro and Amstrad, all competing for the market share during the 1980s.

▲ C:\ prompt on the Commodore 64

In these early designs, when switching on the computer, the user would be faced with an almost blank screen with just a C:\ prompt, as with operating systems such as MS DOS. Usernames were requested by some operating

Activity 13.2

Alternative keyboard command
The forward slash (/), used to access a menu command in Lotus, is still operational today in MS Excel – try it!

systems and, in some cases, followed by the need for a password. Developments such as Lotus spreadsheets still relied on user knowledge to interact with the program, as drop-down menus and GUIs had yet to be invented.

Probably the most widely recognised GUI today is the one used by Microsoft Windows – this was originally based on the Macintosh model. The introduction of Windows by Microsoft promoted the use of a mouse as an alternative and, some might say, easier way to give and respond to commands. Other input devices and output tools which are now available are discussed in sections 13.3.1.2 and 13.3.2.2 on pages 148 and 149.

Activity 13.3

Planning for design

1   You need to plan the steps in designing HCI – using a flow chart approach may be the easiest method. The steps needed include the following (in the wrong order):

   a)   what software the user currently runs on the system – this may influence the type of interface and the way it functions

   b)   identification of who you will send the letter to and who you wish to interview (may be the same person)

   c)   follow up letter identifying what you intend to do next

   d)   work out the cost

   e)   the purpose of the GUI

   f)   the outcome required

   g)   a profile of the users and how many users there will be – this may influence the design

   h)   evaluation of effectiveness

   i)   a letter of permission to the organisation explaining that you want to carry out an interview to identify an interface to design

   j)   identifying what the user wants (which may be different from what is required)

   k)   time needed (for them and you)

   l)   draft stages

   m)   maintenance

   n)   the key components.

2   Put the steps into the correct order and add any more of your own.

3   Bring your list to class and share it with your peers.

Activity 13.4

Crystal ball gazing

1 Carry out further research into the developments of the GUI from 20 years ago to the present day. Make notes.

2 Include the changes and developments in HCI for either PCs or Macintosh and concentrate on one specialist system such as Sun or Unix.

3 Include the changes and developments that have taken place in one other device, such as mobile phones, cash registers or calculators.

4 Now list your prophesies – what do you envisage could develop in the future in each of the areas you have researched

5 Present your findings in a short report of between 250 and 500 words. Include all your references.

6 Read ahead to the section on future development (section 13.1.1.6 on page 132).

13.1.1.2 Extended command line editor (CLE)

Before the introduction of GUIs, the only way to interact with a computer was to enter a series of codes into the computer's operating system.

What does it mean?

CLE (command line editor) enables you to edit text files using the command line.

For example, the user would go into DOS (the operating system) and the C:\ prompt would appear on the screen. By entering a series of codes, the user could create a structure such as copying, renaming and moving files – such structures are now built into modern day computers and accessible through other means. The important thing about CLE was that it was a line of code, terminated by the Return key which handed control back to the computer. Typed text was ignored until the Return key was hit; then the computer interpreted the command and a response appeared on screen (or maybe not!).

13.1.1.3 Graphical user interface (GUI)

Microsoft Windows and associated application software, such as the Office suite, rely on the extensive use of GUIs. These provide users with easy ways to access programs and carry out and give commands using **dialogue boxes** (see Figure 13.3).

What does it mean?

In Office applications, clicking on a menu item with three dots (…) after it will open a **dialogue box**. A dialogue box is a window that responds to a command and allows you to make choices (see Figure 13.3).

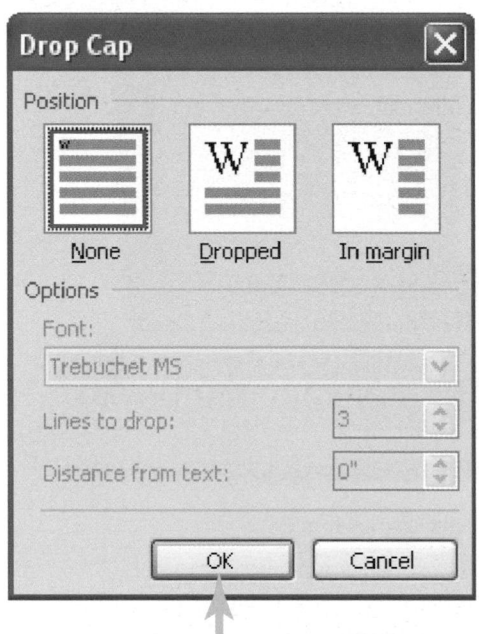

'OK' is the default option and identified by the bold outline. It guides the user to the most likely or preferred option

▲ Figure 13.3 Office dialogue box

13.1.1.4 Visual systems

Software developments have led to visual systems such as 3D pictures of the earth's structure (See Figure 13.4) and reproductions of images such as a scan of an unborn baby. Other types of visual systems include **LCD** screens and holograms such as those seen in Star Trek.

What does it mean?

LCD stands for **liquid crystal display** – used, for example, in cash machines and mobile phones.

▲ Figure 13.4 A 3D picture of the Earth's structure

You are likely to be familiar with the display used to control a laser printer – this is very different from the primitive controls used on a dot matrix printer (see below).

▲ A dot matrix printer

Developments to HCI have led to specialised interfaces. It is only after mainstream development paid for itself that manufacturers started using their expertise to branch out into specialised markets and meeting specialist needs of users. The development of specialist interfaces for users who have visual or hearing impairments has enabled users with such disabilities to access and input information using computers. For example, the National Library for the Blind has developed access to library services for users who are visually impaired, while the British Sign Language Society, in collaboration with teachers and hearing impaired users, has recently developed a bank of sign language covering ICT terms for use by teachers. A range of adaptive and assistive technology is now readily and cheaply available to support users with disabilities. For example, a tracker ball (see below) for a user with **RSI** or arthritis.

What does it mean?

RSI stands for **repetitive strain injury**. This common complaint can result from overuse of a computer mouse.

In extreme cases, RSI can cause a permanent disability. Caused by overuse of muscles of the hands, wrists, arms and shoulders when using a computer, RSI can be worsened by awkward posture, excessive use of the computer and badly designed equipment. When using the computer, avoid resting your wrists on the keyboard

▲ A tracker ball

and typing intensively for long periods. Make sure you take regular breaks and have frequent changes in activities.

Some disabilities, such as back pains, might be avoided by using a properly designed computer chair. Regulations state that both the seat and back of a computer chair should be adjustable by height and angle. It should have a five-star base so it does not tip over. Ideally, computer chairs should not have arms and they should always be tested and adjusted if necessary for every change of user. Always check and, if necessary, adjust the height and angle of the seat and back before sitting at a computer. Do not slump or lean in the chair and ensure your feet are not resting on the five-star base.

Another adjustment to be made where possible is the positioning of the screen to prevent glare. Brightness and contrast can be adjusted on the screen itself and avoiding direct daylight falling on the screen through windows is recommended.

▲ Chair seats should be adjustable and have five-star bases

Activity 13.5

Adaptive technology

1 Ask your teacher/tutor for a list of the specialist technology available in your school/college.

2 Identify what each item is for and how it is used. Perhaps you could try it out.

3 Test out your computer chair and adjust it to ensure you are sitting at the right height and angle with your feet either flat on the floor or on an angled footrest if available. Aim to do this every time you sit at any computer.

13.1.1.6 Present and future development

Section 13.1.1.5 looked at specialist interfaces for users with disabilities. Other developments include robotic systems for the visually impaired and realistic computerised images used in virtual reality computer games – 3D images that appear to leap off the screen.

If you have ever watched a 3D movie or played a 3D game, you will have experienced the 'pop out' effect. This effect can be greatly enhanced by the use of **E-D** glasses.

What does it mean?

E-D stands for **eDimensional**. E-D glasses make computer games appear more vividly 3D.

Speech-activated software has improved greatly since its infancy in the 1990s, when the user had to speak slowly and with great clarity. Instructions were easily confused with narrative. For example, when the user spoke into a microphone, a lengthy pause was often needed to differentiate between words and punctuation. Developments have improved the speed at which the user can talk to the computer and speech recognition is now extremely accurate.

Software has been developed to provide exercises for the brain and claims to boost cognition. For example, thought input type software claims to have enabled patients to communicate through the software where speaking or gesturing has not been possible by other means.

13.1.2 Society

Developments in HCI have brought about a culture in which computers are used in everyday lives. Much of the population now uses a computer of some form or another every single day. Lives depend on computers – consider, for example, their use in hospitals, transport and medical research. This section of the unit explores how technological developments both support and protect us. As well as the relatively simple GUIs used every day in homes and offices, there are also some extremely complex ones.

13.1.2.1 Improving usability

Users benefit from developments in HCI by being able to easily log into computers and load programs. Developers such as Microsoft use a consistent approach to their tool bars, menus and GUIs. This consistency means that the user needs fewer technical skills and less specialised knowledge. For example, someone who has used Word but not Excel should already be familiar with some of the commands in Word. So, when using Excel for the first time, they feel more comfortable, as menus are in a similar format and location, the colours used in GUIs are usually the same, etc. This consistency simplifies input/output and is user-friendly because user confidence is increased.

Domestic appliance displays (see right) are often simple to understand and there is less need to read the instruction book first. Another user-friendly aspect is the use of simple, almost cartoon-like images. This approach has the universal benefit of allowing use of the appliance by people who speak different languages.

One technological development that has impacted on most lives is the mobile telephone. This device is explored in detail in Unit 35 in Book 1. Its relationship with the way humans interface with computers is fascinating. Much research has been carried out, in particular into the 'multi-tap' feature which enables one

Activity 13.6

Location, location, location

Notice how GUIs generally appear in the same location on the desktop, that the colours are relaxing on the eye and that the terminology and format are usually consistent. Colours are explored in more detail in section 13.2.1.1 on page 139.

1 Compare the page setup GUIs in MS Excel and PowerPoint with the GUI in Figure 13.3 on page 130, and make a list of all the similarities and differences between them.

2 Drag and drop one of the GUIs to another location on the desktop. Close it, then open it again. What happens? Try opening another GUI. Does this land in the same or a different location? Now try the original GUI again. Where does it land? Does the same happen when you use another Office package? If you have the chance, try other software and see what happens.

3 Keep a log of each activity, details of software and system, the response time by the user, the response time from the system and the date it was carried out.

4 Compare your list with that of one of your peers.

▲ Icons help to improve the usability of domestic appliances

key to represent more than one entity. This is not the same as StickyKeys, which are referred to in Activity 13.23 on page 147.

13.1.2.2 Specialised interfaces

Specialist software has been developed to enable those with sight or speech impairments to use computers.

- Voice recognition software converts spoken text into electronic text. The user speaks to the computer through a microphone (which may be built into the computer). The computer then interprets what is being said and the text appears on the screen as if it is being typed. In the very early days of voice recognition software, the user had to use very clear diction and identify clearly when saying 'stop' whether a full stop was required or the word 'stop' should be typed. The user had to talk very slowly and the reaction time before the text appeared on the screen was also slow. It took time to 'train' the computer to accept the user's voice and, in some cases, it only recognised one user. See also section 13.1.1.6 on page 132.
- Software that converts text to speech, called speech synthesis, is also available. This works in a similar way to voice recognition, only in reverse. The user types in the text and the computer responds. An example is the software that enables the famous physicist Stephen Hawking to interact with other people. He uses a rod-like tool to tap out his text and the computer then speaks for him. The method used is a type of artificial intelligence and is also used in automated telephone services. It accounts for the occasional stuttering you may have noticed when using automated services on the phone when you are asked to press different keys on your telephone key pad. Try an automated service such as a telephone weather report or a satellite navigation system, and you will experience slight delays between responses (in the case of the weather report) and instructions (in the case of directions for travel).
- People who are visually impaired can now access library books through specialist interfaces, as identified in section 13.1.1.5 on page 131, while those with hearing impairments can turn on subtitles to television programmes, DVDs and many Internet sites.

13.1.2.3 Hostile environments

Robots with remote control devices are particularly useful and often life-saving in situations and activities in locations that are too dangerous for humans, such as locating landmines or landing a rocket on Mars to take samples. In these instances, remote control is necessary as it allows the user to be a considerable distance away and therefore danger free. A remote controlled robot designed to gather information on Mars will include a data logger to record measurements such as temperature.

13.1.2.4 Complexity

As well as the relatively simple GUIs used every day in homes and offices, there are also some extremely complex ones. For example, fly by wire systems are used in aircraft to replace human actions. Virtual reality systems used to train pilots, astronauts and racing drivers provide opportunities to gain experience and learn from potentially life threatening activities without risking human life. These methods of training are also more cost-effective, as they avoid the need for aircraft or racing cars, racing tracks, fuel, etc. Additional equipment such as a **head up display** enhances the virtual experience – for example, simulated skiing down snowy slopes in the Alps.

What does it mean?

Head up displays are worn on the head like glasses and can be used to watch DVDs or experience a virtual activity.

The latest developments in virtual activities require the user to make physical movements in order to interact with the gaming device in simulated sports such as golf and tennis.

13.1.3 Economy

The rapid developments in computers and the features offered have changed the way the economy operates. For example, automation by interacting with computers enables greater productivity, which equals reduced costs.

The range and accessibility of interfaces and the devices where they feature support employees in the way in which they are able to interact with computers – for example, adjusting a robotic machine to cut sheet metal, operating a till in a supermarket or instructing a machine to bake another two dozen cakes.

In the world of business, time is money. Users being able to more easily and quickly give and respond to commands from devices through interfaces results in greater productivity. For example, it takes considerably less time and expertise to analyse data and produce a graph using a **wizard** than to produce one without a wizard or, indeed, without a computer.

What does it mean?

A **wizard** is a programme that enables a user to carry out a complex task by following a series of simple steps using dialogue boxes.

Another example is the speed and reliability with which a database can be constructed, also by using a wizard. When considering such benefits, you will need to consider the length of time it takes to develop HCI, the cost of production and how to make it user-friendly. The cost of producing interfaces has become more competitive due to the increased worldwide number of experts with the knowledge and skill required.

When developing HCI, you will need to consider how to reduce the amount of effort or knowledge for the user to input and whether the use of **text readers** might be beneficial.

What does it mean?

A **text reader** is software that translates text into speech.

An example of a text reader is the BT voice message which relays a text message sent to a landline. Although the message is somewhat inhuman, it does enable the recipient to listen to a message while carrying out another task.

■ Automatic judgement of output

Another example of where increased automation has impacted on the economy is automatic judgement of output. An example of this in use is the grading of produce, such as apples, eggs or potatoes, by size and weight – they pass along a conveyor belt containing holes – a predetermined grade of produce drops through the hole, thus batching items of equal size. In some wineries, for example, in Chile, this method is used for separating the leaves and stalks from grapes before turning them into wine. In Tasmania, however, they still grade apples by hand.

Technology has impacted on organisations that are able to use computers to measure overall output. For example, in the nuclear industry, processes use online monitoring systems to test chemical makeup and ensure the quality of the end product. Technology now allows the decision maker to be the customer – for example, where a consumer is able to provide an example of a desired colour and the paint manufacturer provides an exact match to the customer's requirements.

■ Voice input

Voice input has provided organisations with the opportunity to reduce the need for call centres. An example of this is telephone banking, which uses automated voice input to request, record and relay bank account details straight into a computer for fielding or dealing with enquiries. Utility suppliers also use this method for users to phone in with their meter readings. Some global satellite systems (GPS) respond to voice input and are an example of the consumer becoming part of the process – the GPS instructs the user to turn right, go straight on, etc.

■ Thought input

There are different ideas about what thought input actually means. Some might say that since the introduction of computers, thought input from the individual has been minimised because computers often make decisions for us. An exaggerated example was portrayed in the TV comedy series Little Britain: a customer asks for a bank loan, the bank teller types the details into the computer and responds with, 'The computer says no.' The computer had a set of criteria which it used to make a decision and the human interacting with it could not affect that decision.

Another example of the user's thought input being unnecessary is when the computer carries out a task such as generating a graph from a spreadsheet. The user only needs to enter the figures and the computer does all the work of creating the graph (see also section 13.1.3.1 on page 135).

Research is being carried out in America into the use of micro chips implanted in the skull to test whether a user could 'think' commands to a computer. Users incapable of speech or movement would benefit from being able to interact with computers and possibly carry out a number of tasks. Research has also shown that similar devices have been used to enable a stroke victim to generate signals which move an on-screen cursor to select messages.

13.1.3.3 Varied working environments

Employees are experiencing an ever-changing working environment because of advances in technology. The equipment used in the workplace has changed considerably over the last 20 years. In the 1980s fax machines had only just been introduced, mobile phones were the size of bricks and very rare, and most administrative tasks were carried out manually, with little help from computers.

Today, not only is the equipment more varied, but also the environments within which we work. For example, there has been a considerable shift to home and remote working. Technological developments have made this possible (refer also to Unit 35: Impact of the Use of IT on Business Systems in Book 1).

The range of mobile communications available, such as PDAs (see page 149), mobile phones, wireless Internet connection and Bluetooth, has had a huge effect on the working environment, allowing people to work in locations away from the traditional office.

13.1.4 Culture

The increased opportunities for humans to interact with computers help break down cultural barriers. For example, computerised translators enable users to type in words in their native tongue and vast dictionaries respond with translation in the chosen language. These translators are relatively cheap to buy and easily carried in a pocket or bag. Alternatively, translations are also provided on the Internet.

Activity 13.7

Je ne sais pas! Ich weiß es nicht!

1 Where else can you translate text, apart from using computerised translators and the Internet?

2 Find out which languages are available within operating systems (such as Windows). How many languages are provided?

3 What other language features are available?

Activity 13.8

HCI influences
Investigate the following influences of HCI.

1 Society – how HCI features in our lives. Keep a log over a week identifying every time you use a computer or computerised device. List the item, what you used it for, the day and date.

2 Economy. Investigate the impact of HCI on one of the following:

a) wealth: of a nation or an individual or the exploitation of workers

b) job changes: due to automation or the paperless office

c) market: growth in products, availability, desire to own the latest gadgets, etc.

3 Culture. Find examples of how HCI helps to break down barriers.

4 Be prepared to discuss your findings in class.

Activity 13.9

Technology in the working environment

1 Investigate the use of IT in BT (British Telecom).

2 Identify the way it is used and how it has impacted on jobs.

3 Put together a case for and against those developments – include the impact in the workplace and on the environment, society and culture.

4 Contribute to a debate in class. You will be asked to represent a team that is either for or against increased use of technology in the working environment.

13.1.4.1 How people use computers

Technological developments have supported employees and workers in carrying out everyday activities and have contributed to the growth in numbers of people working from home. For example, texting has grown rapidly and can be used as an alternative to speaking in order to confirm meetings with people in other organisations or to advise on delivery schedules. PDAs and other devices are used in addition to or as replacements for paper diaries and enable remote access to the Internet and file documents such as spreadsheets and databases. Emails have now mostly replaced internal **memos** and in some cases formal letters.

What does it mean?

Memo stands for **memorandum** and is a short note used within an organisation between colleagues.

On the more social side, portable music has developed with the use of MP3 players and iPods. Increasingly sophisticated games are readily available through Xbox and PlayStation. However, there are some adverse effects of the increased use of computers, such as the reduction in verbal and face-to-face communication and the opportunity for employees to hide behind a computer

rather than give verbal instructions or criticism. Some people might say that professionalism is being lost through the widespread use of emails, as there is currently no universal protocol for email language and layout.

Remember!

Domestic appliances rely on in-built computers.

Activity 13.10

I couldn't live without . . .

1 Produce a list of all the technology you can identify.

2 Differentiate between technology that is used for domestic appliances, communication, leisure activities, identification, etc.

3 Having written your list, identify all the items that you possess. Select the item you consider to be the most useful device and that you could not live without. Explain why.

4 Identify the device that, in your opinion, is the least useful and also explain why.

13.1.4.2 Psychological and sociological impact of IT

There is a psychological impact on workers and employees as a result of the development of HCI.

There is less variety of work in some environments, such as where robots are used in manufacturing, and the work is often less specialised. This is called deskilling and can lead to workers feeling less valued and motivated. Automated machinery has taken away the need for some specialist trades such as wood machining and milling or turning as automation reduces costs considerably.

Activity 13.11

It's an automated world!

1 Identify several users who have a portable VCR/DVD player or a laptop. Carry out a survey of these users using the following questions. You can add your own questions to this list.

   a) Is the device used for work and, if so, what for?

   b) What difference does it make to the user's life?

   c) How does the user access the activities available on the device – by GUIs, menus or 'run'?

   d) How useful is the device and why?

   e) Is the user confident with using all the features of the device (e.g. setting the DVD recorder)?

   f) How easy (or not) was the device to use initially?

   g) How easy (or not) did they find accessing the activity/software/feature when they first started using it?

   h) Does the user take the device on holiday? If so, what do they use it for?

   i) What difference has it made to the user to be able to interact with the device?

2 Carry out at least four interviews and bring the results to class.

3 What difference has it made to the users you surveyed to be able to interact with their computers through GUIs?

Some trades are in danger of dying out or being so seldom available that costs have escalated. Examples include traditional furniture manufacture, stained glass making, dressmaking and tailoring. The division of labour and technological development have led to the reduction of the scope of an individual's work to one, or perhaps a few, specialised tasks. Work is fragmented and individuals lose the integrated skills and comprehensive knowledge of the craftsperson. (Read more about the impact of technology on businesses in Unit 35 in Book 1.)

Activity 13.12

'In their shoes'

1 Put yourself in the shoes of a worker who is affected by deskilling. Do the same for the worker's family and then for the employer. What will be the psychological effects for each of these people? The employer is possibly quite content with the developments, as productivity is more reliable and costs reduced. However, the worker will not necessarily feel the same and this might also have effects on their family.

2 Research Samsung and LG products (from South Korea), Sony (Japan), Quanta (Taiwan) and China (more recently the microchip and iPODs) and consider:

   a) if workers feel useful and motivated and whether they have job satisfaction

   b) the impact that changes in production methods have had in developing nations

   c) the impact of production shifting to the Far East on UK industry and jobs

   d) the way in which their 'new found wealth' impacts on nations such as China.

3 Be prepared to discuss your findings.

Test your knowledge

1 What does multi-tap mean?

2 What is E-D and what is it used for?

3 Give two examples of activities where remote control robots might save lives.

4 What does speech-activated software do?

5 What type of software provides exercises for the brain? Does it have other uses?

6 What does a head up display do?

7 What features does Microsoft apply to GUIs to make the user feel comfortable?

This section helps you to understand the essential values to apply when designing an interface.

13.2.1 Perception

Perceptions vary between the developer and the user. The user might not be aware of the fine detail in a GUI, such as the importance of colour or the positioning of the GUI on the desktop and how these aspects may affect the ease with which it can be used. The developer may not be the same person as the designer or the one carrying out the interview with the client, so may not be fully aware of the client's needs. The client may not always be the user and most certainly won't be able to fully represent the desires or requirements of all the users.

13.2.1.1 Colour

When designing GUIs, you need to be very aware of the use of colour. Microsoft Office uses grey as the predominant colour, blue for the title bar and for enhancing drop-down lists and highlighting some text. Many users feel that grey is boring or dull. However, if bright red or black had been used, it would soon become uncomfortable on the eye.

Colours affect different people in different ways. For example, some individuals find yellow easier to read, while others find it difficult to deal with as it can appear fuzzy. Users with certain medical conditions such as dyslexia may be affected by colour in different ways.

If you decide to design a GUI with a 3D effect, you will discover the importance of the **trichromatic system**.

What does it mean?

The **trichromatic system** uses combinations of the three colours that are the basis of 3D vision: red, blue and green.

Activity 13.13

What's in a colour?

1 Study three different types of GUI.

2 Identify the impact different colours have on you. Write down your experiences.

3 Identify any aspects of consistency and special features that you find useful. Make notes on what and why.

4 Compare your findings with some of your peers and note down any differences.

■ Luminance

The three colours of the trichromatic system are detected by three different types of cells on the retina of the eye, which are known as receptors. There has been a lot of work done on developing the theory of this system into a definition of the signals that these receptors generate and it is believed that these signals take the form of red-green, yellow-blue and black-white signals. These signals are called opponent colour channels because they relay information about opposite colours. The word luminance is used to describe these and the theory goes on to say that there is a hierarchy of luminance, red-green – yellow-blue – black-white and the early colour pairings cannot effectively display detail. This leads to a fundamental rule of design … to display the best detail we should always use luminance contrasts.

Activity 13.14

1 Create a screen background of graduated shades of one colour from lightest at the top to darkest at the bottom. Now type a piece of text in a different colour from top to bottom of the screen. Where do you get most detail and the sharpest image. Try this with different colour combinations.

■ Pop out effect

Where a display has a lot of symbols or imagery, how do you make one symbol or image stand out? It can be done by aligning them differently, colouring them differently or by adjusting to a different shape. This makes the symbol or piece of text or image, etc. stand out and is known as the pop out effect. More correctly it is called the Preattentive Processing Theory. It is something with which you can experiment.

Our eyes observe colours using the trichromatic system, which comprises the three colours red, blue and green (not the primary colours red, blue and yellow). We can be tricked into believing that a wider range of colours has been used. Some devices rely on the luminance of colours. DayGlo colours might have value in some games, but unconsidered or excessive use can be irritating and might have adverse effects on individuals with certain health or sight conditions, as might the use of flashing images and lights. Nevertheless, if designing a GUI to be used in poor light or at night, then luminance might be essential.

Most important is the market value of your GUI. In order to achieve credibility and status, it will need to look professional and stylish. Therefore, over-use of colours and extremes of colour will reduce its professionalism. It needs to be 'fit for purpose'.

13.2.1.2 Pattern

The user might think of pattern as the picture on the GUI or its layout, whereas to the designer the word pattern might mean a template. For example, Microsoft uses a template for its dialogue boxes. The template provides consistency and evenness (symmetry). It aids the way the user relates to the interface, providing user-friendliness and **connectedness**.

What does it mean?

Connectedness is the ease with which users move from one location to another, such as between software applications which appear familiar and therefore less threatening.

Consistency helps the user to feel comfortable with what happens next (for example, clicking on **Save As …** allows you to save with a new filename). Templates are likely to include colour, format, layout and common groupings (with menus, options). Early GUI designs (see page 128) laid the foundations and subsequent developments and changes have resulted in apparent simplicity (from the user's point of view), standardisation and consistency of interfaces (see page 133).

Activity 13.15

Connectedness

1 Pick up a GUI on your computer desktop and move it to another position. What happens the next time you instruct the same action, before closing and re-opening the application?

2 What happens when you close and re-open the application, then re-open the same GUI?

3 Try the same exercise with other applications and note down what happens with each GUI.

4 Open three applications by the same software producer (e.g. Microsoft) and make a list of the similarities and the differences between the applications.

4 Compare your findings with other members of your group.

Pattern perception is one of the fundamental processes in our perception of displays and objects. A set of laws, originally the Gestalt laws, have been formulated to describe our pattern perception and form rules for our designs:

- **Proximity:** we view things which are close together as a group.
- **Continuity:** smooth continuous lines are more easily interpreted than rapidly changing lines.
- **Symmetry:** we see symmetrical shapes easier than unsymmetrical shapes.
- **Similarity:** we see similar objects as a group, dissimilar objects tend to be viewed as individuals (a manifestation of the pop out effect).

Common Groupings

- **Fate:** we see objects which move together as a group.
- **Region:** we see objects which are enclosed together in some way, as a group.
- **Connected:** we see objects connected by continuous lines as related to each other.

13.2.1.3 Objects

All components of a GUI or any other form of image display are built using a number of separate objects. Each object appears in a hierarchical system; in other words, the images are layered. It is crucial to identify which image appears first and the subsequent images which overlay the first image. Otherwise, an interface might appear to the user as an incomplete object. If images are sitting behind or in front of other images, then the entire interface will not be visible. An example is that the GUI should appear in front of any text on the desktop. If it is built incorrectly, it could appear behind the existing image on the desktop, which is visually confusing (see Figure 13.5).

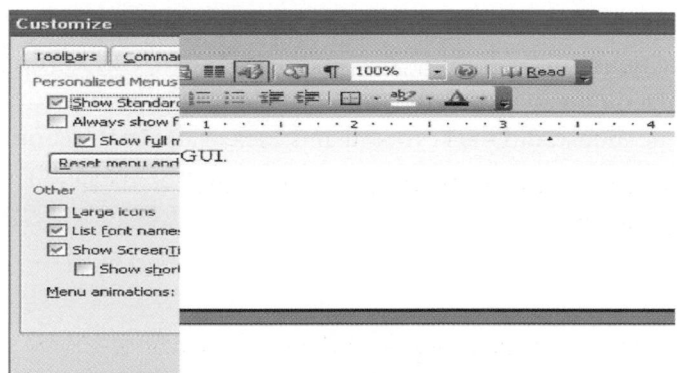

▲ **Figure 13.5 Desktop image on top of GUI**

■ Positioning

To expand on the concept of positioning and layering further, if the positioning of the object has not been accurately arranged then the GUI, or parts of the GUI, may appear behind the main screen. The user will not be able to access the full range of commands, if at all.

Another consideration is the positioning on the face of the interface. If the GUI appears too far across the screen, it may be difficult to see or it might obscure other features that need to be visible.

■ Geons and gross 3D shapes

Geons and gross 3D shapes are used to provide some consistency when reproducing images.

What does it mean?

Geons are 2D images that are quickly recognisable by the user from almost any angle.

Geons are uncomplicated objects that are made of a range of essential properties that enable the viewer to identify the image from almost any angle. Geons are less complex to design and easier to recognise than 3D images. They are also relatively cheap to produce. In contrast, 3D images can more easily be misinterpreted due to the perception of the observer. You will need to consider how a user might view an object when designing your GUI.

Activity 13.16

All is not as it would seem

1 What springs to mind when you look at Figure 13.6 (see following page)?

2 Compare your results with those of your peers.

Gross 3D shapes are used in video games and are also relatively cheap to produce. They do not require exact reproduction and are used to transmit images in **real time**, for example, large screens at football matches and other sporting events or security X-ray machines.

As well as the cost involved in the time taken to design and produce an image, you also need to consider the cost and speed of running such an image (read more in section 13.4.1.2 on page 151).

What does it mean?

Real time transmission results in audio and video signals being transmitted almost instantaneously.

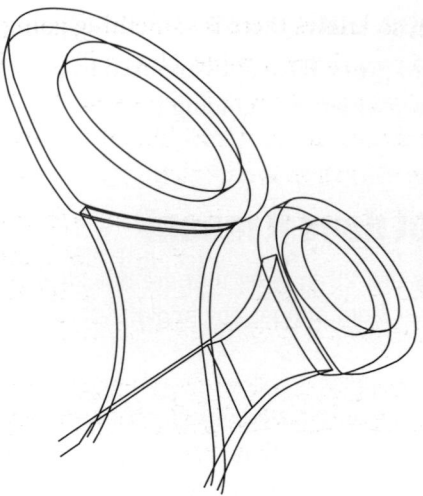

▲ **Figure 13.6 What is this 3D image?**

In some instances cost becomes less of an issue. For example, the use of a gross 3D image produced from a robot on a lunar landing might be essential to present a realistic picture, and would be used almost regardless of cost.

Activity 13.17

An icon

1 Design a very simple image that could feature on a dialogue box/GUI as an icon to represent an action or instruction (e.g. a door representing exit, a pointing finger, etc.).

2 Produce a storyboard identifying the stages for producing the image.

3 Produce your icon.

4 Note down exactly how long it takes to carry out stages 1–3 of this activity.

5 Ask one of your peers to review your icon and provide constructive feedback.

6 Storyboards are discussed in *Unit 21: Website Production and Management*.

13.2.2 Behaviour models

There are a number of models that predict the way in which an interface or user will behave. Some of these are identified in this subsection.

There are a number of **predictive models** that provide guidance when designing interfaces and systems. This is a way of pre-empting what will happen without having to carry out lengthy research and delay the introduction of the interface while lots of people test it out.

The reaction time to respond to a command from a GUI will vary depending on the user. Consideration must be given to whether or not the interface will be responsive to time, e.g. shut down if a reaction or command takes too long.

What does it mean?

A **predictive model** is an equation or calculation used to forecast an event.

■ The keystroke-level model (KLM)

KLM recognises very low-level actions. The model breaks down each sequence of operations into individual actions, such as hitting keys on the keyboard, clicking on the mouse, pointing the mouse, moving between using the mouse and the keyboard and back again. Each action is assigned a time in order to calculate how the system will respond.

Activity 13.18

I predict . . .

1 Write down how long you predict it will take to power up your computer, log in and access one application.

2 Carry out the activity while timing. Write down the results and compare with your peers.

3 Try the same activity using all mouse actions and then again using all keyboard actions where possible.

4 Identify how long it takes for the system to respond.

The throughput (TP)

TP relates to the productivity of the computer. Throughput measures include the amount or speed of processing in response to a command. Other measures of productivity include performance in terms of speed of processing and any variation in relation to the number of tasks and complexity. This is called response time.

Fitts' Law

Fitts' Law is a method for calculating throughput in advance for any system design by predicting human movement and motion based on time and distance (called psychomotor behaviour). It was developed in 1954 to counteract the assumption that the time taken for something to travel from A to B is likely to be based on the distance between the two points. Fitts' Law identified that time depends upon the size of the object to be moved and the size of the object with which to move it. User time will vary according to user, the location of an icon, menu or GUI, the click of the mouse button or hitting a key and even the pressure applied.

13.2.2.2 Descriptive modelling

This section considers three descriptive models:

- the key-action model (KAM)
- Buxton's three state model (see Figure 13.8)
- Guiard's model (see Figure 13.9).

The key-action model (KAM)

KAM identifies the need to evaluate how the user will expect the computer to behave or react and how this may be different from how the computer actually reacts to commands. For example, when a user who is completely new to computers is logging on to a computer, they are likely to find it difficult to understand why they have to type in the username and password completely accurately, otherwise they cannot log on. Similarly, users will get confused and frustrated when they think they have selected 'Shift F' but the File menu drops down because they have accidentally hit 'Alt F'.

Sometimes, there is a delay in the computer carrying out a command, maybe because it is carrying out a background save, but the user receives feedback with the

egg timer, so knows there is something going on and that they need to wait for a while. How will you give your users feedback and how will you make sure that they know what it means and how long they have to wait before the operation is complete?

Other feedback examples include the depression and suppression of buttons on dialogue boxes and invitations or steering to the next most likely command by highlighting a button (see Figure 13.7).

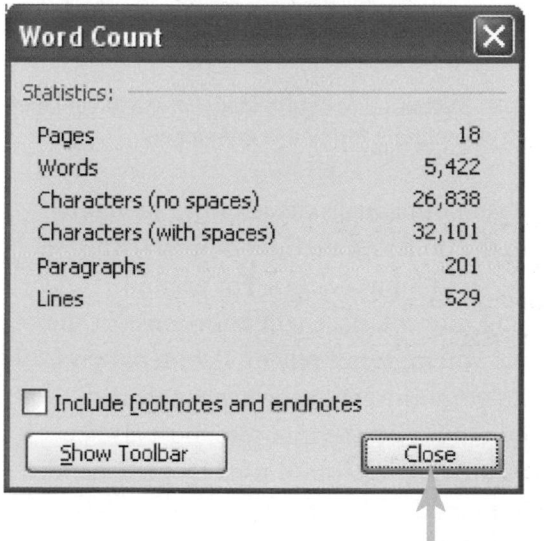

Note the highlighting around this button

▲ **Figure 13.7 A dialogue box with highlighted button**

Buxton's three state model

Buxton's three state model (see Figure 13.8) is concerned with the pressure and dexterity with which users make movements using mice and touchpads. When designing the interface, you should consider the amount of effort or pressure the user will need to make to give or respond to a command. For example, the interface will need to be responsive whether the command is via the mouse, a touchpad on a laptop or a roller button in the keyboard.

This model also identifies the ease of use by many users with a mouse as opposed to a touchpad. This may depend on the regularity of use by a user. For example, someone who frequently uses a touchpad might argue that it is far easier and quicker to use than taking a hand away from the keyboard to reach for the mouse. The same argument might apply to a predominantly keyboard user who prefers keystrokes to mouse use.

■ Guiard's model of bimanual skill

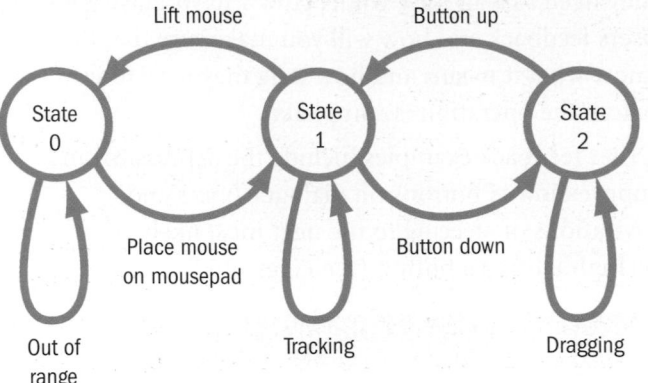

Figure 13.8 Buxton's three state model of graphical input with labels appropriate for mouse interaction

Guiard's model of bimanual skill as shown in Figure 13.9 relates to the preferred method of interacting with computers and input devices. For example, when designing your interface you must consider the ease of use and you must not rely on the user always inputting data or mouse actions using a preferred hand. The positioning on the interface must also be accessible and logically laid out if used by a left-handed person. Guiard's model identifies that users with two hands are unlikely to be able to carry out similar actions to the same degree of effectiveness with either hand.

Activity 13.19

Preferences

1 Select two different interfaces. One might be on the computer while another might be on a standalone game that uses a joystick. Alternatively it might be the same interface using two different command methods, such as a game operated by a mouse or joystick and the same game using keystroke actions.

2 For each of the two interfaces, using your preferred hand, which interface is easier to use and why? Make a list of each action you carry out and its degree of ease. You can use a four-point scale to do this (1 = very easy, 4 = very difficult) and the time (in seconds) it takes to carry out.

3 Identify response time and user time.

4 Now carry out the same actions but with your other hand and answer the same questions.

5 Compare the differences in your findings. Overall, which method was easier and with which hand? Why was this? Was the same method easier for both hands? Be prepared to discuss your findings.

STOP Test your knowledge

1 What are the main features of the KAM model?

2 When would you apply the Guiard model?

3 What is the difference between descriptive and behaviour modelling?

4 What does predictive modelling mean?

▼ **Figure 13.9 The Guiard model**

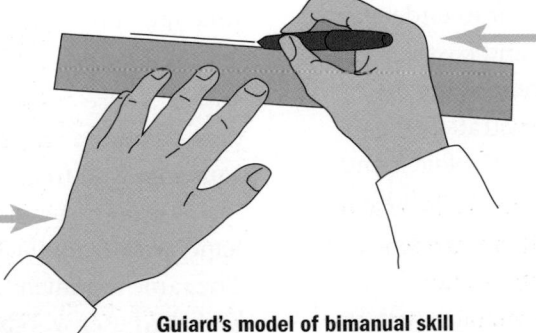

Non-preferred hand
· leads the preferred hand
· sets the spatial frame of reference for the preferred hand
· performs coarse movements

Preferred hand
· follows the non-preferred hand
· works within established frame of reference set by the non-preferred hand
· performs fine movements

Guiard's model of bimanual skill

13.2.3 Information processing

This section explores information processing – in other words, how information is processed (or to be processed) and how fast this is done.

Activity 13.20

This would be even better if . . .

The interface may require the user to make a decision and some decisions take longer than others to make.

1 Identify an interface, perhaps one you use regularly.

2 Make a list of the adaptations that you think would improve the way it currently processes information and/or the speed with which it does this.

3 Be prepared to discuss your results.

13.2.3.1 Humans as a component

One of the key variables in HCI design is the human end user! The human factor is not only difficult to manage but it can also be difficult to identify people's needs and expectations. One way to prepare for all eventualities is to carry out a **risk assessment**. For example, if the user selects option X before option Y, what happens?

What does it mean?

A **risk assessment** is an analysis of a task against each of the steps that could be taken to achieve the task.

13.2.3.2 Human information processing (HIP)

Human information processing (HIP) means the way in which we absorb information, analyse it, use it and do something with it. Our brains (which can be compared to the hardware of a computer), take the

Activity 13.21

How much of a risk?

1 Refer to Guiard's model opposite (see also Figure 13.9) and produce a risk assessment based on this question: What happens if the user gives an instruction to the interface with the mouse in the left hand and uses the right-hand mouse button instead of the left?

2 Repeat Question 1 for this situation: If a key or the spacebar is selected instead of the mouse, what does the user have to do next if the 'Esc' key is selected?

3 A flow chart approach is effective in identifying possibilities of the type 'If this route is taken what will happen?'. In other words, 'What are the risks?' Be prepared to discuss in class.

4 Carry out some Internet research into 'human information processing' and make notes on what you find out.

information, then use the mind (the software) in order to process it. The output depends on our previous knowledge, our ability to interpret information and even our willingness to do something with it (as the decision maker).

Improvements in HIP may be achieved by altering the information provided, by improving the ability of decision makers and by the construction of formal models of human decision making, such as the one shown in Figure 13.10.

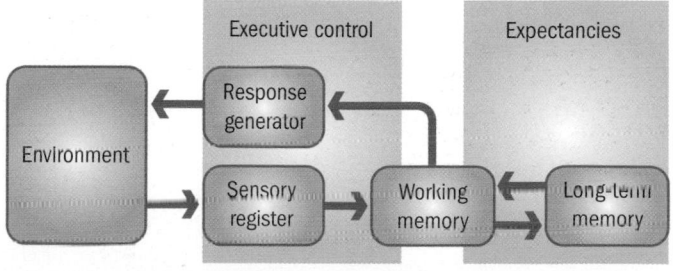

▲ **Figure 13.10 A model of human information processing**

The **GOMS** model can predict the time it will take for an action to be carried out or a command followed. The designer identifies a goal (outcome of intended action) when using a series of operators and lists the method and selection (i.e. mouse or keystroke) in order to carry out the action (or command). This enables the designer to calculate the time it will take to execute the action and identify any risks or loopholes – assuming the user carries out instructions as anticipated. The designer can use the results to identify which method of user interface is more efficient, based on the user's requirements.

What does it mean?

GOMS stands for **goals, operators, methods and selection**. It provides a model for how the user will behave when carrying out a series of well-known tasks.

Test your knowledge

1 What is HIP?

2 Why are humans one of the key variables in HCI design?

3 How could we improve the way in which we process information?

Designing and producing simple interactive computer input and output based on HCI principles

When designing and producing your own simple interactive computer input and output, you will need to demonstrate that you have taken care to base all your decisions on the HCI principles covered in section 13.2. This section focuses on how these principles apply to input, output and specialist situations.

13.3.1 Input

This subsection relates to the tools which a user is likely to use to input information, such as the keyboard, mouse and monitor.

13.3.1.1 Using the keyboard, mouse and monitor

A simplified input might rely on mouse use only, with minimum use of keystrokes, which generally rely on memory. However, some users prefer to use mainly keystrokes and some of these users may wish not to use the mouse at all. Your system might rely on the mouse or keyboard for some commands or you could offer your users a choice, so that there is more than one way of carrying out the same action. If there is the chance of more than one user, then there is likely to be more than one preference.

For any single Microsoft command, there are very often at least four different ways to carry it out (e.g. to save a file: File, Save; Ctrl S; Shift F12; the Save icon on the toolbar). In some cases there is the shortcut menu option as well. The user may be particularly experienced (a power user) and equipped with a wealth of knowledge and techniques which they expect to use. Equally, the user may be a novice, new to interacting with computers (this is discussed further in Unit 28 in Book 1).

Activity 13.23

How long?

1 Select one of the actions you identified in Activity 13.22 and time how long it takes to carry out each of the methods. Write the times next to the method and then compare with your peers.

2 Once you have made these comparisons, consider whether they are fair comparisons. For example, if you click on the toolbar button to print a document, does the overall action take longer or less time than selecting from the menu and is the result the same? Bring your results to class for further work.

Activity 13.22

More than one way

1 Compile a list of at least 20 different actions and list three (or more) alternative methods to carry out the same action.

2 Go back over the list and identify your preferred method for each action.

3 Compare your results with your peers or family members.

4 Continue to add to the list every time you discover another action and the alternative methods of carrying it out.

Another consideration is the use of the mouse and how this will interact with the computer. For example, if the GUI interacts with the mouse, you will need to ensure that the user knows which mouse button and how many clicks are required in order to carry out a command. When designing your interface, you will also need to consider what is happening with the other mouse button as it cannot just lie redundant.

To simplify your system and maybe reduce the development time, you might decide to minimise the number of keystrokes and mouse movements. Pay attention to the layout of the interface so that users can locate commands and input areas without having to move around the interface in an illogical order – this would rely too heavily on the dexterity of the user. You must consider whether a logical sequence to perform an action is necessary or whether it should be up to the user. For example, if your system expects the user to save after instructing a command or inputting data, this may not suit all users, some of whom may wish to save first or during the action to avoid losing the data. You will need to ensure the system responds in a consistent way whether the user clicks softly or hits keys firmly.

Activity 13.24

'Office extras'

1 Try the Microsoft option StickyKeys. What is its purpose?

2 Who would find it beneficial and why?

3 What is the narrator?

4 How can visually impaired users receive feedback from the keyboard?

5 Find out if there are any other adaptations included for users with disabilities.

6 What other extras do Microsoft provide within Windows?

13.3.1.2 Use of other input devices

This subsection explores devices that may be preferred by the user. For example, an end user might want to use a **concept keyboard** (see below).

You might be asked to design a system that responds to voice input or operates by using a **joystick**.

What does it mean?

A **concept keyboard** (or overlay keyboard) has keys that have been preset to specific functions. The keys often have images or symbols to guide the user. A concept keyboard can do anything a QWERTY keyboard and/or a mouse can do. For example, it can be used to access the Internet, run programs, play movies and music.

 A concept keyboard

What does it mean?

A **joystick** is an input device which can be used for playing video games.

The benefits of using a joystick are that they are easy to use and no specialist knowledge or dexterity is needed to play a game. For example, in early versions of space invader games and flight simulators, specific keystrokes such as Ctrl + Shift + arrow keys were required.

Research states that most, if not all, of us will experience a disability of some degree at some stage of our lives. The disability could be, for example, a broken wrist, **RSI**, a bad back or even headaches. Each affects ways of working and may require specialist input devices.

 ## Remember!

RSI stands for **repetitive strain injury**. This common complaint can result from overuse of a computer mouse.

Activity 13.25

What does it do and how much is it?

1 Carry out some research to identify and produce a comprehensive list of adaptive technology and techniques available, what each is for and how much it costs. You can build on the list you obtained from your teacher (refer also to section 13.1.1.5 on page 131). Disabilities for which assistive technology exists include arthritis, visual and hearing impairments and RSI, though there are many more which you will discover during your research (e.g. StickyKeys).

2 You will need to bring this list to class for further work.

13.3.1.3 Designs for input on other devices

Until now the focus has been mainly on designing a GUI for a computer, but GUIs are also needed for other devices, such as mobile phones and **PDA**s, as well as voice-activated systems for **DAB** radios. Designing a DAB radio display requires similar skills to those needed when designing for projection to an audience.

What does it mean?

PDA stands for **personal digital assistant** and is a hand-held computer.

DAB stands for **digital audio broadcasting** – these radios require no tuning and provide a clearer, crisper sound than traditional radios.

13.3.2 Output

This section explores systems designed for the output of information.

13.3.2.1 Output to monitor or printer

You will already be familiar with some examples of output devices, such as the interface on a scanner or printer. Some printers do not require a computer to read

the data or image in order to provide a print out. These printers either take a memory card containing digital images from a camera or connect to the camera direct by **USB** port.

These types of printer can be used by someone who has little or no knowledge of how to use a computer, yet wants to print out photographs with ease.

What does it mean?

USB stands for **universal serial bus** and enables files to be transferred and stored by inserting the flat end into a computer with a USB port.

Activity 13.26

Finite steps

1 Identify the steps you would expect to take when printing directly from a digital camera to a printer. Include how to put a memory card into the printer and obtain print-outs.

2 Draw a flow diagram to set out these steps.

13.3.2.2 Output to other devices

There are other output tools which use on-screen GUIs such as data projectors for projecting images and presentations onto a screen. **Interactive whiteboards** have a list of menus which are activated by the mouse or touching the board with a special pen or using a finger.

What does it mean?

An **interactive whiteboard** is a screen which has a touch-sensitive display and can connect to the Internet, file servers and computer applications. Information can be written on the screen with a special marker pen and changes can be made and stored in the same way as when working on a computer.

These menus are used to access many of the features available on a computer with additional features such as writing on the board, underlining text from the Internet and saving note pages for accessing later. Specialist software for interpreting text into speech is another output example.

13.3.3 Specialist input and output

To avoid producing an interface that is not accessible for a user with a disability, you might consider designing an interface that uses speech-activated software. However, you will need to consider how easy it will be to use if your user has a speech impediment such as a lisp. Would the interface work at all? Would it respond differently to such a user?

If you refer back to the subsection on the pop out effect (page 140) you can consider how it could enhance the appearance and usability of your interface for users with visual impairments.

Other specialist software is available for users with a physical disability who may require adaptive or assistive technology (see pages 131 and 134). Remote control devices can also be used to input or receive output from the interface.

STOP

Test your knowledge

1 What does "pop out effect" mean?

2 Name at least five different methods for giving instructions to a computer.

3 What does RSI mean?

4 Why might you decide to minimise the number of keystrokes and mouse movements used?

5 What does a concept keyboard offer?

6 Give some examples of where output devices do not require a PC.

This section considers how to identify differences between different input and output designs and how to measure their effectiveness. The most effective and reliable way to identify differences and make comparisons is to carry out both **quantitative** and **qualitative research**. Research methods might include use of questionnaires or surveys, interviewing and reading. This section helps you to identify some areas you should include in this research.

What does it mean?

Quantitative research involves collecting data that can be measured and counted. The data collected can usually be presented in the form of graphs, tables and charts. It is important to use a large enough sample to ensure that you have used sufficient 'quantity' for the results to be valid and not guesswork.

Qualitative research involves collecting information about people's opinions, views and preferences about something. It allows you to make 'quality' judgements about your findings (based on fact, not on your own opinions).

13.4.1 Quantitative measures of effectiveness

Research can return different results depending on the number (quantity) of responses to each question. This will determine the value of the research outcomes.

For example, if you ask three young people from a large city if they prefer ITV to Channel 4 and two out of three say yes, does this mean that the majority of the whole population of the UK also agree? You might have unknowingly asked predominantly ITV viewers, whereas if you asked another group of people (perhaps from a different place or of a different age or background), they might give you different answers.

You need to make sure that you ask a large enough sample of people who are representative of all the people who will be using your interface.

When you carry out research you will need a checklist containing the questions you are going to ask. Otherwise, you may ask different questions to different people and the results of the research will not compare exactly. The saying often used is 'you can't compare apples with pears'.

Quantitative measures of research include speed, costs and comparisons with the original needs and with other systems. These all produce quantitative data that can be measured.

13.4.1.1 Speed

One of the features of an interface that is fundamental to its effectiveness is the speed at which it interacts with the user. Issues of speed include:

- how quickly the user can input a command
- the speed at which the user can (or has to) type in any data (does the GUI 'time out' if reaction isn't fast enough?)
- the speed of throughput (such as the response back from the interface)
- the length of time it takes the user to comprehend the result.

13.4.1.2 Comparative costs

Another major factor is the running costs of the interface in comparison to what was used before, which may have been a more traditional approach. If there are a large number of images on the interface or it relies on other programs to support it, then it is likely that the cost of power increases. You will need to consider whether the interface requires additional staffing costs to use or maintain it.

13.4.1.3 Comparison with original needs

You will also need to make a comparison between the product you have provided and the original needs of the user. How closely does it match the original design or requirement of the originator? To find this out, you will need to ask questions such as:

- How many features are fully included?
- How many are partially included?
- How many features are not included?
- How closely does it meet the needs of the client/user?

13.4.1.4 Comparison with other systems

It is important for you to compare your system with other similar systems, as these will provide ideas for further improvements. However, bear in mind that 'you can't compare apples with pears' and be realistic with your evaluation. For example, if the system your interface is running on does not have the power or performance of the system you are comparing it with, it will not be a fair comparison.

13.4.2 Qualitative measures of effectiveness

Qualitative measures are more subjective and the value of the information you obtain will depend largely on the quality of the questions you ask. For example, if you ask a closed question such as 'Do you like food?' the answer is likely to be simply 'Yes'. This doesn't tell you what the person likes about food or what types of food they prefer. Therefore, any evaluation of the answers provided would not provide sufficient information to ensure the food was to the person's liking. However, if you asked an open question such as 'What type of food do you like best?' the answer would be far more informative. If you were then to ask 'Why?' you would be even better informed. The main difference between these questions is that the first question is a closed question (which returns a yes/no answer) and the subsequent questions are open and more meaningful.

Always try to avoid asking leading questions, as they encourage people to provide the answer wanted rather than what they really think. This makes the answer unreliable. An example of a leading question is 'Do you like tomatoes best because they have a better flavour?'

Qualitative measures of effectiveness include user satisfaction. This will provide qualitative data because you will be collecting the users' opinions.

13.4.2.1 User satisfaction

An essential question is the level of satisfaction by the end user. The end user might not be the same person as the commissioner or originator. Therefore the questions you ask are likely to be different.

To establish the level of user satisfaction you can provide the user with a number of statements or questions and ask the user to grade each statement according to whether they agree/disagree or are satisfied/unsatisfied. Your grading system could use number 1 as the highest level and 4 as the lowest. It is a good idea not to use five grades, as many people tend to go for the middle number, which is the easy option.

Using numbers makes the survey quick and easy to complete and is an easy way to make comparisons and identify trends. For example, you can identify whether the lowest level of satisfaction occurs among a particular type of user.

Don't forget to ask the people you are surveying to give details such as their job title and department, where they work and perhaps what they use the interface for (if there are different uses). Asking for their age and level of computer experience might also be useful. Questions you should include in order to determine user satisfaction should cover the following areas:

- knowledge required
- skills/expertise required
- time to use the interface
- ease of use
- limitations
- usefulness of results
- closeness to original requirement.

13.4.2.2 Comparison with other systems

When carrying out your research, include a question asking the user to make a comparison with other similar systems they have used. This type of question can be graded 1–4 as discussed in section 13.4.2.1. It might also be a good idea to include an open-ended question to get their opinion, e.g. 'In what ways is the new system better than the old one?' and 'In what ways is it worse?' This will help with your evaluation.

13.4.3 Evaluation of interfaces

Once you have carried out your surveys, using these guidelines and including some questions of your own, you need to aggregate your results. It is also a good idea to present the results in a graph, as this can be easier to evaluate.

13.4.3.1 Judgements of effectiveness

Every design must be tested during its build to ensure it meets the users' expectations and requirements. When you carry out these staged checks, use a checklist to remind you what you are going to test and how you are going to measure its effectiveness.

You will need to measure effectiveness and evaluate interfaces to demonstrate your understanding and analytical skills. You should relate to some of the experimentation, such as speed and ease of use. You will also need to identify how closely the system matches the original goal, i.e. the degree to which it is fit for purpose.

Although you do not need to include exact costings, you should compare costs between interfaces and to what degree the interface is value for money. You will need to identify the good points and bad points against which improvements can be made.

13.4.3.2 Improvements

Having carried out the evaluation, you will know what needs to be improved. You will need to identify a plan in order to achieve those improvements. It is also important to evaluate why each improvement is needed and how it enhances the design. For example, does the change make the design more effective or simply more colourful?

Where something doesn't work as well as anticipated or when compared with another system, it should be seen as an opportunity, as it informs improvements. Where something really works well it is harder to see how to improve it, although you should be able to identify how to maintain this level of effectiveness.

Test your knowledge

1 Give at least three examples of questions you would ask the originator of the design and three questions you would ask the end user. Why are these questions different?

2 Explain the difference between open, closed and leading questions.

3 Suggest when each type of question might be used to best effect and which type of question should be avoided.

4 Give three examples of types of research that might be unreliable or of little value.

5 Name three methods of carrying out research.

6 What is the difference between quantitative and qualitative research?

Preparation for assessment

The assessment tasks in this unit are based on the following scenario.

You are working in a temporary position for the local council as a software designer. You have been given an assignment in the department working for the local nurseries, schools and colleges. You have been told that if this project is a success, you will be offered permanent employment and, depending on the quality of the outcome, promotion might also be likely.

The council is eager to provide pupils and students in all their schools, at any age, a range of methods by which to learn and be assessed. However, you will need to enlighten managers in the council that your proposals and designs will benefit the end users based on sound research and simple, easy-to-use products. This provides you with lots of scope for creativity and enables you to demonstrate your abilities in your quest to show how indispensable you are.

Task 1 (P1, M1, D1)

Your starting point on this project is to identify the age range for your designs in order to choose the most appropriate devices for HCI development.

Do one of the following.

- Describe one impact of HCI in recent years on each of society, economy and culture.
- Explain how modern advances in HCI design have contributed to the impact of computers on society, economy and culture.
- Evaluate the HCI developments over recent years, relating them to the impact on society, economy and culture, and predicting one potential future development and what impact that may have.

Task 2 (P2)

To enlighten council managers, explain two fundamental principles of HCI design. In order to help them overcome their limited understanding and experience, provide examples that illustrate or demonstrate these principles, including all your planning material.

Task 3 (P3, M2)

Council managers have formed a review group with representative teachers from the local nursery, primary and secondary schools and colleges. Although very keen on your project, some of the teachers are unsure of how their pupils and students will benefit from it. However, seeing your proposals, they have agreed that they want to see the next stage. They have asked to see your working examples at their next meeting in two weeks' time. At this meeting, they have asked to see an interactive computer input and output based on HCI principles. As the group only comprises representatives, they have asked if there is any way their colleagues might be able to experience your presentation. One of these ways might be to blog it.

As a result of this meeting, the group has requested that you design and create three input HCI to meet given specifications, using a variety of techniques. As all the schools and colleges in the area have a number of learners with specialist needs, you have been asked to design one of the interfaces dedicated to specialist needs. You are reminded that, as you are the 'expert', you will need to indicate some of the principles applied and how the specialist needs are met.

One member of the group has also asked you to design a DAB radio display or perhaps something for projection to an audience. At this stage, the request is only for the design as it might not be taken any further.

Task 4 (P4, P5)

The group has met again to review your designs and is fairly confident that the concept of the project could revolutionise the way pupils and students of all ages and abilities learn. The group has now requested that you design and create three output HCI to meet given specifications, using a variety of techniques.

To develop their understanding and provide some context as to how these HCI might be used, you must briefly describe how each of the input and output HCI you have created meets the specifications provided. You will also compare and contrast, using HCI principles, the effectiveness of different designs of input and output by testing out your designs and gaining feedback.

The group has also asked for comparative costings in terms of 'system A costs more for data input than system B'. You will need to give some indication as to whether the cost differences are considerable or minimal. Therefore, you will need to have some knowledge of where and how costs are derived.

Task 5 (M3, D2)

The project is almost complete but, in order to persuade managers that the project should be extended, you must produce a report describing how to measure the effectiveness of your HCI. Provide user evidence by carrying out surveys and analysing and evaluating the results.

To provide your boss with a conclusive report, compare the HCI you developed with HCI that have been commercially produced for similar products. Include the good and not-so-good features of each and any improvements which could be made.

Event Driven Programming

Introduction

Many modern programming languages are event driven, as this is an approach that works well with computers using GUI operating systems such as Windows. This type of programming uses events such as clicking on a button or moving the mouse pointer over an object as the trigger to run the appropriate code handler, whereas the older style of programming, often called flow driven, only started from one point at the beginning of the code.

As you study this unit you will increase your programming skills, as well as learn how to design and test event driven programs. The design of such a program should meet identified needs so that it fulfils the defined purpose.

You will need to be able to use the tools and techniques of an event driven language by placing controls on to a form and writing code to respond to the events they receive. Code for these event handlers will use constants, variables, loop and selection structures to produce appropriate pathways through the code. You will also recognise the importance of thorough, structured testing of your code using various techniques and be able to review completed code against the original requirements to see how well they have been met.

After completing this unit, you should be able to achieve these outcomes:

- Understand the characteristics and uses of event driven programming
- Be able to use the tools and techniques of an event driven language
- Be able to design and create an event driven application
- Be able to test and review an event driven application.

Grading criteria	Activity	Page number
To achieve a pass grade the evidence must show that the learner is able to:		
p₁ Describe the key features of event driven programs	20.1, PFA	160, 190
p₂ Describe, with examples, typical uses and advantages of event driven programs	20.2, PFA	163, 190
p₃ Demonstrate the use of event driven tools and techniques	20.5, 20.6, 20.7, 20.8, 20.102, PFA	170, 172, 174, 179, 190
p₄ Design and implement two different working event driven applications to meet defined requirements	case studies, PFA	181–184, 191
p₅ Test and document event driven applications	case studies, 20.12, 20.13, 20.14, PFA	181–184, 188, 189, 191
To achieve a merit grade the evidence must show that, in addition to the pass criteria, the learner is able to:		
m₁ Explain how an operating system can be viewed as an event driven application	20.3, PFA	165, 190
m₂ Improve the user interface and functionality of an event driven program based on a formal review	20.13, 20.14, PFA	188, 189, 191
m₃ Compare the use and effectiveness of global and local variables	20.10, PFA	179, 190
To achieve a distinction grade the evidence must show that, in addition to the pass and merit criteria, the learner is able to:		
d₁ Evaluate the suitability of event driven programs for non-graphical applications	20.4, PFA	165, 190
d₂ Justify the tools and techniques used in the production of an event driven application	20.9, PFA	175, 190
d₃ Evaluate an event driven application	20.14, PFA	189, 191

Note: 'PFA' stands for 'Preparation for assessment'.

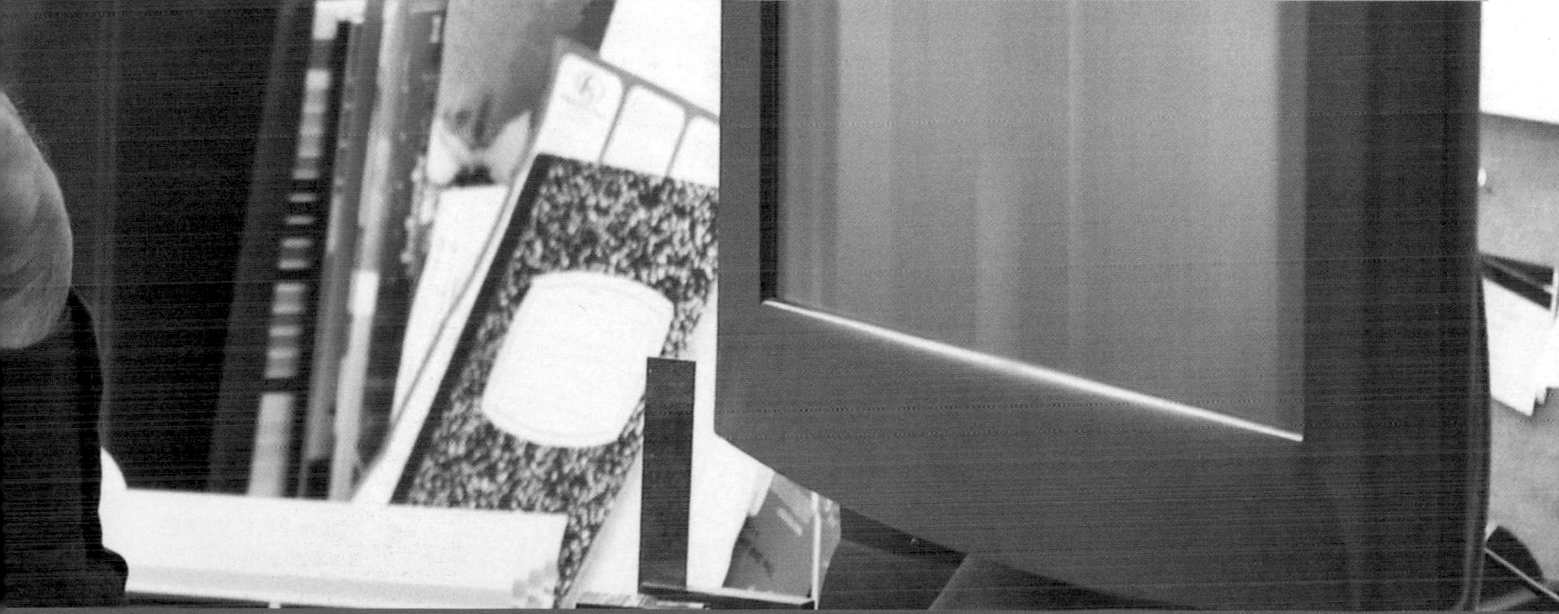

This section identifies the key features that differentiate event driven programming languages from the more traditional flow driven programming languages such as Pascal.

Event driven programs are typically used with **GUI** operating systems, as events are generated when the user clicks the mouse on a button or other object. Typical uses of event driven programs include: word processors, spreadsheets, databases and drawing packages. This list is just the beginning as almost all modern software is event driven.

What does it mean?

A **GUI** is the name given to a modern operating system such as Windows or Linux. GUI stands for **graphical user interface**, meaning that the operating system can be controlled with a mouse by clicking on buttons, menus or similar objects.

Event driven programming techniques can also be deployed in scenarios other than GUIs and forms – they are typically applied in networking and file-handling operations to handle streams of incoming data within indefinite loops.

20.1.1 Key characteristics

These are the key characteristics of event driven programming languages:

- they have event handlers, i.e. code that runs when an event occurs
- trigger functions are the mechanisms that decide which code runs when an event occurs
- event loops are built into the programming language to keep checking to find out if an event has occurred
- forms are used to contain objects which experience events.

20.1.1.1 Event handlers

Most modern programs have forms with controls on them that show when the program runs. **Controls** are **objects** on the form such as a label, button, check box, etc. Many event driven programming environments such as VB.NET (see Figure 20.1) have a toolbox showing objects that can be added to forms.

What does it mean?

Controls and **objects** are the parts of an event driven programming language that have events happen to them. A control is a visual object such as a button or a combo box. An object may be either visual or non-visual. An example of a non-visual object is the PrintDocument object of VB.NET which can be used by a program to produce hard copy on to paper.

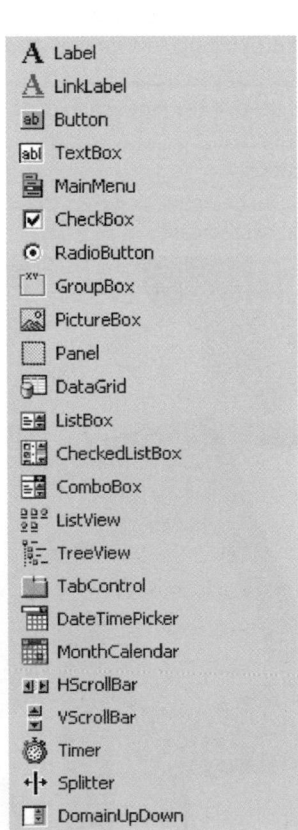

Figure 20.1 VB NET toolbox objects

Most objects have a large variety of possible **events**, which might include click, double click, mouse down and many more.

Different types of objects have different collections of events. The events appropriate for a text box are not the same as the events for a button, as they are used in very different ways.

An event triggers the appropriate **event handler**.

What does it mean?

An **event** is anything that happens to an object when the program is running.

An **event handler** is the code that runs when an event occurs.

VB.NET uses **subroutines** for event handling, with the name of the object followed by an underscore then the name of the event. The following code is the event handler for a command button named cmdQuit, which closes the program when this button is clicked.

```
Private Sub btnQuit_Click(ByVal sender As System.
Object, ByVal e As System.EventArgs) Handles
btnQuit.Click
    End
End Sub
```

What does it mean?

A **subroutine** is a self-contained section of program also known as a **procedure**. Subroutines in VB.NET must have **Sub** and the name of the subroutine in their first line with **End Sub** as their last line. The first line of a subroutine often has extra code to define how it is to be run.

To create the above code, the button tool in the toolbox was selected with the mouse then placed on to the form by dragging. The button name property was set to btnQuit. VB.NET started the code when this command button was double clicked in design view. VB.NET took the name of the object (btnQuit) and the default event (Click) to create the start and end lines of this code.

The code keyword (End) was typed by the programmer.

20.1.1.2 Trigger functions

Event driven programming languages use trigger functions to select which event handler to run according to which event occurred.

Every object has a range of trigger functions, one for each possible event that can happen to it. A text box in VB.NET has a trigger function for the **GotFocus** event, another for the **TextChanged** event and others for all the other events.

VB.NET also allows the programmer to create a user-defined control that can be used in a similar way to other objects in a program. When creating this control, the programmer must define the trigger functions, otherwise there will be no properties or methods for the control.

A **Get** structure is written for every property that can be retrieved from the control. **Set** structures are used for properties that can be changed by the programmer. This part of programming a new control is called exposing the interface.

20.1.1.3 Event loops

Event driven programming languages need to have event **loops** built into them at a level the programmer would not normally be aware of. The event loops are needed to keep testing the user interface to detect whether anything has happened, such as clicking on a button or typing into a text box.

Remember!

A control **property** defines things such as whether it is enabled, the background colour and every other aspect of a control.

A **loop** is a part of a program that repeats itself. Another name for a loop is an **iteration**.

If an event is detected, the event is passed to the trigger functions, which then call the appropriate event handler to run any code in the program that was designed and written for the event.

Event driven programming languages often include provision for programmers to create bespoke event loops (also known as event listeners) to enhance the functionality of their applications and make them more flexible. This is because it would be impossible for the designers of programming languages to provide events for every imaginable circumstance.

20.1.1.4 Forms

Forms are a major feature of most event driven programming environments, as they are what the user sees when the program runs.

Forms are used to hold all the controls the programmer used to create the program.

Forms are also a type of control so have a collection of events that may be used by the programmer. These form events are a very powerful way of controlling a program, especially when the program loads and ends. Here are two examples of form events.

- **Load** is the event that occurs when a form is first used. The load event is useful for code which needs to set variables, default values and other matters which need to be done just the once.
- **Activated** is an event that occurs every time the form is brought up. The activated event is very useful for updating a form when the user returns to it from another form. A program might call another form to enter details of a sale. When returning to the main form, the activated event could bring up a summary of the sale on the main form.

Activity 20.1

Key features of event driven programs

1 Produce a diagram to show how event handlers, trigger functions and event loops work with components on a form.

2 Write an explanation of the diagram.

20.1.2 Advantages of event driven programming

20.1.2.1 Flexibility

Flexibility is a great advantage of event driven programming, as the programmer has enormous control over where to place code and how to start it. Every object has a good choice of events that a program can respond to. These events give the programmer excellent control over exactly what the program will respond to when the user does something.

A good example of this is the text box. Usually there is a choice of events giving fine programming control over anything typed into it. C# includes these choices:

- Enter, when the text box becomes the active control (receives the focus)
- KeyDown, when the text box is active and at the start of when a key is pressed
- KeyPress, when a key is pressed
- KeyUp, when a key is released.

KeyDown, KeyPress and KeyUp events all respond in slightly different ways to when a user types into the text box. Many programmers would choose the KeyPress event as this summarises the other two, but there are times when more control is needed, so the program could respond to when the user presses the key (KeyDown event) as well as the exact moment when key is released (KeyUp).

Similarly, there are good choices of events for all the other controls. Figure 20.2 shows some of the events VB.NET offers for a button. Figure 20.3 shows some of the events C# offers for a button.

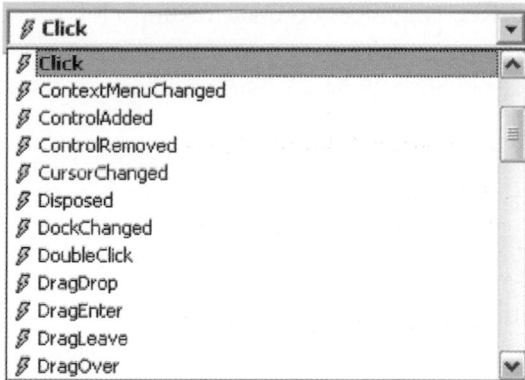

▲ **Figure 20.2 Some VB.NET button events**

VB.NET events are all available by default, whereas events for C# need to be selected from the Properties box before they are available for coding. The screenshot in Figure 20.3 shows that there is no code for any event of the control shown, apart from the Click event.

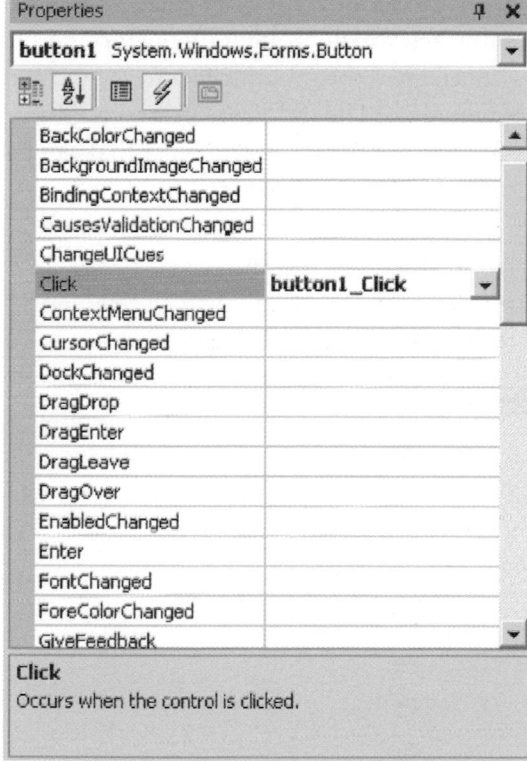

▲ **Figure 20.3 Some C# button events**

Event driven programs are very suitable for graphical interfaces (GUIs) as they are an excellent match for each other.

A GUI presents the user with a wide variety of graphical choices and menus that can be used with the mouse or keyboard (or other input devices), usually with no set sequence that the user must follow. An event driven programming language will use this GUI approach to give the user a variety of controls. Each control reacts to events with code that is just right for each event and for how the program is expected to be used.

Most controls are quite independent from each other, so the code will be modularised into event handlers.

20.1.2.3 Simplicity of programming

Event driven programming languages can make programming very simple compared to traditional flow driven languages, because the programming language is very visual.

A control such as a button can easily be put on to a form from the toolbox. When it is on the form, the programmer can see it. The programmer may choose to see the properties of the control while writing the program (see Figure 20.4). This can simplify programming as there is a lot more information available.

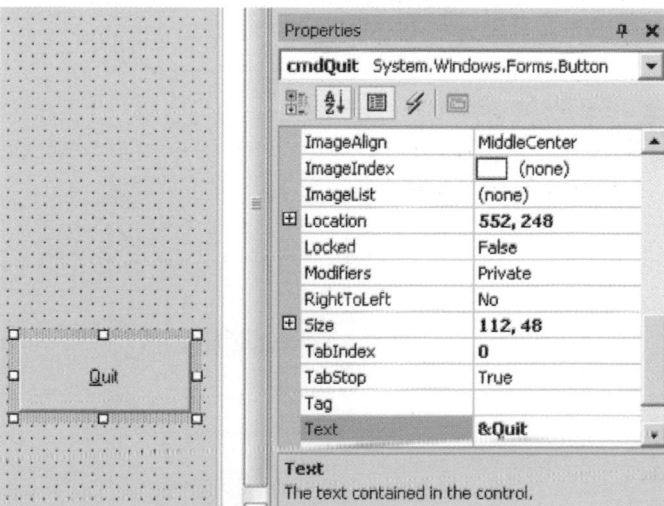

▲ **Figure 20.4 C# button properties**

It is very simple to start an event handler subroutine for the default event of an object. All the programmer needs to do is to double left click on the object.

Writing the code can be a lot more complex, as the programmer needs to understand the commands available to the language and the syntax required to make the commands work correctly.

Some languages (e.g. C#) are **case sensitive**, so commands written without proper capitalisation are not recognised.

What does it mean?

Case sensitive languages need the right mix of capital and lower case letters. A case sensitive part of a program will see System and SYSTEM as very different.

Other languages (e.g. VB.NET) are not case sensitive, so commands can be written with any mix of capitalisation and are still recognised. When coding moves on to another line VB.NET will add capitals for the programmer.

Many event driven languages do make coding a lot simpler by providing floating menus of possible commands (see Figures 20.5a–c). These make programming much easier as they:

- show the programmer the choice of commands that are possible for that part of the code
- allow the programmer to choose the appropriate command without actually typing it – this makes coding both quicker and more accurate.

The screenshots in Figures 20.5a–c are from C#. They show how a variable (StringVar) is assigned a value that is converted from another type of data to string. When the programmer typed **System.** (with full stop), the menu in Figure 20.5a was shown. The programmer highlighted **Convert**, then used the tab key to copy Convert from the menu to code. They typed a full stop (.) which brought up the menu in Figure 20.5b.

The programmer highlighted **ToString**, then used the tab key copy ToString from the menu to code. They typed an open bracket, which brought up the prompt in Figure 20.5c – this helped the programmer to appreciate what this code would do. The up/down arrows in the prompt move around the different data types that can be converted to string by this function.

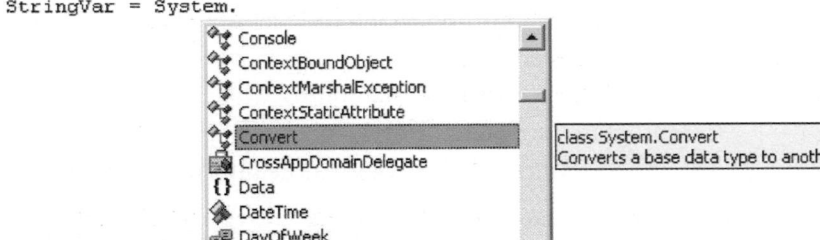

▲ Fig 20.5a C# command menus

▲ Fig 20.5b C# command menus

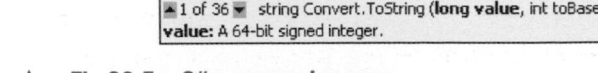

 ▲ Fig 20.5c C# command menus

Program development can be easy with an event driven language, as the programmer only needs to work on one event of one control at a time.

Flow driven languages need to be reasonably complete before they can run and be tested, whereas an event driven language will run with as little as only the code for a single event completed.

Testing is also easier because each event can be tested in turn.

20.1.3 Disadvantages

Event driven languages can be slow, as a lot of processing power is soaked up by the need for event loops to keep checking the GUI to find out if anything has happened. Yet more processing power is taken up by the trigger functions as they match the type of event with the event handler needed to respond to it.

Many modern event driven languages have long, complicated commands. Often these can be inserted into code by selecting from floating menus, but there are still many situations where the programmer must type them.

As with all programming, structured testing is essential to make sure all the program works as expected. The event handlers mean that code is quite isolated, with many subroutines not affecting others. So, the test plan needs to be able to prove that everything works by making sure that each part of the program is run.

Testing should also ensure that the **HCI** aspects of the program are good and effective.

What does it mean?

HCI is the human–computer interface. HCI is the art of making programs easy and intuitive to use.

Many, many programs have been produced that work only in limited ways because the programmers didn't think about different user preferences. For example, a program might be designed to be used just with the

mouse, whereas some users might prefer to use the program in a different way. Perhaps they prefer to use the tab key to navigate forms, only to find that the controls are then selected in a very random sequence because the programmers didn't think of setting the **TabIndex** properties.

What does it mean?

TabIndex is the property of controls that defines the sequence in which they are selected when the Tab key is used to navigate a form.

Some users like to use accelerator keys to control a program, e.g. Alt+Q to press a button with Quit as its text, so programmers should include these.

Activity 20.2

Typical uses of event driven programs

1   Describe six examples of events and how they are handled by event driven programs. To do this:
   - identify six events that could be triggered, with their objects
   - describe what causes these events
   - describe the actions the program needs to implement when handling them. **P₂**

   For example, in Word you might choose **click** as an event on the **Bullets** button object. Describe how selected paragraph(s) then have a bullet point format applied (or removed, if already there), causing the screen to refresh showing the paragraph(s) with(out) bullets.

2   List as many examples of advantages as you can find of event driven programs. **P₂**

20.1.4 Examples

Operating systems for personal computers have always been event driven. Back in the days of **DOS** the operating system was event driven to respond to interrupts from peripherals to the processor.

What does it mean?

DOS stands for **disk operating system**, the name given to a family of operating systems produced for PCs. MS-DOS was the Microsoft product, PC-DOS was from IBM and DR-DOS by Digital Research.

Here are just a few of the many, many events that peripherals send to the operating system for handling:

- keyboard when a key is pressed
- keyboard when Ctrl + Alt + Del are pressed together
- printer when it wants data for the next page
- printer when it jams
- hard disk when a data transfer is completed.

Interrupts are passed to the operating system through the **BIOS** so they can be dealt with.

What does it mean?

BIOS stands for **basic input output system**. It is a chip on every PC motherboard that connects the operating system to hardware, as well as holding the boot program and start-up settings.

Modern operating systems have to deal with all the events that previous systems had as well as all the modern events such as mouse when a button is clicked, when a touch screen is touched and many, many more.

Modern PC operating systems have a GUI (known as a **WIMP** system) so the user can control the computer using a mouse or similar input device such as a graphics tablet. The PC family use Windows (or sometimes Linux) for their operating system. The Apple Macintosh family (Mac and iMac) use MacOS for their operating system.

GUIs make a computer much easier to use, as the options are on show on the screen. Non-GUI systems (know as **CLI** systems) such as DOS needed the user to type commands into an on-screen prompt. These needed the user to remember operating system commands and to type them accurately.

What does it mean?

WIMP stands for **windows, icons, mouse, pointer** and is used to describe a GUI system. The windows are used to show running programs, the icons to start programs, the mouse to control the system and the pointer is an arrow on screen to show the position of the mouse.

CLI stands for **command line interpreter** (or **command line interface**) and is used to describe a non-GUI operating system.

GUIs meet the requirements for an event driven system very easily as almost every part of the GUI is a graphical object with events that need to be handled.

Opposite are some examples of how event driven programming can be deployed in applications other than form-based GUIs.

Activity 20.3

Operating systems as event driven applications

1 Take a screenshot of an operating system, such as Windows. Annotate it to identify where a variety of user-initiated events occur – e.g. right clicking on the desktop, left clicking on the Start button, double left clicking on a program icon, etc. **m**

2 Write explanations of each event you identified in task 1. Structure your explanations with these subheadings:
- Why the user would want to initiate the event
- How the user initiates the event
- What actions the operating system does to handle the event. **m**

3 Draw a diagram identifying the events from hardware that are handled by the operating system – e.g. a printer needing more paper, a key being pressed, etc. **m**

4 Write explanations of each event identified in task 3. Structure your explanations with these subheadings:
- Why the hardware device needs to initiate the event
- What actions the operating system does to handle the event. **m**

- Within **API** development, event driven programming is used extensively to allow other developers access to event functionality from inside the components that make up the operating system. MS Windows provides a rich collection of API functions that are within DLL (Dynamic Link Library) files that are automatically included when the operating system is installed.

What does it mean?

API stands for **application programming interface** – it represents a collection of functions that can be used by programmers to access programs outside the application they are writing.

These allow programmers to use common Windows features such as a print dialogue box.

- A software developer may write an API (a collection of classes) to interact with MSN servers. It will fire off appropriate events (such as a server pinging a client, a message being received, or personal status being changed to 'away' or 'busy').
- Event driven programming is used within both the server and client side of networking protocols: the IRC (Internet Relay Chat) protocol is an example of a protocol suitable for event driven programming techniques.
- Event driven programming can be used for data sorting and sifting. It can coincide with data mining to respond to events around using datasets.

Activity 20.4

Non-graphical event driven applications

1 Evaluate the suitability of event driven programs for non-graphical applications. To do this:
- identify two or more applications that either use a text-based interface or have no graphical components – a program with no graphical components might be PC-based or could be a control application for a device such as a burglar alarm
- identify the events that each of these applications would receive and say how suitable an event driven language might be to handle those events. **d**

20.1.5 Programming languages

20.1.5.1 Visual Basic

Visual Basic (VB) was produced by Microsoft for the Windows systems (see Figure 20.6). It was a popular programming language from the initial release date in 1991 until 2001 when Visual Basic.NET (VB.NET) was released. VB.NET was intended by Microsoft to replace Visual Basic but many programmers preferred the older system rather than reskilling to the newer product.

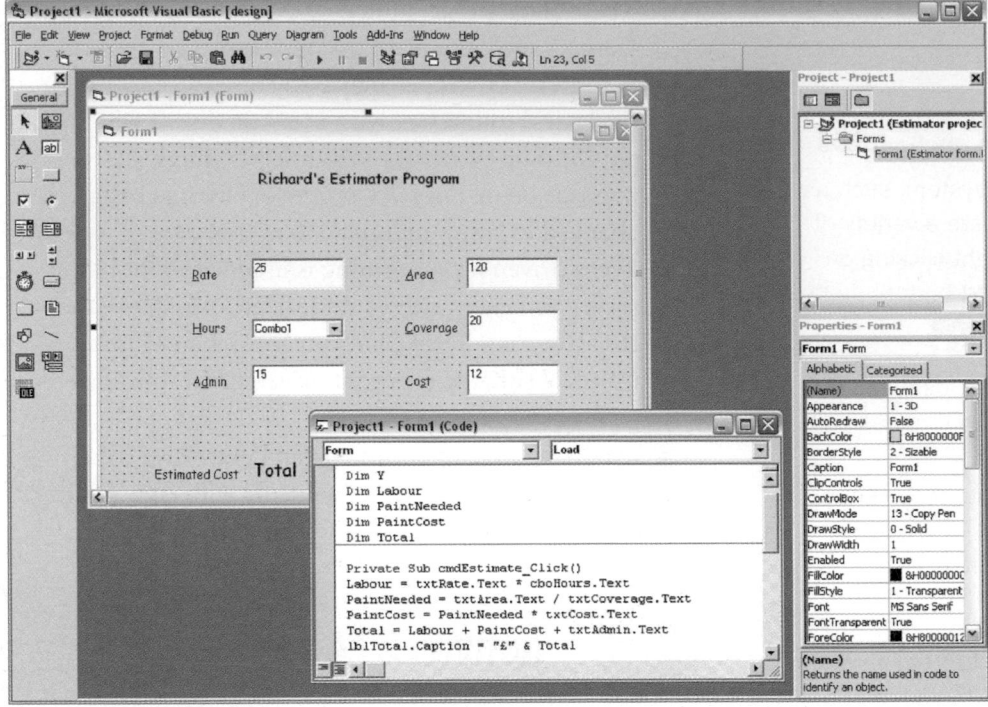

Figure 20.6 Visual Basic 6

Figure 20.7 VB.NET

20.1.5.2 VB.NET

VB.NET (see Figure 20.7) is one of the programming languages in the current Microsoft Visual Studio and is the natural successor to Visual Basic.

20.1.5.3 Visual C++

C++ has always been respected as a very powerful programming language – it is able to combine different levels of code from low (close to machine code) to high, using visual tools and controls (see Figure 20.8).

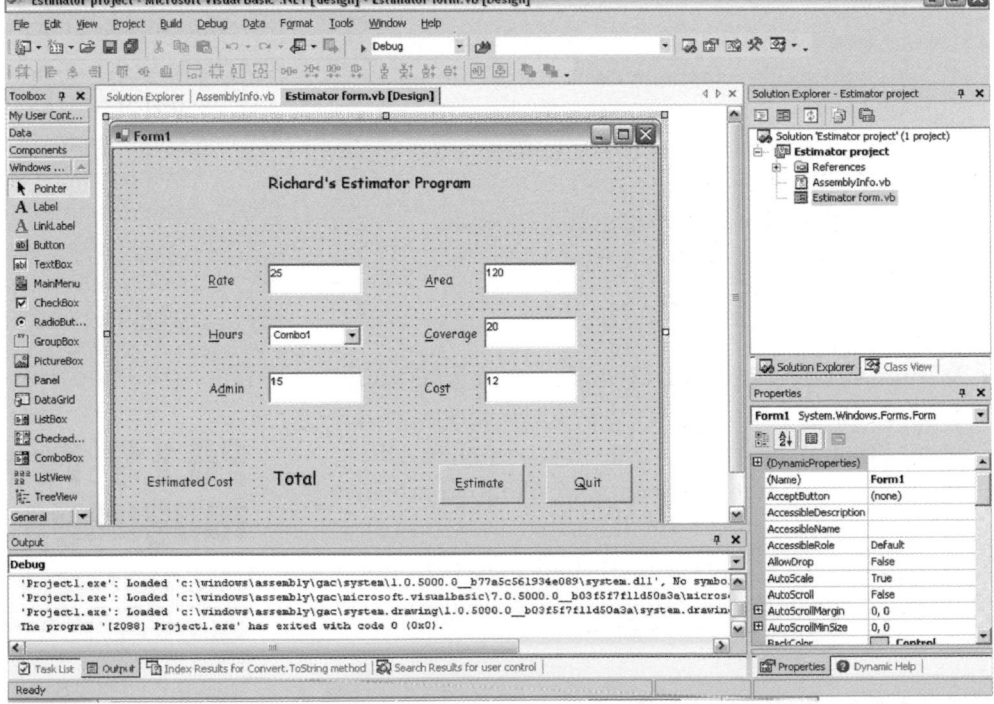

20.1.5.4 Visual Basic for Applications

Visual Basic for Applications (VBA) is the macro programming language that Microsoft includes with its Office suite of programs. VBA (see Figure 20.9) is a version of Visual Basic specifically designed to integrate with the Microsoft Office products such as Access, Excel, PowerPoint and Word.

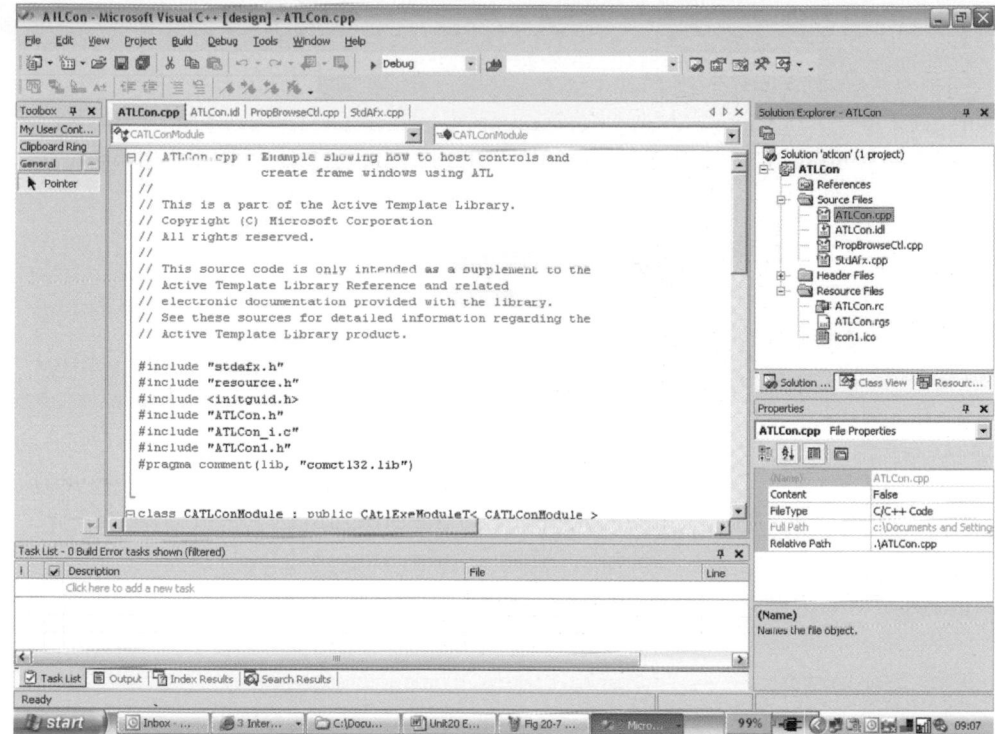

Figure 20.8 Visual C++

1 Can you write a single sentence using the words event handlers, trigger functions, event loops and forms to show how they relate to each other?

2 What features of event driven programming could slow it down?

3 How is event driven programming flexible?

4 In what ways can an event driven language make programming simple?

5 Provide examples of why an event driven language can make development easy.

6 Compare GUI and non-GUI operating systems.

7 How many event driven programming languages can you name?

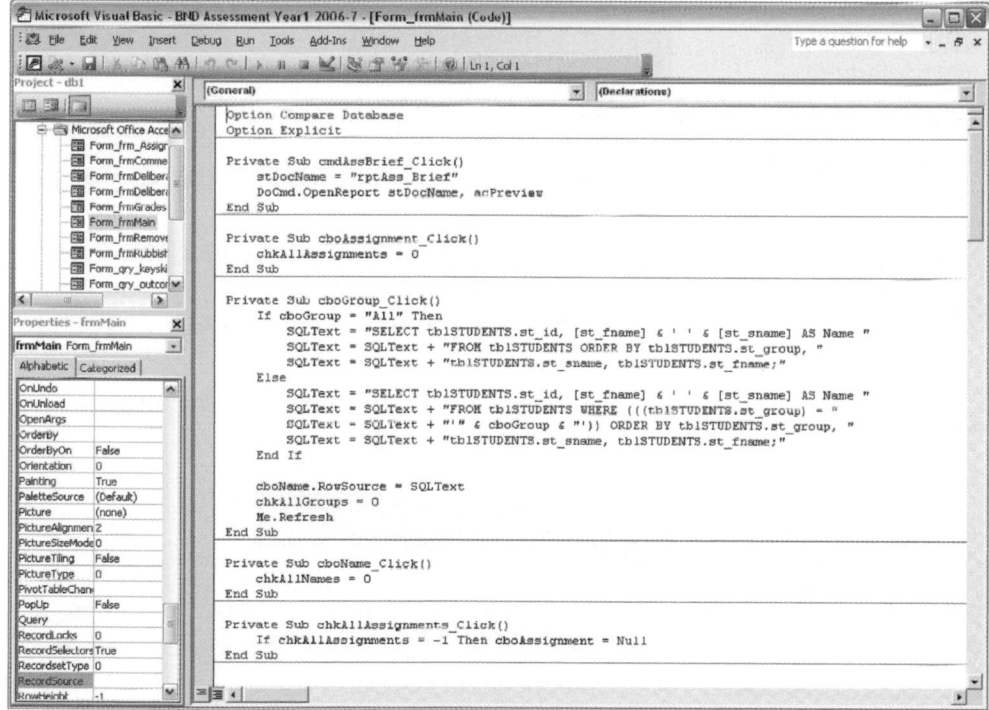

Figure 20.9 Visual Basic for Applications (VBA)

To achieve this part of the unit, you will need to demonstrate that you can use the tools and techniques of an event driven language.

20.2.1 Triggers

Triggers are a wide variety of occurrences that cause events. They include:

- key press to trigger events from the keyboard – e.g. pressing a key
- alarm triggers – e.g. a printer running out of paper
- system event triggers – e.g. the session ending or low memory
- touch screen events – e.g. the coordinates of where a stylus has pressed a touch screen
- mouse click to trigger events – when the user moves or clicks their mouse.

20.2.1.1 Key press

The key press trigger can be very powerful for programs that need to respond to selected keys, particularly to validate data entry or to control the program.

Validation should be used wherever possible to make sure that data entering a program is reasonable, realistic and complete. If bad data is let into a program there can be dire consequences, such as inaccurate results being output from the program or even the program crashing.

Remember!

The acronym **GIGO** has been used by IT professionals for years to remind them that **garbage in** can easily result in **garbage out**!

The key press trigger could be used in a game where different keys have different results, such as changing a direction of travel.

Many business applications use the key press event to respond to the enter key being pressed – this triggers code to accept and use a data entry.

20.2.1.2 Alarm

An alarm is an event that may be triggered by a control such as a timer or by an external device such as a network switch reporting a problem back to a server.

Timers are used by programmers who want an event to fire off regularly so the program can respond to it. For example, a simple animation may use a timer to move a picture box, as in this VB.NET code:

```
private void tmrAnimate_Elapsed(object sender,
System.Timers.ElapsedEventArgs e)
{
    Y = Y + 5;
    pctCartoon.Location = new Point(15, Y);
}
```

20.2.1.3 System event

C# system events include:

- `DisplaySettingsChanged` – when the user changes the display settings
- `LowMemory` – when the system is running out of available RAM
- `SessionEnding` – when the user is trying to log off or shut down the system
- `SessionEnded` – when the user is logging off or shutting down the system.

20.2.1.4 Touch screen events

Devices with a touch screen have a driver to read input from the hardware, then convert that into an event that is fed into the input system.

The driver will submit points while the stylus is touching the touch screen, then when the stylus is removed from the touch screen, an event will indicate that the stylus was removed.

20.2.1.5 Mouse click

C# and VB.NET mouse events include:

- `MouseDown` – when the mouse pointer is over a control and the primary mouse button is pressed
- `MouseEnter` – when the mouse pointer enters the form/control
- `MouseUp` – when the mouse pointer is over the form/control and the mouse button is released
- `MouseLeave` – when the mouse pointer leaves the form/control
- `MouseMove` – when the mouse pointer is moved over the form/control
- `MouseWheel` – when the mouse wheel moves while the form/control has focus
- `MouseHover` – when the mouse pointer hovers over the form/control.

20.2.2 Tools and techniques

20.2.2.1 Use of tool boxes and controls

Controls are objects that can be placed on to a form, usually by selecting the control from the toolbox then dragging the mouse on to the form to place and size the object.

The VB.NET toolbox (see Figure 20.1 on page 158) is quite similar to the C# toolbox (see Figure 20.10). Both have collections of tools:

- Windows Forms tools for adding controls to a form
- components for adding objects such as a timer to the form
- data for connecting to a data source.

20.2.2.2 Selection

Selection is where program code has a structure that allows a choice of routes, with a **condition** deciding which route the program takes.

There are two main structures for selection:

- `If...Then...Else` for when a simple decision is made to choose between two routes.

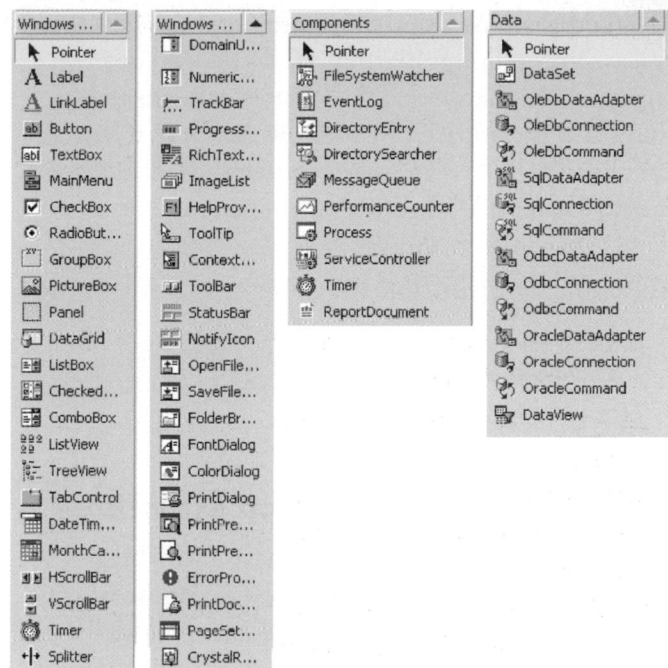

▲ **Figure 20.10 C# toolbox objects**

- `Select Case` for when a decision is made where there are many routes.

■ If...Then...Else

This structure has a condition between the If and Then keywords to choose the route the program takes. The Else part of the structure is optional and, if present, the code inside this part of the structure will run if the condition is False.

The following VB.NET code shows an If...Then...Else structure where a message box pops up to show whether the variable, MyVar, is larger than 14:

```
If MyVar > 14 Then
   MsgBox("more")
Else
   MsgBox("less")
End If
```

What does it mean?

A **condition** is part of a statement which the program understands as representing True or False. For example, **MyVar < 3** would give True if MyVar is a variable containing 2 or False if it contains 3.

Many programmers find they introduce bugs into their code with conditions like this one, as they do not consider what happens if the variable contains the number it is compared with. In this example, if MyVar contains 14 the 'less' message box will show. If the 'more' message is wanted when MyVar contains 14, the condition should be MyVar>=14.

This is the same structure using C#:

```
if (UserScore > 14)
    MessageBox.Show ("more");
else
    MessageBox.Show ("less");
```

■ Select Case and switch structures

Select Case and switch structures have a variable or object containing a value that is used to choose which route the program takes. Each Case statement in the structure has a value to test against. If the value is met, that section of the structure runs. After a section runs the program jumps to the end of the structure, so only one of the Case sections can be run. If none of the Case statements are met, none will run.

This VB.NET code shows a Select Case structure where a message box pops up to show whether integer variable MyVar is smaller than 12, 12–14, 15–16 or above 16:

```
Select Case Size
    Case Is < 12
        MsgBox("under 12")
    Case Is < 15
        MsgBox("12-14")
    Case Is < 17
        MsgBox("14-16")
    Case Is > 16
        MsgBox("over 16")
End Select
```

This is a switch structure using C#:

```
switch(MyVar)
{
    case 12:
        MessageBox.Show ("12");
        break;
    case 13:
        MessageBox.Show ("13");
        break;
    default:
```

```
        MessageBox.Show ("Not 12 or 13");
        //dostuff;
        break;
}
```

Activity 20.5

Program using controls, selection and object properties

1 Write a small program to demonstrate the use of these event driven tools and techniques:
   - tool boxes and controls
   - selection
   - objects and object properties.

   For part of the P3 assessment evidence, you could ask for a signed and dated observation record to prove that you have used appropriate debugging tools. **P₃**

2 Produce a screenshot of the program as it runs. Paste it into a document which has your name, program title and which tools and techniques the program demonstrates. **P₃**

3 Produce an annotated code print of the program taken directly from the integrated development environment (IDE) using the File, Print menu option. **P₃**

Activities 20.6, 20.7, 20.8 and 20.10 (see pages 172, 174 and 179 also contribute to criterion **P₃** *and learners may need to complete all of these tasks to evidence this criterion fully*

20.2.2.3 Loops

A loop is a program structure that allows a section of code to be repeated a number of times.

Remember!

Iteration is the technical term for a loop.

As with other programming languages, event driven languages usually offer two types of loop:

- **definite** – the loop repeats for a known number of times, set by the programmer
- **indefinite** – the loop repeats until a condition is met, such as reaching the end of a data file being read into the program.

■ Definite loops

The classic definite loop is the For structure. The For line defines a variable used to keep track of the repetitions, the start and end values of this variable and by how much it changes each time through the loop.

This example of a For loop in C# uses a loop variable named ComboNo, which has a start value of 2, an end value of 10 and increases by 2 each time through the loop:

```
for (ComboNo  = 2; ComboNo<= 10; ComboNo+= 2)
{
cboNumbers.Items.Add    (ComboNo-1);
cboNumbers.Items.Add    (ComboNo);
}
cboNumbers.SelectedIndex=2;
```

The code above, uses curly brackets {} to enclose repeating code. The end result of this code is to put the numbers 1 to 10 inside a combo box named cboNumbers then show 3 in the combo box (SelectedIndex=2 will select the third item, as SelectedIndex starts at 0).

■ Indefinite loops

An indefinite loop will repeat until a condition is met.

This condition may be at the start of the loop, called pre-test, which means the code inside the loop may never run if the condition is not met. The condition may be at the end of the loop, called post-test, which means the code inside the loop will always run at least once, even if the condition is not met.

The indefinite loops available to VB.NET are shown in Table 20.1.

20.2.2.4 Event handlers

Using event handlers can be as easy as double clicking on an object in design view and then typing code. These actions would create the default event handler for the object.

One of the great advantages of event driven languages is flexibility – the programmer has a lot more choice of which events to write code for than simply the default event.

Look at Figure 20.3 on page 161 to see the C# events tab of a properties window with the default click event showing. If the programmer wishes to write code for another event, such as DragDrop, they simply need to double click on it here.

Other languages, such as VB.NET (see Figure 20.2 on page 161), have a combo box in the top right of the code window where event handler code can be initialised.

Type of Do Loop	Explanation	Example
Do While ... Loop (pre-test)	• Evaluates the condition and, if true, evaluates the statements following the condition. • When it has finished doing this, evaluates condition again and, if true, it evaluates them again. • Continues repeating until the condition is false. • If the condition starts as false, the statements will never be evaluated.	Do While condition Statements Loop
Do Until ... Loop (post-test)	• Similar to Do While ... Loop, except it repeats until the condition is true rather than while it is true. • If the condition starts as true, the statements will never be evaluated.	Do Until condition Statements Loop
Do ... Loop While (post-test)	• The Do ... Loop While will evaluate the statements at least once. • It then evaluates the condition and, if true, evaluates the statements again. This process continues until the condition is false.	Do Statements Loop While condition
Do ... Loop Until (post-test)	• Similar to Do ... Loop While, except that it evaluates the statements until the condition is true.	Do Statements Loop Until condition

Table 20.1 The indefinite loops available to VB.NET

Activity 20.6

Program using loops

1 Write a small program to demonstrate the use of these event driven tools and techniques:

- a definite loop
- an indefinite loop.

For part of the P3 assessment evidence, you could ask for a signed and dated observation record to prove that you have used appropriate debugging tools. **p₃**

2 Produce a screenshot of the program as it runs, pasted into a document which has your name, program title and which tools and techniques the program demonstrates. **p₃**

3 Produce a code print of the program taken directly from the **IDE** using the File, Print menu option. **p₃**

See the note to Activity 20.5 about referencing criterion **p₃** *(page 170).*

What does it mean?

An **IDE** is an **integrated development environment** – it is the name given to a programming language that is open for creating and editing a program. Modern IDEs include a toolbox for adding new components, views for designing and coding the application, windows for properties of components and what disk files are in the project, as well as debugging tools and help screens.

20.2.2.5 Triggers

Triggers start events and come from the user, controls in the program or the system.

- A trigger from the user might be clicking the mouse.
- A trigger from a control might be a timer.
- A trigger from the system might be a broken network connection.

One of the great skills needed for designing programs is to identify which triggers are likely to produce which events and therefore which event handlers are needed and what code they should run.

20.2.2.6 Objects and object properties

Event driven languages such as VB.NET and C# make it very easy to place the visual objects (components) on to a form. Usually it is enough to click on the toolbox button representing the object then drag to place it on the form.

There are also non-visual objects that may be used by the program, such as PrintDocument, message queues, timers and event logs.

Some event driven languages offer an object browser (see Figure 20.11), which allows the programmer to see the classes and objects that are available to the project.

Remember!

A **class** is an abstract representation of something, whereas an **object** is a usable example of the thing the class represents.

Activity 20.7

Program using triggers and event handlers

1 Write a small program to demonstrate the use of these event driven tools and techniques:

- triggers
- event handlers.

For part of the P3 assessment evidence, you could ask for a signed and dated observation record to prove that you have used appropriate debugging tools. **p₃**

2 Produce a screenshot of the program as it runs, pasted into a document which has your name, program title and which tools and techniques the program demonstrates. **p₃**

3 Produce a code print of the program taken directly from the IDE using the File, Print menu option. **p₃**

See the note to Activity 20.5 about referencing criterion **p₃** *(page 170).*

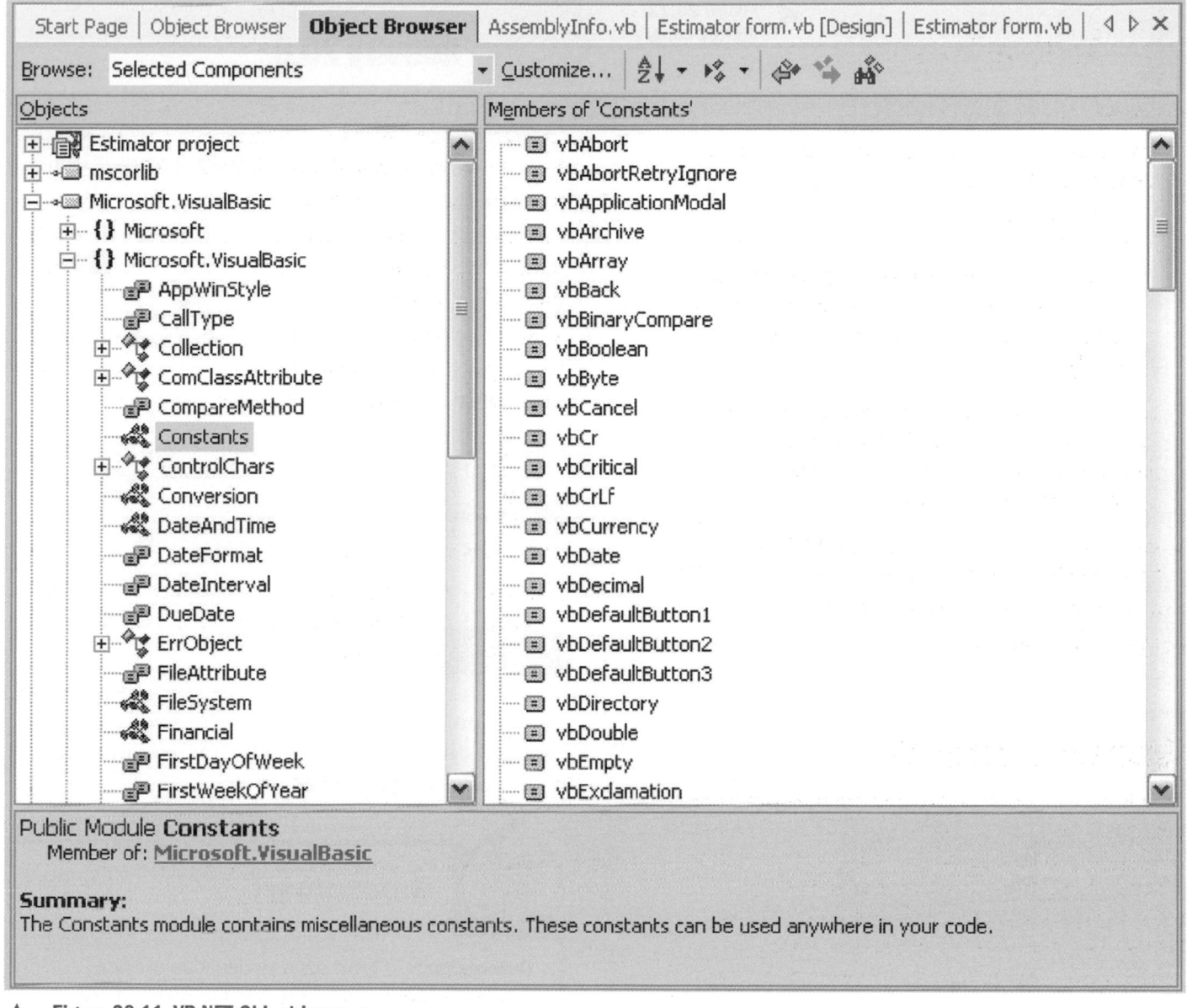

Figure 20.11 VB.NET Object browser

Objects have properties, methods and events that can be used in a program.

- Properties control the state, behaviour and appearance of objects, such as a form, document or control. Properties affect aspects of the object, such as text alignment, size, font, location and the name of the object.
- Methods are actions that can be carried out on the control by code, such as copy or clear.
- Events are actions that happen to objects, such as click or lost focus.

20.2.2.7 Menus

Event driven languages usually have a way of adding a menu to a form, if required.

VB.NET and C# have a MainMenu button in the toolbox. Double clicking on this button adds the MainMenu control to the bottom of the form (see Figure 20.12). The programmer can then right click on this control and select Edit to type in the menu options.

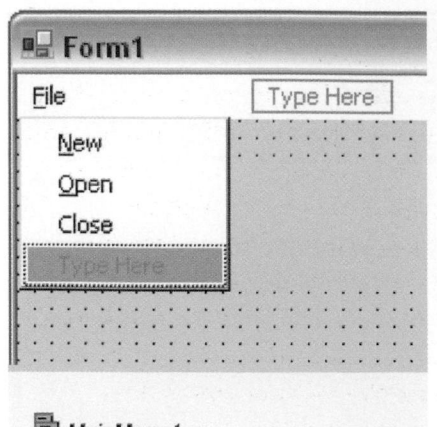

Figure 20.12
VB.NET menu

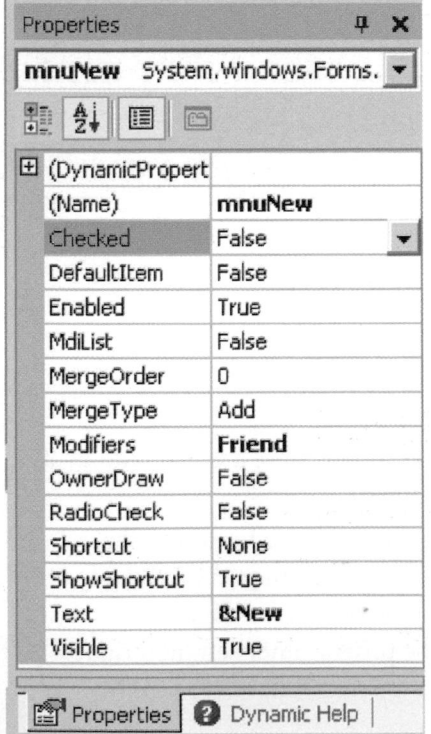

Figure 20.13
VB.NET menu
properties

Underlines can be assigned by typing an ampersand before the letter to be underlined. In Figure 20.12 File was typed as &File. Underlines allow the user to control the program using the Alt key with the underlined letter as an alternative to the mouse.

Each menu item has properties (see Figure 20.13) that may be used to define the name of the menu item (and therefore the event handler that will run when selected), as well as other aspects of the menu such as whether it shows a tick next to the item (the Checked property).

Code can be started for a menu option by double left clicking on it in a similar manner to other objects.

Activity 20.8

Program using menus

1 Write a small program to demonstrate the use of menus.

   For part of the P3 assessment evidence, you could ask for a signed and dated observation record to prove that you have used appropriate debugging tools. **p**₃

2 Produce a screenshot of the program as it runs, pasted into a document which has your name, program title and which tools and techniques the program demonstrates. **p**₃

3 Produce a code print of the program taken directly from the IDE using the File, Print menu option. **p**₃

See the note to Activity 20.5 about referencing criterion **p**₃ *(page 170).*

20.2.2.8 Debugging tools

Modern programming environments provide a wide choice of debugging tools to help programmers find and resolve problems with code.

Remember!

Debugging is a term used to describe actions needed to make a computer work properly. It was first coined when the American programmer Grace Hopper removed dead moths (bugs) from first generation computer hardware to free up electronic switches.

VB.NET and C# provide a Debug menu (see Figure 20.14) in the IDE with options to help the programmer identify and correct problems in their code.

The Debug menu options include:

- **Breakpoints window** – used to show the breakpoints that have been set in the code – this window is particularly useful for disabling breakpoints temporarily then reinstating them later (without the need to find each line of code that needs a breakpoint again).

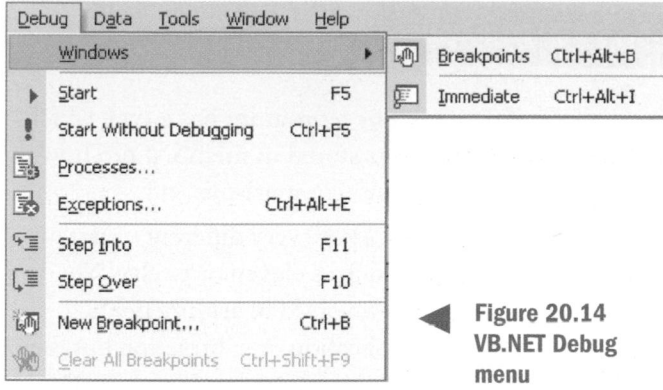

Figure 20.14
VB.NET Debug
menu

- **Immediate window** – used to run small sections of code independently from the main program or to see what value is inside a variable or control.
- **Start** – can also be used to restart the program if it has been paused by a breakpoint or other method.
- **Start Without Debugging** – runs the code without the warnings that VB.NET usually gives if it finds anything in the program that looks wrong – this may be useful if you want to focus on getting a section of code to work properly and ignore problems elsewhere.
- **Processes** – brings up a window showing processes running on the computer, similar to the Windows Task Manager, but with a lot more detail and control over which processes are shown; includes the ID numbers of each process which could be useful if the programmer wishes to hook into them.
- **Exceptions dialogue box** (see Figure 20.15) – gives control over how the IDE handles errors and allows the programmer to instruct the IDE to ignore and continue if a specified type of error occurs, e.g. division by zero, by replacing the system message with one the programmer prefers.
- **Step Into and Step Over** – both run code a line at a time, very useful when the program has been paused by a breakpoint – when code calls a subroutine, Step

Into runs the subroutine line by line, whereas Step Over runs all the subroutine as one step.

- **New Breakpoint** – adds a breakpoint to the code; this looks like a brown highlight on the line and will pause the program when it gets there – very useful to show the program actually runs the code with the breakpoint or to pause the program so Step Into can be used to run the lines of code one at a time.
- **Clear All Breakpoints** – removes all the breakpoints that have been placed in the program at once.
- **Enable All Breakpoints** – activates them if the Breakpoints window has been used to disable some of the breakpoints.

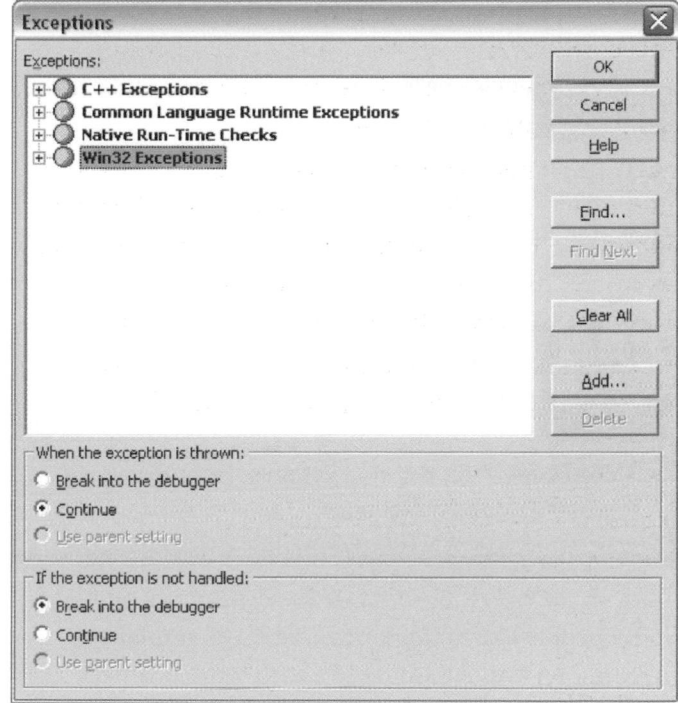

Figure 20.15 C# Exceptions dialogue box

Remember!

IDE is the **integrated development environment** – the name given to VB.NET, C# or other languages when they are running so the programmer can write code.

Activity 20.9

Justifying tools and techniques

1 Design and implement two different working event driven applications.

2 Create a report justifying the tools and techniques used in the production of these event driven programs.

20.2.3 Data

Most programs need **data** to work. Data is the name given to numbers, words or other values that are used by a program.

Remember!

Data is the plural of the Latin word **datum**, so sometimes you will see it written in expressions such as 'the data are valid'.

20.2.3.1 Variables

A variable is a name used by a program to represent a value that can change (vary).

Remember!

A **constant** is similar to a variable, but the value it represents does not change.

Some people like to think of variables as similar to pigeonholes (see Figure 20.16), each with a name, e.g. BookingRef, and holding a value, e.g. Br2034.

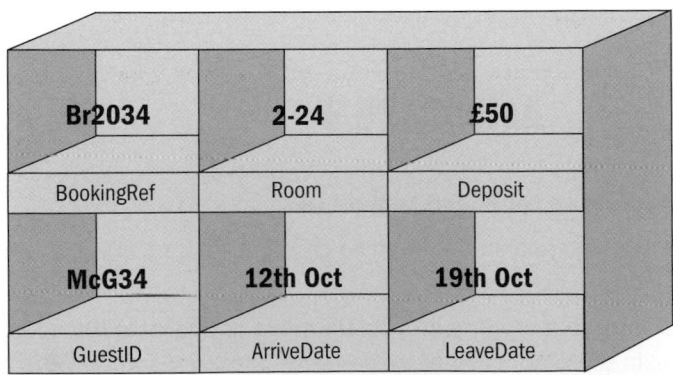

▲ **Figure 20.16 Variables as pigeonholes**

20.2.3.2 Data types

Every piece of data used by a program has a type which defines the way the data is stored in memory and how it can be used in calculations, comparisons, etc.

Numerics such as **11** or **12** have very different requirements to **strings** such as **eleven** or **twelve**. Not only can the numerics be involved in arithmetic operations such as multiplication or subtraction but they will be stored differently in memory (see Figure 20.17).

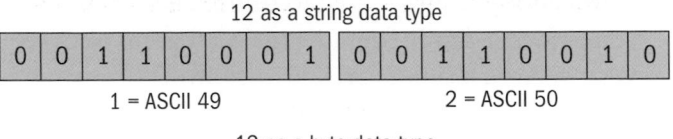

12 as a string data type

| 0 | 0 | 1 | 1 | 0 | 0 | 0 | 1 | | 0 | 0 | 1 | 1 | 0 | 0 | 1 | 0 |

1 = ASCII 49   2 = ASCII 50

12 as a byte data type

| 0 | 0 | 0 | 0 | 1 | 1 | 0 | 0 |

8 bit unsigned binary

▲ **Figure 20.17 Data types in memory**

Some event driven programs allow variables without having to declare the data types. If there is no data type for a variable, it takes on a default type of **variant**.

What does it mean?

Variant variables respond to the data given to them and adapt as the program runs to whatever is put inside them.

Using variant variables is considered bad practice as it places unnecessary overheads on the program and reduces reliability.

Data types enable programmers to define what sort of data is to be held in each variable. This is useful for two main reasons:

- **speed** – the program will run faster as it will keep data in the most suitable format in memory, allowing faster, easier data manipulation.
- **reliability** – the program will show run-time errors early in testing if unexpected data are assigned to a variable with a declared data type. The program will become more reliable as the programmer will have to reconsider exactly what type of data is correct for the variable and either change the data type declaration

or modify the program so the unexpected data arrives in the correct form.

These are some of the many data types available:

- **Boolean** – holds one of two values: true or false.
- **Char** – holds Unicode characters, including those from virtually every language in the world (see Figure 20.18).
- **Date** – holds a calendar date, useful for calculations such as how long between two dates.
- **Floating point** – holds virtually any number.
- **Integer** – holds whole numbers; the integer data type usually has a definite number of bytes in memory:
  - Byte, using 8 bits to store **unsigned** integers in the range 0–255.
  - Smallint, using 16 bits to store **signed** integers, giving a range of -32,768 to 32,767.
  - Int, using 32 bits to store signed integers, giving a range of -2,147,483,648 to 2,147,483,647.
- **String** – holds words and sentences.

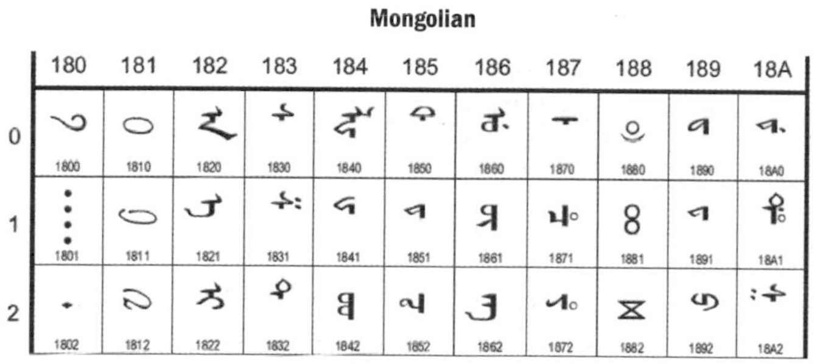

What does it mean?

Signed means that a number can be positive or negative. In programming, signed usually means that the most significant digit (MSD) of a binary number (the leftmost digit) is used to define whether the number is positive (MSD is 0) or negative (MSD is 1).

Unsigned means that a number is treated as positive. In programming, unsigned usually means that the most significant digit (MSD) of a binary number (the leftmost digit) is simply part of the number.

The names given to data types may be different in different programming languages (see Table 20.2).

Figure 20.18 Unicode Mongolian characters

Storage size	VB	Visual C++	C#	JScript
16 bytes	n/a	VARIANT	n/a	Object
Decimal	Decimal (.NET Framework class)	DECIMAL	decimal	decimal
Date	Date (.NET Framework class)	DATE	DateTime (.NET Framework class)	System.DateTime Also the JScript Dates Date object
(varies)	String (.NET Framework class)	n/a	string	String
1 byte	Byte	BYTE, bool	byte	byte
2 bytes	Boolean	VARIANT_BOOL	bool	boolean
2 bytes	Short, Char (Unicode character)	signed short int, __int16	short, char (Unicode character)	short , char
1 byte	n/a	signed char, __int8		Sbyte
4 bytes	Integer	long, (long int, signed long int)	int	int
8 bytes	Long	__int64	long	long
4 bytes	Single	Float	float	float
8 bytes	Double	Double	double	double

Table 20.2 Names given to data types in different programming languages. Source: Microsoft Corporation (Visual Studio help pages)

To declare a variable the programmer inserts a line of code defining the name of the variable. Usually the declaration includes the data type for the variable.

Different programming languages have different **syntax**.

What does it mean?

Syntax is the structure and order of the language. In English, 'door to go the' is not understandable as the syntax is wrong, whereas 'go to the door' is very clear as the syntax is correct. Similarly, programming languages need the syntax to be correct or the code cannot be understood.

The VB.NET code for declaring a variable named UserScore with data type of integer is:

```
Dim UserScore As Integer
```

The C# code for declaring a variable named UserScore with data type of integer is:

```
Int UserScore;
```

A variable is said to be definitely assigned if it is given a value when it is declared.

The VB.NET code for the definite assignment of a variable named UserScore with data type of integer and value of 12 is:

```
Dim UserScore As Integer = 12
```

The C# code for the definite assignment of a variable named UserScore with data type of integer is:

```
Int UserScore = 12;
```

20.2.3.4 Scope of variables

Using a variable outside its **scope** should return an error stating that it has not been recognised.

What does it mean?

The **scope** of a variable is how much of the program the variable is usable within.

- **Local variables** have their scope restricted to only the procedure where the variable is declared.
- **Form variables** are declared within the general declarations section at the top of the code for the form. They can be used inside any of the procedures associated with that form.
- **Global variables** can be used anywhere in a project.

Professional programmers are very aware of the scope of variables and ensure that their scoping is tight, with variables only holding values in the parts of the program that need them. Tight scoping limits the available places where values may be changed in variables and thus decreases the likelihood of errors.

Good coding leads on from good design and the closer the program keeps to the design specification the better.

20.2.3.5 Constants

Constants are very powerful for programs where a value is needed which does not change, but might be different at some point in the future.

For example, VAT is currently 17.5 per cent for the standard rate and has been for years, so a programmer might be tempted simply to use the number in calculations. The code for a VAT calculation using the number might be:

```
VATcharged = SubTotal * 0.175
Total = VATcharged + SubTotal
```

If the VAT rate changes, in order to carry out **maintenance**, the programmer will need to find every place in the program where the VAT figure occurs and change it. This could be time-consuming and one or two calculations might be missed, resulting in the program giving inconsistent results.

What does it mean?

A **constant** is similar to a variable in that it is a name in code that represents a value, but different in that the value does not change.

Program **maintenance** is the stage in the systems development life cycle (SDLC) when programs are tweaked to remove bugs that are found during use and to make small improvements.

The code for a VAT calculation using a constant might be:

```
VATcharged = SubTotal * VATrate
Total = VATcharged + SubTotal
```

In this case, if the VAT rate changes, the programmer only needs to change the one line of code where the constant was defined. This will be quick to do and will also result in a program that gives consistent results.

Some event driven languages have a number of constants built into them so the programmer can use these constants instead of awkward **hexadecimal** or other values.

What does it mean?

Hexadecimal is the numbering system using base 16 – i.e. 10 in hexadecimal represents 16 as we know it in denary (base 10). Hexadecimal is important to programmers because it is often used to represent binary values with 2 hexadecimal digits being an exact match for any 8-digit binary value.

VB6 used constants such as vbAbort and vbRed in code. For example, the following line of code sets the background colour of the active form to red in VB6:

```
Me.BackColor = vbRed
```

VB.NET takes a different approach, using the Drawing. Color.Red class of the System namespace to set the colour:

```
Me.BackColor = System.Drawing.Color.Red
```

Activity 20.10

Program using constants and variables

1 Write a small program to demonstrate the use of these event driven tools and techniques:
   - constants
   - variables.

   For part of the P3 assessment evidence, you could ask for a signed and dated observation record to prove that you have used appropriate debugging tools. **p₃**

2 Produce a screenshot of the program as it runs, pasted into a document which has your name, program title and which tools and techniques the program demonstrates. **p₃**

3 Produce a code print of the program taken directly from the IDE using the File, Print menu option. **p₃**

4 Include evidence that you understand the scope of variables. This evidence can be a document explaining:
   - the differences between global and local variables
   - why using each scope was appropriate in your programs
   - how and where these variables were declared in your code. **m₃**

See the note to Activity 20.5 about referencing criterion **p₃** (page 170).

Test your knowledge

1 How many examples of triggers can you think of?

2 Name and describe six tools in the toolbox of an event driven language you know.

3 Identify the programming keywords needed to make a loop work.

4 Identify the programming keywords needed to make a selection work.

5 What is meant by the scope of a variable?

6 Give three examples of data types.

7 Identify the similarities and differences between constants and variables.

As an IT practitioner you should be aware of how programs are produced, particularly:

- specification – to define what the program needs to do
- design – to plan how the program will look and run
- creation – to produce the program and eliminate the initial bugs.

The stages used to design and create an event driven application are very similar to any other type of program, except that the program is treated as a collection of events with each event identified and its actions defined.

20.3.1 Specification

20.3.1.1 User need

The user need is a sensible starting point for most programming projects. A recognised user need is often the initiation of a development life cycle and should be recorded in the specification to ensure the proposed program meets the need.

20.3.1.2 Purpose

The purpose of the program is stated in the specification. This will be linked to the user need.

An example of a commercial, off-the-shelf application

20.3.1.3 Input

All inputs into the program should to be identified, as they must be incorporated into the design. Inputs will be both data and how the controls are to be used.

■ Data inputs

Data needed by the program should be understood and defined. For instance, if a program is to calculate the amount of paint needed to decorate a wall, the data input will need to include the length and height of the wall so the area can be calculated. The other item of data needed is the paint coverage, i.e. how many square metres can be covered by a litre of paint.

Data inputs should also have their ranges defined.

■ Control inputs

How controls such as text boxes are used is a vital aspect of planning an event driven program. Processing will need to be planned for each of these anticipated events, such as testing each key press to validate it as a number or to check for the Enter key.

It is important to identify early in the planning what events are expected and what each should do. This will be the basis for which events need coding.

20.3.1.4 Output

The specification of an event driven application program will include the outputs required, just as for any other type of application. This will usually be the screen and print designs, but may also include any other output device the application will use.

20.3.1.5 Processes

Processes need to be identified and described in the specification. There will be a process for each anticipated event, as well as processes for shared code, such as a subroutine to update data shown on the form which may be called from any of several controls that take data.

Case study

Job estimator for Pete Lumber

Pete Lumber is a self-employed plumber who finds producing estimates for new work difficult and time-consuming. There are often errors in his calculations which have resulted in him carrying out work for very small profit and sometimes losing work because his estimate was too high.

Pete has approached Apps'R'Us to get a **bespoke** program written so that his estimates become a lot quicker and more accurate.

What does it mean?

A **bespoke** program is written especially for a client. Usually more expensive than 'off-the-shelf' software and more likely to have bugs when first delivered, bespoke is a good option where a client has software needs that are not easily met by commercial, off-the-shelf applications.

The cost of a job includes these elements:

- Labour at £40 per hour
- Travel at £1 a mile
- Plastic pipes at £2 per metre
- Copper pipes at £3 per metre
- Chrome pipes at £4 per metre.

Pete requires the program to run on his laptop, which has a current processor, 1GB of RAM, 50GB of free disk space and a current version of the MS Windows operating system. The laptop attaches to an inkjet printer that he would like to use to print completed estimates.

1 From these user requirements, produce a design for the form(s) needed by the program. Do this using pencil and paper or a drawing package such as Paint.

2 From these user requirements, produce a design for the estimate printout needed by the program. This must be actual size, and should be drawn using pencil and paper on to a blank sheet of A4. Careful measurements can then be drawn on to the paper from the top of the page to the top of each object (such as text) on the page and from the left of the page to the left of each object. These X,Y distances will be needed in code to print the estimate.

3 Identify which events are to be used by your program. These will probably be three buttons to produce the estimate, print the estimate and to quit the program.

There are many ways a program like this can use events to meet the requirements – if you design the program to work in a different way, that is fine.

Produce a document entitled **Data Dictionary: Procedures** with a subheading for each of your identified events (use Activity 20.11 for guidance). Under each of these subheadings write a description of what the event will do.

4 Identify which variables are to be used by your program, then create a document entitled **Data Dictionary: Variables** using Activity 20.11 for guidance.

5 Produce a test plan for your program using Activity 20.12 for guidance.

6 Start a new programming project, produce the form and write code for the events.

7 Test the program to confirm it meets the requirements. Update the test plan with the results of your testing. Document any changes you make to the program when a test is failed.

Note: Any two of the case studies from this one and those on pages 182, 183 and 184 would contribute to criteria **P**4 and **P**5.

Case study

Cartoon for Anny Mation

Anny Mation runs a small music store and wants to purchase a program that will project cartoons on to a large flat screen in the shop.

The cartoons are from a collection of 800 × 600 JPGs and the program should show them in sequence on a form.

She requires the program to run on a PC which has a current processor, video at 1024 × 768, 1 GB of RAM, 250 GB of free disk space and a current version of the MS Windows operating system.

1 From these user requirements, produce a design for the form(s) needed by the program. Do this using pencil and paper or a drawing package such as Paint.

2 Identify which events are to be used by your program. These will probably be two buttons to start the cartoon and to quit the program.

There are many ways a program like this can use events to meet the requirements – if you design the program to work in a different way, that is fine.

Produce a document entitled **Data Dictionary: Procedures** with a subheading for each of your identified events (use Activity 20.11 for guidance). Under each of these subheadings write a description of what the event will do.

3 Identify which variables are to be used by your program, then create a document entitled **Data Dictionary: Variables** using Activity 20.11 for guidance.

4 Produce a test plan for your program using Activity 20.12 for guidance.

5 Start a new programming project, produce the form and write code for the events.

6 Test the program to confirm it meets the requirements. Update the test plan with the results of your testing. Document any changes you make to the program when a test is failed.

20.3.2 Design

After the specification is produced, the needs of the program are understood and the design can be created.

The design is useful as a guide to the programmer(s) and as a communication tool to help management and users understand how the new application will work. This helps avoid wasted effort, as unwanted aspects of the program can be identified before they are actually produced.

20.3.2.1 Screen layouts

Screen layouts are needed to plan the appearance of forms and how they will be used. Screen layouts may be produced using pencil and paper or using drawing software, as both these methods allow the design to be modified if needed. IT professionals do not use ink for planning, as it is difficult to rub out if changes are needed.

20.3.2.2 Data storage

Most programs need to store data so that information or documents used by the program are available the next time it runs.

The design will need to identify where data is stored as well as the structure of data. The structure defines what gets saved to disk:

- the sequence – e.g. the data file may have a header section, the main data as records, then a section with **checksums** to ensure no corruption has occurred
- records – what fields are in each record with their data types and sizes.

What does it mean?

A **checksum** is a calculation on data that is a form of validation, often used during transmissions. The calculation produces a result that is worked out before transmission then sent as a checksum in the last section of data. The receiving computer carries out the same calculation on the data received then compares it with the checksum – if it is different, the data is corrupted and needs to be resent.

Case study

Booking Form for X Ercise

X Ercise is a gym that has approached Apps'R'Us to have a bespoke booking program written to accept bookings and print out confirmation for the client.

The confirmation print needs this information:

- date of the booking
- time of the booking
- equipment that has been booked
- name of the member of the gym.

The program is to run on a PC which has a current processor, 1GB of RAM, 50GB of free disk space and a current version of the MS Windows operating system. The PC attaches to an inkjet printer to be used for printing confirmations.

1 From these user requirements, produce a design for the form(s) needed by the program. Do this using pencil and paper or a drawing package such as Paint.

2 From these user requirements, produce a design for the confirmation printout needed by the program. This must be actual size, and should be drawn using pencil and paper on to a blank sheet of A4. Careful measurements can then be drawn on to the paper from the top of the page to the top of each object (such as text) on the page and from the left of the page to the left of each object. These X,Y distances will be needed in code to print the confirmation.

3 Identify which events are to be used by your program. These will probably be two buttons to print the booking confirmation and to quit the program.

There are many ways a program like this can use events to meet the requirements – if you design the program to work in a different way, that is fine.

Produce a document entitled **Data Dictionary: Procedures** with a subheading for each of your identified events (use Activity 20.11 for guidance). Under each of these subheadings write a description of what the event will do.

4 Identify which variables are to be used by your program, then create a document entitled **Data Dictionary: Variables** using Activity 20.11 for guidance.

5 Produce a test plan for your program using Activity 20.12 for guidance.

6 Start a new programming project, produce the form and write code for the events.

7 Test the program to confirm it meets the requirements. Update the test plan with the results of your testing. Document any changes you make to the program when a test is failed.

20.3.2.3 Event procedures and descriptions

The event procedures relate back to forms and controls and how they are expected to be used. Each event needs a name and description. The description explains what will happen when the event is triggered. This will probably be a paragraph or two of writing for each of the events.

20.3.2.4 Appropriate ways of representing the processing tasks

There are many approaches to representing processing tasks, including: flowchart, structure diagram, pseudocode and action list. The choice of which method(s) to use may depend on the organisation's standards or on the programmer's own view of which method best explains the algorithm.

■ Flowchart

A flowchart is a diagram that is particularly good at showing program flows. Flowcharts use standard

Activity 20.11

Produce a data dictionary

1 Produce a document entitled **Data Dictionary: Variables** for the program you wrote to meet the requirements of one of the case studies in this section. This data dictionary could be a table in a document with these headings:

- name of variable
- description of how the variable is to be used
- data type
- example of data to be kept in the variable
- scope of the variable.

Include a row in the table for each variable you identify for your program.

2 Produce a document entitled **Data Dictionary: Procedures** to describe the subroutines and functions of the program. This could be structured using subheadings for each of your events. Under each of these subheadings write a description of what the event is to do, a description of the **parameters** (if any) and what the code does. **P**₅

What does it mean?

Parameters act as local variables (see page 178) where values are passed into a subroutine or function. A parameter is usually inside brackets after the name where it is declared, e.g. Sub LoadData(FName) has FName as a parameter.

symbols (see Figure 20.19) to represent code, joined by lines to represent the flow of the program from symbol to symbol. These lines are assumed to flow downwards or to the right. Arrow heads may be used on the lines to show if the flow is in a different direction.

■ Structure diagram

Structure diagrams are good at helping to plan code using a top down approach. Structure diagrams have an implied sequence of top to bottom and left to right (see Figure 20.20).

Case study

Car for Ray Seeng

Ray Seeng runs a nursery for children aged 2 to 4 years old.

The nursery wants a program that can be used by the children to improve their awareness of numbers. The children will choose a number on the keyboard, then drive a car from the form, using the number as the speed of the car.

The nursery requires the program to run on a PC which has a current processor, 1 GB of RAM, 250 GB of free disk space and a current version of the MS Windows operating system.

1 From these user requirements, produce a design for the form(s) needed by the program. Do this using pencil and paper or a drawing package such as Paint.

2 Identify which events are to be used by your program. These will probably be two buttons to start the car and to quit the program.

There are many ways a program like this can use events to meet the requirements – if you design the program to work in a different way, that is fine.

Produce a document entitled **Data Dictionary: Procedures** with a subheading for each of your identified events (use Activity 20.11 for guidance). Under each of these subheadings write a description of what the event will do.

3 Identify which variables are to be used by your program, then create a document entitled **Data Dictionary: Variables** using Activity 20.11 for guidance.

4 Produce a test plan for your program using Activity 20.12 for guidance.

5 Start a new programming project, produce the form and write code for the events.

6 Test the program to confirm it meets the requirements. Update the test plan with the results of your testing. Document any changes you make to the program when a test is failed.

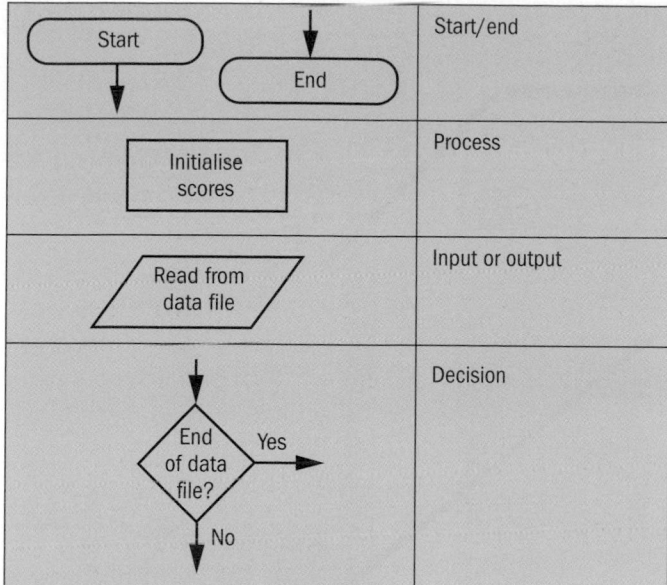

▲ **Figure 20.19 Flowchart symbols**

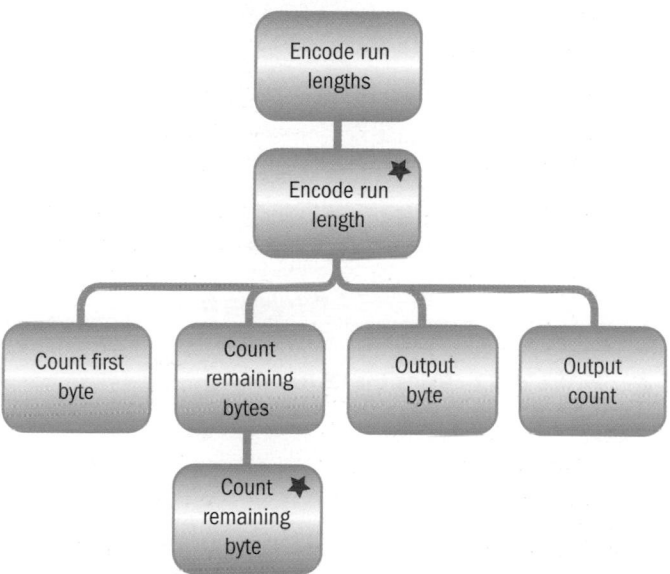

▲ **Figure 20.20 Example of a structure diagram**

■ Pseudocode

Pseudocode is a mix of English and program code and provides a strong feel for how the code will be written, but without the need to actually write and debug it at the design stage of the development.

■ Action list

An action list consists of bullet points that give the sequence and summarise what the code will do when it is written.

20.3.3 Creation of an application

20.3.3.1 Use of a development environment

Modern event driven languages use an integrated development environment (IDE) (see page 172) to make programming and debugging easier for the programmer – all the tools and facilities are available in the same environment.

Using a modern IDE often has this sequence:

- Start the IDE, then either open an existing project for more development or create a new project – for a new project you will need to select the type of application.
- Save the new project, giving it a name and creating a new folder for it.
- Add controls to the form(s), giving each control a meaningful name.
- Add code to the control events that are to be used in the application.
- Run the code to correct syntax and simple run-time errors.

Once the program is running reasonably well, the structured testing plan can be implemented.

The VB.NET IDE has these features (see Figure 20.21):

- **Solution Explorer** – used to keep track of the forms, modules and anything else in the current project, with their names and file locations.
- **Main window** – shows the forms, code and help screen – the current view is selected using tabs at the top of the window.
- **Toolbox** – used to select components for the program that can then be dragged on to the form.
- **Properties window** – gives information and control over the many aspects of components, such as name, position, size, colour, etc.
- **Output window** – gives debugging information about the current project when it runs, help choices and other information that is selected using tabs at the bottom of this window.

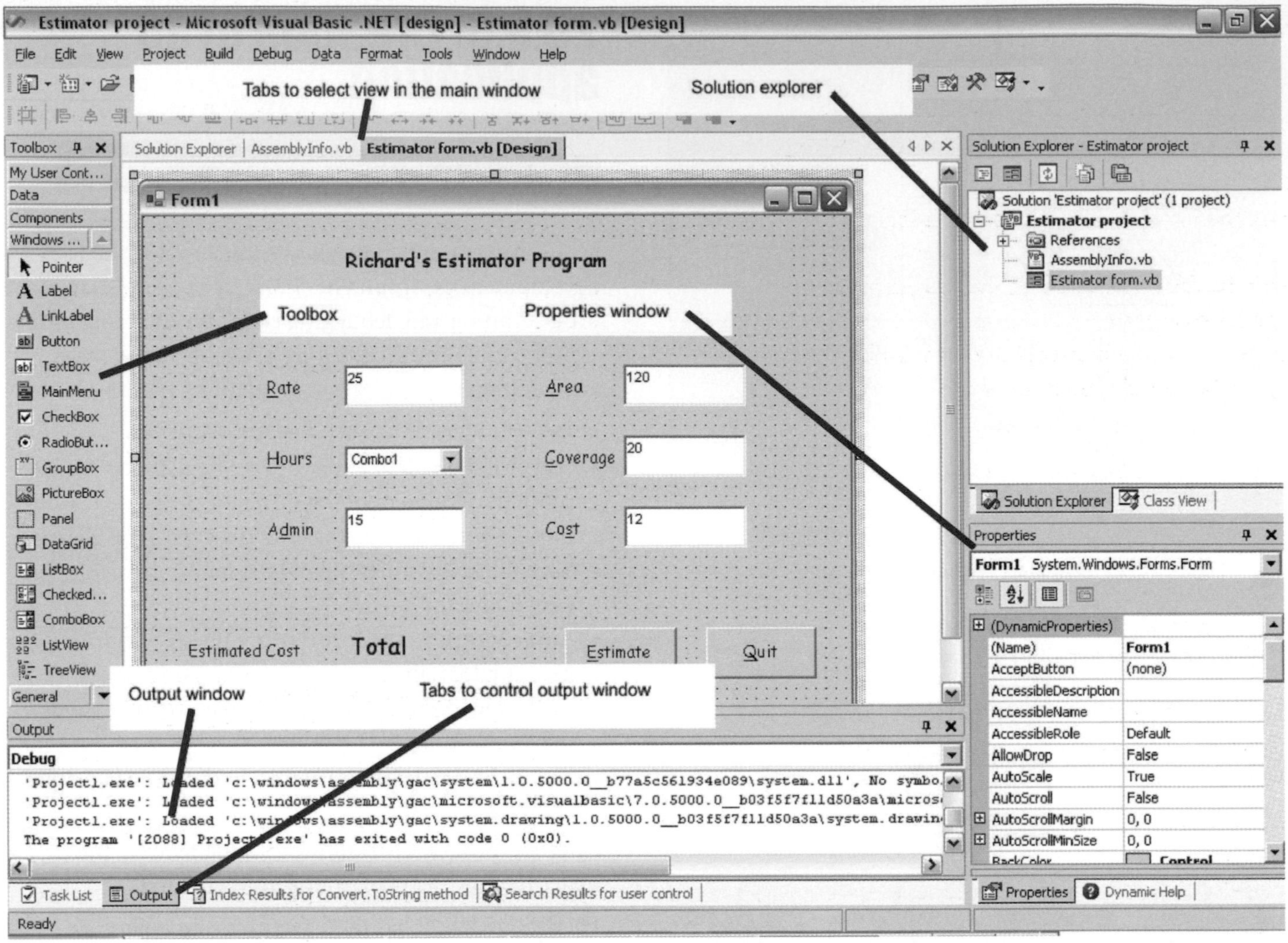

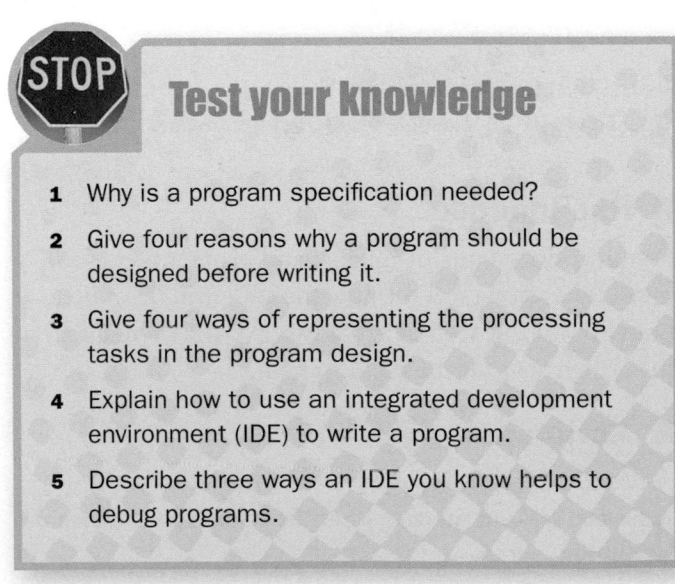

- Estimator project - Microsoft Visual Basic .NET [design] - Estimator form.vb [Design]
- File Edit View Project Build Debug Data Format Tools Window Help
- Tabs to select view in the main window
- Solution explorer
- Solution Explorer | AssemblyInfo.vb | **Estimator form.vb [Design]**
- Solution Explorer - Estimator project
- Toolbox: My User Cont..., Data, Components, Windows ..., Pointer, Label, LinkLabel, Button, TextBox, MainMenu, CheckBox, RadioBut..., GroupBox, PictureBox, Panel, DataGrid, ListBox, Checked..., ComboBox, ListView, TreeView, General
- Form1 — Richard's Estimator Program
- Toolbox
- Properties window
- Rate 25 Area 120
- Hours Combo1 Coverage 20
- Admin 15 Cost 12
- Estimated Cost Total Estimate Quit
- Output window
- Tabs to control output window
- Solution 'Estimator project' (1 project)
  - Estimator project
    - References
    - AssemblyInfo.vb
    - Estimator form.vb
- Solution Explorer | Class View
- Properties — Form1 System.Windows.Forms.Form
  - (DynamicProperties)
  - (Name) Form1
  - AcceptButton (none)
  - AccessibleDescription
  - AccessibleName
  - AccessibleRole Default
  - AllowDrop False
  - AutoScale True
  - AutoScroll False
  - AutoScrollMargin 0, 0
  - AutoScrollMinSize 0, 0
  - BackColor Control
- Properties | Dynamic Help
- Output
- Debug
  - 'Project1.exe': Loaded 'c:\windows\assembly\gac\system\1.0.5000.0__b77a5c561934e089\system.dll', No symbo...
  - 'Project1.exe': Loaded 'c:\windows\assembly\gac\microsoft.visualbasic\7.0.5000.0__b03f5f7f11d50a3a\micros...
  - 'Project1.exe': Loaded 'c:\windows\assembly\gac\system.drawing\1.0.5000.0__b03f5f7f11d50a3a\system.drawin...
  - The program '[2088] Project1.exe' has exited with code 0 (0x0).
- Task List | Output | Index Results for Convert.ToString method | Search Results for user control
- Ready

▲ **Figure 20.21 Using the VB.NET IDE**

Every program needs to be debugged as it is written, otherwise it will not run. There will be a structured test plan later, after the program has been completed, to confirm the program meets the specification.

Event driven languages offer the programmer many tools to help with features such as:

- pausing the program when an error is found, with a message to inform the programmer of the type of error
- Command window (this VB.NET tool is similar to the Debug window of VB6), which can be used to create a test log or to test code when the program is paused
- Watch window to test values of variables and other objects as the program runs.

STOP Test your knowledge

1 Why is a program specification needed?

2 Give four reasons why a program should be designed before writing it.

3 Give four ways of representing the processing tasks in the program design.

4 Explain how to use an integrated development environment (IDE) to write a program.

5 Describe three ways an IDE you know helps to debug programs.

esting is always needed when a program is written to nsure it works as expected. Reviewing an event driven pplication is also needed in order to:

- compare the final product with the original user need
- compare the final product with the program design
- evaluate the ease of use
- identify whether requirements were met and if there are any further development needs.

20.4.1 Testing and ebugging

20.4.1.1 Test strategy

esting needs a strategy to make sure that everything at needs testing is checked and to avoid unnecessary uplication of effort.

he test plan strategy may include these sections:

- **event testing**, to ensure that each of the planned events works without errors and produces the expected results
- **black box testing**, to ensure that pre-prepared test data produces the expected outputs from the program

What does it mean?

Black box testing is when a program is tested without taking into consideration the code inside the program. The program is the 'box' which is 'black', as the tester does not see anything inside it.

- **white box testing**, to ensure that all the selections and pathways inside the program code work properly and without errors.

The test plan needs to be kept in a document and should record that corrective actions that are taken each time a test fails. The test should then be re-run to prove the fix worked.

Diagnostic software might be used as part of the testing strategy.

What does it mean?

White box testing is when a program is tested to make sure each line of the code works. The program is the 'box', which is 'white' as the tester does see inside it.

Diagnostic software attempts to diagnose a problem; it identifies possible faults and offers solutions.

20.4.1.2 Test plan structure

The test plan is often a table (see Table 20.3). Each row is used for an individual test, with the columns holding information such as:

- the test number – useful so that other parts of the program documentation can easily refer to the test if needed
- a description of what the test is designed to achieve
- the test date – to be filled in when the test is actually carried out
- expected result – so the tester knows what to look for and how the test can be passed

Number	Description	Date	Expected result	Actual result	Passed?
1	Main form loads	1/4/08	Form loads without errors	Form loads without errors	Yes

Table 20.3   An example of a test plan

- the actual result must be recorded to show whether the test has passed – if the test fails, this provides useful information for the debugging that must follow
- any corrective action that was taken to fix the bug – this may be a separate section of the test plan documentation.

Activity 20.12

Produce a test plan

1. Produce a test plan for one of the programs you wrote to meet the requirements of a case study in this unit. You could use a table with the headings shown in Table 20.3. **p**₅

2. Run the tests and complete the table with the actual results. **p**₅

3. Add a section to your document with descriptions of the actions that were needed to solve any tests that failed. Include the code, copied from both before and after the fix. **p**₅

20.4.1.3 Error messages

The programmer must be aware of every error message that the IDE shows as the program is written and tested.

Some of these messages can be disregarded, as they will refer to parts of the program that have not yet been written or completed. However, all the other messages will need to be responded to with the issues they identify resolved.

20.4.1.4 Specialist software tools

Every programming environment provides specialist software tools, such as Debug, which assist in correcting code by giving extra information to the programmer, when needed.

Debug is available to VB.NET, C# and other event driven languages. It can be used to create a log when the program runs and the programmer can examine the log later to see what happened. This can be a very powerful aid to finding errors, as the programmer has a lot of control over when items are added to the log and there is no need to pause the program.

Other specialist software tools for debugging include:

- Locals window – shows the local variables that are in use when the code pauses
- Watch window – creates a collection of variables, the contents of which can be seen 'at a glance' when code pauses.

20.4.2 Review

A review is needed of every project to confirm that the project is delivering the needed outcomes and is not missing any of the requirements.

Activity 20.13

Review a program

1. Prepare a form for people to complete to give you feedback on a program that you wrote to meet the needs of one of the case studies in this unit. Include sections on the form to get information about:
   - how easy it is to use
   - any problems with using it
   - any improvements they would like to make it more usable. **p**₅

2. Ask some fellow students to use your program and then complete the form. **p**₅

3. Improve the user interface and functionality of your program based on the feedback. **m**₂

20.4.2.1 Review against specification requirements

It is essential to review the program against the original specification requirements in order to confirm that the end product is what was originally wanted. Some programmers get side-tracked in their development work (perhaps as a result of solving some programming problems) into producing work which appears to be correct at the time, but which strays away from the original requirements.

This review is also a good check that the end product fulfils the original user needs.

20.4.2.2 Interim reviews

Interim reviews are useful to check progress both against timescales and in terms of meeting requirements.

Timescales have always been difficult to plan for and meet in programming, as unexpected problems can be discovered during coding which can have considerable impact on the delivery date. The sooner such a problem is discovered the better, as users and management can then be informed of likely delays and, if necessary, extra resources can be put into the project to bring it back to predicted timescales.

Meeting requirements is crucial for the success of the programming. If there is a drift away from the requirements during development, it is important to identify this early on, so that the program can be brought back on course while it is still easy and relatively inexpensive to do so.

Activity 20.14

Check a program against the specification

1 Check the program you produced to meet the needs of a case study against the original specification. Produce a document identifying the parts of the specification it meets and any parts it does not. **p**₅

2 Improve the user interface and functionality of your program, based on your check against the original specification. **m**₂

3 Produce a written report to evaluate the application you produced. **d**₃

Test your knowledge

1 What is a test strategy?

2 What is black box testing?

3 What is white box testing?

4 Identify four error messages you have seen and what caused them.

5 Describe how Debug can be used.

Preparation for assessment

The assessment tasks in this unit are based on the following scenario.

Apps'R'Us is a small software house that produces bespoke software for a range of national and international clients, such as programs to operate door entry systems, shop tills, calculate job estimates and so on. Apps'R'Us employs 24 people, to market the company, liaise with clients to analyse their needs, to produce program requirements and to write and support code.

Most of the marketing work is done through the website.

You are new to Apps'R'Us and your role is junior programmer. You are part of a team of three programmers, led by Sabrina who is an analyst-programmer. Your role is to write programs, produce documentation and any other supporting tasks as directed by Sabrina.

- Produce a document that can be downloaded from the website to explain how an operating system, such as Windows, can be viewed as an event driven application. Include annotated screenshots with written explanations of a variety of events that occur when the operating system is used and the actions the operating system takes for each of these events. **m**₁

- Produce a document that can be downloaded from the website to evaluate the suitability of event driven programs for non-graphical applications. Identify two or more applications that either use a text-based interface or have no graphical components. A program with no graphical components might be a control application for a device such as a burglar alarm. You need to identify the events that each of these applications would receive and identify how suitable an event driven language might be to handle those events. **d**₁

Task 1 (P1, P2, M1, D1)

Sabrina has asked you to produce some materials to help potential clients understand what event driven programs are and some examples of how they can be used. These will be pages for the Apps'R'Us website and downloadable documents.

- Produce page(s) for the website that describe the key features of event driven programs. Include a diagram to show how event handlers, trigger functions and event loops work with components on a form. The page should also include text to explain the diagram. **p**₁

- Produce page(s) for the website that describe, with examples, some typical uses and advantages of event driven programs. **p**₂

Task 2 (P3, M3, D2)

Your team leader, Sabrina, needs to prepare for your first appraisal – a meeting you will have with her to formally review your performance as a junior programmer.

As your job has a strong programming element, she needs to have evidence of your abilities and understanding of event driven programming in preparation for the meeting.

She has asked you to produce some small programs to demonstrate the use of these event driven tools and techniques:

- toolboxes and controls
- variables with declarations defining data types
- constants
- selection

- loops
- event handlers
- triggers
- objects and object properties
- menus.

Create as many programs as you need to show how each one of these tools and techniques are used. Some programs may demonstrate several of them.

As evidence you should provide:

- screenshots of each program as it runs, pasted into a document which has your name, program title and which tools and techniques the program demonstrates
- a code print of each program taken directly from the IDE.

You will also need a signed and dated observation record for your appraisal to prove that you used appropriate debugging tools. **p**₃

If you are to be considered for progression from junior programmer, you will need to include evidence that you understand the scope of variables.

For this evidence, provide a document comparing the use and effectiveness of global and local variables. The document should explain:

- the differences between global and local variables
- why using each scope was appropriate in your programs
- how and where these variables were declared in your code. **m**₃

Another requirement for being considered for progression in the team is your skill in report writing. You need to produce a report justifying the tools and techniques used in the production of your applications. **d**₂

Task 3 (P4)

Your team has been allocated four jobs from clients:
- job estimator for Pete Lumber (see page 181)
- cartoon for Anny Mation (see page 182)
- booking form for X Ercise (see page 183)
- car for Ray Seeng (see page 184).

As the junior programmer, you have been given first choice on these jobs so you can choose to produce two programs that are within your capabilities.

You will design and implement a working application to meet two of these defined requirements.

As evidence you should provide:

- screenshots of each program as it runs, pasted into a document which has your name and the program title
- a code print of each program taken directly from the IDE. **p**₄

Task 4 (P5, M2, D3)

The programs you produced for Task 3 need to be tested and documented.

The documentation for each program will consist of:
- data dictionary
- written test plan
- feedback from users
- checks against the original specifications.

Improve the user interface and functionality of one or both of your programs, based on the feedback from the users and the checks against the original specifications. As evidence, provide written documentation recording the changes made and an observation record of you demonstrating the changes. **m**₂

Evaluate an application you produced for Task 3 in the form of a written report. **d**₃

Website Production and Management

Introduction

The Internet is perhaps the most important IT development in the last few decades; it has provided new ways to communicate and share information and, in doing so, it has revolutionised the way people and businesses use IT.

In this unit you will learn how to design and create interactive websites. You will also discover the factors that can improve website performance, security issues and legislation affecting websites.

After completing this unit, you should be able to achieve these outcomes:

- Be able to design an interactive website
- Be able to create an interactive website
- Understand the factors that influence website performance
- Understand the constraints related to the production and use of websites.

Grading criteria	Activity	Page number
To achieve a pass grade the evidence must show that the learner is able to:		
p₁ Define the specific purpose and requirements for a website	PFA	225
p₂ Design a multi-page website to meet stated requirements	PFA	225
p₃ Using a design, build a functional multipage, two-way interactive website	PFA	225
p₄ Review a website M4 demonstrate that a created website meets the defined requirements and achieves the defined purpose	21.14, PFA	214, 225
p₅ Describe the various factors that influence the performance of a website	PFA	225
p₆ Successfully upload a website to a web server	21.15, PFA	215, 225
p₇ Identify the potential security issues and legal constraints involved in a particular website	21.19, 21.20, PFA	221, 223, 225
To achieve a merit grade the evidence must show that, in addition to the pass criteria, the learner is able to:		
m₁ Explain the tools and techniques used in the creation of a website	21.9, PFA	203, 225
m₂ Adapt and improve the effectiveness of a website on the basis of a formal review	PFA	225
m₃ Explain techniques that can be used to minimise security risks to websites	21.19, PFA	221, 225
m₄ Demonstrate that a created website meets the defined requirements and achieves the defined purpose	PFA	225
To achieve a distinction grade the evidence must show that, in addition to the pass and merit criteria, the learner is able to:		
d₁ Compare and evaluate two different designs created to meet a particular specification and justify the one chosen for Implementation	PFA	225
d₂ Produce a website that is W3C compliant	PFA	225
d₃ Compare 'user side' and 'server side' factors that can influence website performance	21.18, PFA	219, 225

Note: 'PFA' stands for 'Preparation for assessment'.

Before a website can be created, it must be designed. If this stage is skipped, major problems are likely to occur when building the website and errors might not be found until the website **goes live**.

What does it mean?

When a website **goes live**, it is uploaded to a web server and made available to the public for the first time.

21.1.1 Identification of need

By investigating the requirements of a project, a web designer can ensure that the website fully meets both the client's needs and those of the users.

21.1.1.1 Nature of interactivity

Most modern websites involve interactivity; **static websites** risk losing users.

It is important to decide how much interactivity will be in a **dynamic website**.

What does it mean?

A **static website** is one with no interactivity and is usually just a presentation of information. Changes have to be hard-coded into the site.

A **dynamic website** can involve any level of interactivity from a simple feedback form to a database that personalises the website for each individual visitor. Changes can be made on the fly.

Too little interactivity on a website and users may lose interest; too much and they may feel overwhelmed. It is important to get the balance right.

If a website is to be an e-commerce site, the designer also needs to decide how online transactions will be carried out. There are two parts to this issue:

1. How will the user browse the catalogue?
2. How will they make purchases?

Activity 21.1

Browsing and buying

1. Visit five websites that have e-commerce facilities. Note the URL and business name of each website you visit.

2. Make notes on the design decisions that have been made for each website.

3. Describe the interactivity possible on each website.

21.1.1.2 Client needs and user needs

Web designers must always have two sets of needs in mind: those of the client and those of the users. The client is the person who has commissioned the site to be made and usually they are also the person who holds the purse strings. If the client is not happy with the site, you may not get paid for your work.

The users are the visitors to the site. They need to be attracted to the site initially to make their first visit, and then encouraged to revisit. This may be for several reasons: for example, to make more purchases, to look at new content or to take part in discussions on forums. One aim of websites is to persuade their users to bookmark the website, therefore increasing the probability of their returning on a regular basis.

Activity 21.2

Bookmarks

1 Think about websites you have bookmarked in the past. Why did you choose them? What persuaded you to become a potentially regular visitor?

2 If you haven't bookmarked a website before, why do you think that is? Would you like to bookmark any you use frequently?

■ Image

A website must convey the correct image, especially if it is for a business. It should be professional and demonstrate that the organisation behind the website can be trusted. Image can be conveyed through a clear layout, choice of colours and pictures and the content of the text.

Activity 21.3

Business image

1 Find three e-commerce websites: one for children, one for teenagers and one for adults. What meanings are the images trying to convey? What techniques have the designers used to suggest these meanings? Have they successfully portrayed appropriate images for each business?

■ Level of security

A level of security must be decided upon at the design stage, as this will impact on both the design of the website and its management. You will need to ask questions such as:

● Can anyone access the site or will there be an account system with passwords, or a mixture of both?

● What protective methods will be used on the web server? (See section 21.4.1 on page 220.)

■ Development timescales

Development timescales must be agreed upon at the start of the project, preferably in a written form which both client and developer have agreed and signed. The schedule should be broken down into stages, with clear points of review (see Unit 4, section 4.2.2.3, on page 16) where the client can check that the project is progressing to their satisfaction.

■ Support and maintenance contracts

Support and maintenance contracts are important factors which need to be decided at the beginning of the project. The web developer might be contracted just for designing and building of the website, or they might also be contracted to provide maintenance, updates and support when needed. The type of contract agreed on will affect the cost of the project.

■ Costs

Pricing a website for a client is difficult. Items to consider when estimating costs include the size and content of the website, the timescale of the project and the aftercare requirements. Some developers charge by the hour for as long as the project takes. Others charge for each element in the website – the more elements that are in the website, the more expensive it will be. There might be very few overheads involved in website development (e.g. a freelance developer working from home), but on the other hand, it is a very specialised area, so deciding on how much to charge can be difficult. Sometimes a price might be selected purely to undercut the competition.

■ Other client needs

Other elements which a client may need include:
● logo design
● original images and photographs
● **search engine visibility**
● online advertising.

What does it mean?

Search engine visibility is getting a website listed as high as possible on a search engine. This will increase the number of visitors to a site.

The user and client requirements are used as a benchmark of the success of a project. After testing, the website should be evaluated, including checking whether the requirements have been met. An explanation should be included for any requirements that have not been met (see section 21.2.4.3 on page 214).

(see section 21.2.4.3 on page 214).

21.1.1.3 End user need

The other set of needs a web designer has to consider are those of the users. This can be a difficult task where sites are intended for a large target market.

The website must be appropriate to the audience. The content must be suitable, which involves not using inappropriate language or technical jargon. The image should also be suitable for the wide range of people who may look at it. For example, the website for Disneyland Resort Paris needs to be suitable for both children and adults and has to be careful to avoid excluding either of these target audiences. For children, there are colourful images and magical animations; for adults, there is information about the hotels, the parks and all the facilities available. The aim of the website is to encourage parents to book a holiday.

Considering the range of people who may use the website, the complexity of the site must be appropriate. This includes not just the content, but also the method of using it – for example, it must be easy to navigate round the site. Users with little Internet experience must also be taken into consideration.

One problematic area of web design is ensuring that the client and user needs are compatible. For example, the client might want to use a colour scheme of yellow and magenta but you know this would not be appropriate for the website's users – you will need to manage the situation and attempt to come to a compromise, such as using a header of yellow and magenta, but designing the rest of the website in more easily read colours.

21.1.2 Design tools

Several tools can be used to ensure that all areas are considered when designing websites. By producing a thorough design using the tools presented in this section, and using this to communicate with your client, you can ensure that your client is happy with your plans before you build the site. This should reduce the problems that you could encounter if there was a mismatch between client expectations and the actual outcomes.

21.1.2.1 Concept designing

What does it mean?

Concept designing means outlining the overall design of the product. This gives the general feel of the website and the effect it should have on its users.

To convey the concept of a site, you might use one or both of the following tools: **mood boards** and **storyboards**.

What does it mean?

Mood boards are a collage of images, textures and other items aimed at providing an idea of the look and feel of a product. They are usually A3 size.

A **storyboard** shows the sequence of a project. In web design, it shows how different pages will interrelate.

The aim of a mood board (see Figure 21.1) is to produce something with the same feel as the finished website. They are useful to focus the design and demonstrate initial ideas to the client.

Storyboarding (see Figure 21.2) is key to structuring a website clearly and is a way of expressing a navigation design (see section 21.2.1.2 on page 204). Storyboards are used in the design of moving images, such as animation or film, as well as in web design.

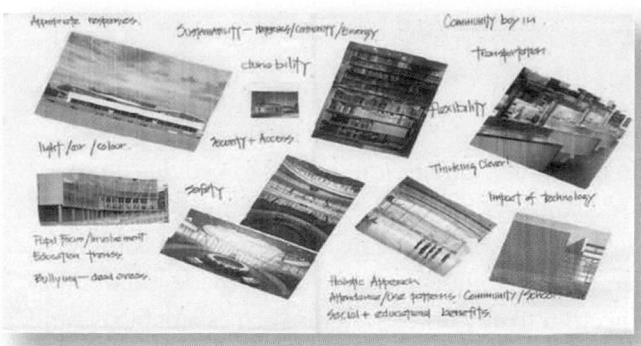

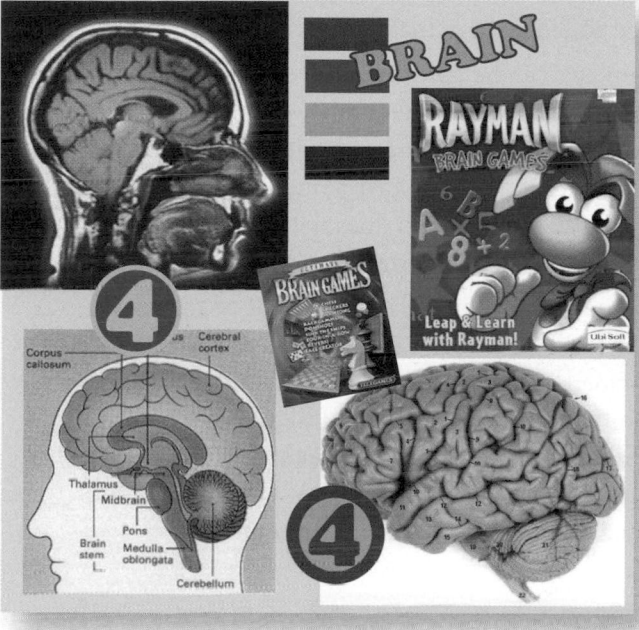

▲ **Figure 21.1 Examples of mood boards**

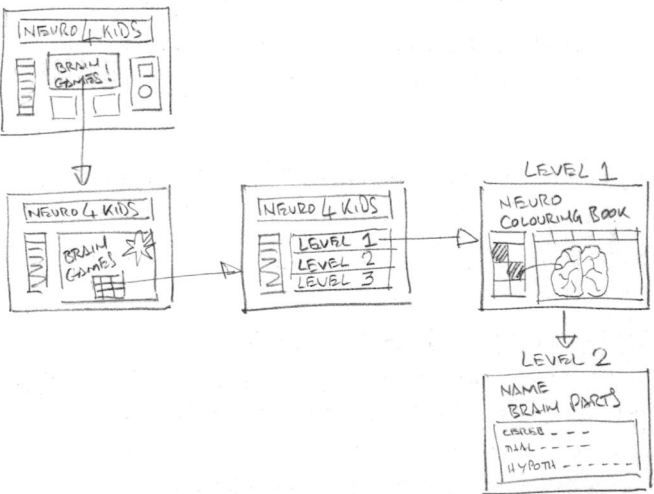

▲ **Figure 21.2 Examples of a storyboard**

Activity 21.4

Storyboarding

1 Think of a scene from your favourite cartoon or film. Create a storyboard to show what happens. Use a minimum of 10 boxes and a maximum of 20. Add any notes underneath each box to explain what is happening.

21.1.2.2 Layout techniques

As well as the structure of the overall site, the layout of the individual pages must be designed. There are several methods that can be used to arrange items on a web page, including frames, tables and DIVs and SPANs.

■ Frames

The simplest method of layout is to use frames (see Figure 21.3), but these are considered old-fashioned in the industry. Each part of the page is contained in its own file and there is a master page which pulls each part in like a jigsaw.

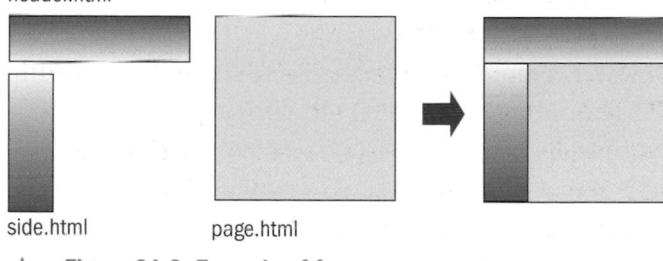

▲ **Figure 21.3 Example of frames**

■ Tables

A table (see Figure 21.4) holds all the content on a web page, with each cell having an individual part of the content. It is a good method of ensuring that the layout is retained on the different browsers that users may use to view the page. However, the more complicated the table, the longer it will take to load for the user. If a page takes too long, a visitor may lose patience and leave the site, perhaps never to return.

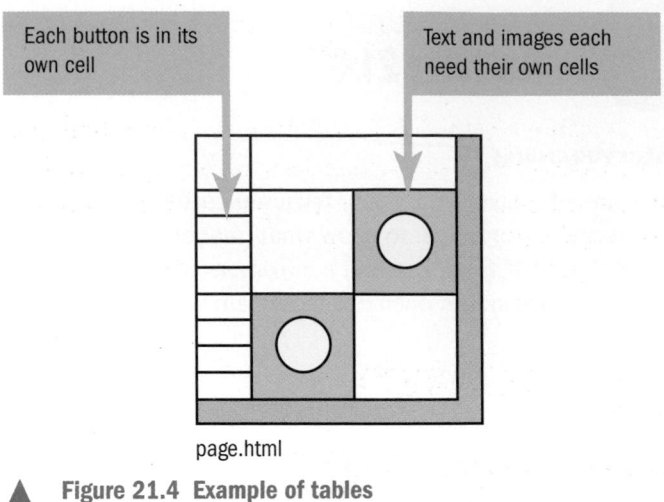

Each button is in its own cell

Text and images each need their own cells

page.html

▲ **Figure 21.4 Example of tables**

■ DIVs and SPANs

What does it mean?

A **DIV** is a method of defining a style for a block of HTML (HyperText Markup Language). It includes an automatic paragraph break.

A **SPAN** is also a method of defining a style for a block of HTML (HyperText Markup Language).

DIVs and SPANs are used to define styles within blocks of HTML; for example, `<span class="red small">some text</span>`.

However, a more useful method is to combine them with CSS (cascading style sheets) formatting style. For example, in the code `<span class="warning">some text</span>`, the "warning" style would be defined earlier in the CSS (see section 21.2.3.6 on page 213).

The main difference between DIVs and SPANs is that a DIV includes a paragraph return, whereas a SPAN does not. They are efficient methods of laying out and formatting a page, especially when used in conjunction with effective CSS.

21.1.2.3 Templates

Templates are used to make the process of adding content simpler, and are often used to provide an easy maintenance system for users with minimal web knowledge. A template keeps the design and content separate. Generally, a template will provide full design, connection to any other systems such as a database and all interactive coding. The only thing that usually needs to be added is the actual content.

Templates can be quite expensive, depending on the level of design, especially if a company has asked for a unique creation. However, using templates can mean that a business that does not have someone with web skills within the organisation does not need to employ someone to create the website.

A recent development is the concept of 'takeaway' websites. This is where all the parts of a website are provided and a user can add the content. These are mainly targeted at non-technical people who want to put their own personal website on the Internet. The result could be a high number of websites that look very similar and have low-quality content.

21.1.2.4 Colour schemes

The colours selected for a website can encourage or deter users, so the selection must be made with care. Several questions must be asked when deciding on a colour scheme.

- Do the colours combine well? Are they aesthetically pleasing?
- Are the colours appropriate for the target audience? For example, primary colours might be used for a children's website.
- Is the text readable? Black text on a purple background may produce an atmospheric effect, but is not east to read.
- Does the colour scheme fit with the business's **house style**?

What does it mean?

House style is a standard design that is carried throughout an organisation's website. It can also be extended throughout the business, e.g. on promotional brochures, letterheads, etc. It can include logos, colour combinations and layouts.

Activity 21.5

House styles

1 Find three websites with distinctively different artistic styles. Describe the artistic style used on each website.

2 For each of your chosen websites, describe how a house style has or has not been carried through the website.

3 Explain why a house style has or has not been used for each website. In your opinion, is this effective for that website?

21.1.2.5 Screen designs

To visualise what the pages will look like before building them, designers create screen designs (see Figure 21.5). These are mock-ups of the actual page and concentrate on layout rather than content.

Activity 21.6

Screen designs

1 Choose an existing website and produce a screen design to show how the designer has created the layout (following the example shown in Figure 21.5). Label the colours, fonts and other specifications. Estimate sizes and give the images suitable labels.

21.1.2.6 Outline of content

As screen designs deal with the layout of the page, the content must also be considered. Generally, at the design stage, only headings will be defined.

▼ **Figure 21.5 An example screen design**

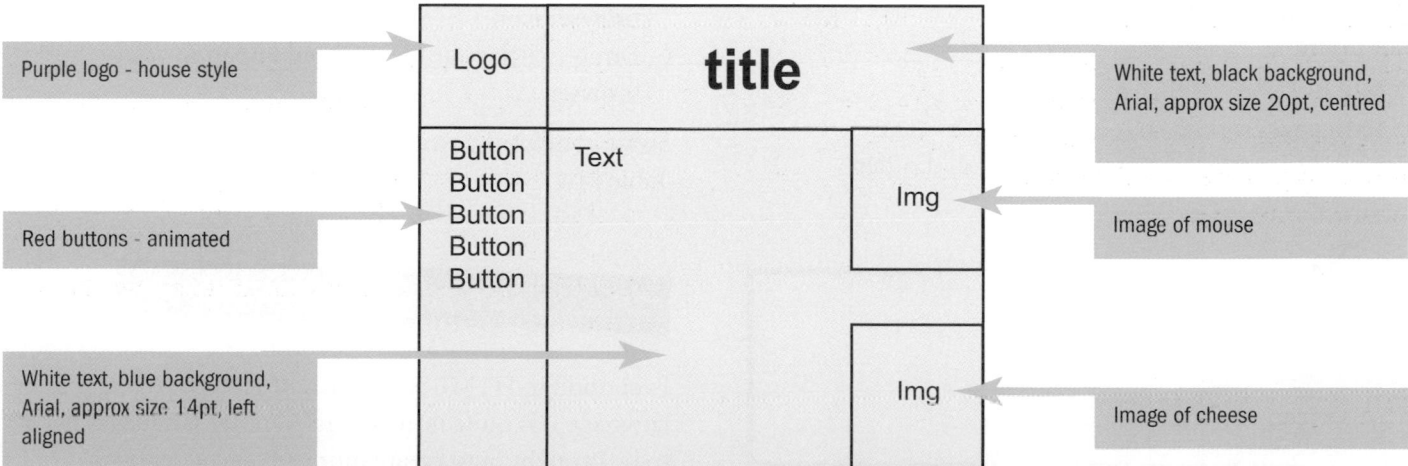

21.1.3 Software

It is only possible to choose the correct web development software once you know exactly what will be in your website. Otherwise, part of the way through a build, you may find you need another piece of software which will cost money and may take time to learn.

21.1.3.1 Markup languages

HTML (Hypertext Markup Language) is the most commonly used markup language. So much so that all the others are just about extinct. HTML forms the basis of all World Wide Web pages, even where other languages are also used.

HTML uses a system of tags (indicated by angle brackets, < and >) which contain the instructions. Almost all tags come in a pair of open and close tags which enclose the content to be affected.

For example, `<font color="red">Some text</font>` would produce: Some text.

HTML pages should start and end with `<html> </html>` tags to declare the language being used. If other languages are used, they will need to be declared (see section 21.1.3.2 below).

Every web page is divided into a head and body section, each of which is defined by its tags. The head section is unseen by the user and can be thought of as the brains of the page. It contains all the information for the page to function correctly. The body is the part seen by the user and contains all the content of the page. A well-designed page should have reusable code in the head and minimal code in the body.

■ How to create a simple HTML web page

1 Open Notepad (or a similar text editor).

2 Enter this code:

```
<html>
<head>
<title>My First Web page</title>
<bgcolour="white">
</head>
<body>
<font color="blue"><b>Hello World!</b>
</font>
<font color=#000000><i>This is my first ever
web page.</i></font>
</body>
</html>
```

3 Click File / Save As.

4 Delete the Filename and type **mywebpage.html**, then click Save.

5 Navigate to where the file is saved using My Computer. Notice how the file icon is your Internet browser icon.

6 Double click your file. It should open in your browser.

Some commonly used HTML tags are shown in Table 21.1.

21.1.3.2 Client side scripting languages

Even though HTML is the basis of all web pages, as a language it is quite limited and so other languages need to be brought in to create more advanced features.

Remember!

American spelling is used in HTML.

Open tag	Close tag	Purpose	Example
`<font>`	`</font>`	Changes text. Open tag can have parameters such as color, size, face (i.e. typeface).	`<font face="Arial" size="16">Text</font>`
`<b>` or `<strong>`	`</b>` or `</strong>`	Makes text bold.	`<b>Text</b>`
`<i>` or `<em>`	`</i>` or `</em>`	Makes text italic.	`<i>Text</i>`
` `	No close tag	Starts a new line. One of the rare tags that is not in a pair.	`Text` ` ` `Text`
`<ul>`	`</ul>`	Creates a list with bullet points. `<li></li>` creates each list item.	`<li>first item</li>` `<li>second item</li>`

`<table>`	`</table>`	Creates a table.
		`<tr></tr>` creates rows.
		`<td></td>` creates columns.
			`<table border=1>`
			`<tr>`
			`<td>top left</td>`
			`<td>top right</td>`
			`</tr>`
			`<td>bottom left</td>`
			`<td>bottom right</td>`
			`</tr>`
			`</table>`

`<img />`	No close tag	Inserts an image. One of the rare tags that is not in a pair.	`<img src="Images\logo.gif" />`
`<a href>`	`</a>`	Creates a hyperlink. Can be used around text or an image.	`<a href="index.html">Go to home page</a>` `<a href="index.html"><img src="Images\logo.gif" /></a>`

Table 21.1 Common HTML tags

Activity 21.8

Using HTML

Even though there are several web design environments available, it is still important to understand HTML. The best way to do this is to use Notepad (or a similar text editor) to create a web page using purely your own code.

1 In a browser, open a website with which you are familiar, such as your school or college website. View the HTML (e.g. in Internet Explorer, click View / Source or Tools / View Source). Examine the code and compare it with the visual version in the browser.

2 Write down all the tags you recognise and what effect they have on the display of items on the web page. Try to find examples of all the tags in Table 21.1.

A **client side scripting** language is code which is embedded into the HTML. When the web page is downloaded onto the user's browser, the script is run on the user's computer.

What does it mean?

Client side scripting is when the script is executed on the user's computer.

This is the opposite of server side scripting, which is executed on the web server. **Server side scripting** is used for more advanced interactive features, such as connecting to a database and is not covered in this unit.

There are several languages available for a web designer to use. All websites must have a foundation in HTML, even if it is just used to support the other languages.

CSS (cascading style sheets) is used to ensure standardised formatting across a website – this also makes the site easier to maintain. In order to make a formatting change to a website that is formatted in HTML, the designer would have to search through the whole code, finding every instance of the format that needs to be changed. There could be hundreds of entries, so this is a very time-consuming method and it is likely to produce errors in consistency. By using CSS, on the other hand, only one formatting entry need be changed and it will be immediately applied throughout the whole site for every instance of the formatting style.

ASP (Active Server Pages) and **PHP (Hypertext Preprocessor)** are server side web languages. This means that the code is executed using the web server's processing power. The result is that the code and the data are very secure and can be executed efficiently. Both these languages can create interaction on a website, particularly involving connecting to databases.

VBScript and **JavaScript** are client side web languages. This means that the code is executed using the user's computer and not the web server. This frees up the processing power which would otherwise have been used. Both languages can create interaction on a website, such as forms, searching and even games.

There are several software development environments available. Microsoft FrontPage is the most popular web authoring application for beginners, as it uses a similar layout to the other Office programs and is very user friendly. However, the functionality can be limited.

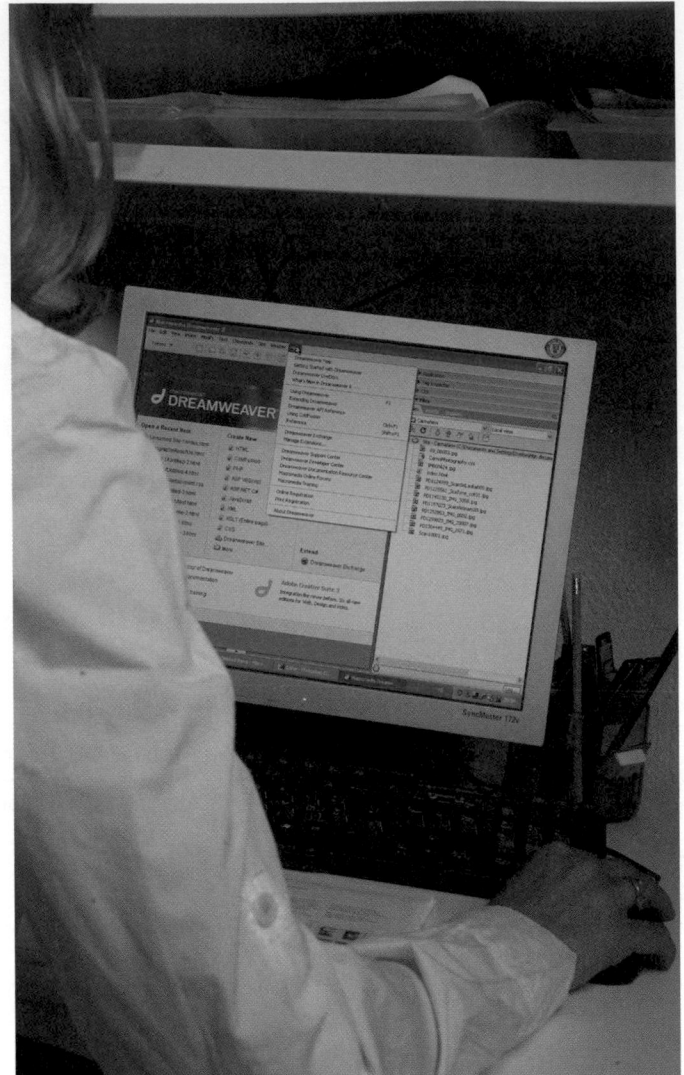

▲ A web designer using Adobe Dreamweaver

Adobe Dreamweaver is the current industry standard. Although more difficult to learn, it provides a wide range of tools to create a website and supports several client and server side scripting languages.

Using a development environment such as FrontPage or Dreamweaver is not absolutely necessary – as you have seen from the previous examples, it is possible to write the code using a text editor. However, using a development environment can make coding quicker and formatting easier.

Activity 21.9

Web design software

1 Explain the advantages and disadvantages of using a text editor (e.g. Notepad) for creating a web page.

2 Explain the advantages and disadvantages of using web authoring software (e.g. FrontPage or Dreamweaver) to create a web page. **m**

Test your knowledge

1 What is interactivity?

2 What is the difference between a static and a dynamic website?

3 Which two sets of needs must always be borne in mind when designing a website?

4 State the three methods that can be used in web page layout.

5 What is a house style and why is it used?

6 What do HTML and CSS stand for?

7 What two parts are all HTML web pages divided into?

21.2 Creating an interactive website

Once the design is entirely completed and the client is happy with it, the website can be built. Prototyping is often used in the first instance. This is where a test version of the website is built to ensure that the functionality is correct and that the specifications and look and feel are to the client's liking. By using a prototype the designer can save time and money.

The first element of the creation of a website is the structure. This will provide a solid basis for the content, which can then be easily inserted. Extra features, such as interactivity and audio-visual elements can be added. At this point the website should be complete. All parts must then be tested to ensure they are functioning correctly. Once the developer is happy that there are no bugs in the site, it can be uploaded to a web server and go live on the Internet.

21.2.1 Structure

Before adding any content, the fundamental structure of the page should be put in place, otherwise, you may have formatting problems later in the implementation.

21.2.1.1 Layout of pages

In your design, you will have decided whether you are going to use frames, tables or DIVs and SPANs. You should also have your layout exactly planned in your screen designs.

■ How to create tables in Adobe Dreamweaver

1 Open a web page in Dreamweaver.

2 Select Insert / Table or click on the Table icon in the top toolbar (see Figure 21.6).

3 Enter the number of rows and columns required.

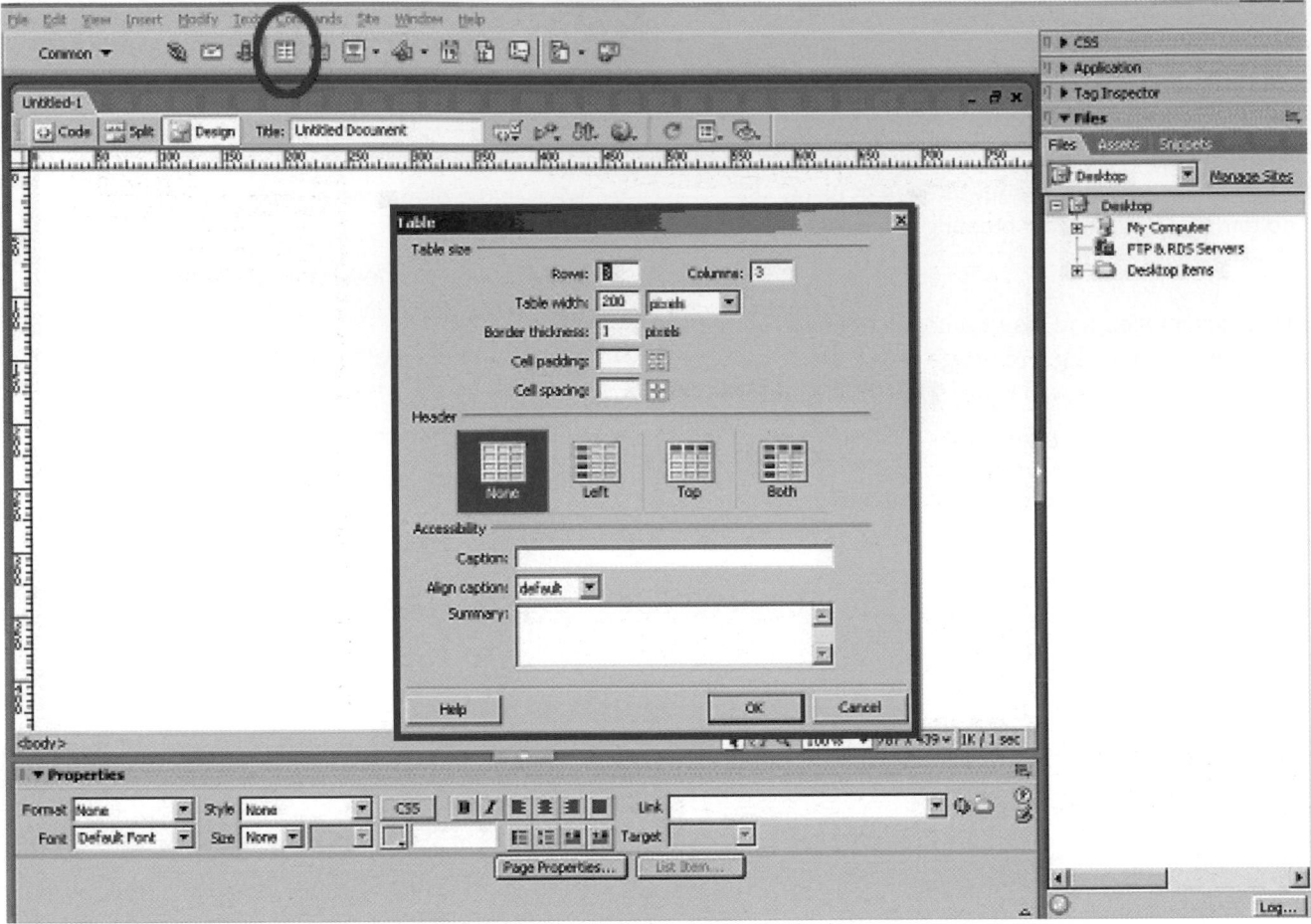

▲ Figure 21.6 Dreamweaver Table icon and Table Properties box

4 Select border thickness (0 is invisible, 1 and over is increasingly thick).

5 Test your page in the browser by pressing F12 or selecting File / Preview in Browser.

21.2.1.2 Navigation

The location of your buttons and **hyperlinks** should appear in your screen designs. Your storyboard will show how the pages will link together. For example, in a matrix style website all the pages will have buttons to all the other pages.

What does it mean?

A **hyperlink** is a method of connecting two pages together. It can be applied to text or an image. When clicked, it will take you to a predefined location.

■ How to create flash buttons in Adobe Dreamweaver

1 Open a web page in Dreamweaver.

2 Select Insert / Media / Flash Button (see Figure 21.7).

3 Choose your settings: the style of the button, the text written on the button, font and font size, where the button should link to, and the 'save as' name – note that each Flash button is saved as a separate image.

4 Once you have selected the settings, click OK.

5 Test your page in the browser.

21.2.1.3 Formatting

There are several ways of formatting text on a web page, including font, size, emphasis (bold), italics, underline and lists. In Dreamweaver, when text is selected, the Properties Inspector (see Figure 21.8) will change to offer all the font formatting options.

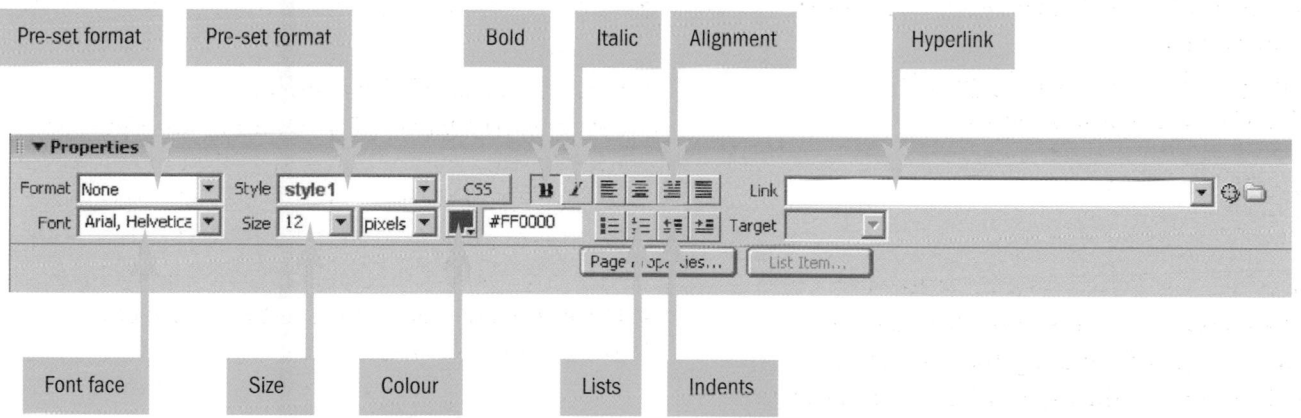

▲ Figure 21.7 Dreamweaver Flash Buttons Properties box

Pre-set format Pre-set format Bold Italic Alignment Hyperlink

Font face Size Colour Lists Indents

▲ Figure 21.8 Font Properties Inspector

Formatting can also be done using CSS (see section 21.2.3.6 on page 213), which will ensure that the formatting is efficient and consistent throughout the website.

Interactivity involves two-way communication between the user and the computer. In other words, it requires input from the user which provokes a response from the computer. This could include giving feedback, searching a catalogue of products or purchasing a product from a website. To have a full catalogue of products would require a database and server side scripting, which are not covered in this unit. However, the functionality can be simulated using client side scripting.

■ How to create a feedback form in Dreamweaver

1 Open a web page in Dreamweaver (either a blank one or one you have prepared for the form).
2 Change the toolbar drop-down to show the Forms toolbar (see Figure 21.9).
3 Place your cursor where you want the form to go and select the red dotted square (see Figure 21.10) that has automatically been drawn on your web page.

Everything within that red square will be part of the form.
4 Using the Forms toolbar, insert the fields you want, e.g. a textbox with the label Name.
5 When you have all your fields, insert two buttons at the bottom, still inside the red square, with no labels. They will automatically both be called Submit. Leave one as Submit and change the other to Reset using the Properties Inspector at the bottom of the screen.
6 Using the tag selector at the bottom left of the page (see Figure 21.11), select the Form tag. The Properties Inspector will show an action box. Into it, type mailto: followed by the email address to which you want to submit the form.
7 Test your page in the browser.

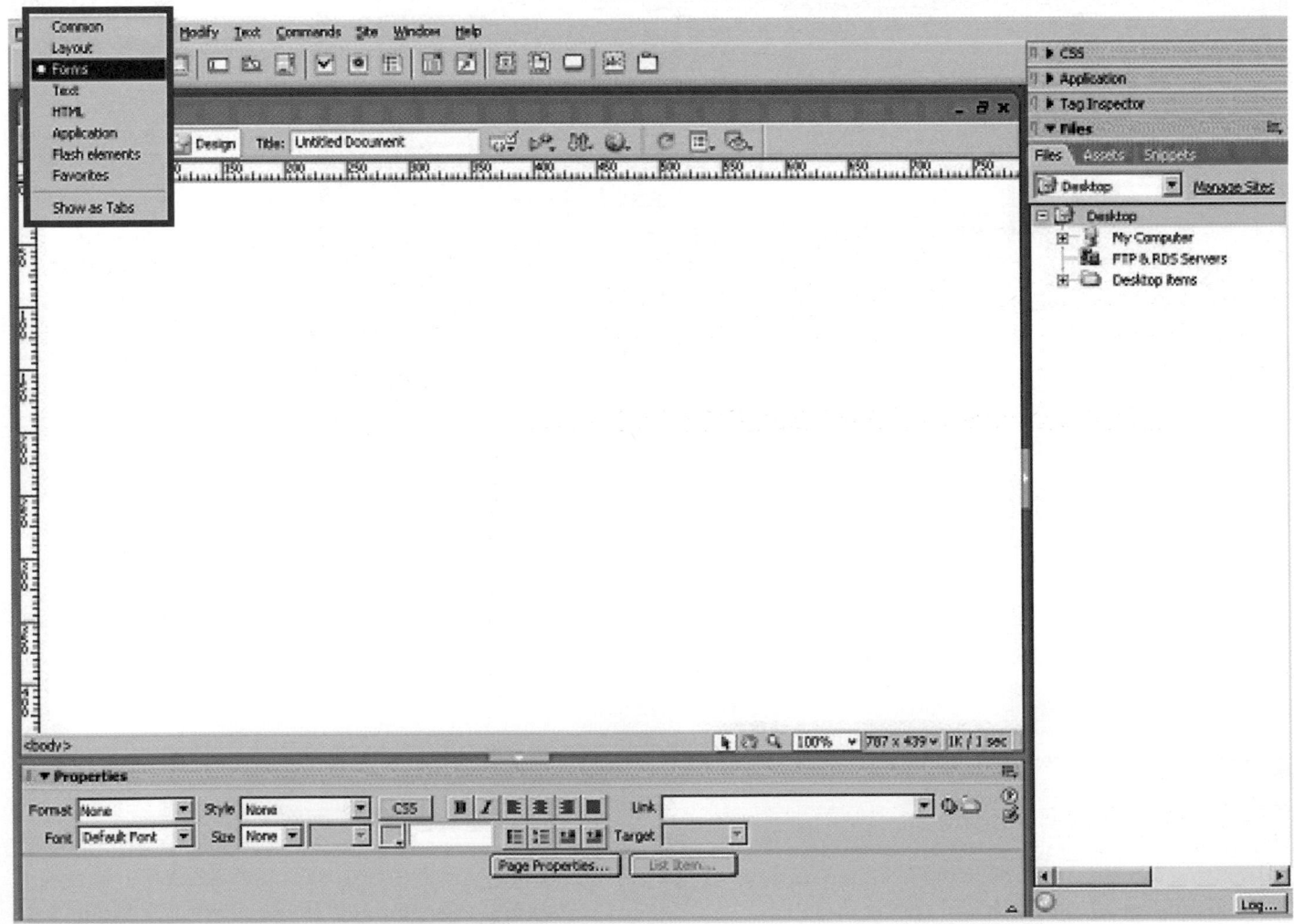

▲ Figure 21.9 Dreamweaver Forms toolbar

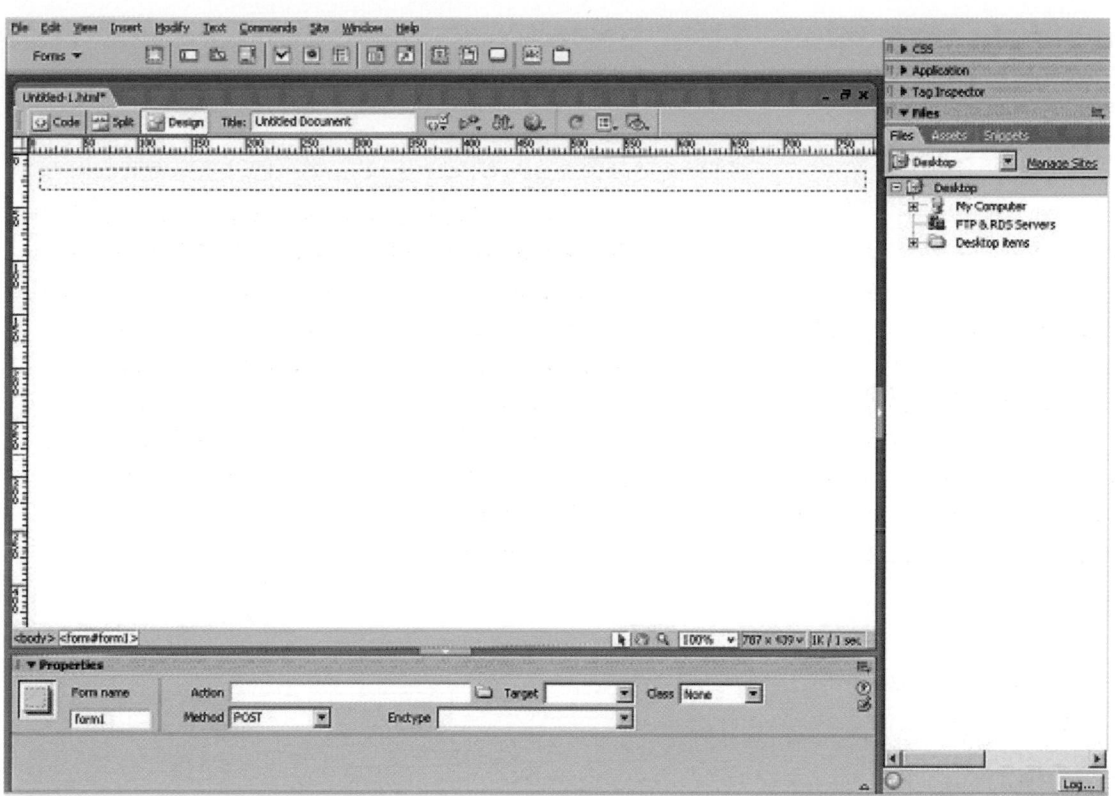

Figure 21.10
Dreamweaver form
outline

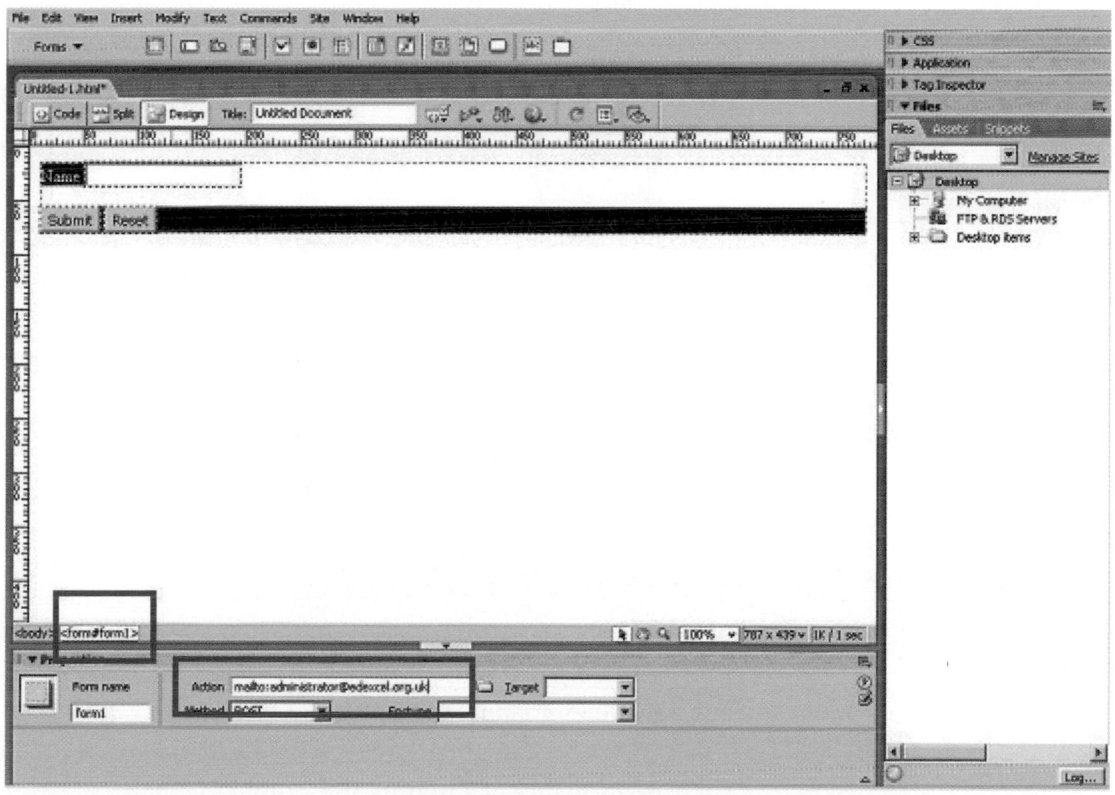

Figure 21.11
Dreamweaver tag
selector and
completed action
box

How to create a simple catalogue search using JavaScript

1 Create a web page for your catalogue.
2 Above the </body> tag, enter this code:

```
<script>
necklace = 1
chocolates = 2
toy = 3
product=prompt("Please enter search product", "")
if (product=="necklace")
  {document.write("Item found. Catalogue number
  " + necklace)}
  else
  if (product=="chocolates")
    {document.write("Item found. Catalogue
    number " + chocolates)}
    else
    {document.write("Item found. Catalogue
    number " + toy)}
</script>
```

3 Amend your code to match three different products (by changing the words in red).
4 Run the page in a browser and test if it works for all three products.

How to create a shopping cart system

1 Open a web page in Dreamweaver (a blank one or one you have prepared for the form).
2 Above the </body> tag, enter this code:

```
<script>
necklace = 25.99
chocolates = 5.95
toy = 4.51
product=prompt("Please enter product to be
purchased", "")
document.write("You have purchased ")
if (product=="necklace")
  {document.write("a fabulous necklace: £" +
  necklace)
  total = necklace}
  else
  if (product=="chocolates")
    {document.write("a luxury box of chocolates:
    £" + chocolates)
    total = chocolates}
```

```
  else
  if (product=="toy")
    {document.write("a cuddly toy: £" + toy)
    total = toy}
    else
    {document.write("nothing")
    total = 0}
document.write("<br />Total to pay is £" + total)
if (total != 0)
  {alert("Are you ready to enter your details?")
  name=prompt("Please enter your name:","")
  dob=prompt("Please enter your date of
  birth:","")
  ccnum=prompt("Please enter your credit card
  number:","")
  document.write("<br /><br />Customer details:
  <br >Name: " + name + "<br />Date of birth: "
  + dob + "<br />Card number: " + ccnum)
  alert("Thank you for making your purchase.")
  }
</script>
```

3 Amend your code to match your three products.
4 Run the page in a browser to test that it works for all three products.

Remember!

This unit will not show you how to process customer purchases, only how to collect their order and payment details.

21.2.1.5 Images and animation

A web page should not be littered with images because they increase the download time of a site (see section 21.3.1.1 on page 216) and can make the page look amateurish. Choose images and animations wisely so that they enhance the content of the website.

Similarly, animation can have a serious effect on the performance of a website and should therefore be limited to only where it is essential. There are several

Activity 21.10

Using JavaScript

1 Using your knowledge of JavaScript, and referring to books and the Internet as necessary, amend the shopping cart code so it allows the user to purchase more than one item at a time.

2 Change one of the prices in the shopping cart exercise to £4.50. Notice how the zero is missed off when it is written to the web page. Research why that happens and how it might be fixed.

animation programs available, the most popular being Adobe Flash. When creating a Flash animation, the working file is saved in the .fla format, but is then converted to a movie file (.swf) so it can be added to a website. The user will need the plug-in Flash Player to be able to view the Flash animation. However, most modern browsers already have the player built in. Animated GIFs can also be used as animations on a website. These provide a smaller file type but a lower image quality in playback and are therefore more suitable for small, simple animations. Animated GIFs can be made by several programs, including Adobe Photoshop and Corel Draw, and can be rendered on most browsers without the need for a plug-in.

21.2.2 Content

After the web page has been structured and all the coding features are finished, the content can be inserted. This includes text, more images and other features that give information to the user and are not part of the structure. It is pointless to have a website that looks stunning but which does not hold well-written, accurate, informative content. The content of each page should be carefully planned, remembering that generally users will not want to read an essay, but they must be able to obtain all the information they need. The use of language should be concise and precise.

21.2.2.1 Proofreading for accuracy and appropriateness

All text in a website should be proofread for both spelling and grammar mistakes. The website you are creating will be your client's presence on the web and as such it is an extension of them and their business. If it is an e-commerce site and there are mistakes in it, customers may not trust the site and decide to shop somewhere else.

The content should be correct, accurate and up to date. If the descriptions of products are incorrect your client could be prosecuted under the Trade Descriptions Act (1968). The prices must also be correct; if they are lower than they should be, your client may lose money.

Check also that there is no inappropriate content on the site. Not only could inappropriate content deter potential users, it might also contravene the Obscene Publications Act (1964), which can be applied to UK websites. In legal terms, "an article shall be deemed to be obscene if its effect is … such as to tend to deprave and corrupt persons who are likely, having regard to all relevant circumstances, to read, see or hear the matter contained or embodied in it." (Quoted from the website of the Internet Watch Foundation – to access this website, go to www.heinemann.co.uk/hotlinks and enter the express code 231SP.)

21.2.2.2 Reliability of information source

It is essential that the information given on a website is correct; otherwise users may lose trust in the site and stop visiting. This is most important for an e-commerce site. When creating the content of the website, if a designer is taking information from other places, they must ensure that it is reliable. If the designer puts out incorrect information, even though it is from another source, they could be held responsible.

A legal disclaimer is usually included on the bottom of a website home page to ensure that the owners are not held responsible for incorrect or changing information. It can also include other legal information about viruses, data protection, copyright and trademarks.

Case study

Edexcel

Edexcel is the largest awarding body in the UK and offers a wide range of opportuntities to help people achieve their full potential.

Their website provides information for teachers, students and others involved in teaching and learning.

1 Visit the Edexcel website and read the disclaimer.

2 Find two more websites with disclaimers.

3 Compare the three disclaimers.

   a) What elements do they have in common?
   b) What elements are different?

4 Write a disclaimer for the website you are designing.

Case study

Nestlé

Nestlé is a multinational organisation with products ranging from Nescafé coffee to KitKat chocolate bars and Ski yoghurts. Their UK website is well-designed and rich with content.

The website uses several techniques to present a high volume of textual information effectively.

1 Go to the Nestlé website (go to www.heinemann. co.uk/hotlinks and enter express code 2315P) and find examples of these formatting features:

   a) bold text
   b) upper case
   c) bulleted list
   d) highlighting with colour.

2 How has the web designer ensured that the text is clear and readable? List a minimum of five methods.

21.2.2.3 Structured for purpose

The content of a website should be structured so it is easy for the user to read. Lists should be put into bullet points and complex data should be put into tables. Prose should be ordered in a logical sequence.

21.2.3 Tools and techniques

There are several tools and techniques that can be used to create a website. It is only by combining these that an effective site can be produced.

21.2.3.1 Navigation diagram

There are three main methods of connecting web pages together in a **navigation diagram**: linear, hierarchy and matrix (see Figure 21.12).

What does it mean?

A **navigation diagram** shows how the different parts of a project will combine. In web design, it shows how different pages will interrelate.

Activity 21.11

Navigation structures

1 Analyse each type of structure. Name two positive points and two negative points about each one. Consider the needs of the designer, client and user.

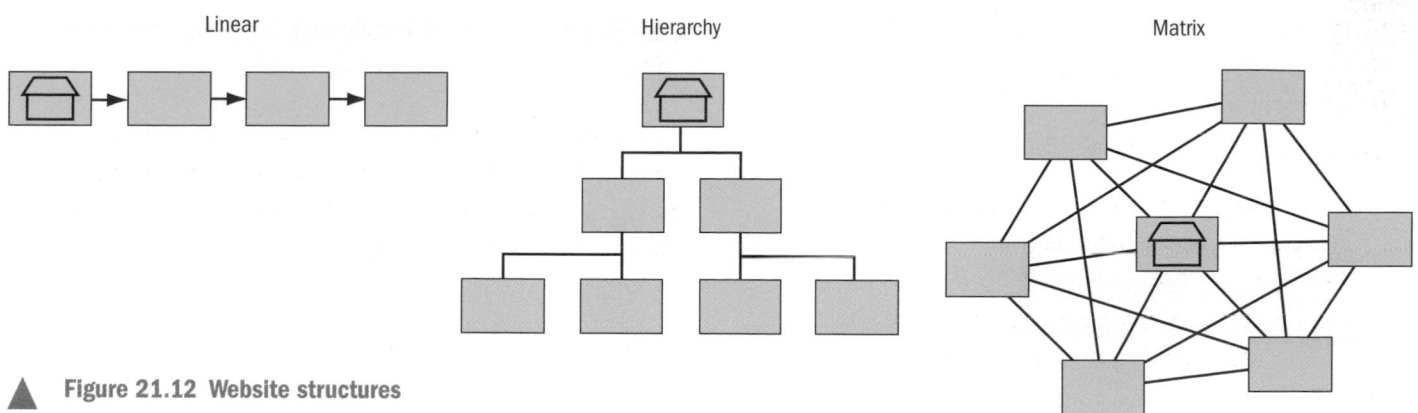

Linear   Hierarchy   Matrix

▲ **Figure 21.12 Website structures**

21.2.3.2 Building interactivity tools

Client side scripting languages include JavaScript and VBScript. These can be used to create items from simple feedback forms which are emailed to an address when submitted to complex arcade-style computer games. The essential purpose of the languages is to create two-way communication between the user and the website.

■ How to create a simple JavaScript web page

1 Open Notepad (or a similar text editor).
2 Save the file as myjavascript.html
3 Enter this code:

```
<html>
<head>
<title>My JavaScript</title>
</head>
<body>
<script>
age=18;
document.write("My age is: ");
document.write(age);
</script>
</body>
</html>
```

3 Save the file.
4 Navigate to where the file is saved using My Computer
5 Double click your file to open in your browser.

Activity 21.12

Using JavaScript

1 To receive input from the user, the following JavaScript can be used:
```
age=prompt("Please enter your age: ","").
```
Use this new code to alter myjavascript.html so the user can input their own age.

2 Add the ability for the user to input their name so it will be displayed on the web page.

■ Pseudocode

Pseudocode is a method of designing code, forming an intermediary step between an explanation in English and the coding language – see Table 21.2. (See also section 18.2.2.5 on page 228 of Book 1.)

Pseudocode	JavaScript
age = input from user	`age=prompt("Enter age","");`
if age >= 18 then	`if (age>=18)`
print onscreen "i am an adult"	`{document.write("I am an adult");}`
else	`else`
print onscreen "i am x years old"	`{document.write("I am " + age + " years old");}`

Table 21.2 Example of Pseudocode used to plan JavaScript

By using pseudocode, a designer can plan what the code will do, without having to worry about ensuring that the correct words and syntax are used. It is also easier to convert into the full programming language by using this transitional step.

21.2.3.3 Adding animation and audio-visual elements

It is good practice to save your images and animations in a folder called **Images**, and to store this folder in the same folder as your web pages. Keeping all your website files in one place means that when you come to upload them, there is less chance you will miss any out. Also, it reduces the amount of code needed to link to an image or create a hyperlink.

■ How to insert an image in Adobe Dreamweaver

1 Open a web page in Dreamweaver.
2 Select Insert / Image.
3 Browse to the image you want to insert and click OK.
4 Test your page in the browser.

■ How to insert a flash animation in Dreamweaver

To use a Flash animation in Dreamweaver, it needs to be saved as a .swf file. This compiles it into a movie file which can then be linked to a web page.

1 Open a web page in Dreamweaver.
2 Select Insert / Media / Flash.
3 Browse to the animation you want to insert and click OK.
4 Test your page in the browser.

Remember!

You must insert the silver .swf file, not the red .fla file.

■ How to insert sound in Dreamweaver

To insert sound as a link:

1 Open a web page in Dreamweaver.
2 Highlight the text or image you want to link for the sound.
3 In the Link box in the Properties Inspector, type in or browse to the music file.
4 Test your page in the browser.

To embed as a background sound:

1 Open a web page in Dreamweaver.
2 View the code by selecting View / Code or by clicking the Code button in the top left.
3 Between the <head> and the </head> tag, enter <bgsound src="mysound.wav" loop=50>. But instead of mysound.wav enter the file name of your sound, and instead of 50 set the loop number to the amount of times it should play. (Note: loop can be set to infinite.)
4 Test your page in the browser.

21.2.3.4 Ensuring compliance with W3C

W3C (World Wide Web Consortium) is a body which promotes the standardisation of web design, especially of HTML. This is to ensure universal accessibility, including the ability of websites to be displayed on a variety of browsers and resolutions and be used by users with special needs. For more details on W3C compliance, see section 21.4.3.1 on page 221.

21.2.3.5 Meta-tagging

Search engines do not literally search the whole Internet every time a search word is entered. Instead, they use enormous databases to store information about all the websites of which they are already aware and it is these databases that are searched. Search engines use **spiders** to trawl the Internet for websites to include in their databases.

What does it mean?

Spiders are automated bots which are used by search engines to find websites.

The spiders examine each web page encountered and send information back to be stored in the database. To ensure that the spiders list the web page correctly, the web developer can include meta-tags in the coding for the web page.

■ How to create meta-tags in HTML

1 Open your home page.
2 Below the <head> tag, enter this code:

```
<meta name="description" content="Cheeseworld –
all you need to know about cheese">
<meta name="keywords" content="cheese, fromage,
brie, cheddar, dairy">
```

Notice there are no spaces between the keywords and commas.

3 Change the description and keywords so they are relevant for your site.

This code cannot be tested, but can be read by spiders to be listed in search engines.

21.2.3.6 Cascading style sheets

CSS (cascading style sheets) can be used to control the formatting of a website efficiently. They can appear in the head of a particular web page to which they are to be applied or in a separate file so that they can serve the whole site. CSS makes formatting easier. All the formatting is done in one place, making it easier to preserve a house style. If alterations are required later on, only one change in the CSS needs to be made, rather than several in the HTML, which may be hard to find.

■ How to create a simple CSS page

1 Open Notepad (or a similar text editor).
2 Save the file as myCSSwebpage.html.
3 Enter this code:

```
<html>
<head>
<title>My CSS Web Page</title>
<link rel="stylesheet" type="text/css"
href="myCSS.css">
</head>
<body>
Here is some normal text.
<br>
```

```
<h1>Here is the text with CSS formatting.</h1>
</body>
</html>
```

3 Save the file.
4 Create another new file and save it as myCSS.css
5 Enter the following code:

```
h1 {
font-family: Arial;
color: red;
font-size: 20pt;
}
```

6 Save the file.
7 Navigate to where the .html file is saved using My Computer.
8 Double click your html file to open in your browser.

Remember!

Make sure the .html and .css files are saved in the same folder.

Activity 21.13

Using CSS

1 In myCSS.css, change the font to Wingdings. Save the .css file and refresh the .html file in the browser.

2 In myCSS.css, change the colour to blue and the size to 100pt. Save the .css file and refresh the .html file in the browser.

21.2.4 Review

After the website is built, it is essential to test it to make sure all parts work correctly. This allows an opportunity for bugs to be removed and for the website to be perfected before it goes live.

21.2.4.1 Functionality testing

All the elements of the website should be tested. For example, when the page loads, the correct images should load in the right places. Also each hyperlink should be tested to ensure it goes to the right page.

The user environment needs to be tested as well, to make sure it is in fact easy to use. This is often done using a usability group. This is a group of people who fit into the target market who will use the system. They provide feedback on the website before it goes live when there is still time to make changes.

▲ **Keep your target market in mind when carrying out functionality testing**

A test plan such as the one shown in Table 21.3 can be used.

21.2.4.2 Content

The content of the website must be proofread to check there are no spelling and grammar errors, that the information is accurate and that it is appropriate for the target audience. (See also section 21.2.2.1 on page 209.)

21.2.4.3 Check against user requirements

The final website should be compared with the user requirements which were defined in the design. The requirements that have been met should be assessed according to how well they have been met. If any requirements have not been met, this must be justified, giving valid reasons.

Activity 21.14

Meeting user requirements

1 Choose a website with which you are familiar. Identify the target audience and write a list of ten user requirements this site would need to meet.

2 For each user requirement, state how the web designers have or have not met it.

3 If any requirements have not been met, explain how the designers could improve the website to ensure that all requirements are met.

Test number	Test element	On page	Test data	Expected result	Actual result	Success or failure	Screenshot reference
1	Home button	About.html	Left click	Load index.html	Load index.html	Success	S1
2	Logo.gif	Index.html	Load page	Appear in top left corner	Appear in centre of page	Failure	S2

Table 21.3   Example test plan

21.2.4.4 User acceptance

Once the website has been tested for functionality and been corrected, it is necessary to test if it is suitable for the designated audience. A focus group of people from the potential target market are selected to test the website and provide feedback. One very useful aspect of this will be to test whether the website is user friendly, as this is difficult to measure using other methods.

21.2.4.5 Audit trail of changes

An audit trail will track all the changes made to a web page. This can be used to trace all the developments made, especially useful when making changes due to testing.

In addition, tracking the changes made allows the possibility of reverting to a previous version if an amendment has caused a problem. For example, testing the JavaScript might produce an incorrect result, but when the code is changed it could stop asking the user for data to be inputted. If the developer has tracked the changes, instead of trying to repair this new error, they can easily change back to the original version and redo the repair of the script.

21.2.5 Uploading

To allow a website to be seen across the Internet, it must be **uploaded** on to a web server.

21.2.5.1 Tools

The process of uploading involves a protocol called **FTP (File Transfer Protocol)**. FTPing can be done directly through a browser or by using a program such as CuteFTP.

What does it mean?

Uploading is the process of putting a website on to a web server so it can be distributed across the Internet.

FTP (File Transfer Protocol) is the protocol used to upload web pages on to a web server. Unusually, the term is used as both a noun and a verb.

It is not only the web pages that must be uploaded on to the web server, but all other associated files. This includes images, video and sound files. This is because these files are not embedded into web pages, but are linked to them, remaining as separate entities.

Activity 21.15

Uploading to a web server

1 Upload a website through a browser and a dedicated program. Make notes for future use in your coursework.

21.2.5.2 Web servers

A **web server** holds the live copy of the web page that can be seen by the public.

There are several web server software applications, such as Internet Information Services (IIS), which comes bundled with modern versions of the Windows Server operating system or Apache HTTP Server.

What does it mean?

A **web server** is a server that distributes web pages on the Internet.

Test your knowledge

1 What is the best way of organising the file structure for web page files and the associated images and animations?
2 Which Flash animation file type can be inserted into a web page: .fla or .swf?
3 Name the three types of navigation structure.
4 How can meta-tags help a website to be listed high in a search engine?
5 What are the advantages of using CSS?
6 What is the purpose of the File Transfer Protocol?

If a website is slow to download, it is likely that it will struggle to gain new users or retain visitors. There are various methods that can be used in conjunction with each other to reduce download time and make a website more efficient.

21.3.1 File types

By using smaller file types which use compression methods, the website will have a faster download time. When deciding on which file types to use, a developer must make a judgement in order to balance quality and file size because the higher the quality, the larger the file size.

21.3.1.1 Image files

There are two image file types available: **bitmap** and **vector** (see Figure 21.13), which are compared in Table 21.4.

What does it mean?

A **bitmap** is literally a map of bits; each pixel is saved in its location.

A **vector** is an image which is saved as a mathematical algorithm. Each line is saved as co-ordinates of each point and details of colour, width, etc.

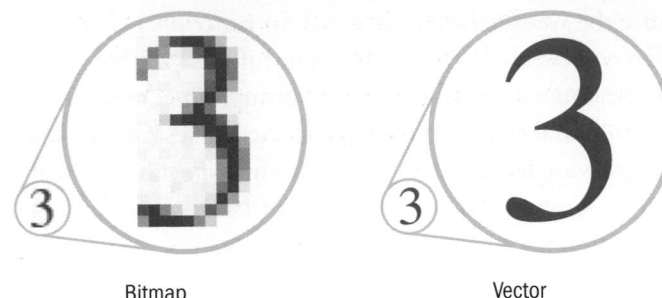

Bitmap   Vector

▲ **Figure 21.13 Bitmap and vector images**

Bitmap file types include GIF and JPEG. A GIF has a maximum palette of 256 colours, and should therefore be used for low-colour images. A JPEG has a larger palette, and is therefore better for higher-colour images.

Activity 21.16

Image file types

1 Look at an existing website, perhaps the one for your school or college. Open the code of the web page (in Internet Explorer click View / Source). What image file types have been used and why?

Bitmap	Vector
• Each pixel is saved individually with its location, colours and other details.	• Co-ordinates of points and curves are saved as a mathematical equation.
• Generally has a large file size.	• Generally has a small file size.
• When resized, the image will become pixellated.	• When resized, the image will retain clarity.
• File formats include .bmp, .gif and .jpg.	• File formats include .pdf and .eps.
• Created by programs such as Microsoft Paint and Adobe Photoshop.	• Created by programs such as Adobe Illustrator and Corel Draw.
• Usually used in web pages as they are rendered by all graphical browsers.	• Often used for graphics such as logos which need to be resized.
	• Shapes drawn in Adobe Flash are vectors.

Table 21.4 Comparison of bitmap and vector

21.3.1.2 Sound files

Sound travels in waves. These are continuous and are called analogue. Digital sound waves are sampled at regular intervals with gaps so small the human ear cannot perceive them (see Figure 21.14).

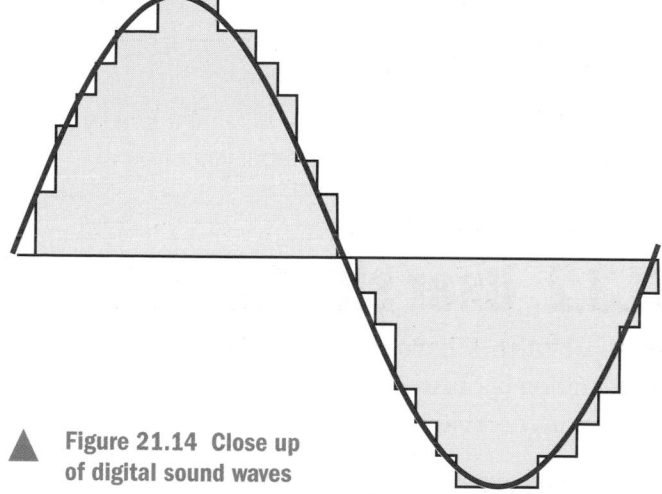

▲ Figure 21.14 Close up of digital sound waves

Once these signals are combined, the whole piece is a series of waves which denotes the characteristics of the sound (see Figure 21.15).

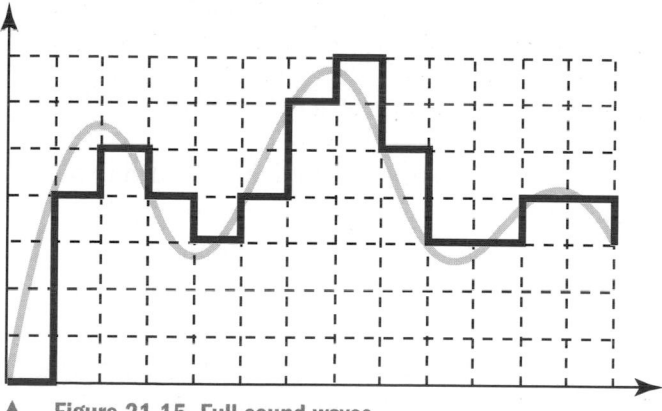

▲ Figure 21.15 Full sound waves

There are several types of sound file type available, each with its own method of sampling and **compression**.

What does it mean?

Compression is where a mathematical calculation is performed on a file in order to 'squash' it and make it smaller.

A .wav file has a high sample rate, which means the sound quality is closest to that produced by the actual instruments, but it is a relatively large file.

An .mp3 file has a low sample rate and therefore produces a smaller file size. This is how MP3 players manage to store such a high volume of music. However, there is a loss of quality, dependent on the compression rate chosen. The higher the rate, the better the quality but the larger the file size.

Also a consideration must be made as to what types of music **plug-ins** a user is likely to have, as this may restrict the choice available. It could be like giving someone a CD when they only have a cassette player.

What does it mean?

A **plug-in** is software which will play specific types of files. For example, modern versions of browsers like Internet Explorer come with Flash Player, which is a plug-in to allow the user to play Flash animation. Most browsers have a range of plug-ins automatically installed or available for download.

21.3.1.3 Video and animation files

Video and animation can seriously affect the speed of a website and, in general, should be used sparingly. Both video and animation can produce very large file sizes.

When uploaded on to a website, for a user to view video or animation files, usually they must click on them and download them. Due to the size of the files, this will most often take a relatively long time and control a large proportion of bandwidth for the duration of the download, even with a high-quality Internet connection. A file such as this will also take a large proportion of web server space. The more video and animation files used, the more web server space used and the slower the website will be.

A possible solution to this problem could be to **stream** the video file instead of the user downloading it in one go (see Figure 21.16).

What does it mean?

Streaming means feeding the video file to the user's computer in a continuous smaller volume of data, buffered by temporarily storing it and feeding to the player gradually so it is displayed steadily on the screen.

▲ Figure 21.16 Video stream buffered to a user's computer

21.3.1.4 Conversion between formats

To convert a bitmap to a vector, the image has to be **traced**. This can be done in programs such as Adobe Flash, Adobe Illustrator and Corel Draw.

What does it mean?

Tracing is the process of the individual pixels of a bitmap being converted into the mathematical algorithm of a vector.

The conversion of a vector to a bitmap is a much simpler process, as it consists of opening the vector in a bitmap program and saving it. As the package's native file format is bitmap, anything saved in it will be saved as a bitmap. Programs such as Microsoft Paint and Adobe Photoshop will perform this process, which is called rasterisation.

To convert between sound files involves using the compression algorithm, either to make a file into a smaller MP3 or to convert back to a file type such as .wav. CD creation programs such as Nero have the facilities to perform this conversion. It is very important to check that the conversion of the file and inclusion on the website will not break copyright law.

Activity 21.17

Image file conversion

1 Design on paper a new logo for your school or college.

2 Create this logo in a vector program such as Adobe Flash or Corel Draw.

3 Convert the logo into a bitmap using a program such as Microsoft Paint or Adobe Photoshop.

4 In both programs, try increasing the image size by 200 per cent. Make notes on the effects you observe.

21.3.2 User side factors

The capabilities of the user's system must be taken into consideration because, if not, people who may become potential users could be prohibited from using the site.

21.3.2.1 Modem connection speed

The speed of the user's Internet connection will also determine how quickly the web page is downloaded.

- **Dial-up** is the traditional method of connection and remained popular for many years. The earliest type had an average speed of 56 Kbps. Dial-up uses the existing analogue telephone lines.
- To achieve faster speeds, digital lines needed to be connected: **ISDN (Integrated Services Digital Network)** could reach speeds of 128 Kbps.
- Using these digital lines, **DSL (Digital Subscriber Line)** was introduced, which is the basis for broadband. The most common in the UK is **ADSL (Asynchronous Digital Subscriber Line)** and can currently reach speeds from 1 Mbps to 8 Mbps, although **Cable** is also gaining popularity with a current average speed of 6 Mbps.
- **Broadband** technology is constantly being developed and faster speeds are already conceivable in the near future, with even 100 Mbps being proposed in Japan.

You should ensure that your website will work satisfactorily on a 56K modem as well as the latest broadband speeds. This way you will not exclude any potential users from accessing your website.

As the connection speed will determine the rate of download, so the computer's components will affect the speed with which it is displayed and with which users interact with it.

You must take into consideration that a user may not have a fast processor or large memory capacity and so you must decide between a high level of user specification requirements and a high number of visitors.

21.3.3 Server side factors

As well as the capabilities of the user's computer, the capacity of the web server must be taken into account. This is true whether the web server has been bought or rented.

Bandwidth determines how much traffic can be handled by the web server – specifically, how much material is able to be downloaded at any one time. Bandwidth can be thought of as a pipe from the web server to the users. The bigger the pipe, the more that can be sent down it. The larger the web page and its associated files, the fewer users can download it at any one time.

What does it mean?

Bandwidth is the capacity that a network connection can conduct at one time.

Server side scripting on a website will also take up bandwidth. The more that is to be performed before page load, the slower it will be to download on a user's computer. Client side scripting does not have the same issue, as it is executed on the user's computer rather than the web server. As a general rule, server side scripting should be carried out only where absolutely necessary and as efficiently as possible.

Activity 21.18

Client and server side factors

1 Investigate the Internet service providers (ISPs) that currently provide broadband over ADSL. Create a table comparing the speeds and prices.  **(partial evidence)**

2 Find out the Internet connection method and speed at your school or college.

3 Find out the specification of the computers at your school or college.

4 Discuss the choice of connection and specification, explaining whether you would make any changes to it. Take financial factors into account. **d₃ (partial evidence)**

STOP

Test your knowledge

1 What is a bitmap?

2 What is a vector?

3 What is compression and how does it aid website performance?

4 How does bandwidth affect website performance?

Any business which operates online is at risk from Internet threats and therefore security is vital to its successful operation.

21.4.1 Security

There are several risks to the security of a website, which is especially important for e-commerce sites where hackers and viruses can steal customers' details and use them for fraud, such as **identity theft**.

What does it mean?

Identity theft is where a victim's details are stolen and someone poses as them, applying for financial products and making purchases, pretending to be the victim.

Developers must build protection mechanisms into their websites in order for users to feel comfortable using them. This is especially important for e-commerce sites. For more information, see Unit 34: e-Commerce in Book 1.

21.4.2 Security protection mechanisms

There are several security protection mechanisms available, such as anti-virus. However, those which relate specifically to websites are discussed below.

21.4.2.1 Firewalls

A **firewall** builds a protective 'barrier' around a computer or a network of computers so that only authorised programs can access the data.

What does it mean?

A **firewall** is a piece of software that protects the system from unauthorised access. This is especially important for web servers.

The firewall sets up a 'gateway' and only allows authorised traffic through the gateway. Incoming data is inspected and only allowed through if it is legitimate. This is done by the opening and closing of ports. Ports connect protocols and IP addresses together. Each computer has several ports for data to pass through. They are virtual so they cannot be seen. Ports are like doors: each has a number to identify it and can be open or closed. There are some default ports – for example, port 25 is usually for email and port 80 is usually for the Internet, although these can be changed. For a web server, it is good practice to close all ports that are not being used. Otherwise, hackers can take advantage of open ports to get into the system.

21.4.2.2 Secure sockets layers (SSL)

SSL is a cryptographic protocol which provides secure communication on the Internet. It provides endpoint authentication – this means that both the server and the client need to be identified and confirm they are who they say they are. This is done by **public key encryption** and **certificate-based authentication**.

What does it mean?

Public key encryption is a method of coding information so only the people with the right key at both ends of the communication can decode it.

Certificate-based authentication is a method of coding information so the people at either end are identified by a digital certificate, coupled with a digital signature. These can confirm the identity of the sender or recipient.

21.4.2.3 Adherence to standards

It is vital for all computer users to use strong passwords. This is especially important for web servers and other e-commerce systems.

A strong password involves:

- both letters and numbers
- both capitals and lowercase
- symbols such as * or #
- being over eight characters long.

Hackers can take advantage of weak passwords, especially those which are easy to guess. If a password is related to the user, e.g. a pet's name, it will not take too much effort for a hacker to guess it. There are software programs which can run through many possible combinations of characters and test each one to see if it is the chosen password. The stronger the password, the longer this software will take to work it out, and the more likely a hacker will go on to try a different website. They are less likely to spend time working their way into a well-protected site.

Activity 21.19

Security

1 Select a website and identify any threats to it, including hackers and viruses. Make notes for future reference in your coursework. **p**₇

2 Research and explain the methods to protect websites, including firewalls. Make notes for future reference in your coursework. **p**₇ **m**₃

21.4.3 Laws and guidelines

For a website to operate correctly, it needs to follow the appropriate legislation. These laws protect both the business and the consumer. All the legislation discussed in this section relates to the UK only.

21.4.3.1 W3C compliance

Accessibility is concerned with the users who can access the website. If a website uses some newer technologies, it could be inaccessible to users with lower-specification computers or low-speed Internet connections.

In addition, a website should be accessible by users with special needs, such as partially sighted users or users who are hard of hearing. This might be done by creating a site which can be used by as many people as possible, or by giving options, such as to make the text larger.

What does it mean?

Accessibility is the ease with which websites can be accessed by users, especially referring to those with particular technologies or special needs.

The W3C produces guidelines and tools for standardising websites which contribute towards increased accessibility.

Case study

W3C

The World Wide Web Consortium (W3C) develops guidelines and tools to create standards on the web to ensure it grows and continues to be an important resource.

Go to the W3C website (www.w3.org/) and answer the following questions.

1 Who is Tim Berners-Lee? What has he achieved and what is his role in the W3C?

2 What are the Web Content Accessibility Guidelines and why are they needed?

3 How does the W3C attempt to standardise HTML?

4 The W3C uses the terms 'deprecated' and 'obsolete' with regard to cetain tags. What do these terms mean?

5 The HTML Validator is a tool provided on the W3C website. What does it do and how can it help a web developer?

Data Protection Act 1998

The Data Protection Act was designed to protect sensitive data held in databases. It was originally passed in 1984, with an update in 1998 which was brought into effect in 2000. It is upheld by the Information Commissioner. Every business that stores data, for example information about customers, must register and state the data that they plan to hold.

There are eight principles in the Act (see Figure 21.17).

The data subject is the person to whom the data refers. Under the Act, the data subject has several specific rights, including:

- the right to compensation for unauthorised disclosure of data
- the right to compensation for unauthorised inaccurate data
- the right to access data and apply for verification or erasure where it is inaccurate

- the right to compensation for unauthorised access, loss or destruction.

Computer Misuse Act 1990

The Computer Misuse Act was introduced due to the increasing threat from hackers and viruses, and has three new offences:

- unauthorised access to computer programs or data
- unauthorised access with the intent to commit further offences
- unauthorised modification of computer material (e.g. programs or data).

Health and Safety at Work Act 1974

The Health and Safety at Work Act was designed to protect all employees in any organisation. This included ensuring the safety, health and welfare of workers, the controlling of dangerous substances in the workplace and monitoring certain emissions into the atmosphere. All employees have the right to work in a safe

▼ **Figure 21.17 The eight principles of the Data Protection Act**

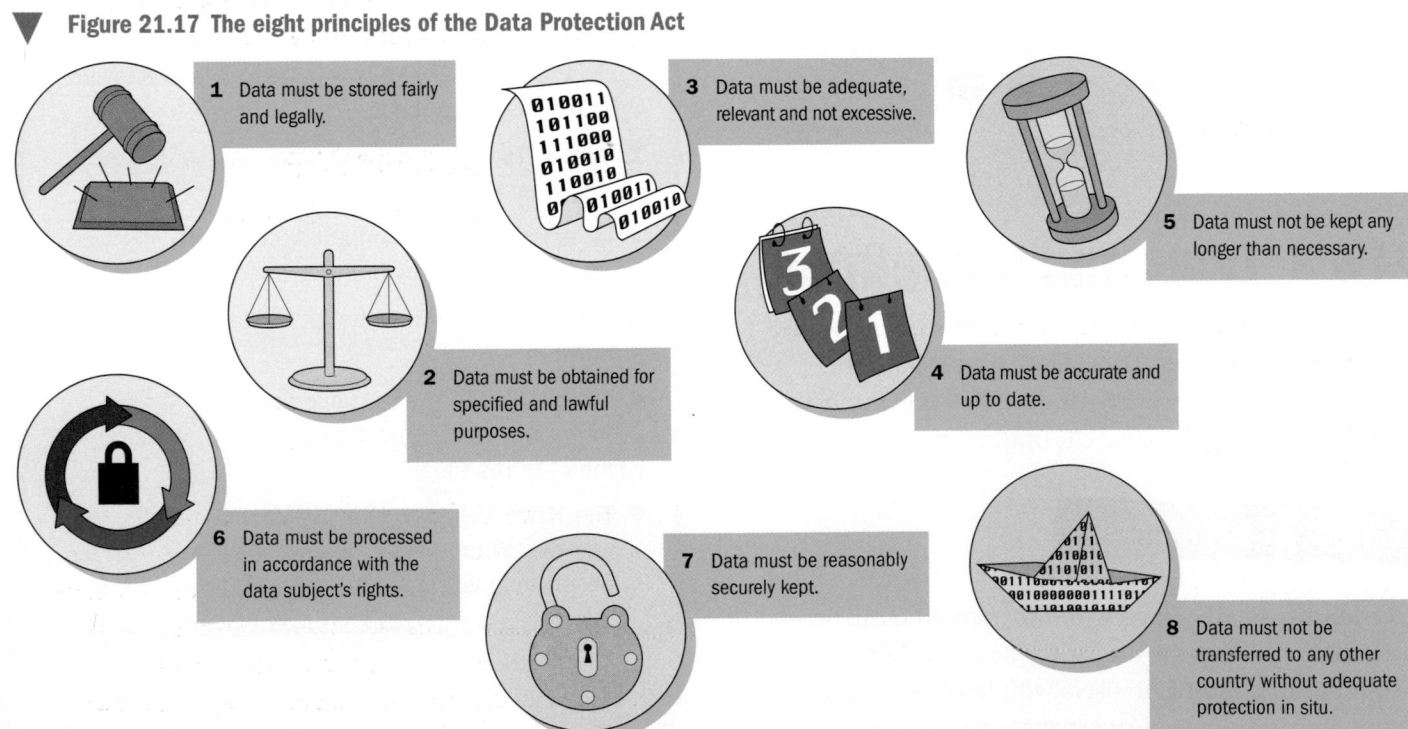

1 Data must be stored fairly and legally.

2 Data must be obtained for specified and lawful purposes.

3 Data must be adequate, relevant and not excessive.

4 Data must be accurate and up to date.

5 Data must not be kept any longer than necessary.

6 Data must be processed in accordance with the data subject's rights.

7 Data must be reasonably securely kept.

8 Data must not be transferred to any other country without adequate protection in situ.

environment; here are some of the measures that are advised for working in an ICT environment.

- Monitors should be adjustable and be between 45 and 60 centimetres away from the user's face.
- Keyboards should be adjustable and allow room to rest wrists.
- Chairs should support the back and be at a height so that the top of the monitor is no higher than the user's eyes.
- Tables and desks should provide sufficient leg room.
- Appropriate lighting and window coverings should be used to prevent glare.

■ Copyright, Designs and Patents Act 1988

The Copyright, Designs and Patents Act protects all works such as music, art, writing and programming code once it is tangible, which means in a fixed form. As the Internet has grown, the question of whether websites are subject to protection under copyright has often been discussed. It is now accepted that a website becomes tangible once it is coded and saved onto storage media, especially if the source code is also printed. Websites are therefore protected by copyright.

Activity 21.20

Legislation

Think about a website with which you are familiar, such as your school or college website.

1 How do the laws listed above affect the content and running of the website? **p**₇

2 What might happen if one of these laws was contravened? **p**₇

21.4.4 User perception

One of the most difficult issues for web developers is the user's perception of both the Internet and the specific website being developed. Although general opinion appears to be improving with regard to the Internet, there is still a proportion of the public who are mistrustful of websites.

21.4.4.1 Concerns over privacy of information

Most modern websites, especially e-commerce sites, take details from their users and some people may fear that their personal information will not be secure. Threats exist from hackers and identity thieves, and web developers must use a high level of security and also demonstrate to their users that the site is safe. This can be done with systems such as firewalls and SSL (see section 21.4.2.1 and section 21.4.2.2 on page 220) and also by demonstrating to users that these security measures are in place.

In addition, users may be worried that their contact details will be passed on to direct marketers and they may receive junk mail, **spam** or direct marketing telephone calls, which they find a nuisance.

What does it mean?

Spam is the term used for junk email.

21.4.4.2 Security of financial transactions

The biggest worry for e-commerce customers is that their financial details will not be safe, that the business may use them in some unauthorised way or may have minimal security so the customers' identities could be stolen by other people. In the early days of e-commerce, customers could either pay by cheque through the post (which meant the transaction could take several days) or email their credit card details (which was a concern as email security was not as good as it is today).

Nowadays, there are several very secure methods of making online purchases, including online credit and debit card transactions, electronic cheques, digital payment methods such as PayPal or NoChex, and Splash Plastic, which is a prepay card for online transactions.

Test your knowledge

1 How does a firewall use ports to protect a web server?

2 Give three examples of strong passwords.

3 What is the purpose of the W3C?

4 Name the eight principles of the Data Protection Act 1998.

5 Name the three offences defined by the Computer Misuse Act 1990.

Preparation for assessment

The assessment tasks in this unit are based on the following scenario.

Fancy That! is a business selling fancy dress costumes. It wants to create a website to advertise its business with a catalogue the customers can look through. It hopes to sell its products online in the future.

To work towards a Distinction you will need to achieve all the Pass, Merit and Distinction criteria in the unit and have evidence to show that you have achieved each one.

You are advised to research wherever possible and use correctly referenced sources.

Task 1 (P1, P2, M1, D1)

Fancy That! wants a website with at least five pages and at least one interactive feature.

Define the purpose of the website and ten user requirements.

Create two designs with the following elements:

- concept design
- house style
- screen design (describing choice of layout method)
- outline of content.

Compare and evaluate the two designs, select one and create a report to justify why you have selected this design.

Task 2 (P3, P4, P6, M2)

Using your design, build the website for Fancy That! This includes the HTML, CSS and server side scripting. You should use a web authoring package.

Once built, test the website thoroughly to ensure it works. For the tests that fail, show the changes you need to make to fix them.

Upload the website on to a web server.

Task 3 (P5, D3)

Prepare a report for Fancy That! to describe the factors that can affect the performance of the website: for example, the image file types used. Compare the user and server side factors that can affect the website.

Task 4 (P7, M3)

Create a reference booklet for Fancy That! which the company can use to explain:

- security threats to the website
- methods to protect the website
- legislation that affects the website.

Task 5 (M4, D2)

Write an evaluation of the website to explain how you have met the user requirements and how it is W3C compliant.

Digital Graphics and Computers

Introduction

Digital graphics are found in many places, including promotional materials, documents and websites. This unit will give you an awareness of the software currently available to create and manipulate images. It will show you techniques that you can practise to enhance your graphical skills, as well as the hardware required to capture, edit and print digital images.

When you have completed this unit you will have improved your technical skills in using both vector and bitmap software packages. You will learn the importance of choosing an appropriate file format for saved graphics, with an appreciation of the issues around resizing images and pixellation distortion. You will need to understand how to use formal checking to ensure that a final product meets the requirements and that artwork keeps within the laws of copyright.

After completing this unit, you should be able to achieve these outcomes:

* Know the hardware and software required to work with graphic images

* Understand types of graphic image and graphical file format

* Be able to use editing tools to edit and manipulate technically complex images

* Be able to create and modify graphic images to meet user requirements.

Grading criteria	Activity	Page number
To achieve a pass grade the evidence must show that the learner is able to:		
p₁ Describe hardware and software used to create and edit graphics	24.1, 24.3, case study	229, 240, 247
p₂ Identify two graphics related hardware upgrades to an existing system and describe the potential benefits when working with graphic images	24.2, case study	232, 247
p₃ Define and document a client and user need for three related graphic images	24.5	254
p₄ Create and review three original graphic images to meet a defined user need	case study, 24.5, 24.6	237, 254, 255
p₅ Capture existing images using a scanner and a digital camera and edit them to meet a given user need	24.6	255
p₆ Explain potential legal implications of using and editing graphical images	24.7	256
To achieve a merit grade the evidence must show that, in addition to the pass criteria, the learner is able to:		
m₁ Compare the limitations of at least two different hardware devices and two different software packages utilised for the capture, manipulation and storage of graphics	24.2, 24.3, case study	232, 240, 247
m₂ Demonstrate the use of two advanced techniques in graphics manipulation	24.6	255
m₃ Demonstrate the impact that file format, compression techniques, image resolution and colour depth have on file size and image quality	24.4	253
To achieve a distinction grade the evidence must show that, in addition to the pass and merit criteria, the learner is able to:		
d₁ Justify the following in connection with the production of graphic images to meet a client and user need: software and tools used, file format, image resolution, colour depth	case study, 24.6	237, 255
d₂ Evaluate the impact of evolving output media on the designing and creation of graphic images	24.2, case study	232, 247
Note: 'PFA' stands for 'Preparation for assessment'.		

Working with graphic images requires suitable **hardware** and **software** to produce the best results. The hardware used can have a dramatic impact on the ease of working with graphical images. Large amounts of data need to be moved between components such as the hard disk and RAM and video display, which can result in a frustratingly slow system if the components are not ideal.

What does it mean?

Hardware is the physical part of a computer system, including components inside the system unit, peripherals such as monitor and printer, as well as specialised devices such as a digital camera.

Software is the collection of programs installed on the computer.

Slow systems are not only more difficult to use, but they can also stifle the creative side of anyone using the system. If a 'wrong' click of the mouse makes the system unusable for a minute or so while the hardware struggles to catch up, then there is less incentive for the user to try new things.

Graphics should be fun and any computer system that is used to work with graphics should be fast enough to make it a pleasure.

24.1.1 Hardware

Suitable hardware for a graphics system should include these components at appropriate performance levels:

- graphics card – needed to produce a display at a **resolution** and **colour depth** that meet the needs of the user within the capabilities of the monitor
- internal memory (RAM) – to hold the running software and graphic images
- processor – to run the software and work out the calculations needed to manipulate digital graphics
- digital card reader – to quickly and easily accept graphic images from a digital camera
- file storage – to save the graphic images

- input devices – to capture graphical images and transfer them to the computer system.

For a computer system used for graphics, the higher the spec the better. A high-resolution display with good colour depth is essential for most graphic designers.

24.1.1.1 Graphics cards and their features

The graphics card takes digital information from the operating system specifying what is to be shown on the screen and makes this into a signal that the display understands. The signal usually travels along a video cable to the monitor, which uses it to create the picture.

Most modern graphics cards are very capable of producing an image that meets the highest needs of any monitor without noticeably slowing the system down.

Professional graphic designers value a **DVI** (**Digital Visual Interface**) connection between graphics card and monitor in preference to the older **VGA** (**Visual Graphics Array**) cable connection, as it gives a better picture.

Professional graphic designers often work with 32-bit colour depth, which gives 'truecolor' – this is a system where 32 bits are used for each pixel: 24 bits for the colour and the other 8 bits giving transparency information of 256 values from fully opaque to fully transparent.

What does it mean?

Resolution is the number of **pixels** on the screen or other output device. The resolution is usually written as two numbers, the number of pixels across then the number down, so a 1024×768 resolution has 1024 pixels across and 786 down giving 786,432 dots on the screen.

A **pixel** is a dot of colour on a screen or other output device. The word pixel is short for 'picture element'.

The **colour depth** is the number of bits used by the graphics system to hold the colour of each pixel on the screen. A 24-bit colour depth means the number of colours available on a computer system will be 16.7 million.

Activity 24.1

What is a digital graphics computer system?
Research each of the following and produce
presentation slides to explain your findings.

1 Describe what each of the following items does in a
computer system used to manipulate digital graphics:

- mouse
- screen
- graphics tablet
- digital camera
- scanner
- flash cards
- USB storage devices.  **(partial evidence)**

2 Describe how the following hardware components
affect the performance of a computer system used
to manipulate digital graphics:

- hard drive
- graphics card
- processor(s)
- RAM. **(partial evidence)**

24.1.1.2 Role of the internal memory

The internal memory of a computer system is called
RAM. It is primarily used to hold programs when they
are running and any documents or graphic files that the
user has opened.

What does it mean?

RAM stands for **random access memory**. It is the
name given to the electronic memory plugged into the
main motherboard inside the system unit. RAM is
often 1 GB or more in a modern computer system.
This component is often replaced when a PC has a
memory upgrade.

There is a constant flow of data between the hard disk,
the RAM and the processor (see Figure 24.1). When a
software application is run, the program is first copied

from the hard disk to RAM. Once in RAM, the program
can travel at very high speed to the processor where the
program code can be run. RAM works at the speed of
electricity, much faster than a hard disk, which works at
the speed the disk spins.

Similarly, when a document or data file is opened, it is
first copied from the hard disk to RAM. Once it is in
RAM, the file can be worked on by the user.

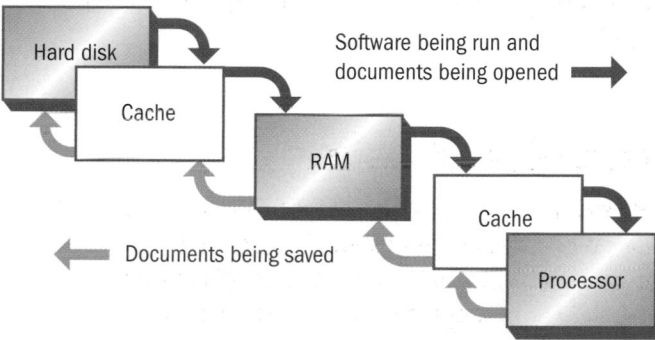

▲ **Figure 24.1 Data flows in a computer system**

Most modern hard disk drives have **cache memory** built
into the control electronics to help the drive work faster.
The cache is used so that:

- the **FAT** is copied from the disk to cache to make
  finding disk addresses faster, as fast electronic cache is
  used rather than slow disk to access FAT

What does it mean?

Cache memory is very fast electronic memory
between RAM and another device, used to make the
system run faster.

The **FAT (File Allocation Table)** is held on the disk to
connect names of files and folders to where they
actually are on the disk. When a file is opened or
saved, the disk address needs to be looked up in the
FAT before the file can be found. FAT can be likened to
a phone book holding the addresses of files on the
disk.

- if data is needed from a drive, the required data is
  brought to cache, as well as the next data on the disk,
  so if the computer needs this as well, it is already in
  the cache, ready to go

- when data is written to disk, it is very quickly sent to cache so the drive electronics can then write the data to disk at slow disk speed without reducing performance in the rest of the system.

Usually there is also some cache memory between processor and RAM. This cache may be on the motherboard or part of the processor. The processor works a lot faster than RAM, so needs a good supply of data and software to keep running without slowing the system down. Processor cache is a type of very fast RAM, keeping the processor from slowing down in a similar way to how disk cache helps the hard drive work faster.

Graphic files can be huge, so everything that the hardware can do to make rapid transfers of data helps.

24.1.1.3 Role of processors in relation to the manipulation of graphic images

The processor (or **CPU**) is the heart of a computer system, allowing the operating system and other programs to run. Every program consists of instructions for the processor that are decoded and actioned inside the processor to make them work.

What does it mean?

The **CPU (central processing unit)** is another name for the processor. This is a chip that fits into a socket on the motherboard. Modern CPUs are often made by AMD or Intel. The AMD family of CPUs include Athlon and Opteron. Intel processors include Pentium and Celeron.

When running a program, the processor has to make every instruction work, usually one after another, but some modern processors can run processes side by side. The quicker the instructions are run, the quicker a program responds to the user.

The processor is very important to maintaining performance with complex digital images, so a computer with two or more processors – such as with a system using a dual or quad Xeon motherboard or similar – helps to keep the computer responsive.

Some graphics manipulations are easy for the processor, e.g. loading a graphic from disk to RAM, which is delegated to the **DMA** controller(s).

What does it mean?

DMA (direct memory addressing) is the name given to circuits on the motherboard which are used to move large amounts of data from one part of the system to another.

Many graphics operations involve a lot of processor work, such as:
- rescaling an image, so the picture is a different size
- saving or exporting the image into another format, e.g. converting a bitmap file into a JPEG file
- applying a complex effect to a graphic, such as adjusting the tone or colour balance.

Any of these operations needs good, fast processor(s) to operate effectively.

24.1.1.4 Digital card reader

IT professionals who work with digital graphics often need to bring pictures from a digital camera into the computer system. There are three methods for doing this: cable, card and wireless.

■ Cable

Most digital cameras have a cable to connect the camera to the computer so pictures can be transferred, usually from camera to hard disk. The cable will probably be USB, but other standards, such as the faster FireWire, are also available.

■ Card

Virtually every digital camera on the market uses a card to store the pictures taken with it.

There are several types of card currently available (see opposite), each with different sizes and different connections:
- SD (Secure Digital) – a secure stamp-sized digital camera memory card

- SDHC (Secure Digital High Capacity) – offers high storage capacity, currently to 32GB
- CF (Compact Flash) – the world's most popular type of digital camera memory
- Memory Stick – from Sony, used in a wide range of Sony products
- MMC (MultiMedia Card) – a very small card which can also operate in SD devices
- XD – from Fujifilm and Olympus, with a very small footprint of only 20 × 25 × 1.7 mm
- SM (Smart Media) – from Toshiba, now becoming less popular.

▲ Digital camera cards

Usually only one type of card will fit the camera, but many computers used for digital graphics have a card reader (see below) which can accept many types of card, often in the same slot.

The card can easily be removed from the camera and then inserted into a card reader to allow a very quick and effective data transfer of the pictures from camera to computer.

▲ Card reader

■ Wireless

Wireless cameras are now appearing on the market, offering **WiFi** radio connection to a network or PCs. This allows a fast data transfer of the pictures without the need to use cables or remove the memory card (see below).

What does it mean?

WiFi is an increasingly popular standard for wireless networking and connection of PCs and other devices such as printers. WiFi is based on the 802.11 standard for wireless transmissions.

▲ Nikon Coolpix P3 wireless camera

Bluetooth is a wireless technology that can be used to transfer images between a mobile phone and a computer.

24.1.1.5 Other hardware devices

■ Camera cradle

Some digital cameras use a cradle to attach them to the computer system. This is a quick and easy method for transferring pictures to the computer as the camera simply pushes into the cradle that is already cabled to a computer (see following page).

 Digital camera cradle

Many cradles recharge the camera and can create a slide show of pictures.

A cradle is similar to most hardware, in that it will need a driver to make it work properly, probably on an installation CD that is bundled with the cradle.

■ SCSI

SCSI (Small Computer Systems Interface) is a system in which several devices, such as scanners, external or internal hard drives and similar, can be **daisy-chained** together.

What does it mean?

Daisy-chained is a term used to describe when a number of devices are connected together with a cable connecting each device to the next. Daisy-chained devices usually need a terminator at the two ends of the chain to keep the data signal inside the cabling.

An SCSI card is located inside the computer with a cable connecting from the card to external devices such as a scanner or internal devices such as a hard disk (see Figure 24.2).

SCSI has always been popular with digital graphic professionals, who have respected the high data transfer rates and the flexibility of types of connected devices it offers.

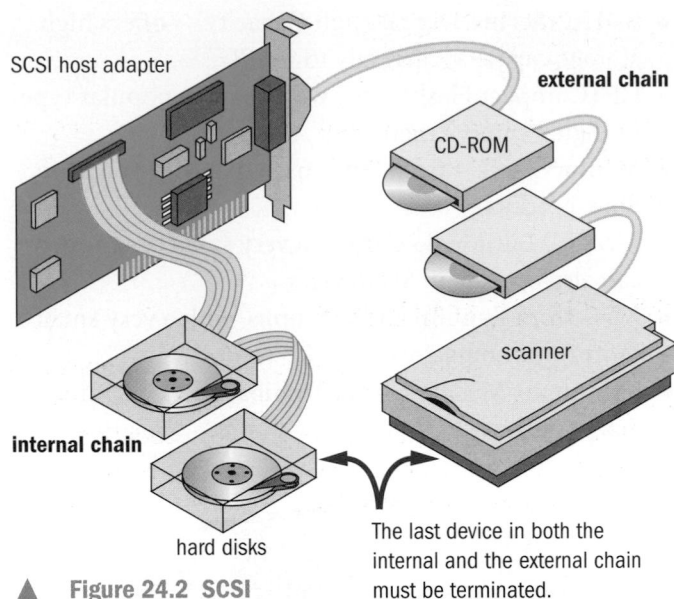

▲ **Figure 24.2 SCSI**

Activity 24.2

Upgrading a digital graphics computer system

1 Identify two graphics-related hardware upgrades to the system described here. Describe the potential benefits these upgrades will bring when working with graphic images.

System specification:
- Intel Pentium D 'Dual Core X2' CPU (5.3 Ghz)
- VIA Chipset 1066 Mhz Motherboard – slots available: AGP8X (1), PCI (3), RAM (2); ports available: LAN (1), USB (6)
- 512 MB RAM
- 80 GB HDD (SATA300)
- 18X DVD+/-RW Dual Layer & Dual Format
- onboard UniChrome PRO 3D Graphics with 64 MB shared memory
- mouse and keyboard
- 15" flat screen
- cheap inkjet printer **p₂**

2 Identify a choice of products for each of the proposed hardware upgrades for the capture, manipulation or storage of graphics. Compare their limitations.
m₁ (partial evidence)

3 Evaluate the impact of evolving output media on the design and creation of graphic images. You will need to research how output media products such as large flat screens, printer technologies, etc. are developing. Then evaluate them against cost, speed, usage and any other criteria you discover. **d₂**

24.1.1.6 File storage

Graphic files need to be stored so they can be used again, modified, **backed up** or sent to a third party, such as a client.

What does it mean?

To **back up** means to copy computer work to another place so that it is kept safe in case of emergency such as file corruption, fire, flood or theft. Many users back up to CD-ROM then store these somewhere secure, such as a fireproof safe or off-site in another location.

■ Hard drive

The hard drive is the obvious place to store graphical files as it is quick and the graphical software will look there first to open or save work because it is part of the computer system.

Modern hard disks are very quick and spacious, with lots of room for work.

Remember!

Even the best computer systems fail sometimes, so you should regularly back up your work.

■ Optical drives

Most computer systems have CD-ROM and/or DVD drives – these are optical disks used to install software, play DVDs and to store files.

For an optical drive to store files, it must be of the right type . Table 24.1 (on the following page) shows the bewildering choice of standards available for optical drives. Fortunately for most IT professionals, the choice is a simple one: usually a DVD +/- RW drive for reading and writing DVDs that also handles the CD-RW standard for writing and reading CD-ROMs.

■ Flash cards

Digital cameras and other devices often use a flash card to store pictures or other data.

There are many types of flash card, each with a different size, shape and connectors (see section 24.1.1.4 on page 230).

■ USB storage devices

There are many USB storage devices currently available to plug into the USB port of a computer system.

External USB hard drives are quite popular as a means of backing up data and to take a substantial amount of work between computers.

USB pen drives are **solid state** devices that have become increasingly popular as they are cheap, robust, quick and offer reasonable capacity for storing files, especially to move from office to home or client. A lot of organisations now find them cheap enough to send through the post or even to give to a client with their completed graphic images.

What does it mean?

A **solid state** device has no moving parts. USB pen drives are solid state because they store data onto electronic circuits which hold their values even when unplugged. USB hard drives are not solid state because the hard disk spins (moves) when used.

24.1.1.7 Input devices

An input device is anything that can be used to feed data into a computer system.

The mouse is an almost essential input device for a computer system used for digital graphics, but some IT professionals who specialise in this area prefer a graphics tablet.

■ Graphics tablet

A graphics tablet often has a special pen to operate it in a similar way to how a mouse is used. The great advantage of the graphics tablet is that it is much more precise than a mouse and positioning is absolute, because when the pen is touched to a point on the tablet it will always

CD-R	Compact Disc-Recordable: also referred to as Compact Disc-Write Once (CD-WO). A type of disk drive that can create CD-ROMs and audio CDs, allowing users to 'master' discs for subsequent publishing.
CD-ROM	Compact Disc-Read Only Memory: a standard for compact disc to be used as a digital memory medium for personal computers. The 4.75-inch laser-encoded optical memory storage medium can hold about 650MB of data, sound and limited stills and motion video. A CD-ROM player will typically play CD-DA discs, but a CD-DA player will not play CD-ROMs. The standard used for most CD-ROM formats is known as Yellow Book, based on the standard published by Philips.
CD-ROM XA	CD-ROM Extended Architecture: a hybrid format, promoted by Sony and Microsoft, that combines CD-ROM and CD-i capabilities. The extension adds ADPCM audio to permit the interleaving of sound and video data to animation and with sound synchronisation. It is an essential component of Microsoft's plan for multimedia computers and also the physical format for Kodak's Photo CD format.
CD-RW	Compact Disc-Rewritable: once known as CD-Erasable, or CD-E.
DVD	Digital Versatile Disc: the replacement for the ubiquitous compact disc. Like the CD, it is available in a number of different formats. Unlike the CD, it is available with a number of capacities ranging from 4.7GB to 17GB.
DVD Multi	A logo program that promotes compatibility with DVD-RAM and DVD-RW. Putting the emphasis for compatibility on the reader, not the writer, it defines a testing methodology to ensure drives are able to read both DVD-RAM and DVD-RW media.
DVD+R	A write-once optical media format designed for use by devices using DVD+RW technology.
DVD+RW	A competing (with DVD-RAM and DVD-RW) rewritable DVD standard being promoted by Hewlett-Packard, Philips and Sony. Unlike the DVD-RAM standard, DVD+RW allows the use of bare discs. All three standards are incompatible. At one time the DVD-Forum – which does not support the standard – was insisting on the name being changed to '+RW' – but this appears to have had little effect.
DVD+RW Alliance	A voluntary association of industry-leading personal computing manufacturers, optical storage and consumer electronics manufacturers.
DVD-R	DVD Recordable: the write-once DVD format. DVD-R discs are the DVD counterpart to CD-R discs.
DVD-RAM	A rewritable compact disc format that provides much greater data storage than today's CD-RW systems. The caddy-mounted discs will initially provide 2.6GB per side on single or double-sided discs.
DVD-ROM	The read-only format supports discs with capacities of from 4.7GB (enough for an MPEG-2 compressed full-length movie) to 17GB and access rates of 600 KBps to 1.3 MBps. Backward-compatible with CD-ROMs.
DVD-RW	Pioneer's rewritable DVD format, incompatible with the rival DVD-RAM and DVD+RW formats but generally compatible with DVD-ROM drives and consumer DVD players.
DVD-Video	A consumer DVD format for displaying full-length digital movies. DVD-Video players attach to a television like a video cassette player. Unlike DVD-ROMs, the Digital-Video format includes a Content Scrambling System (CSS) to prevent users from copying discs. This means that today's DVD-ROM players cannot play DVD-Video discs without a software or hardware upgrade to decode the encrypted discs.

Table 24.1 Optical drive formats

▲ **Graphics tablet**

represent the same spot on the screen. In contrast, if a mouse is lifted and then put down on a different part of the surface, the mouse pointer will continue from where it was on the screen.

Some top of the range graphics tablets have LCD screens built into them so the graphic designer can use the pen directly on the image (see below).

▲ **Graphics tablet with LCD screen**

■ Digital camera

Digital cameras have become better and better and are now very impressive devices with **high resolution** and low costs.

■ Scanner

Scanners are still the best way to input paper images into a computer. They have a similar mechanism to a photocopier, with a scanning bar moving across the length of the scanner under glass (see Figure 24.3).

Remember!

Resolution is the term given to describe how many pixels (dots) are used to make up a picture. A **high-resolution** image has more pixels across and down than a **low-resolution** image, giving it more detail and making it more suitable for printing onto large areas.

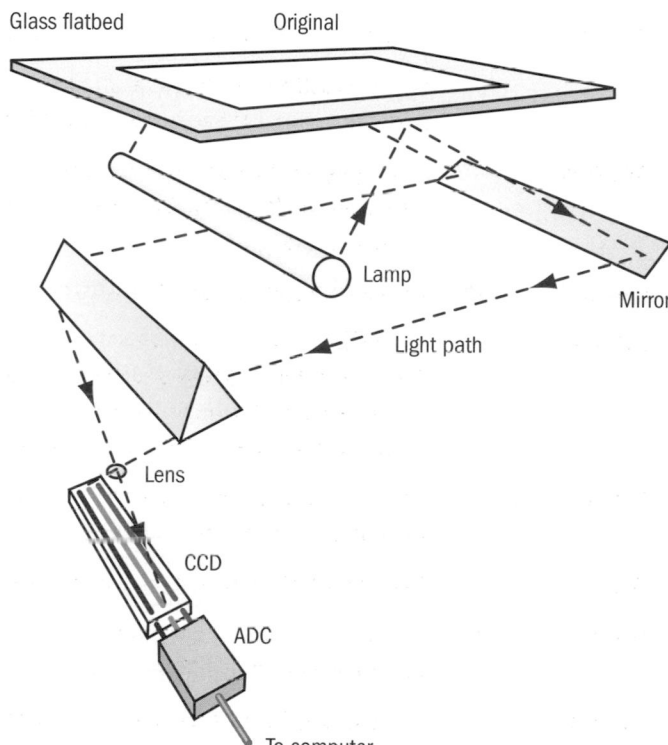

Glass flatbed   Original

Lamp

Mirror

Light path

Lens

CCD

ADC

To computer

▲ **Figure 24.3 Flatbed scanner mechanism**

The document is placed face down onto a glass window, and a scanning mechanism moves back and forth underneath the glass. Light from the lamp bounces off the original and is reflected by the mirror into the lens. This focuses the image into the **CCD**, which digitises the

What does it mean?

A **CCD (charge-coupled device)** is an image sensor used in digital cameras and other devices that converts the image to digital signals.

results via an analogue-to-digital converter (ADC), to send the resulting information to the scanner's own hardware and then to the host PC.

24.1.2 Output media

Output media for digital graphics include: printers, computer monitors, mobile phones, PDAs, plotters and vinyl cutters.

24.1.2.1 Printer

A printer is a device that produces hard copy by printing onto paper or another medium such as an overhead projector transparency or T-shirt.

There are different printer technologies available, each with their own characteristics, strengths and weaknesses. The choice of printer technology should match the user needs.

Below are the printer technologies that are of most interest to IT professionals working with digital graphics.

- **Inkjet printers** have small nozzles that squirt tiny droplets of ink onto the paper. They are cheap to buy and run, but can be slow for complex printing.
- **Colour laser printers** have cyan, magenta, yellow and black toners. They are usually more expensive than inkjets with similar running costs and can be a lot faster, especially when printing the same page many times.
- **Dye-sublimation printers** use dyes which vaporise and seep into the paper surface. They are usually more expensive than colour laser printers to buy and run, but are quite slow. The great strength of these printers is that they produce real photo-quality prints.
- **Solid ink printers** make use of sticks of a wax-like substance, which are melted and then applied to the page. They produce quick, quality prints. They are usually more expensive to buy, but have low running costs, which can make them a cheaper option over time if they are well used.

Inkjet technology is the most well accepted of these technologies, with laser printer technology next.

24.1.2.2 Computer monitor

A computer system needs a monitor or display so the user can see what is happening. Traditionally, monitors have used **CRT** technology, which has many disadvantages, especially the space the monitor occupies and the heat produced. CRT screens have now been largely superseded by flat screen displays.

What does it mean?

CRT (cathode ray tube) is a screen technology that uses a phosphor-coated glass tube to display images. The tube makes the unit quite deep, especially for large screens, as electron rays need to be fired at the display from the back of the tube, with room to spread out to the size of the display. This technology uses a lot of electricity and older models can produce some radiation, which concerns many users.

Some professional displays feature hardware calibration to adjust and match the screen display colours to printers, image setters and other digital devices. A **colorimeter** is used to help with this (see the case study on page 247).

Flat screen monitors have become much larger and cheaper in recent years and are now the natural choice for any new computer system.

24.1.2.3 Other

There are other media that can display digital graphics, including the following.

- **Mobile phones** can use images that may be captured using the phone camera or downloaded from another source
- **PDAs** (personal digital assistants) small hand-held devices offering a calendar, contact list and other useful programs (right). Many PDAs have a built-in camera that can take pictures to be displayed on the device screen.

Palm Tungsten PD

- Plotters are used for large prints onto paper, material or other materials (see below)

◀ **Plotter**

- vinyl cutters are used to cut signs from vinyl (see below) in the shape of the graphic image; the sign can then be peeled from its backing fabric and stuck onto a surface, such as the side of a van.

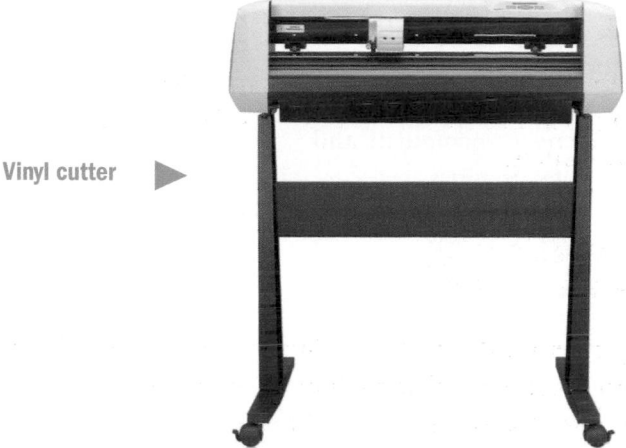

Vinyl cutter ▶

Case study

Figure 24.4 ▶
Vizual Impact
website

Vizual Impact

Vizual Impact (see Figure 24.4) is a thriving shop (www.vizualimpact.co.uk), producing signs and graphcs for:

- car graphics
- van signs
- registration plates for vehicles.
- shop signs
- sun visors

The proprietor, Martin Oxenham, has seen your website and is so impressed by your graphical skills that he has approached you to help him with some current jobs.

1 Produce documentation to define the user needs for the images required in tasks 2–4 below.

2 A client has asked Vizual Impact to produce some graphics to be vinyl cut and then stuck to the sides of their BMW car. You are to produce a vector graphic using up to three colours that could be used to produce this graphic. You should produce two prints of the graphic:

  1 the graphic onto A4 paper
  2 the graphic rescaled and superimposed onto a photograph of a BMW to show what the completed job will look like. **p**₄ (partial evidence)

3 Microsoft has approached Vizual Impact to produce some displays for its stand at a show to be held in the Birmingham NEC publicising its newest operating system. Produce a graphic that could be printed onto a large piece of card to be used on the Microsoft stand. **p**₄ (partial evidence)

4 An organic foods mobile fast-food service has requested a roadside sign. It will be used on a stand so when its van is parked in a lay-by offering quality burgers and all-day breakfasts, passing motorists will notice it. This sign is to be in full colour and must be eye-catching. **p**₄ (partial evidence)

5 Produce a report for Vizual Impact to justify how the production of your graphic images met the client and user needs. Include justification of the software and tools used, the file formats, the image resolutions and colour depths. **d**₁

24.1.3 Software

Software is the term used to describe the programs that run on a computer. Application software is used to help people produce work. There are many types of application that can be used to create, manipulate and view digital graphics.

24.1.3.1 Dedicated vector graphics software

Vector graphics are different from bitmap graphics. The main features of vector graphics are:

- small file size when saved to disk
- no loss of print quality when enlarged or reduced in size
- vector pictures are made from objects such as circles and rectangles
- each object has an outline and/or fill
- objects may be grouped together.

Vector graphics are very good for diagrams.

Examples of vector drawing packages include CorelDRAW (see Figure 24.5), Autodesk AutoCAD (see Figure 24.6) and Microsoft Visio (see Figure 24.7 on the following page).

What does it mean?

Vector graphics define objects as coordinate points and use mathematics inside the software to calculate how to display the image onto the screen or printer.

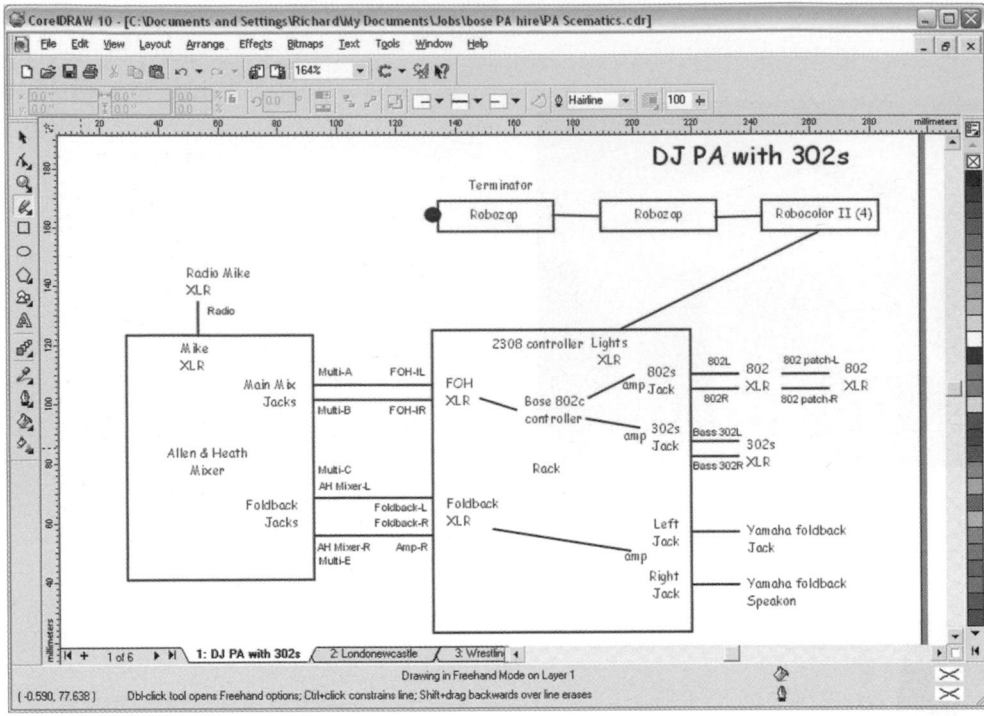

▲ **Figure 24.5 CorelDRAW**

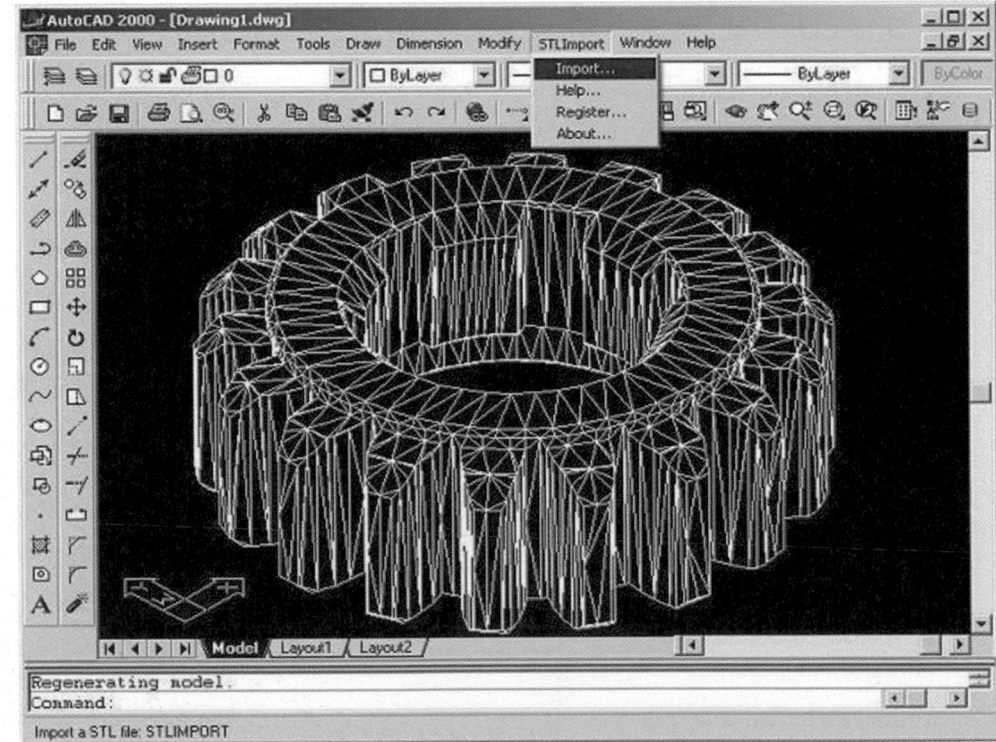

▲ **Figure 24.6 Autodesk AutoCAD**

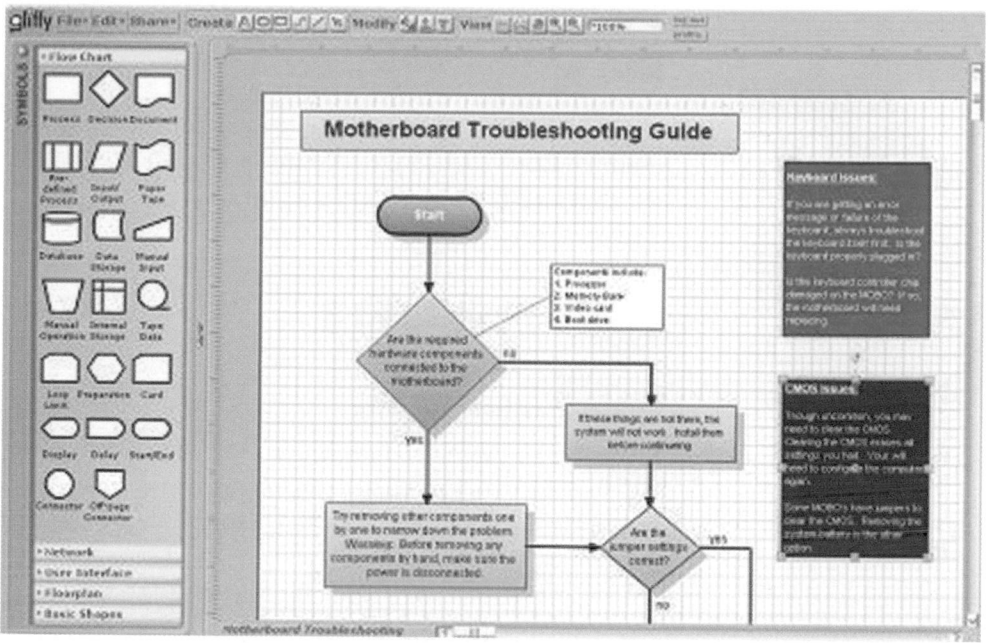

Figure 24.7 Microsoft Visio

What does it mean?

Bitmap graphics are made from lots of pixels, each with a colour. They are also called **raster** graphics.

24.1.3.2 Dedicated bitmap software

Figure 24.8 Corel Paint Shop Pro

Bitmap graphics are different from vector graphics. The main features of vector bitmaps are:

- large file size when saved to disk
- print quality can become 'blocky' when enlarged or reduced in size
- bitmaps can be created when a picture is scanned into a computer system using a scanner or from a digital camera.

Bitmap graphics are very good for screenshots and web page illustrations.

Examples of bitmap drawing packages include Corel Paint Shop Pro (see Figure 24.8) and Microsoft Paint (see Figure 24.9 on the following page).

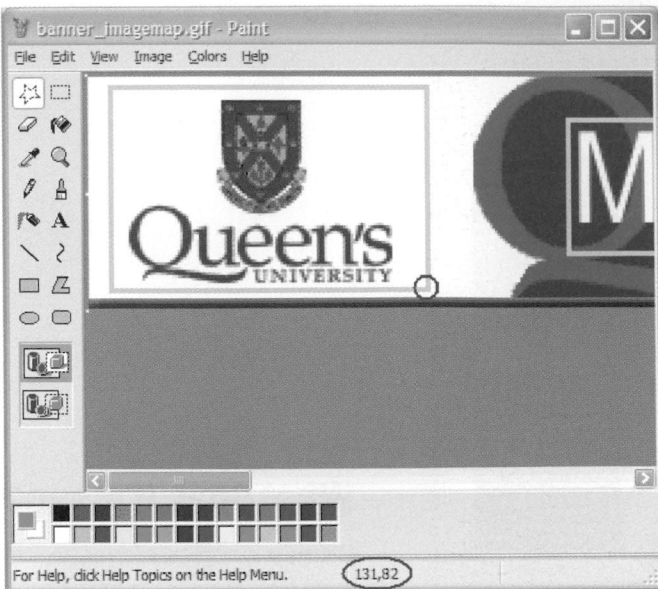

Figure 24.9 Microsoft Paint

Other software tools are available to IT professionals, for example CorelTRACE (see Figure 24.13 on page 242), which converts a bitmap graphic into a vector graphic.

Activity 24.3

Digital graphics software

1 Identify software used for digital graphics and produce presentation slides to give an impression of how graphical software can be used. Explain the differences between:
   - vector graphics software, such as CorelDRAW
   - bitmap software, such as Paint
   - photo manipulation software, such as Photoshop
   - graphics facilities embedded within other application packages, such as Word.

   Note: This test should be completed in conjunction with Activity 24.1 to evidence criterion **p** fully.

2 Compare the limitations of two different software packages used for the capture, manipulation or storage of graphics. **m**

   Note: This test should be completed in conjunction with Activity 24.2 task 2 to evidence criterion **m** fully.

24.1.3.3 Dedicated photo manipulation software

Photo manipulation software applications are specialist bitmap programs that are very good for manipulating photographs.

Examples of photo manipulation software applications include Corel PHOTO-PAINT (see Figure 24.10) and Adobe Photoshop (see Figure 24.11 opposite).

24.1.3.4 Graphics facilities embedded within other application packages

Many applications have graphical capabilities built into them. For example, Word (see Figure 24.12 opposite) is a word processing application that also has very impressive graphical features allowing you to easily include photographs and other digital graphics in a document.

Figure 24.10 Corel PHOTO-PAINT ▶

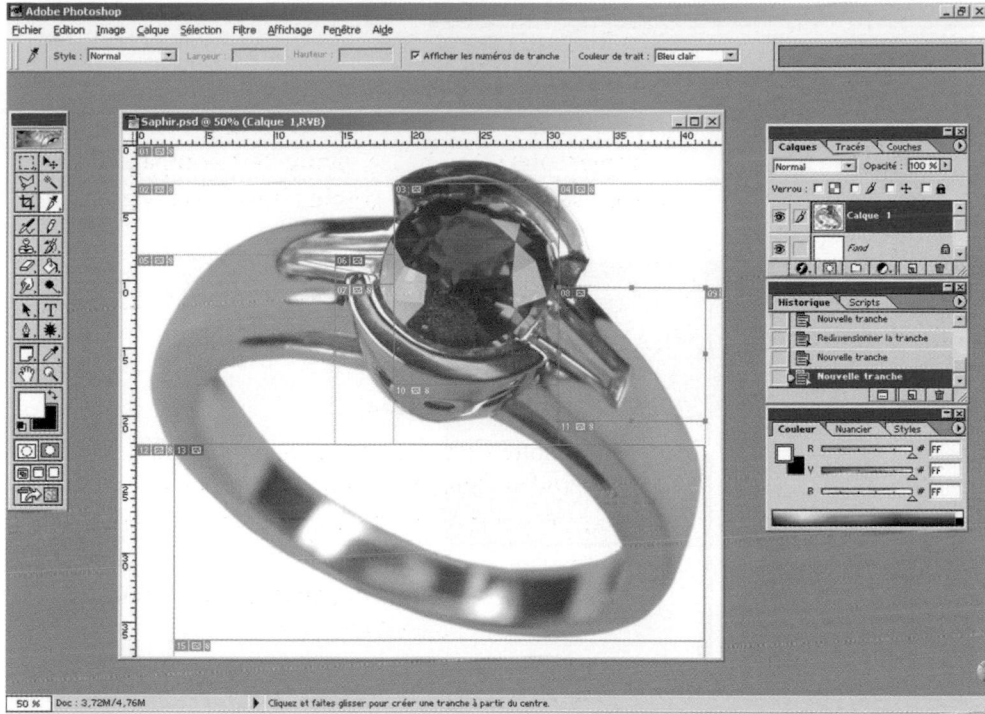

Figure 24.11 Adobe Photoshop

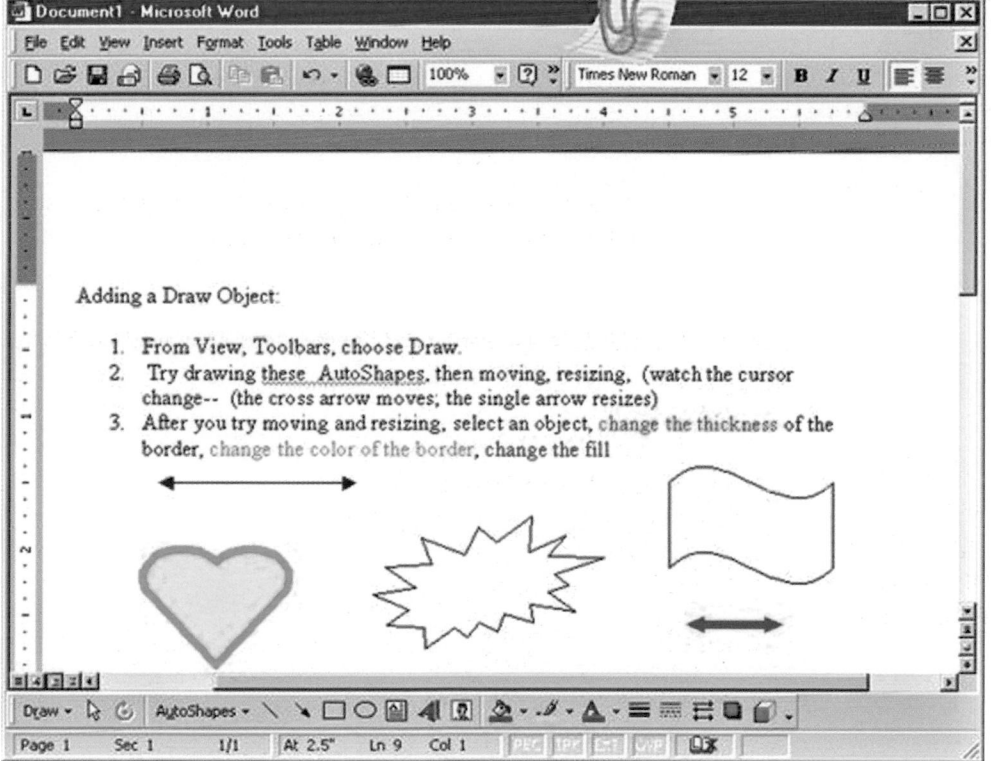

Figure 24.12 Microsoft Word

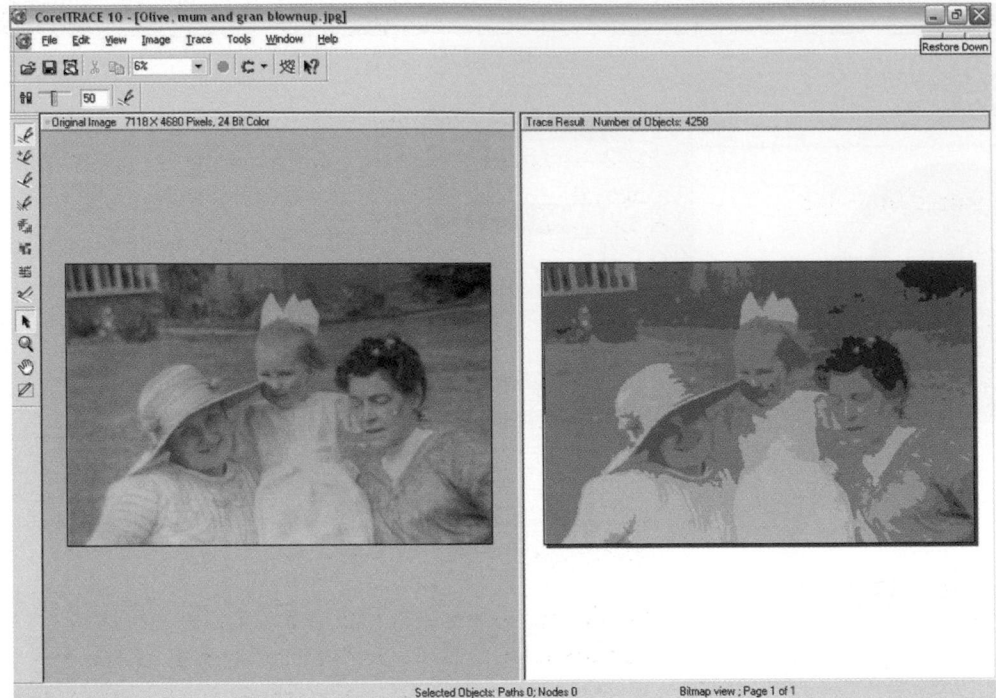

Figure 24.13 CorelTRACE

Test your knowledge

1 What parts of a computer system help the production of digital graphics?

2 How do the different types of memory work together to edit digital graphics?

3 How can photographs be captured and transferred to a computer system?

4 What is SCSI?

5 How can digital graphic files be stored?

6 What input devices are suitable for a computer used for editing graphics?

7 What output devices are suitable for a computer used for editing graphics?

8 Identify some software applications suitable for creating and editing images.

There are two main types of graphic images and many graphical file formats.

The bitmap (also called raster) type stores an image as lots of pixels, each with a colour.

Vector type stores the image as a collection of objects, each with coordinate points to define size and position, as well as mathematical formulae defining line curvatures and thickness.

Each of these two types can be saved in many different formats to the disk.

24.2.1 File handling

24.2.1.1 Converting files

Files can usually be converted from one format to another. Many IT professionals simply use the File menu of their favourite graphical application to export or save as a new file type.

There are also utility programs available that convert between formats and may offer batch options in order to automatically convert a collection of files from one format to another.

24.2.1.2 File sizes

The size of a bitmap graphic file saved to disk depends upon the format of the file and the options taken when saving it. Vector files are usually a lot smaller and do not have save options for controlling file size.

The same graphic would have different sizes in different formats (see Table 24.2).

BMP	GIF	JPG	PNG	TIF
2305 KB	209 KB	440 KB	348 KB	2305 KB

Table 24.2 Graphic sizes in different formats

Controlling the file size is achieved by setting the compression or quality level when saving the graphic. The same graphic file might have the sizes shown in Table 24.3 using JPEG quality settings.

100%	90%	60%	40%	10%
440 KB	216 KB	116 KB	92 KB	41 KB

Table 24.3 Graphic sizes with different JPEG quality settings

24.2.1.3 File formats

The file format is the way the graphic is internally structured. Each file format uses a different structure – a program using that format must be able to understand the structure so it knows how to show the graphic on the screen, print it, edit it and so on. Table 24.5, on the following page, shows some of the more common file formats.

24.2.1.4 File management

File management involves the methods used to look after work saved to disk or USB drive, including the following.

- File naming simply means giving names to your files. Students often give files joke names making them very difficult to identify later. IT students and professionals recognise that naming a file is important because the name must represent what the file is. Look at Table 24.4. Which type of file name would you rather see if you were looking for the second assignment for Unit 24 about vector software?

Joke file names	Professional file names
Itchy	Unit 24 assignment 1 Bitmap software
Scratchy	Unit 24 assignment 2 Vector software
Bart	Unit 24 assignment 3 Utility software

Table 24.4 Showing filenames

File extension	Graphics type	Proper name	Description
.ai	vector	Adobe Illustrator Artwork	Vector format for Adobe Illustrator (originally a subset of PostScript, if an appropriate file header was present).
.bmp	raster	Windows Bitmap	Commonly used by Microsoft Windows programs and the Windows operating system itself. **Lossless compression** can be specified (RLE), but some programs use only uncompressed files.
.cdr	vector	CorelDRAW Document	Default proprietary format for Corel CorelDRAW 2D documents. Features include multiple import/export filters, 3D special effects and object/image layering.
.cgm	vector	Computer Graphics Metafile	Defined by ISO Standard 8632. Often used for complex engineering drawings, e.g. in the aviation industry (CGM members).
.cpi	raster	Cartesian Perceptual Compression	Hyper-compressed format for black-and-white raster images. Typically compresses images 5–20 times smaller than corresponding TIFF or PDF versions, leading to dramatic reductions in download times and server network traffic.
.cpt	raster	Corel Photo-Paint Image	Default proprietary format for Corel Photo-Paint documents. Has many extra features such as image layering. Supported by very few image editing programs other than Corel Photo-Paint. Photo-Paint images are usually smaller than Photoshop documents.
.dxf	vector	ASCII Drawing Interchange	Standard ASCII text files used to store vector data for CAD programs.
.eps	raster/vector	Encapsulated PostScript	A PostScript file that describes a small vector graphic, as opposed to a whole page or set of pages.
.emf	vector	Windows Enhanced Metafile	An enhanced version of Windows Metafile. Supported in Windows NT and later.
.exr	raster	Extended Dynamic Range Image File Format	OpenEXR is the Open Source high dynamic-range (HDR) file format developed by Industrial Light & Magic for advanced imaging in movie production. The main advantages of that format are up to 32-bit floating-point pixels and multiple lossless image compression algorithms up to 2:1 lossless compression on film grained images.
.fh	vector	Macromedia Freehand Document	Vector format for Macromedia Freehand.
.fla	vector	Flash Source File	Shockwave Flash source file, only usable by Adobe (previously Macromedia) Flash authoring software.
.gif	raster	Graphics Interchange Format	GIF is used extensively on the web. Supports animated images. Supports only 255 colours per frame, so requires **lossy compression** for full-colour photos (dithering); using multiple frames can improve colour precision. Uses lossless LZW compression, which used to sometimes make GIF undesirable due to LZW patent (now expired) issues.

Table 24.5 Graphic file formats

continued ▶

What does it mean?

Lossless compression of images allows the original image to be rebuilt from the compressed image.

Lossy compression of images does not allow the original image to be rebuilt from the compressed image.

File extension	Graphics type	Proper name	Description
.igs	vector	Initial Graphics Exchange Specification	IGES is an ASCII text neutral data format used extensively for CAD/CAM data exchange. It supports 2D and 3D curves and surfaces, as well as solid models and annotation.
.jpeg .jpg	raster	Joint Photographic Experts Group	JPEG is used extensively for photos and other continuous tone images on the web. Uses lossy compression by trying to equalise eight by eight pixel blocks; the quality can vary greatly depending on the compression settings.
.jpg2 .jp2	raster	Joint Photographic Experts Group 2000	JPEG 2000 is the successor of popular JPEG. A new wavelet-based file format that includes both lossy and lossless compression options. It is commonly considered the actual 'state-of-the-art' lossy format for photographic imaging, but its support in modern systems is still weak due to heavy requirements for hardware and many patents for software.
.mng	raster	Multiple-image Network Graphics	Animation format using data streams similar to those of PNG and JPEG, originally designed to replace the use of animated GIF on the web. Free of the patent (which expired in 2003) associated with animated GIF.
.pcx	raster	PCX	Developed by ZSoft Corporation. Uses a simple form of run-length encoding. Supports palette-based and 24-bit RGB images.
.pdf	raster/ vector	Portable Document Format	A page description language (loosely based on PostScript, but not a programming language), which allows for files containing multiple pages and links. Works with Adobe Acrobat Reader or Adobe eBook Reader, or third-party compatible software. It is the 'native' metafile format for Mac OS X.
.pict .pct .pic	raster/ vector	Picture	Default for Macintosh operating systems before version OS X.
.png	raster	Portable Network Graphics	PNG is an image format with lossless compression, offering bit depths from 1 to 48. It was mainly designed to replace the use of GIF on the web. Free of the patent (which expired in 2003) associated with GIF.
.ps	vector	PostScript	Generic vector-based page description language, created and owned by Adobe. PostScript is a powerful stack-based programming language. Supported by many laser printers.
.psd	raster	Photoshop Document	Default proprietary format for Adobe Photoshop documents. Has many extra features, such as image layering. Also supported by some other image editing programs than Adobe Photoshop.
.sgi .rgb .rgba .int .inta .bw	raster	Silicon Graphics Image	Native image format for Silicon Graphics workstations.

Table 24.5 Graphic file formats – continued

continued ▶

File extension	Graphics type	Proper name	Description
.svg .svgz	vector	Scalable Vector Graphics	An XML-based vector graphics format, as defined by the World Wide Web Consortium for use in web browsers.
.swf	vector	Small Web Format (commonly referred to as Shockwave Flash)	Flash is a web page plug-in that displays vector-based animations contained in SWF files. Several applications can create SWF files; these include the Flash authoring tool from Adobe (previously Macromedia).
.tiff .tif	raster	Tagged Image File Format	TIFF is used extensively for traditional print graphics. Lossy and lossless compression are available, but many programs only support a subset of available options.
.wmf	vector	Windows Metafile	Stores vector graphics and raster graphics as a sequence of commands to be issued to the graphics layer of the Microsoft Windows operating system.
.xaml	vector	XAML	The XML-based file format for representing a document built using a Windows Presentation Foundation application (pre-installed on Vista). Can declare 2D vector graphics (and include references to external bitmaps for imaging), textual documents (with or without page fidelity), 2D user interfaces and renderings of 3D models (with a fair amount of baseline support for lighting, materials, etc.).

Table 24.5 Graphic file formats – continued

- Folder structure is one of the most powerful tools that IT professionals can use to help organise their work. Folders give a structure to the disk that can be used to help locate files easily and quickly. There are many ways to organise folder structures. The correct one is usually the one that is most obvious to the user.
- Moving a file involves cutting it from a folder then pasting it to another folder or drive. You may need to move files when tidying up your folder structures, so that the files are in their correct locations.
- Deleting a file removes it from the drive so it cannot be used again.

24.2.1.5 Compression techniques

Compression techniques are used to reduce the disk size of a file. Making a file smaller is useful if there are issues around the size of the file. File size is important if the file is to be transmitted to another location (a small file arrives faster) or if there is a small amount of storage space (the file needs to be reduced in size to fit).

24.2.2 Graphic images

24.2.2.1 Vector graphics

Vector graphics follow mathematical rules. Shapes are understood by vector graphic software as coordinate points joined by lines with a defined fill (see Figure 24.14).

▲ Figure 24.14 A vector image

Case study

Vision Design UK

Vision Design UK (see Figure 24.15) is an independent design studio (www.vduk.co.uk) offering a range of services to local businesses and TV production studios, including:

- digital photography
- display materials
- digital prints
- web design
- TV props.

The proprietor, Ralph Ferrand, has decided to replace his main computer with a new cutting edge PC to make editing large, complex digital graphics easier and quicker. He particularly wants the new system to have at least two processors, preferably more, on the motherboard.

A lot of his work is involved with editing photographs to high professional standards, so the system needs a screen that features hardware calibration – this is so his **colorimeter** can match the screen display colours to his printers, image setter and other digital output devices.

What does it mean?

A **colorimeter** is a device that can measure the colours of a device for calibration.

The new system is also an opportunity to replace his graphics tablet, so he is interested in the features offered by current devices.

You have been introduced to him by your uncle, who is an old friend of Ralph, as you have a real talent in IT and your recommendations will be valued and carefully considered.

Ralph would like you to produce a report for him containing the following sections.

1 Identify the hardware and software used in a typical system used to create and edit graphics,

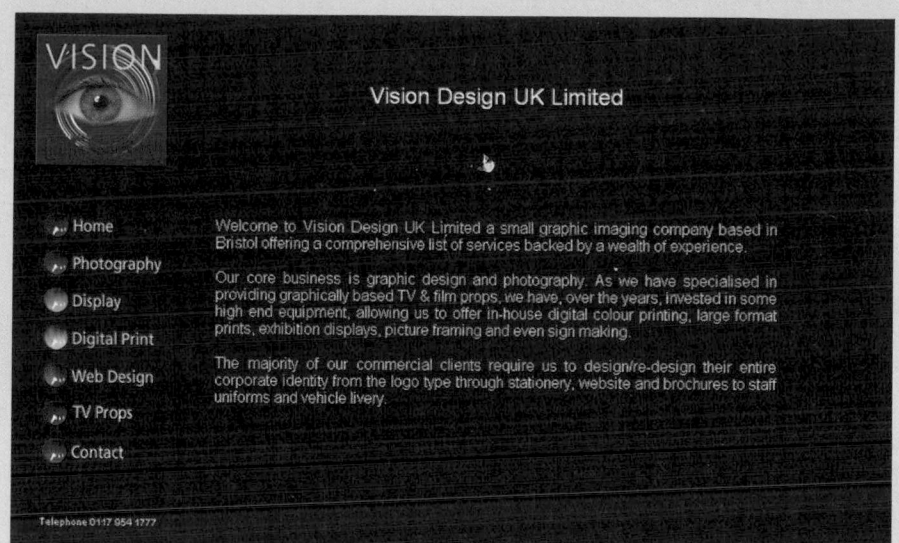

▲ Figure 24.15 Vision Design website

with explanations of the role of each part of the system. Ralph wants this so he can have confidence in your understanding of these systems. **p₁**

2 Specify the hardware components needed inside the system unit (motherboard, video card, processor(s), etc.) to produce an effective computer for manipulating graphics. **p₁**

3 Specify a display device to meet the needs of Visual Design for its new system and explain the potential benefits this will bring to the business. **p₂**

4 Specify a graphics tablet to meet the needs of Visual Design for its new system and explain the potential benefits this will bring to the business. **p₂**

5 Find alternative products to your hardware upgrade recommendations in sections 3 and 4 of your report and compare their benefits and limitations. **m₁**

6 Identify two graphical software packages that could be used by Visual Design and compare their benefits and limitations. **m₁**

7 Research how the choice of output media is changing and report back current developments in this area, evaluating how they could be used by the business. **d₂**

A line joining points may be straight or curved and has properties such as thickness, colour, solid or dashed and so on.

There could be no fill, making the shape transparent, or it could have a colour, more than one colour, texture, etc.

Bitmap (or raster) graphics are pixel-orientated, meaning that a bitmap image is made from a lot of pixels. Each pixel is a tiny dot in the image with a colour. Bitmap software can usually zoom the graphic large enough to edit individual pixels (see Figure 24.16).

 Figure 24.16 Bitmap pixels

There are big differences between vector and bitmap images (see Table 24.6).

The mathematical way in which vector images are stored and manipulated by software makes them easy to edit and resize and results in small file sizes.

Bitmap images allow editing that is much more complex than that possible with vector images, which means that skilled IT professionals can manipulate photographs into anything they can imagine.

Resizing a bitmap needs software to analyse the pixels in the image, then recreate a new set of pixels to make the image the new size. Modern software can be amazingly good at this complex task, but there will still be a loss of quality. There will always be a limit to how large a bitmap image can be acceptably enlarged.

As the colour information of every pixel needs to be stored in a bitmap image, the file size can be enormous.

	Vector	Bitmap
File size	Small	Large files sizes, especially big pictures with large colour depth
Scaling	Very scalable to any size without loss of quality	Pixellation occurs
How created	User created with mouse or graphics tablet	Scanner or digital camera
Typical uses	Diagrams	Photographs

Table 24.6 Relative features of vector and bitmap images

Vector file formats are usually **proprietary**, with few open or common standards to share between vector software applications.

What does it mean?

Proprietary means owned, often by a company. In computing, proprietary often refers to the way a document file is structured, e.g. CorelDRAW uses a CDR format for its vector files, which are structured so that CorelDRAW can open them.

There are many file formats commonly used for bitmap files – bitmap applications can usually open, edit and save many of them. Bitmap file formats are less likely to be proprietary than vector files.

BMP bitmap files are often used for scanned images that need to be saved at best quality. Because of this, BMP files are often quite large.

JPEG bitmap files are often used when a smaller file size is needed, for example so that Internet graphics take less time to download and to show in the browser.

Test your knowledge

1 What are the differences between vector and bitmap images?

2 Explain ways that the size of a graphics file may be controlled.

3 Identify four graphic formats, with examples of where their use would be appropriate.

24.3 Tools to edit and manipulate technically complex images

Editing tools are designed to help the user change a graphic and can be very powerful. This section explains the uses of some of these tools.

24.3.1 Graphic creation

Graphic images can either be obtained from another source, or created using specialist software.

24.3.1.1 Obtaining images

Many digital graphic artists use editing tools to enhance an image that is obtained from somewhere else, usually photographs or other sophisticated graphics. Images may be obtained by:

- scanning – using a scanner to capture an image from paper or other hard copy
- importing – using the File, Import menu option to bring in a graphic file in from another program
- digital camera – transferring a photograph taken by yourself or another person to your computer system.

24.3.1.2 Image creation

Many tools exist to help the user create an image, including freehand drawing techniques, which allow the user to draw with a mouse or graphics tablet directly into the application.

It is more common to create images with vector software rather than bitmap software, as vector graphics are often logos, diagrams or similar that do not already exist and so need to be created.

24.3.2 Tools and techniques

The computer can be a very powerful and in creating or editing graphics, enabling the user to do things that would be very difficult otherwise.

24.3.2.1 Standard software tools

Most graphics software applications include several standard tools, including rotate, flip, crop, group/ungroup and resize.

■ Rotate

Rotate is a common tool for both vector and bitmap applications. As you might expect, this tool turns the selected image round by a specified amount. The rotation might be done using the mouse to drag it round or by selecting an angle to rotate.

Flip

Flip is a common tool for both vector and bitmap applications. It is used to create a mirror image of part of an image. Often there is an option to create a new flipped image while keeping the existing selection, or to change the selection so that it is mirrored. Mirroring an object horizontally flips it from left to right; mirroring an object vertically flips it from top to bottom.

Crop

Crop is usually a bitmap tool used to 'cut off' the edges of an image so that the parts of the image that are not wanted are removed. The overall size of the image becomes smaller, but the contents of the image remain the same size. For example, a photograph of a person may be cropped to remove some of the background but the size of the face stays the same.

Group/Ungroup

Group/Ungroup is usually a vector tool. As vector images are created using many objects, it is often sensible to group some or all of them together to make it easier to work with them. For example, if a logo is created using several objects, then grouping them creates a single object that is much easier to select and work with. Grouped objects can be ungrouped to split them up into the original collection of objects – this is useful if one or two of the objects in the group need changing. They can then be grouped again once the changes have been made.

Resize

Resize is a common tool for both vector and bitmap applications. Using this tool makes the selection bigger or smaller. Vector images resize without losing quality because the image is kept inside memory as coordinates, with the computer recalculating the image to whatever resolution is needed for the screen, printer or any other device. When a bitmap is resized the software needs to examine the existing pixels, then determine the colours of the new pixels to reproduce the image – this is a complex operation that inevitably reduces image quality. Resizing bitmaps well is one of the benefits of using expensive, professional software applications.

24.3.2.2 Special effects

Special effects give you a lot of control and power over the image. The skilled IT professional can use these bitmap tools to make a bad picture spectacular – unfortunately, an unskilled user can use the same tools to make a spectacular picture bad!

Soften

The soften tool is used to smooth and tone down the harsh edges in an image without losing much of the important image detail.

Sharpen

Sharpening an image can increase the contrast, enhance image edges or reduce shading.

Watermark

A watermark in a word processor such as Word places an image behind the page giving the appearance of printing using watermarked paper.

Similarly, specialist graphic software may also have this tool, which can be used, for example, for adding a translucent copyright watermark over the image to identify it as your own work.

Invert

The invert tool reverses the colours of an image. Inverting an image creates the appearance of a photographic negative.

24.3.2.3 Colour

Specialist IT professionals can use colour tools to enhance and edit images.

Colour balance

The colour balance tool or filter lets you adjust an image by shifting colours between complimentary pairs of primary RGB (red, green and blue) colour values and secondary CMY (cyan, magenta and yellow) colour values. For example, to tone down red in a photo, you can shift the colour values from red to cyan.

■ Colour depth

Colour depth is also important as it controls the file size and overall quality of the image. **8-bit** (256 colours) is still popular for web images as they load up a lot quicker than 16-bit (64,000 colours) or 24-bit (16.7 million colours), while still maintaining an acceptable picture quality.

What does it mean?

8-bit means that a single byte is used for each item of data. A byte has 8 bits, each of which can be set to a one or zero. This gives 256 different combinations of bit patterns.

24.3.2.4 Layering

Layering is a very useful technique for creating and editing images, in which an image is divided into layers. A layer can be selected for editing with all the other layers locked, making it impossible to accidentally change part of the image which is completed.

Layers can also be set as not visible, allowing the user to see only the part of the image they want to work on.

Printing is another operation where layering can help the user. Unwanted layers can be marked as non-printable, so the hard copy will only show the parts needed by the user.

24.3.2.5 Advanced techniques: three-dimensional images

There are many ways of representing three-dimensional images using digital graphics, including:

- 3D drawing tools in a vector drawing package
- rendering a wire-frame model in a CAD application
- defining a digital landscape using games generation software.

■ 3D drawing tools

Using 3D drawing tools in a vector drawing package can produce some excellent effects. For example, CorelDRAW offers the Extrude dialogue box. This gives control over how the 3D effects are applied, including which direction the object is lit from and the position of the vanishing point – shown in Figure 24.17 as x under the shape.

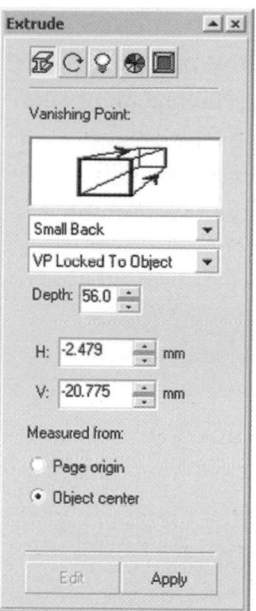

Figure 24.17 CorelDRAW 3D Extrude tool

■ Rendering a wire-frame model

CAD applications such as AutoCAD allow the user to define complex and precise objects using **wire-framing** (see Figure 24.6 on page 238 for an example). The object might be a component designed for manufacture, an architectural drawing or other 3D design. Many CAD applications can add texture to the wire-frames to produce a realistic impression of what the design will look like when it is produced (see Figure 24.18).

What does it mean?

Wire-framing is used to draw an image of a 3D object that shows only the edges of the object.

Figure 24.18 A 3D graphic created using AutoCAD

■ Using games generation software

Games generation software such as DarkBASIC brings the power of games programming within reach of all software developers. This type of software makes defining a digital landscape and using animated creatures or machines much easier than you might expect (see Figure 24.19).

24.3.2.6 Advanced techniques: masking

What does it mean?

Masking means selecting a certain area of an image to protect it from changes, such as applying colour, filters or other effects.

A regular mask is a selection tool such as a simple rectangle, circle, freehand shape or lasso to isolate the area that you want to protect from changes.

The image can be cropped to a mask, so only the part inside the mask remains.

A colour mask is used to protect colours in an image – the mask will apply only to the pixels within the colour range that you specify in the mask, using the magic wand, lasso or colour mask tool. This technique can be used to separate part of an image such as a car or person from the background.

Test your knowledge

1. Give three examples of how a digital image may be sourced.
2. Identify and explain how four software tools may be used to edit digital images.
3. Identify and explain how four special effects may be used with digital images.
4. What is layering?
5. Explain three techniques for producing 3D graphical images.
6. What is a wire-frame model?

 Figure 24.19 DarkBASIC

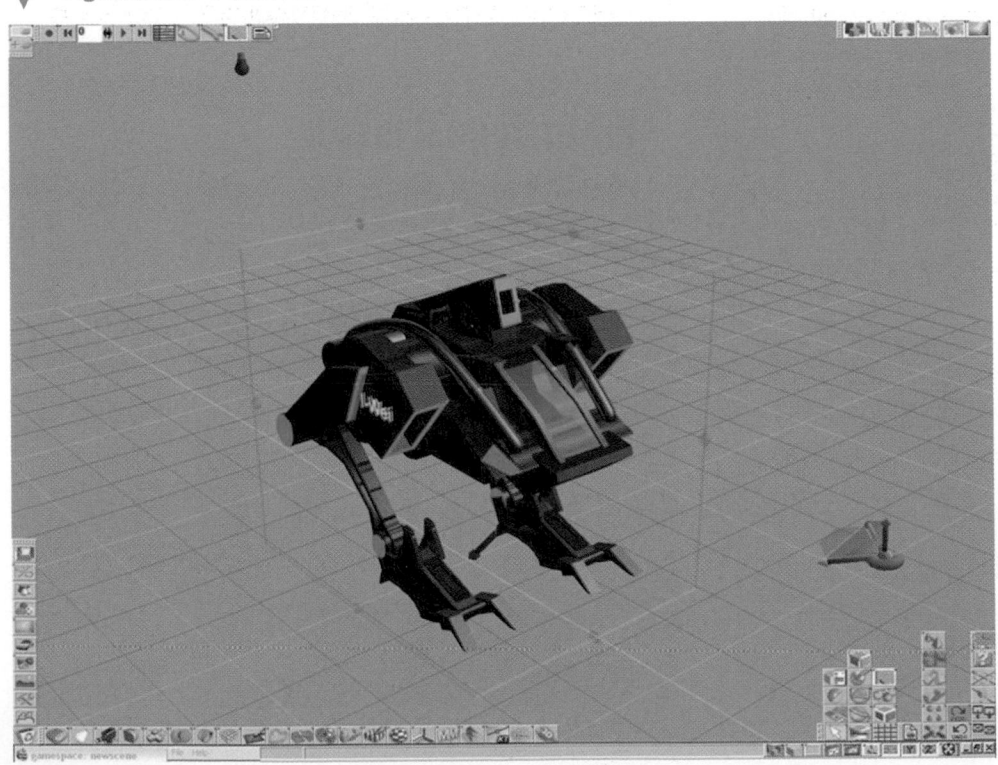

Professional graphical work needs to meet the user requirements, which will be specified at the beginning of a project.

24.4.1 User need

24.4.1.1 Client needs as distinct from user needs

Clients and users may have different needs from digital graphics.

The client is the person or organisation that has commissioned and will pay for the job so their needs are the most important. Their needs might include such aspects as:

- keeping to a corporate style
- using file formats that are compatible with their software
- keeping within their guidelines for file sizes that are appropriate for website download times and any other bandwidth or storage considerations.

The user is anyone who sees the digital graphics. Their needs include:

- images having enough resolution to make the picture quality acceptable
- images that clearly convey intended information.

24.4.1.2 Identifying target audience

Identifying the target audience is important because it will help you to be clear about who will be seeing the completed images and why. Understanding this makes a big difference to the effectiveness of images, as knowing the reasons for creating them will help you to target them better.

When the images are near to completion, you can show them to people selected from the target audience for feedback on how well they meet the user needs.

Activity 24.4

Managing digital images

Produce a guide to managing digital images.

1 Start your guide with a section demonstrating the impact on file size and image quality of:
- file format such as BMP or JPEG
- compression techniques such as WinZip
- image resolution and colour depth.

You need to define each of these terms and include screenshots of an image to show how changing these aspects of an image affects the quality and file size.

2 Include a section explaining how to convert files into other formats using:
- file menu options such as Save As or Export
- dedicated file conversion software.

3 Add a section explaining file management techniques, including naming files, folder structures, moving and deleting files.

4 Finally, write a section identifying some other software tools that can be useful such as image viewers and photo galleries.

24.4.1.3 User requirements

You will need to set out the user needs in a document or part of a document stating what is wanted by the people who will be viewing the end result of the production.

24.4.1.4 Constraints

Most graphic productions have constraints to help make the production practical and useful. Constraints may include:

- house style – so the graphic fits in with the rest of the document and other publications from the client organisation

- image size – to ensure that the graphic meets requirements such as acceptable load times for web pages or acceptable resolution for printing
- intended use – to make sure the graphics are appropriate for their target audience
- file size – particularly important for web page load times, but may also be an issue if the graphics are to be delivered on CD-ROM or other media where there is a limited amount of space
- production costs – to keep within budget and to not make work unprofitable
- timescale – as an image completed after the rest of a job is published is of little use.

Activity 24.5

Defining the client and user needs

You have been asked to define and document the client and user needs for three related graphic images. The client is a family that owns a chain of local shops. The users are existing and potential customers of the shops. The required images are:

- a map showing the location of the shops owned by the family to be used for a website and brochure
- a new logo for the chain of shops
- a poster to display in the shops using the logo and a selection of photographs of products sold by the shops.

1 Produce a document defining the client need and identifying the target audience for each of these images. This document must include any constraints such as:

- house style
- intended use
- production costs
- output media. **p**₃

- image size
- file size
- timescale

2 Produce a document defining user need and requirements for each of the three images. **p**₃

3 Create and review the three graphic images defined in tasks 1 and 2. **p**₄

The output medium is whatever is used to convey the image to the end user. Output media include:

- paper
- vinyl
- textiles
- display
- plates (for printing).

24.4.2 Reviewing

24.4.2.1 Check against client need and user need

When a job is close to completion, it should be checked against the client and user needs to ensure it is fit for purpose and suitable for release. These checks are best made against the original job documentation to confirm the end result will be what is actually wanted.

24.4.2.2 Proofing

Proofing is when the image is output to see (roughly) what it will actually look like when completed. An image may be proofed to an inkjet printer by the designer to check that the parts of the image look right before sending the image to a **bureau** for the final print.

What does it mean?

A **bureau** is an organisation that carries out services, such as printing, for other businesses or clients. A design studio may not have expensive specialist printing facilities, so sends work to a bureau to make use of their printing equipment.

24.4.2.3 Image resolution

Part of the review process is to confirm that the image resolution is appropriate for the purpose of the digital graphic.

Graphics for web pages need to have an acceptable balance between the resolution and picture quality. Lower resolution means poorer picture quality but faster web page loading and downloads.

Graphics for publication need to match the resolution to the printer. Either a lower or higher resolution will result in poorer picture quality when printed.

24.4.2.4 File formats

The review process should involve checking that the file format meets the needs of both client and users. The file format should not cause any compatibility issues that would result in problems loading or using the graphic.

24.4.2.5 Other

Any other identified needs from the image specification, such as the speed of loading, should also be reviewed to confirm that all the image design needs have been met.

24.4.3 Legislation and guidelines

24.4.3.1 Identifying ownership

Identifying ownership is an important first step towards finding out whether a graphic can be reused. Many images have the owner name or copyright printed on or close to the image, which makes this task easy.

If there is no name printed near the graphic, then the ownership will probably be with the publisher of the web page or book where you found the image.

24.4.3.2 Copyright

A piece of work such as an image is copyright when it has an owner with control over how the work is used or copied.

It must always be assumed that an image already has copyright and that permission must be sought from the copyright owner before the image can be reused.

Activity 24.6

Reviewing graphical image production

1 Review the three graphic images you defined and created in Activity 24.5. Your reviews should include:

- the different types of graphic images, image resolutions, file formats and extensions used for each graphic
- an explanation of the relevance of each type of graphic, with reference to the documents to be produced and the file size and clarity of image
- reference to tools you used within the software and the reasons you chose them
- checking each image against the client and user needs
- how the images were proofed
- the speed of loading any graphics intended for web pages. **p**₄

Note: This test should be completed in conjunction with Activity 24.5 task 3 to evidence criterion **p**₄ fully.

2 Use a scanner and digital camera to capture images and use them in your editing to produce some of the graphic images. You must produce a report to accompany these images explaining how you did this. **p**₅

3 Annotate your printed work to identify where you used appropriate advanced techniques, such as creating 3D images or masking. **m**₂

4 Justify your choice of vector graphics or bitmaps for each graphic and the tools used in the completed documents. Refer to how they meet client needs and user requirements.

These tools might include freehand draw, rotate, flip, crop, group/ungroup, resize, soften, sharpen, watermark, invert, colour balance and/or layering.

You should also justify the image resolution, colour depth and file formats. **d**₁

24.4.3.3 Copyright free

Copyright free images can be freely used by anyone. Such images may be found on web pages that are clearly identified as copyright free, included with graphics software or from other sources.

Any image that is not clearly identified as copyright free needs the permission of the owner if it is to be used. Permission should be requested from the owner and this will often involve paying a fee before the image can be reused.

If you take your own photographs of people, you need them to sign a model release form, giving you permission to use the photographs as you wish.

Activity 24.7

Legal implications of using graphical images

1 Produce presentation slides to help you explain the potential legal implications of using and editing graphical images. You will need to identify how copyright limits using images found on the Internet or from other sources. Include some example images and explain the potential implications of using them. Include:

- how to identify the ownership of an image
- what is meant by copyright
- what is meant by copyright free
- how to gain permission to use an image.

Test your knowledge

1 What is the client need?

2 What are user requirements?

3 What is meant by constraints?

4 Give five examples of output media.

5 What are the purposes of reviewing a completed job?

6 Explain the issues around copyright and digital images.

Preparation for assessment

The assessment tasks in this unit are based on the following scenario. In addition to this scenario, the case studies on pages 237 and 247 can also provide assessment evidence for P1, P2, P3, P4, M1, D1 and D2.

You have a part-time job in an off-licence. It is one of a family-run chain of stores in your area. You help to stock the shelves and operate the till.

The owners have decided to produce some marketing material for the shop. They want to produce some graphics to be used on a printed colour leaflet to put through letter boxes in the area, on the website they are hoping to have created and on a poster to display in their shops.

The chain has a recently purchased computer which they hope to use to produce the graphics needed for the leaflet and website.

As they know you are studying to become an IT practitioner, the owners have asked you for your advice on what to do to the existing system to make it suitable for manipulating digital graphics.

They hope that, if the system can be upgraded, you will be able to use it to produce the graphics that they require.

Task 1 (P1, P6)

The owners want you to explain to them the system requirements needed to capture and manipulate digital graphics. They have borrowed a data projector and invited you to show them a PowerPoint presentation.

They would like your presentation to last about ten minutes, describing the hardware and software used to create and edit graphics. You should create a graphic for your presentation to help you explain what each of the following do in a computer system used to manipulate digital graphics:

- mouse
- screen
- graphics tablet
- digital camera
- scanner
- flash cards
- USB storage devices.

They are also interested in how hardware components affect the performance of a computer system used to manipulate digital graphics, so would like you to produce a digital graphic showing how these work together in your presentation:

- hard drive
- graphics card
- processor(s)
- RAM.

The next slides in your presentation will help you explain the software used for digital graphics. These slides will use screenshots taken when you created the other digital graphics in your presentation to give the owners an impression of how graphical software can be used. The slides also need to explain the differences between:

- vector graphics software such as CorelDRAW
- bitmap software such as Paint
- photo manipulation software such as Photoshop
- graphics facilities embedded within other application packages such as Word.

The last slides in your presentation will explain the potential legal implications of using and editing graphical images. You will need to identify how copyright limits the use of images found on the

Internet or from other sources. Include some example images and explain the potential implications of using them. Include:

- how to identify the ownership of an image
- what is meant by copyright
- what is meant by copyright free
- how to gain permission to use an image.

Task 2 (P2, M1, D2)

The owners enjoyed your presentation and found it helped them to understand what some of the computing jargon involved in digital imaging actually means. They now want a written report on how suitable their existing computer system is for the task and whether it should be upgraded.

The existing computer has this specification:

- Intel Pentium D 'Dual Core X2' CPU (5.3 Ghz)
- VIA Chipset 1066 Mhz Motherboard – slots available: AGP8X (1), PCI (3), RAM (2); ports available: LAN (1), USB (6)
- 512 MB RAM
- 80 GB HDD (SATA300)
- 18× DVD+/−RW Dual Layer & Dual Format
- onboard UniChrome PRO 3D Graphics with 64 MB shared memory
- mouse and keyboard
- 15″ flat screen
- cheap inkjet printer.

The report must identify two graphics-related hardware upgrades to this system and describe the potential benefits they bring when working with graphic images.

The report should identify a choice of products for each of the proposed hardware upgrades for the capture, manipulation or storage of graphics. It should also compare their limitations.

You must also compare the limitations of two different software packages used for the capture, manipulation or storage of graphics.

The report will include a section evaluating the impact of evolving output media on the design and creation of graphic images. You will need to research how output media products such as large flat screens, printer technologies, etc. are developing. Then evaluate them against cost, speed, usage and any other criteria you discover.

Task 3 (P3)

The owners want you to define and document the client and user needs for three related graphic images to be used in their marketing materials.

The client needs are those of the family that owns the shops and are different from the user needs, which are those of people receiving the images.

The required images are:

- a map showing the location of the shops owned by the family, to be used for both website and leaflet
- a new logo for the chain of shops
- a poster to display in the shops using the logo and a selection of photographs of products sold by the shops.

Produce a document defining the client need and identifying the target audience for each of these images. This document must include any constraints such as:

- house style
- image size
- intended use
- file size
- production costs
- timescale
- output media.

Produce a document defining user need and requirements for each of the three images.

You have been asked to create and review the three graphic images defined in Task 3.

Your reviews should include:

- the different types of graphic images, image resolutions, file formats and extensions used for each graphic – their relevance should be explained, with reference to the end product and the size of file and clarity of image
- reference to the tools you used within the software and the reasons you chose them
- checking each image against the client and user needs
- how the images were proofed
- the speed of loading the graphics intended for web pages.

You must use both a scanner and digital camera to capture images and use them in your editing to produce some of the graphic images. Write a report to accompany these images explaining how you did this. **p₅**

Use appropriate advanced techniques such as creating 3D images or masking. Provide evidence of this by annotating your printed work. **m₂**

Justify your choice of vector graphics or bitmaps for each graphic and the tools used in the completed documents. Refer to how they meet client needs and user requirements.

These tools might include freehand draw, rotate, flip, crop, group/ungroup, resize, soften, sharpen, watermark, invert; colour balance and layering.

You should also justify the image resolution, colour depth and file formats. **d₁**

The owners have now asked you to produce a guide to managing the digital images you have created to make it easier to add to the collection in the future and to find images.

Start your guide with a section demonstrating the impact on file size and image quality of:

- file format such as BMP or JPEG
- compression techniques such as WinZip
- image resolution and colour depth.

You need to define each of these terms and include screenshots of an image to show how changing these aspects of an image affects the quality and file size.

Include a section explaining how to convert files into other formats using:

- File menu options such as Save As or Export
- dedicated file conversion software.

Add a section explaining file management techniques, including naming files, folder structures, moving and deleting files.

Finally, write a section identifying some other software tools that can be useful, such as image viewers and photo galleries.

Computer Animation

Introduction

Computer animation is the art of creating moving images using computers. It brings together computer graphics and animation techniques. Animation does not require computers, but the increasing power of computers to create and manipulate sets of images has allowed animation to reach new levels of sophistication and realism.

Animation is increasingly created by means of 3D computer graphics, although 2D computer graphics are still widely used for low bandwidth and faster real-time needs. In this unit only 2D graphics are required.

After completing this unit, you should be able to achieve these outcomes:

- Understand the origins and types of animation

- Be able to use software techniques used in animation

- Be able to plan, create and review an animation using digital methods.

The examples given throughout this chapter for animation applications are for Adobe Flash.

Grading criteria	Activity	Page number
To achieve a pass grade the evidence must show that the learner is able to:		
p₁ Describe how persistence of vision is used in animation	PFA	292
p₂ Describe three applications for animations	26.15, PFA	282, 292
p₃ Describe the features, advantages and limitations of animated GIFs and one other animation format	26.11, PFA	276, 292
p₄ Describe two different types of animation techniques	26.14, PFA	280, 292
p₅ Describe the special factors that need to be taken into account when creating animations for the web	PFA	292
p₆ Design, create and review animations for particular purposes that use both vector and bit map graphics	26.19, 26.20, 26.21, PFA	288, 289, 290, 291
p₇ Design, create and review animations for particular purposes that are designed to be incorporated into web pages	26.19, 26.20, 26.21, PFA	288, 289, 290, 291
To achieve a merit grade the evidence must show that, in addition to the pass criteria, the learner is able to:		
m₁ Compare two different animation formats	PFA	292
m₂ Compare two different specialist software package or programming techniques used to create computer animation	PFA	292
m₃ Adapt and improve animations based on formal reviews	26.21, PFA	290, 291
m₄ Explain particular techniques that are used to minimise the file size of animations	26.16, PFA	283, 292
To achieve a distinction grade the evidence must show that, in addition to the pass and merit criteria, the learner is able to:		
d₁ Evaluate one software package or technique that is used to create animations	26.15, PFA	282, 292
d₂ Evaluate the tools and techniques used to create finished animations	PFA	291
Note: 'PFA' stands for 'Preparation for assessment'.		

Animation is a way of creating the illusion of movement. It can be used to create a fantasy world or to recreate reality, and is a medium that is both exciting and popular.

The development of animation technology began as a quest to capture the real world on a fixed medium. Before the invention of the camera, it was impossible to acquire a picture of reality. Before inventions such as the zoetrope and the cinematograph, it was difficult to show natural movement. Nowadays we are quite used to seeing the real world captured in a photograph or a strange new world animated in a movie. But try to imagine that you have never seen such things and think about the dedication and creativity it must have taken to create these exciting visual experiences that we take for granted today.

26.1.1 Basis of and origins of animation

At the core of animation is how the human eyes and brain allow us to see movement, particularly the theory of the persistence of vision (see section 26.1.1.2 below). This theory explains how we can see and make sense of animations. Thanks to the pioneers and inventors of animation and film making, it has become possible to create masterpieces – the scale of modern animations and films would have been unimaginable to the early pioneers. Traditional techniques have paved the way for more modern techniques, although most are still used today in some form.

26.1.1.2 Persistence of vision

Movement in animation can seem very smooth, but in fact what is being seen is a series of individual images joined together and shown at speed. The animation appears continuous due to **persistence of vision** (see Figure 26.1).

An animation appears smoother and less jerky when there are more **frames per second (fps)** and more intermediary steps in the images that build up the illusion of movement.

▲ **Figure 26.1 Separate images which are seen as continuous**

The more frames that are shown during one second, the fewer gaps the eye and brain have to fill in and so the more continuous the motion appears.

An early example of this principle being applied was the **zoetrope** (see section 26.1.1.3 on page 263). The faster the zoetrope was spun, the smoother the animation appeared.

What does it mean?

The **zoetrope** (also known as a daedalum) was invented by William Horner in 1834. It was a machine that spun a strip of images at high speed in order to show movement.

Computer animation is generally created at 12 fps, as this is a sufficient speed to prevent jerkiness in the series of images, although the number of frames per second can be raised if necessary. The higher the rate of frames per second, the more images are needed in the animation. Cartoons that are made on a tight budget sometimes have a reduced rate of frames per second, such as 8 fps, so they need fewer images and the animation can be finished more quickly and cheaply.

What does it mean?

Persistence of vision refers to the ability of the human eye to preserve the image it has just seen for a brief instant. Therefore, when the eye sees a series of images that follow each other, it retains each image and the brain processes the series as one continuous image.

Frames per second (fps) refers to the number of individual images that are shown every second.

Activity 26.1

Persistence of vision

1 Create a **flip book** of at least 20 images to demonstrate persistence of vision in action.

   a) Use either a small book or pieces of rectangular paper cut to the same size and stapled together (see Figure 26.2).

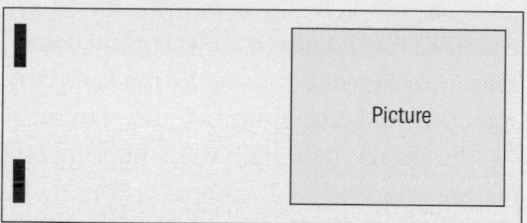

Picture

▲ **Figure 26.2 Layout of a flip book**

   b) Starting with the back page, draw a picture at the right-hand side of the page.

   c) Draw a picture on each page, moving forward, making slight changes on each new page.

   d) Test your flip book by flipping through the pages quickly. Instead of seeing a set of different images, persistence of vision should mean that you see movement.

2 The average speed of an animation is 12 fps. Research the speed for movies, computer screens (refresh rate) and computer games. Why do you think they are different?

What does it mean?

A **flip book** is a very simple type of animation where drawings are put on separate pages and then flicked through to animate.

26.1.1.3 Pioneers and techniques

If it were not for the pioneers of animation who pushed the boundaries of technology, progress would not have been made so quickly. There were numerous people involved in the development of the capture of the still image (the camera) and then the motion picture – each one has contributed to modern animation and film making. Described here are three key people in the history of this technology – without them, modern movies may never have become a reality.

■ William Horner

In 1834, William Horner invented the daedalum (which means 'wheel of the Devil'). The name was later changed to zoetrope ('wheel of life') (see below). It became a popular item, especially as the animations could be changed.

▲ **A zoetrope**

The zoetrope was a cylindrical device, about 30 centimetres in diameter, with slits cut into it at equally spaced intervals. Animation strips were placed inside with images that had slight differences between them. Then the cylinder was spun and, by looking through the slits which were spinning past, the images appeared to be animated. The zoetrope achieved about 14 fps and the images appeared to be moving naturally.

The zoetrope is considered the forerunner of cinema film.

■ Thomas Alva Edison

Thomas Alva Edison was a prolific and successful inventor – he developed three ideas which have become crucial to modern animation and cinematography.

Edison was working to improve the efficiency and quality of the telegraph message, when he noticed that the transmitter would emit a noise that resembled the spoken word. By developing this further, he discovered that he could record and play back voices, using two needles and a wax-coated cylinder. When someone spoke into the mouthpiece, one of the needles would indent the cylinder according to the sound vibrations in the voice. The other needle would then 'read' these indentations and play it back. Edison completed his first **phonograph** in 1877 (see below). It became hugely

▲ **A phonograph**

What does it mean?

The **phonograph** was invented by Thomas Edison in 1877 to record the spoken word.

popular, as it could be used for numerous purposes, such as dictation, books for the blind, children's toys and recording messages.

Edison is most popularly known as the inventor of the electric light bulb. However, he didn't actually invent it, but improved an idea that had been conceived 50 years earlier. His major achievement was that he made electric lighting safe, practical and economical. As a replacement for gas lighting, the electric light bulb was a huge hit and made Edison famous and rich. His company, Edison General Electric, merged with its competitor and became the US company General Electric.

In 1888, Edison was visited by Eadweard Muybridge who was the inventor of the **zoopraxiscope** (see below). This was an early form of projector – images on glass were lit by a lantern and projected onto a screen, producing a continuous moving image.

▲ **A zoopraxiscope**

What does it mean?

The **zoopraxiscope** was invented by Eadweard Muybridge and was a development of the zoetrope. It used light shone through images on glass.

Muybridge was interested in Edison's phonograph and proposed a collaboration of moving images and recorded sound. Edison, possibly considering the zoopraxiscope to be an inefficient way of producing moving images, declined. But he was very much interested in the idea. He invented his own version – the **kinetoscope** (see below) – which became the forerunner of modern projection. It involved a sheet of perforated film being moved over a light to give the illusion of movement.

▲ **A kinetoscope**

What does it mean?

The **kinetoscope** was invented by Thomas Edison and was an early projector using perforated film.

Further experiments to combine a moving image machine with a pre-recorded sound machine were partly successful, but quality was an issue and it was difficult for the technicians operating the machines to keep the images and sound in time.

■ Lumière brothers

There had been several attempts at making motion picture cameras before 1895, but the Lumière brothers created a camera that was portable and could film, process and project all in one unit. The **cinematograph** (see below) is considered the invention that began the era of motion pictures. It used 35 mm perforated celluloid film. Although Edison (and others such as the Skladanowsky brothers) had preceded them in projecting film to an audience, the first screening made by the Lumière brothers is considered by film historians to be the birth of cinema.

▲ **A cinematograph**

What does it mean?

The **cinematograph** was invented by the Lumière brothers in 1895 and used 35 mm celluloid film.

One of their first films, *The Arrival of a Train at the Station*, showed a train entering a station diagonally across the screen and reportedly had audiences screaming and ducking out of the way. This was a new and exciting medium and it was now practical to bring it to a mass audience.

Now the technology had sufficiently developed, filmmakers began to become interested in the entertainment value and make historical, fantasy and horror movies. As demand increased, musical halls, theatres and opera houses were converted to allow the showing of moving pictures and audiences flocked to see the new exciting shows.

There are many techniques available to animators. Some have been developed into more modern methods using technology and some are still used in their original form today.

■ Drawn animation

Drawn animation is where each frame is hand drawn or painted onto a **frame** of film (see Figure 26.3).

What does it mean?

Drawn animation is where animators draw each frame of the film.

A **frame** is a single section of film that contains one image of the animation.

► Figure 26.3
Frame of a film

This method works in a similar way to a flip book, as each frame is drawn slightly differently from the previous one. When played at speed, the frames create movement. The advantage is that every single frame can be drawn in immense detail. The disadvantage is that this is incredibly time-consuming. Saturday morning children's cartoons have always been in high demand and studios are pressured to produce new material every week with very limited budgets. To combat these challenging circumstances, they drew fewer frames per second, which meant that less work and resources were required; however, the animation appeared shakier.

Another method of saving time and money using traditional techniques is to use **limited animation**.

What does it mean?

Limited animation is where the same cels are used over and over again.

Images are drawn on to **cels** and then overlaid to create a composite image.

What does it mean?

A **cel** is a piece of transparent film that can be drawn on and then overlaid with other cels to create a composite image.

One cel would contain the background and others would contain the moving parts. The background could remain the same throughout the scene and only the moving cels would need to be redrawn. This method can be seen in cartoons such as Hanna-Barbera's *The Flintstones*. For example, Fred Flintstone could be running along a street, so he would be the moving part that needed to be redrawn. However, the same background would be used throughout the scene, so he would pass the same house and the same lamppost over and over again, but giving the illusion of distance.

■ Claymation

Claymation is a type of stop-motion animation where a scene is set up, a picture is taken on a camera, then the scene is moved, another picture is taken, and so on.

What does it mean?

Claymation is where models or puppets are moved frame by frame to create an animation.

Although called claymation, models can be puppets or made out of clay, plasticine, wire or any other material that is malleable but can stay still during the taking of the shot. Claymation provides a 3D effect that is often lacking in other traditional techniques. The models can be reused over and over again throughout the filming and this can aid continuity. However, making a claymation film is a very time-consuming process. For example, the makers of the film *James and The Giant Peach* could only film about 10 seconds of the movie each day because of the number of joints belonging to each character – the centipede alone had 72 moving parts.

■ Cut-outs

Cut-outs use a similar method to claymation – they are moved, then a shot is taken, then moved again and so on.

What does it mean?

Cut-out animation is where shapes are laid against a background and moved for each shot of the camera.

A background is created, then the cut-outs (the moving parts) are placed on top. This can be a very quick method of creating animation – much quicker than the other traditional methods discussed – but it can result in quite jerky movements. The cut-out method is rarely used in modern animation; however, Matt Stone and Trey Parker have had worldwide success with their creation, *South Park*. It originally used traditional cut-out methods but moved on to use computer animations to simulate the effect of cut-out.

STOP Test your knowledge

1 What is animation?

2 How does the theory of persistence of vision relate to animation?

3 What does fps mean?

4 Name three pioneers of animation and their key inventions.

5 Give an example of each of the following animation techniques:
   a) drawn animation   c) claymation
   b) limited animation   d) cut-out animation.

26.1.2 Applications of animation

When someone thinks about animation, often the first thing that comes to mind is entertainment: animated films and cartoons. However, animation has so many other uses and is so widespread in our lives that sometimes you may not even realise when animation is being used.

26.1.2.1 Entertainment

Animation used for entertainment can take several forms, from a cartoon 'short' lasting only a few minutes between programmes to feature-length films. The first full-length animated film to be widely successful in the Western world was *Snow White and The Seven Dwarfs*, produced by Walt Disney Productions in 1937. It used traditional animation techniques, took three years to make and was a risky enterprise for Walt Disney – he reportedly had to mortgage his house to finance the project. However, the international success it acquired has justified Disney's decision and it changed the course of animation history. In making this film, techniques (such as realistic human movements and weather effects) were developed that would be used in future films.

Modern animation films generally use computer techniques throughout and examples of this can be seen in films such as *The Incredibles*, *Ice Age* and *Toy Story*.

Audiences can watch unrealistic animation and understand that it is simulation. They can also watch real humans acting and understand that what they are watching is real. As animation becomes increasingly realistic, it is believed to enter the Uncanny Valley. This is an area of perception in which the human brain cannot clearly distinguish whether what they are seeing is real or simulated.

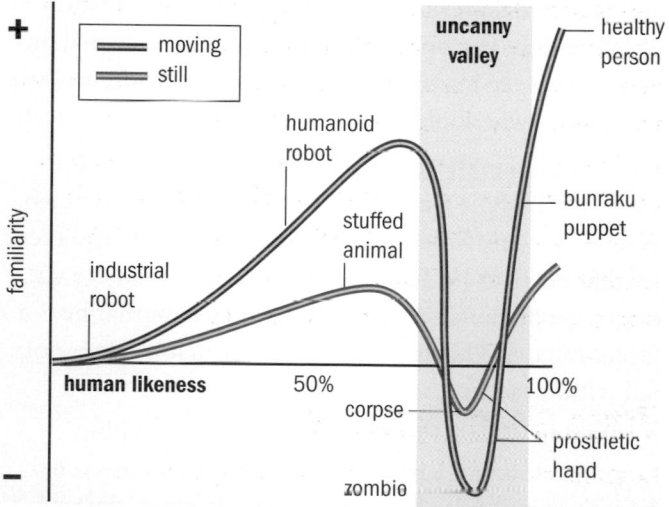

▲ **Figure 26.4 Diagram of the location of the Uncanny Valley**

Case study

The Uncanny Valley

Animated films such as *The Polar Express* and *Monster House* were hailed by critics as being revolutionary for their use of **performance capture** for human characters. However, this acclamation did not translate into as much box office profit as might have been expected. The reason given was a theory called the **Uncanny Valley** (see Figure 26.4).

What does it mean?

Performance capture is where human acting is 'captured' by a computer and then used by animators to create the images.

Uncanny Valley is the theory that if animation looks too real, audiences will feel uncomfortable.

The theory states that humans or humanlike figures (such as androids), which are not real but look very real, make us feel very uncomfortable as our brains have difficulty recognising what they are seeing.

As technology develops, it is thought that the Uncanny Valley will become an increasing problem. For example, as computer game characters become more realistic, players might feel uncomfortable being represented on-screen by a person who is no longer a fantasy figure, but a character who looks and moves completely realistically.

For example, in the game *Gears Of War* (released on Xbox 360 by Epic Games), the main character Marcus Fenix is very realistic in the way that he moves and there is great detail in his face. However, he has been drawn out of proportion, so there can be no doubt that he is a fantasy figure. This means that the animation does not fall within the Uncanny Valley.

Animation can also be used in conjunction within human acting. An early example of this is in the 1964 Walt Disney Productions film, *Mary Poppins*, starring Julie Andrews and Dick Van Dyke. Although most of the film is acted by humans, there is a sequence in which they are acting alongside animated characters. There are some clever interactions where the humans talk to the animated characters and objects are passed between them.

The penguins from the animation in *Mary Poppins* reappeared as waiters and bartenders in the 1988 film *Who Framed Roger Rabbit*, which was a landmark film involving animated characters and humans in a real environment. Bob Hoskins stars alongside a cartoon rabbit called Roger in a world where humans and 'Toons' exist together. The animated characters were all created using traditional techniques after the shooting of the live action, which meant the actors were acting against thin air. This film led to other human/animation interaction movies such as *Space Jam* (1996), *The Pagemaster* (1994) and *Casper* (1995).

CGI (computer generated imagery) is used widely in modern films and can create fantastical scenes such as flying through space. It can also be used to replicate objects and show, for example, a fleet of ships filling the ocean to the horizon. At first CGI used stop-motion techniques which created a slightly unrealistic effect. However, the 1993 film *Jurassic Park* revolutionised CGI technology and proved that convincing digital animation was both achievable and desired by audiences.

Activity 26.2

CGI in movies

1   Research and make notes on how the following films used computer animation:

- *Tron*
- *Flight of the Navigator*
- *Labyrinth*
- *The Abyss*
- *The Mask*
- *The Matrix*
- *Lord of the Rings*
- *Star Wars*.

26.1.2.2 Advertising

Television advertising makes good use of animation to provide imagery that would not be possible in the real world.

Animation can be used to make products look fun and can be especially effective with adverts for children. For example, Kellogg's has used animated characters throughout a long-running series of adverts for Coco Pops. The characters are now well-known to the television-viewing population, even though they are only on-screen for a couple of minutes at a time.

Other uses of animation can involve suspending reality in order to entertain TV audiences during the advert or wow them by the product. For example, in a series of Citroën adverts, a car morphed into a robot figure and took part in activities such as dancing and ice skating. This conveyed an exciting message to the audience about the product that was being sold.

Activity 26.3

Animation in advertising

1 The next time you watch television, pay close attention to the adverts. Choose five adverts and, for each one, write down:
   - the product being sold
   - whether animation is used
   - the purpose of the animation
   - whether, in your opinion, it is an effective advert.

With the rise in popularity of the Internet and the speed at which people can access it in their own homes, there has been an increase in opportunities for advertisers on the Web. There are three main types of advertising on the Internet that use animation:

- banner adverts that appear either across the top of a web page or down the side
- pop-up adverts that open in a new window when a web page is opened
- centre-screen Flash adverts.

Generally, the aim of the animation in these adverts is to attract the attention of the visitor to the web page and to encourage them to buy the product, visit the advertised site or do whatever else the advert wants them to do.

Billboard advertisements now also use animation, due to the increased availability and affordability of the technology. In Piccadilly Circus in London, the famous illuminated adverts span the whole height of the buildings (see below). Traditionally these were made up of fluorescent and neon lighting, but they are now being replaced by full-screen animations. This means that advertisers are no longer limited to one advert but can change it easily whenever necessary.

▲ **Piccadilly Circus then and now**

26.1.2.3 Education

Animation is becoming more frequently used in education: from demonstrating a scientific idea that would be difficult to carry out in the classroom, to grabbing and maintaining students' interest in a topic by using a computer game with strong educational content.

A study carried out for the Department of Education and Skills in 2002 investigated whether computer games could be used as an educational tool and reported:

> 'Games provide a forum in which learning arises as a result of tasks stimulated by the content of the games, knowledge is developed through the content of the game, and skills are developed as a result of playing the game.'

> (TEEM report: *Games in Education*, 2002)

There are many educational games available and most rely on animation to ensure users find them entertaining while they learn. They cover a wide variety of topics including school subjects, such as science, and life skills, such as healthy eating, and they can even be used in training for adults, such as in driving simulators.

Activity 26.4

Animation in education

1 Think about your education to date. Has animation been used in any area to develop your learning?

2 List all the subjects you are currently studying. For each one, name at least one way animation could be used to assist your education.

26.1.2.4 Other uses of animation

Animation can be used for simulations of places or situations that would be too difficult, dangerous or expensive to carry out in the real world. In architecture, animated simulation can predict what would happen to buildings in certain weather conditions, such as hurricanes or floods. Architects can test the buildings for every possible eventuality before the actual building work is done. This means they can refine and perfect the structures to make them as safe as possible.

The military also uses simulations as part of its training. Military personnel are able to take part in realistic, interactive and repetitive military scenarios to develop their reaction times and strategies for similar circumstances in the real world. Animations are also used to model what would happen in situations such as a bomb hitting a certain target, demonstrating the impact on the surrounding areas.

Driving simulators work in a similar way, allowing drivers to gain confidence in driving and a feel for the car before driving in the real world. They can also be used to teach hazard perception, i.e. awareness of potentially dangerous situations and knowing how to avoid them.

Television weather forecasting exposes a huge amount of people to high-quality graphics every day. Early TV weather forecasts were illustrated with hand-drawn symbols held in place on a map with magnets. Now animations are used to show more detailed and accurate forecasts (see below).

▲ **Weather forecasts then and now**

Activity 26.5

Animation in weather forecasting

1 Watch the weather forecasts on BBC 1, ITV and Channel 4 and compare the different styles of animation and artwork used.

STOP Test your knowledge

1 What is the Uncanny Valley and how does it affect viewers' perceptions of animation?

2 What is CGI and where is it used?

3 Name three adverts that use animation that you have seen within the last week.

26.1.3 Types of animation

Animation involves three mains types of progression: movement, masking and morphing.

26.1.3.1 Movement

Movement is the development of an object from position A to position B. Movement can be achieved frame by frame or by using **tweening**.

What does it mean?

Tweening (short for in betweening) is where the animator states where points A and B are and the computer fills in the intermediary movement.

■ How to create a simple motion tween in Adobe Flash

1 Open a new Adobe Flash document.
2 Select the Circle tool.
3 Choose any fill colour and no outline: ☑
4 Draw a circle (hold down the Shift key to make it a perfect circle).
5 Place your circle in the top left of the stage.
6 Right click on the circle and select Convert To Symbol.
7 Call it 'ball' and select the type: graphic. Click OK.
8 On the timeline (at the top of the screen), right click on frame 10 and select Insert Key Frame.
9 Make sure the key frame at 10 is highlighted and move your ball to the bottom middle of the stage.
10 On the timeline, on the grey section between the two key frames, right click and select Insert Motion Tween.
11 The grey part should turn blue and an arrow should point from the first key frame to the second one.
12 Test your movie by pressing Ctrl and Enter together.
13 The ball should move from one position to the other.

Activity 26.6

Moving in Adobe Flash

1 Create the ball described in the How to feature. Make it bounce by adding another key frame at frame 20 and tweening it from the bottom middle of the stage to the top right.
2 Create two more tweens to make the ball bounce back again (at frames 30 and 40).

26.1.3.2 Masking

Masking involves an image being shown or hidden by a **mask**.

What does it mean?

A **mask** is used to cover part or all of an image and can be moved to reveal the image beneath.

Some of the effects that can be produced using a mask resemble a camera lens or spotlight.

■ How to create a simple mask effect in Adobe Flash

1 Open a new Adobe Flash document.
2 Create a text box and type in your first name.
3 Create another text box and type in your last name.
4 Create a new layer – right click on Layer 1 beside the timeline, Insert Layer. (For more on layers, see section 26.2.1.2 on page 277.)
5 Make sure your cursor is on the first key frame in this new layer.
6 Draw a circle and fill it entirely in a solid colour (e.g. black).
7 Animate the circle using motion tweens so it moves around the two text boxes.
8 Right click on the layer name (Layer 2) and select Mask.
9 Test your movie by pressing Ctrl and Enter together. The circle should now act as a spotlight and only the area underneath it should be visible.

Morphing is the changing of an object from shape A into shape B. Morphing can be done frame by frame or by using tweening.

■ How to create a simple shape tween in Adobe Flash

1 Open a new Adobe Flash document.
2 Select the Text tool, draw a textbox onto the stage and enter the text '1'.
3 Format the 1 so the font is Arial and the size is 48 pt.
4 Use the Align palette (Ctrl + K to open) and centre the 1 to the exact centre of the stage.
5 Highlight the 1 and use Ctrl + B to break it apart until the shape is dotty (not highlighted with a blue box).
6 Create a key frame at frame 20 (right click, Insert Key Frame).
7 Replace the 1 with a 2 and ensure it has the same formatting, is in the centre of the stage and is broken apart.
8 On the timeline, on the grey section between the two key frames, left click so the highlight appears on it.
9 In the Properties Inspector at the bottom of the screen, choose Tween: Shape.
10 The grey part should turn green and an arrow should point from the first key frame to the second one.
Note: If the arrow is dotted, the shapes probably need to be broken apart again.
11 Test your movie by pressing Ctrl and Enter together.
12 The 1 should morph into a 2.

26.1.4 Animation formats

When creating an animation, you must consider the format in which you will create it. The choice will depend on the level of complexity of the animation and where it is intended to be used. It may be important to have a relatively small file size, perhaps to be used on a web page, or the animation needs to run equally well on different platforms such as Windows and Macintosh.

Animated GIFs are bitmap file formats which support animations. An animated GIF records a set of images and the instructions of how to run them. For more information on Animated GIFs, see section 26.1.5 on page 274.

Activity 26.7

Morphing in Adobe Flash

1 In a new document, morph a green square into a red circle.

2 In a new document, morph your first name into your last name.

3 Use the Help files to learn how Shape Hints work.
Hint: They are under Modify.
Add Shape Hints to your name morph and see how the transition improves.

■ Dynamic HTML

Dynamic HTML (**DHTML**) is a form of **HTML** combined with client side scripting languages (such as JavaScript), **CSS** and a **Document Object Model**.

What does it mean?

HTML (Hypertext Markup Language) is the language used as a basis for all web pages.

CSS (Cascading Style Sheets) is a language used to create the formatting for web pages.

DOM (Document Object Model) is used to integrate styles, content and formatting for web pages.

DHTML can be used to create animation on a web page, such as a rollover button or drop-down menu, as well as being used to make browser-based games. However, due to the different ways browsers interpret web languages, there were platform problems with DHTML, for example, between users using Internet Explorer and

Netscape Navigator. DHTML has become less popular in recent times and the features of DHTML are now usually created in CSS or client side scripting languages by themselves. The features of DHTML can also be created in Flash, and Flash websites are becoming more popular.

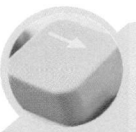

Activity 26.8

Animation formats: DHTML

1 Create a list of the advantages and disadvantages of using DHTML to create animation.

■ Flash

Adobe Flash (previously Macromedia Flash) is a multimedia authoring application, although the term can also be used to refer to Flash Player, the virtual machine used to run animations made in Flash.

The program allows users to create animations frame by frame using vectors or imported bitmaps and scripting in **ActionScript**. Sound and video can also be included.

What does it mean?

ActionScript is a language used in Flash animations, for example to create buttons.

A working Flash file is a .fla, which means that it can be opened and edited in Flash, whereas a compiled, uneditable file is a .swf.

Flash can be used to create animations for entertainment, examples of which can be found across the Internet. Elements of a web page, such as rollover buttons, can be made in Flash. The whole website can even be a Flash animation – this can create an impressive effect but causes problems for users with slow connections or who block Flash content. Flash has also been used more recently in online advertising, either in banner or centre-screen adverts. In addition, Flash games and content for mobile phones are becoming popular.

Flash is becoming the industry standard for lower-end animation and as a teaching tool in education. Due to the thorough help tutorials and its similarity to other Macromedia and Adobe products, Flash is relatively easy to learn, as opposed to many other animation programs.

Activity 26.9

Animation formats: Flash

1 Create a list of the advantages and disadvantages of using Flash to create animation.

■ Shockwave

Adobe Shockwave (previously Macromedia Shockwave) was introduced prior to Flash and was Macromedia's first successful multimedia player. Whereas Flash focuses more on 2D animation, Shockwave specialises in 3D graphics, streaming videos and has a faster **rendering** engine.

What does it mean?

Rendering is the process combining audio and visual elements with any applied effects to produce a file that can be played in real time.

Shockwave was designed to work with the Director application, which can compile several types of **asset** into one multimedia product, on a larger scale than Flash.

What does it mean?

An **asset** is any type of object within a multimedia product, such as an image, movie clip or sound file.

■ QuickTime

QuickTime is made by Apple but can be used on both Macintosh and Windows platforms. It is a multimedia player that supports animation, sound, video and other types of media clips. To accompany it, products such as

QuickTime Broadcaster (for producing live events) and QuickTime Pro (for creating movies) can be purchased.

QuickTime comes bundled with modern Macintosh operating systems (Mac OS) and rivals Windows Media Player which is embedded in Windows platform products. Although sales of Windows are higher than those of Apple (see Table 26.1), Apple is more commonly used in the design industry and the competition is still raging fiercely.

Windows Vista	Mac OS X Leopard
'In the first month of Windows Vista's general availability, sales exceeded 20 million licenses.' (From the official Microsoft site, 2007)	'Sales of Mac OS X Leopard will hit 9m in first year.' (From the official Mac News Network, 2007)

Table 26.1 Comparison of operating systems sales figures

■ RealPlayer

RealPlayer is a cross-platform multimedia player that can support both QuickTime and Window Media formats. Although this player might seem to be a solution to the issue of different formats needed for QuickTime and Windows Media Player, RealPlayer has received a lot of criticism for displaying adverts and pop-up messages during use. RealPlayer has an advertising-free version for businesses. However, this does not give the user access to all the features available in the full program.

A version of RealPlayer is used by the BBC website for playing the audio files of radio shows in its Listen Again service.

Activity 26.10

Multimedia players

1 Create a list of the advantages and disadvantages of creating animations for each of these:
   ● Shockwave ● QuickTime ● RealPlayer.

2 Compare your three lists of advantages and disadvantages. Name situations where you would choose to create an animation for each individual multimedia player.

26.1.5 Animated GIFs

GIF (pronounced either 'gif' or 'jif') is a **bitmap** format, which means that each pixel is saved in its location like a map. This is opposed to a **vector**, in which the graphical information is saved as a mathematical algorithm that is recalculated on each opening of the file.

What does it mean?

GIF stands for Graphics Interchange Format. It is a bitmap image format that can support animations.

Bitmap format is where an image is saved as a map of pixels.

Vector format saves the image as a mathematical algorithm.

26.1.5.1 Features of GIFs

A GIF uses a maximum palette of 256 colours, which means it can hold less colour detail than a **JPEG**.

What does it mean?

JPEG stands for Joint Photographics Expert Group. It is a bitmap image format which can hold more than 16 million colours in an image.

JPEGs are more suited to images, such as photographs, that need more detail to be stored, whereas GIFs are more appropriate for images with fewer colours, such as logos or graphics. One useful feature of GIF is that it supports transparent backgrounds.

GIF is an unusual image file format in that it also supports animation. In the file of an animated GIF, a set of images are stored together with the instructions of how they should be played, including the order of the images (see Figure 26.5).

GIF images are smaller than pure bitmap (.bmp) files, due to compression. They use a type of **lossless**

▲ **Figure 26.5 Frames in an animated GIF**

compression called LZW, which attempts to make the file size smaller without significantly degrading the image quality. The more times a file is saved in a compressed format, the more quality is lost – for example, if a file is saved as a GIF, then saved again as a GIF, the compression algorithm will have been performed on the image twice. It is better to work in a full bitmap (for example, a .psd file in Adobe Photoshop), then compress only once when the image is finished.

What does it mean?

Lossless compression makes the file size smaller, losing minimal quality of the image.

To try to include more colours in a GIF image, a technique called **dithering** can be employed, although this will decrease the amount by which the file size can be decreased and can cause some loss of definition in the image. The aim of dithering is to reduce the 'blockiness' that GIF images can have and give the impression of a more photographic quality (see Figure 26.6).

What does it mean?

Dithering is a technique which uses in-between colours to reduce the harsh contrast of two colours.

26.1.5.2 Advantages of GIFs

The advantages of animated GIFs include:

- lossless compression
- relatively small file sizes
- supports transparent backgrounds
- suitable for inclusion in online content.

▲ **Figure 26.6 Dithering**

26.1.5.3 Limitations of GIFs

The disadvantages of animated GIFs include:

- maximum palette of 256 colours
- colours can appear 'blocky' in photographic-quality images
- dithering reduces the amount the file size can be compressed.

26.1.5.4 Alternatives to GIFs

Alternative animation formats include DHTML web pages, Flash animations and multimedia products created for specific players such as QuickTime or Shockwave.

Activity 26.11

Animation formats: animated GIFs

1 Find or create examples of animated GIFs to demonstrate the following aspects and features of GIFs:
   - transparent backgrounds
   - use in web pages
   - maximum palette of 256 colours
   - smaller file sizes
   - dithering.

2 Using your lists of advantages and disadvantages from activities 26.8 to 26.10, decide which formats you would choose for the following animations and explain why:
   - an animated logo for a website
   - rollover buttons for an Internet website
   - rollover buttons for an intranet website
   - short animated movie to instruct workers in a company how to lift boxes safely
   - animated introduction to a CD being delivered to design companies.

Note: You can choose a combination of formats if required. **p₃**

26.2 Software techniques used in animation

There are several tools and techniques that are used throughout all digital animation development. Although some of the topics discussed in this section will also be applicable to other types of animation, this unit focuses on digital animation, which constitutes the majority of the modern industry.

26.2.1 Tools

Tools such as layers and frames are the basic building blocks of creating animations and are found in all animation applications. Other methods, such as scripting, give an animator more control over their creation and can be used to add interactivity for products such as games.

26.2.1.1 Frames

A **frame** (see Figure 26.7) is a single image within an animation. It is the equivalent of a single frame in a strip of celluloid. Frames are played in sequence at a specified rate (fps) to create the illusion of movement.

Key frames (see Figure 26.7) are special frames at the beginning and end of an animation (see section 26.3.1.3 on page 287).

When using tweening, each tween must begin and end with a key frame.

■ How to use frames and key frames in Adobe Flash

1 Open a new Adobe Flash document.
2 Draw a picture of a bee.
3 Highlight the whole bee, right click on it and select Convert to Symbol.
4 Call it 'bee' and select the type: graphic. Click OK.
5 Create a key frame at frame 10.
6 Motion tween your bee to move from frame 1 to frame 10.
7 Continue animating until your bee flies all over the stage.
8 Test your movie by pressing Ctrl and Enter together.

26.2.1.2 Layers

A layer (see Figure 26.8) is a separate element of an image. When layers are viewed together, they become an amalgamation of the separate images. Layers are similar to the cels used in hand-drawn animations, where transparent films are placed over each other to create a composite image (see section 26.1.1.4 on page 266).

When animating several assets, each asset must be on a separate layer.

■ How to use layers in Adobe Flash

1 Open a new Adobe Flash document.
2 Name the layer 'branch'.
3 Draw a picture of a tree branch, similar to this:

4 Create a new layer and call it 'sun'.
5 Draw a sun in the top right corner.
6 Convert the sun to a graphic symbol.
7 Create a new layer and call it 'caterpillar'.
8 Draw a caterpillar.
9 Convert the caterpillar to a graphic symbol.
10 Animate the caterpillar so it crawls up the tree (from off-screen) and along the branch.
11 Test your animation.

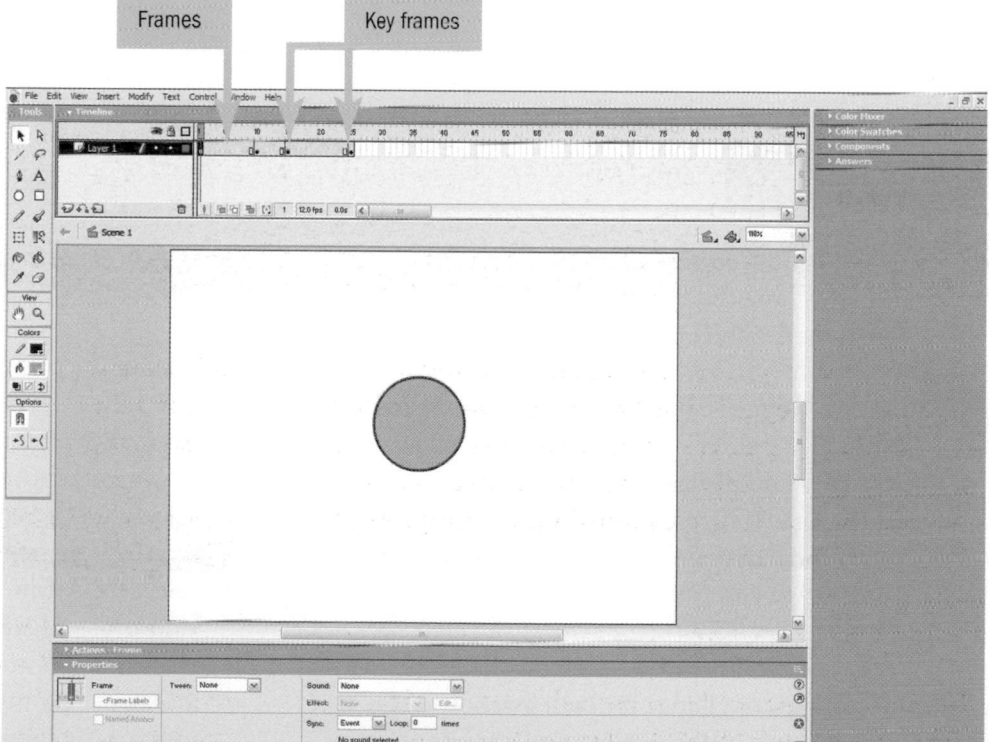

Figure 26.7 Frames and key frames in Flash ▶

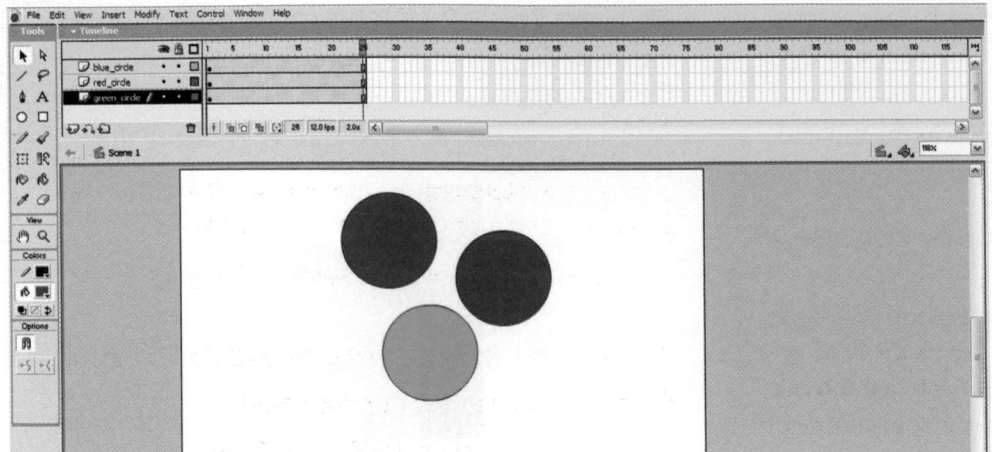

Figure 26.8 Layers in Flash

Activity 26.12

Layers in Adobe Flash

1 Create the animation described in the How to feature about layers. Continue the animation so the caterpillar turns into a chrysalis.
   Hint: You might need to use both types of tweens.

2 Continue the animation so the chrysalis turns into a butterfly and flies off-screen.

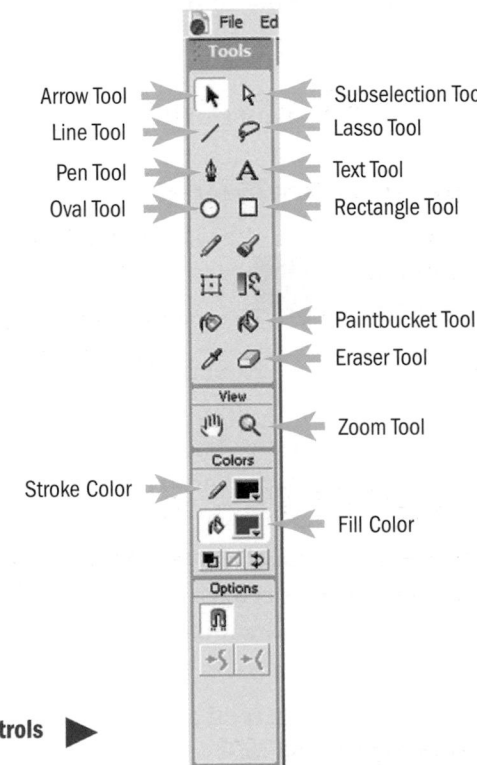

Figure 26.9 Controls in Flash

26.2.1.3 Controls

Controls are the tools available in the animation application that are used to animate. They are usually contained in the Toolbox palette (see Figure 26.9).

■ How to use some controls in Adobe Flash

1 Open a new Adobe Flash document.
2 Select the Line Tool and draw a line on the stage.
3 Select the Text Tool and click on the stage to start a text box – type your name in the text box.
4 Select the Arrow Tool (black arrow) and click on your line and your text – notice how the Properties Inspector options change for each asset.
5 Change the style of the line from solid to dotted.

6 Change the colour and size of the text.
7 Select the Oval Tool and draw a circle.
8 Draw another circle but hold down Shift while drawing it – notice how this produces a perfect circle.
9 Select the Rectangle Tool and draw a rectangle, then a perfect square.
10 Select the Arrow Tool (black arrow), right click on your oval and select Free Transform. Notice how black **handles** appear. These can be used to adjust the shape. Try pulling and pushing the handles and rotating the shape

11 Hold down the Alt key and drag the oval shape to another part of the stage. Notice how, instead of moving the shape, it creates a second copy

12 Select the Subselection Tool (white arrow) and click on the edge of your square. Notice how white handles appear. These can be used to adjust the individual points in a shape. Try turning your square into a diamond.

13 There are two colour tools in the Toolbox: Stroke Color and Fill Color. Change the Fill Color to a colour you have not yet used in this activity and use the Paint Bucket Tool to change the colour of one of your shapes.

Activity 26.13

Controls in Adobe Flash

1 Use the controls described in the How to feature on controls.

2 Use three more tools not yet tried to change the shapes you have created in some way.

What does it mean?

Handles are markers on a shape that show where a shape can be adjusted.

26.2.1.4 Tweening

Tweening can create movement (such as a motion tween) or morphing (such as a shape tween). The tween itself also has properties that can be altered, for example the **ease**.

What does it mean?

The **ease** (also known as the fairing) is the speed at which a tween is performed.

Remember!

Tweening (short for **in betweening**) is where the animator states where points A and B are and the computer fills in the intermediary movement.

■ How to use easing in Adobe Flash

Create a bouncing ball in Adobe Flash:

1 Open a new Adobe Flash document.

2 Draw a line across the lower part of the stage (this will be the 'ground').

3 Create a new layer.

4 On that new layer, draw a circle, convert it to a symbol and call it 'ball'.

5 At frame 10, motion tween the ball to the ground in a straight vertical line.

6 At frame 20, motion tween the ball back into the air vertically, but not as high as it started.

7 Create three more bounces down and up, with the ball moving less high into the air each time.

8 Test the movie and think about how realistic it looks.

For each tween, change the ease:

9 To change the ease, click on the tween itself in the timeline and change the Ease option in the Properties Inspector.

10 Each time the ball moves towards the ground, set the Ease to -100 In.

11 Each time the ball moves away from the ground, set the Ease to 100 Out.

12 Test the movie. Why does this look more realistic than before?

To make the animation even more realistic, squash the ball slightly as it lands on the ground.

13 Create another symbol called 'squashedball' – the same ball but slightly flattened.

14 For a few frames on each bounce, when the ball touches the ground, change the ball symbol to the squashedball symbol.

Activity 26.14

Using easing in Adobe Flash

1 Create the movie described in the How to feature on easing. Describe what easing is. Explain why easing makes the movie look more realistic.

 **(partial evidence)**

26.2.1.5 Other tools

Other tools at the animator's disposal include those below:

- **Buttons.** These can be used to control the play of an animation or alter the sequence. For example, at the beginning there could be a 'Start' button to begin the playing of the animation; at the end there could be a 'Play again' button to restart the animation; there could even be 'Scene selection' buttons like the ones on a DVD which would take the viewer to a particular part of the animation.

- **Libraries.** Symbols, tweens and other assets are stored in libraries within animation software so they are able to be reused. Reusing assets means that the animator does not have to create the same thing over and over, and also it means that there will not be any differences in assests which are meant to be the same. For example, if an animator wants to have three butterflies flying up the screen, instead of drawing three butterflies, they can draw one and reuse it three times. This saves time and means that the butterflies will be identical.

- **Integrated media.** Other types of media can be integrated into an animation, such as video and sound. These can add a powerful effect to the animation, but can sometimes be awkward to include and can raise the file size dramatically.

- **Preloaders**. These can be displayed to the user to indicate that a file is being loaded. They are generally used for larger files which take time to load or files uploaded to the web as the animator does not know what equipment the user has and so cannot predict how long the file will take to open. Preloaders generally display a progress bar and can also have additional information such as the title, the animator's name, a short description and even a mini-animation.

- **Scripts.** To make animations more versatile, scripting languages can be used, such as ActionScript in Flash. These can change a simple linear animation into one with more potential and can also allow user interactivity.

■ How to create buttons using ActionScript to control playing an animation

1 Open a new Adobe Flash document.
2 At frames 1, 2 and 3, create a green, yellow and red circle respectively. These will serve as markers to show the buttons are working.
3 Click on key frame 1 and open the Action palette (just above the Properties Inspector).
4 Make sure you are in Expert Mode (use the Help if you are unsure).
5 Enter the following ActionScript: **Stop**();
6 Enter the Stop command in key frames 2 and 3 in the same way.
7 Create a new layer and add key frames at 1, 2 and 3.
8 Click on key frame 1 and draw a green square.
9 Convert it to the symbol type: button.
10 Do the same for key frames 2 and 3, adding a yellow and a red square respectively.
11 Click on key frame 1 and highlight the green square.
12 Open the Action palette and enter the following ActionScript:

> **on (release)** {
> **gotoAndPlay(2);**
> }

13 Do the same for the button on key frame 2, changing the middle line to **gotoAndPlay(3);**
14 Do the same for the button on key frame 3, changing the middle line to **gotoAndPlay(1);**
15 Test your movie and try clicking the buttons.

26.2.2 Software

There is a multitude of software available to animators, from simple 2D beginner packages to complex 3D applications. Which software to use depends on the animation to be created and its purpose – for example, if it is to be used on a web page or whether the file size is important.

26.2.2.1 Vector graphics

A vector file consists of a mathematical algorithm which is recalculated every time the file is opened. This means that the file size is generally smaller as it only holds data about the picture rather than an actual image. Because the file is a set of calculations, the image can be resized as much as necessary without any loss of quality (see Figure 26.10).

7x Magnification

Vector

Bitmap

Ice Cream

▲ Figure 26.10 A vector image: small and enlarged (not pixellated)

Adobe Flash is a vector-based program – although bitmaps can be imported to be used, any images created in Flash are vectors. Other vector-based programs include Adobe Illustrator (.ai files) and CorelDRAW (.cdr).

26.2.2.2 Bitmap graphics

A bitmap file is made up of individual pixels – essentially, it is a map of where each pixel is and what colour it is. This results in a larger file size than vectors. The files can be compressed to make them smaller using formats such as GIF or JPEG, but this results in a loss of quality. The more times a file is saved in a compressed format, the more quality is lost.

Due to the image being stored with the pixels in place, when it is enlarged, the pixels become stretched and this causes a pixellation effect (see Figure 26.11).

▲ Figure 26.11 A bitmap image: small and enlarged (pixellated)

Applications such as Adobe Photoshop and Microsoft Paint are bitmap-based and file types include .gif, .jpeg and .bmp.

26.2.2.3 Specialist software packages

There is a multitude of specialist animation packages available. Some of the applications used in the design, film and games industries include:

- Dream Studio
- Bryce
- Maya
- Blender
- trueSpace
- LightWave
- 3D Studio Max
- Softimage XSI
- Flash

Some applications specialise in particular areas – for example, Bryce focuses on building environments. Others tackle characters and objects as well. Some are good as learning applications, such as Flash, while others can be quite complex. Most are relatively expensive, but Blender is an open-source program and is free.

Activity 26.15

Animation applications

1 Select three specialist software packages and research each one. Make notes on:
   - who produces it and what other products are available from them
   - how much it costs and how it can be obtained (e.g. general release in stores, download from Internet, etc.)
   - what it is used for in the design industry
   - its key features and in what situations the application may be used. **p₂**

2 Select two of your three packages and compare them using the points from question 1.

3 Select one of your two packages and evaluate it, using your own opinions. **d₁**

26.2.3 Managing file size

The file size of an animation is crucial, especially if it is to be used on the Internet. If the file is too large, it will take too long to download and the user may lose patience and navigate away from the site.

26.2.3.1 Balancing file size against quality of image

Images that are of a very high quality generally have the largest file sizes. In a bitmap, if the **resolution** is high, more pixels need to be stored in that image.

What does it mean?

Resolution is the number of pixels per inch in an image.

The more detail that needs to be recorded about an image, the larger the file size. In addition, if the image is detailed, the more likely it is that compression will have a detrimental effect on the image. When an image is compressed, some loss of quality will always occur and with detailed, photographic-type images, this degradation is usually more noticeable. An animator must choose whether it is more important to have high-quality images and a large file size, lower-quality images and a small file size or to find a happy medium balancing the two.

26.2.3.2 Use of special techniques

Optimisation of animation files is quite a complex process and can involve a detailed understanding of the file type and any compression methods that are used. Two common techniques are frame disposal and autocrop.

Frame disposal is used to prevent **artifacts** appearing. This is where a previous frame remains on-screen and is shown through the transparent areas of subsequent frames. To avoid this happening, frames should be disposed of and the background restored.

Autocrop is used to ensure that only the area that contains images is shown; areas with no images (which are transparent or a solid colour) can be trimmed (see Figure 26.12).

What does it mean?

Frame disposal determines whether the frame continues to be displayed through subsequent frames or is discarded.

Artifacts are unwanted visible elements in a picture or animation.

Autocrop is a function that trims unwanted edges from an image or animation.

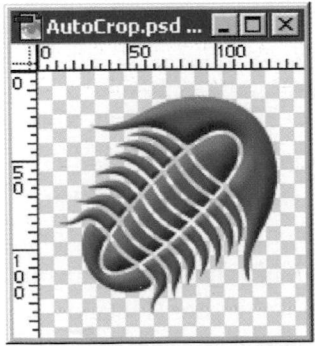 

▲ **Figure 26.12 Example of autocrop**

Activity 26.16

Managing file size

1 Create a simple animation without any optimisation techniques applied.

2 Using your animation, demonstrate and explain how frame disposal minimises the file size of animations.

3 Using your animation, demonstrate and explain how autocrop minimises the file size of animations.

26.2.4 Animating for the web

When animating for the web, file size is not the only constraint. In this medium, the animation is generally not the focal point but is used to enhance the content of the site – for example, buttons or logos. A **house style** may have to be followed so that the animations blend with the site as a whole.

What does it mean?

House style is a standard design carried throughout an organisation's website. It can also be extended throughout all the publications of that organisation, including logos, colour combinations and layouts.

26.2.4.1 Special techniques

Animated rollovers are buttons that perform an action when an event triggers them, for example when a mouse hovers over them. They usually have three states: up (where the button is unaffected), over (where the mouse hovers over the button) and down (when the mouse clicks the button).

■ How to create a rollover button in Adobe Flash

1 Open a new Adobe Flash document.
2 Draw a blue square on the stage.

3 Convert it to a symbol called 'button' and of type Button.
4 Double click button – you are now inside the button. Notice how the timeline is split into four actions: Up, Over, Down, Hit.
5 Add a key frame to the Over action and change the square to green.
6 Add a key frame to the Down action and change the square to red.
7 Add a key frame to the Hit action. This will be invisible when the movie is played but will define the clickable area of the button. Draw a large square over the top of button.
8 Just below the timeline, click Scene 1 to take you back to the main stage.
9 Test your movie and notice how the different actions affect the button.

■ How to create a moving rollover button in Adobe Flash

1 Open a new Adobe Flash document.
2 Draw a red square on the stage.
3 Convert it to a symbol called 'button' and type Button.
4 Double click button.
5 Add a key frame to the Over action and the Down action.
6 Click on the Over action and convert the red square to a MovieClip.
7 Double click the square – you are now inside the MovieClip.
8 Using a shape tween, animate it so it grows longer.
9 Just below the timeline, click Button to take you back to the button.
10 Click on the Down action and change the red square into a yellow square.
11 Just below the timeline, click Scene 1 to take you back to the main stage.
12 Test your movie and notice how the different actions affect the button.

26.2.4.2 Email attachments and e-cards

A popular use for animation is as attachments to emails. They can include humorous jokes, inspirational messages and other entertaining distractions. Once they have been sent to one group of people, they are generally passed on and on and can spread all round the world. In a busy modern life, where people sometimes don't have time to write a full email message, they can send someone an animated email attachment to let the person know they are thinking about them.

Viral advertisers have taken advantage of this new phenomenon and use it as another way of spreading news of their product using digital word of mouth.

E-cards are digital cards that are sent via email in place of traditional paper-based cards. E-cards are generally animated and often have sound as well. E-card sites often offer a few cards for free, but charge for the cards with higher-quality animations or messages. Parts of the e-card are usually customisable, including the heading, the greeting, the main message and the goodbye message. For example, a sender could personalise a birthday card by writing 'Happy Birthday, Simon' instead of the generic 'Happy Birthday'.

26.2.4.3 Output devices

When creating animations, attention should be given to the devices on which it will be viewed.

Monitors can be set at a variety of resolutions so the animator cannot always know which will be used. Common practice is to design animations for the most popular resolution at the time – this will influence the animator's decisions on size of stage and other factors.

Some animations are designed for portable devices such as mobile phones and PDAs. Although a large percentage of these now have full-colour screens, some are still monochrome, which should be borne in mind when creating animations for these devices.

If an animation is to be projected on to a screen, some quality may be lost as it is enlarged, and the animator must take this into account.

26.2.5 Files

Before starting to animate, it is useful to know what file type will be used as this may influence the choice of software or the method of saving used.

Activity 26.17

Animating for the web

1 Research and make notes for future use on factors that need to be considered when creating animations for the Internet.

26.2.5.1 File types and features of each

Each file type is associated with a set of characteristics and the file type will often determine how the files are saved or how they can be played. Table 26.2 (opposite) describes some of the most commonly used file types.

It should be noted that .mp4 and .mp3 (an audio-only file type with which you will be familiar) formats are related, but not as closely as you might think: .mp4 is the MPEG-4 standard, whereas .mp3 is MPEG-1 Audio Layer 3.

26.2.5.2 Converting files

Once files are in a compressed format, it is difficult to convert between them. However, during the editing stages it is possible to save files as many different types.

26.2.5.3 Importing and exporting files

An animation will quite often include images and animations from other sources, rather than all assets being created especially for that project. The animation software being used will determine what can be imported and how, but in general terms, both bitmap and vector static images will be accepted, as well as other animations made in the same program.

Exporting files involves publishing them into a viewable format that makes it possible to distribute. For example, when an Adobe Flash animation is published, it is then viewable using Flash Player and can be watched on a computer that doesn't have the full Flash application installed.

File Types	Full name	Features
.gif (animated)	Graphics Interchange Format	<ul><li>Maximum 256 colour palette</li><li>Supports transparency</li><li>Compresses files using lossless compression</li><li>Generally used for web animations and therefore playable on most platforms</li></ul>
.swf	Small Web Format Shockwave Flash	<ul><li>Created by Adobe Flash</li><li>Locked and uneditable (as opposed to .fla files)</li><li>Files are compressed</li><li>Often used for online content</li></ul>
.mov		<ul><li>Designed for QuickTime media player</li><li>Can contain graphics, video and audio</li></ul>
.mp4	MPEG-4 Part 14 Moving Picture Experts Group	<ul><li>Based on the .mov format</li><li>Can contain graphics, video and audio</li><li>Mainly playable on Apple software or specialist hardware, including iTunes, QuickTime, PlayStation3, Xbox 360, iPod</li></ul>
.wmv	Windows Media Video	<ul><li>Created by Microsoft and popular on Windows platform (Windows Media Player is built into Windows operating systems)</li><li>Can contain graphics, video and audio</li><li>Recently developed to store high definition files as WMV HD</li></ul>

Table 26.2 Comparison of some popular animation file types

Activity 26.18

Converting files in Adobe Flash

1 Create a simple animation to save in Adobe Flash.

2 Save the animation in different formats.
- Save your animation in the normal way (File/Save) – this saves it as a .fla file, a working Flash file.
- Select File/Publish Settings. A new window should open with all the file type options: .swf, .html, .gif, .jpeg, .png, .exe, .hqx, .mov

Save your animation as each file type, then try opening it. Make notes on what happens and try to explain why.

26.2.5.4 File management

Keeping files organised is a skill that you need to develop. One method is to keep all working files in one folder and all finished files in another. This should prevent working on a compressed file such as a GIF and compressing it further each time it is saved.

In addition, backing up is crucial, especially when working on large files, which is common for animations. Saving regularly can also prevent data loss.

Test your knowledge

1 What are a frame and a key frame?

2 Explain how layers work.

3 Name five tools you might find in the toolbox of an animation program.

4 What are the key differences between a bitmap and a vector?

5 Name four specialist animation applications.

6 How can frame disposal and autocrop assist file size reduction?

When creating an animation there are generally three stages that must be performed: planning, creating and reviewing. The planning stage includes all the designing of the animation. The creating stage is the implementation of the design. The review involves testing the functionality of all elements of the animation and evaluating the animation to see whether it fulfils the client brief and is satisfactory for the viewers.

26.3.1 Design

Before beginning to animate, it is crucial to design it first. Although design can take a lot of time, it will save so much more during the actual implementation. Designing animation can involve storyboarding, calculating times and naming scenes.

26.3.1.1 Storyboarding

Storyboarding (see Figure 26.13) is key to structuring an animation and deciding on the sequence of frames. The storyboard can simply be an overview of key scenes or it can be done in extensive detail, almost down to each frame being modelled, depending on how the animation will be made.

▲ **Figure 26.13 Example of an animation storyboard**

annotations can include film or theatre notations if these are understood by the animators involved. For example: 'Boy enters SR to CS, camera pans L → R' (which means: 'Boy enters stage right to centre stage, camera pans left to right').

Storyboarding can be a rough noting of ideas done in draft form or formally drawn for a team of animators to follow throughout the project.

What does it mean?

A **storyboard** shows the sequence of a project. In animation, it shows what happens in each frame or scene and how they will interrelate.

In a storyboard, boxes represent the screen and the designer draws the images to appear on screen within the boxes. (If items are drawn outside the boxes, it means that they are off-screen and invisible to the viewer.) Drawings (or even photographs, if appropriate) are put inside each box to show what will appear in a particular frame or scene.

The designer includes notes under each box about what is happening. For example: 'Boy moves to centre'. These

26.3.1.2 Timings

Timing in an animation is quite an art and can be the element that draws the viewer into the action or leaves them feeling cold. For example, have you ever seen a film in which the speaking is out of sync with the picture? What effect did that have on you as a viewer?

The frames and their times can be planned using a log sheet or a bar sheet. The complexity of the animation will determine the intricacy of the sheets. Figure 26.14 and Figure 26.15 show templates for log and bar sheets that may be suitable for your animations during this unit.

26.3.1.3 Key frames

When designing an animation, you need to identify where key frames occur as these are the beginnings and ends of actions. These can be noted on the log sheet or bar sheet.

26.3.1.4 Frame numbering and naming

It is useful to know the frame numbers of each particular action (for example, when the key frames take place). In addition, it is good practice to name sections so they are easier to refer to, especially when working with a team of animators. If an animation has 2000 frames it is cumbersome to have to keep referring to the frame numbers of a particular scene. You could number the scenes, but again this doesn't give a clear indication of where the scene comes in the animation. It is therefore useful to name scenes in the animation, with meaningful names that reflect the content or action.

Figure 26.14 Log sheet

Log sheet

Title of animation:

Sheet of

Frame	Real time	Layer	Assets	Actions	Sounds
1	00:00				
2					
3					
4					
5					
6					
7					
8					
9					
10					
11					
12					

Figure 26.15 Bar sheet

Bar sheet

Title of animation:

Sheet of

Image:	Image:	Image:
Notes:	Notes:	Notes:
Sound:	Sound:	Sound:

Activity 26.19

Designing animation

Sweet As is a business based in County Durham that produces honey from its own bees. The company has a website but the owners want to improve it by adding animation. They also want to use an animated advert on the Internet.

They have asked you to produce:

- a logo to be displayed large in the centre of the home page and smaller on each subsequent page
- a rollover button that can be used several times on every page for all of the navigation
- an advertisement for their special offer: 25% off for first-time buyers – to be shown on other websites with a link back to the Sweet As website.

Their website has a black background with yellow and white text. The logo must be completely in vectors so it can be resized. The rollover must have an action for up, over and down. The advertisement must involve some bitmap graphics.

1 Produce three draft designs for each animation using a pencil and paper. Choose the best design for each animation to produce for the business.

P₆ P₇

2 Create a detailed storyboard for each animation.

P₆ P₇

3 Create a log sheet or bar sheet for each animation.

P₆ P₇

Note: This Activity should be completed in conjunction with Activity 26.20 and Activity 26.21 task 1 to evidence criteria **P₆** and **P₇** fully.

26.3.2 Documentation

Although at the moment you will be creating animations on your own, in the design industry it is common for animators to work in teams. Therefore, documentation is needed so that everyone in the team understands the process and the progress being made. In addition, if an animator is absent for a period of time, the documentation will allow others in the team to carry on

with the work or bring in another animator. In a situation where there is no documentation, a team member's absence might disrupt creation of the product, resulting in the deadline not being met and the client not paying the fee.

26.3.2.1 Purpose and description

The documentation must clearly state the objective of the project and contain a detailed description of how this will be achieved. This should be based on the client brief.

The purpose should include a clear explanation of the core objective and other details such as where the animation might be displayed. For example, the purpose of an animation might be to provide an introduction to a DVD. More detail could be added as to the subject of the DVD, how many buttons are required, what language it needs to be in, etc.

The description should then add considerably more detail, including:

- any ideas the client has had for the project – this will assist in ensuring that the client is satisfied with the resulting product
- design elements such as storyboards – these should be amended as the project progresses, so that at any time they are an up-to-date representation of the animation
- clear user requirements, which can be used to review and evaluate the project on its completion.

26.3.2.2 Format, target file size and other documentation

The format of the animation needs to be decided before beginning the implementation of the design. The decision will include:

- the platform on which to create it (Apple, Windows, etc.)
- the software to be used and the format of the files
- the choice of bitmaps, vectors or both, as well as the file types and compression methods
- the media players for which they will be designed.

The target file size will help determine the complexity of the animation and also the amount of compression needed in order to make it suitable. For example, if the animation is to be used on the web, the file size will be crucial to its success; whereas if it is to be included on a CD, the file size may not be quite so important.

Storage of the animation during production needs to be decided and known by all animators involved. For projects such as games development, the competition is fierce and robust security is needed to ensure that projects remain secret until the publishers are ready to release them. A breach in security can destroy months of careful and expensive advertising that has built anticipation among consumers. In addition, backing up files is essential. For larger projects, several backups need to be made, at least one of which should be held off-site in a fireproof, waterproof container.

26.3.2.3 Source of images

Animation projects sometimes use images from outside sources. These might be stock images that the company already has or images from services such as Getty Images or Stock.Xchng which provide (mostly photographic) images to subscribers. The documentation should include a record of all images that are not original, so that the legality of using the images can be checked at any time.

In the creative industry, copyright is a prevalent issue and animators must be careful not to breach it. Otherwise, they may find themselves involved in legal disputes. In UK law, copyright exists on any piece of work once it has become tangible (in a fixed form) and is protected by the Copyright, Designs and Patents Act 1988. This means that using other people's work without their permission is a breach of copyright. It also means that your own work is protected by copyright law.

26.3.3 Software

The choice of software can affect a project significantly and, if chosen well, can speed up the process and produce a high-quality result. The choice is generally

based on two factors: appropriateness for purpose and the tools available in the software. However, the cost and availability of the software can also be included in the decision.

26.3.3.1 Appropriate for purpose

The purpose, as defined in the documentation, should make it clear what type of software will be appropriate to the task. For example, if the animation is to be regularly resized, a vector image will be suitable, whereas if transparency is needed, an animated GIF may be the best choice.

26.3.3.2 Use of tools

Animation applications usually have a wide range of tools available and this will influence the choice of the software. For example, if true 3D graphics are required, Adobe Flash will not be suitable, but if the animation is to be in 2D, there is no point using an expensive and complicated 3D modeller, as this will be superfluous and distracting.

Activity 26.20

Creating animation
Using your designs from Activity 26.19, do the following.

1 Document each animation, including:
- purpose and description
- format, file size and storage location
- source of images
- chosen software. **P**₆ **P**₇

2 Create each animation using animation software. **P**₆ **P**₇

3 Update the documentation as each animation is being created. **P**₆ **P**₇

See note at end of Activity 26.19.

26.3.4 Review

It is vital to review a project once it is complete to ensure that it successfully fulfils the client brief and is functionally sound – in other words, that it does what it is supposed to do.

26.3.4.1 Testing functionality

To confirm the functionality of an animation, it must be tested in several ways.

The movie needs to be tested in great detail to see if it plays correctly. It should be viewed scene by scene and all the way through at a much slower frame rate, in order to find small faults. Then it should be viewed at normal speed, to see what the viewer would see, again scene by scene and all the way through.

If there are any elements of interactivity, they should also be tested to make sure they work in the correct way.

It is advisable for not only the original animator(s) to test the movie, but also other members of the team and an external tester or focus group. A focus group could consist of members of the potential target market. For example, the creators of an animated Walt Disney film will invite a focus group of children and their parents to watch the new movie before its release and will even adapt the film according to their feedback if necessary.

26.3.4.2 Reviewing against original purpose and requirements

Using the documentation, it should be possible to review the project to see if it matches the original client brief. Does the animation fulfil its purpose? Does the original description of the project reflect what has been created?

In addition to this, there should be an analysis of the user requirements to see if they have been satisfied by the animation. If there are any requirements that have not been achieved, you must be able to give a suitable reason as to why not – for example, a requirement may have been technically impossible.

26.3.4.3 Improvements

Once testing has been completed, amendments can be made based on the results of testing. If errors or problems with the functionality have been found, they should be rectified and retested.

Once the animation has been fully tested and corrected, the animators should be ready to present the completed project to the client for their approval.

Activity 26.21

Reviewing animation
Using the animations you created in Activity 26.20, do the following.

1 Test the functionality of each animation and review it in terms of the client brief (given in Activity 26.19).

p₆ **p**₇

See note at end of Activity 26.19.

2 Make any amendments necessary resulting from the formal review. **m**₃

3 Evaluate each animation, assessing it against the original client brief (given in Activity 26.19).

STOP Test your knowledge

1 What is storyboarding and why is it important?

2 Why are log sheets and bar sheets used?

3 Why is it important to name scenes within a large animation?

4 What is the purpose of documentation and what should it include?

5 Describe the two ways in which animation can be tested.

Preparation for assessment

The assessment tasks in this unit are based on the following scenario.

Digital Myths is a small business that creates animated stories for primary school children, aged 5 to 11. Some are based on classic fairy tales or nursery rhymes, others are new stories written especially for the animations. The aims are to encourage reading, to educate the children about creative writing and, most importantly, to entertain.

All the stories are subtitled, are approximately 5–10 minutes long and are appropriate for the specific age group. The animations are usually published on CDs which are purchased by schools, although the company has recently begun to set up a website to distribute its animations.

You have recently been appointed as an animator at Digital Myths.

You are advised to research wherever possible and use correctly referenced sources.

Task 1 (P6, M3, D2)

As the new animator at Digital Myths, you have been asked to create a short demonstration piece to advertise the type of work that the company does. This should be an animated story with subtitles, but does not need to be a complete story. It should be 1–2 minutes long. The narrative can be a classic fairy tale or nursery rhyme, or an original new story.

- Create a storyboard for the whole of the story.
- Create the animation, documenting throughout using bar sheets or log sheets.
- Test the animation thoroughly by:
  a) checking it against the storyboard
  b) gaining feedback from another person. **p**₆

Make improvements based on your testing resulting from the formal review. **m**₃

Evaluate the products used in your animation, describing the good and bad points, and what you would use in the future and why. **d**₂

Task 2 (P6, P7, M3, D2)

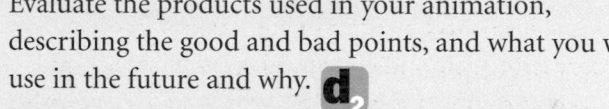

Digital Myths is setting up a website to advertise and distribute its products. The creative director has asked you to create three separate animations for the website: a logo, a title bar and a banner advert. The logo must use vector images and the others must use bitmaps. The logo and title bar will be displayed near each other on the same web page. The advert is to go on other websites.

- Create storyboards for each animation.
- Create the animations, documenting each using bar sheets or log sheets.
- Test the animations thoroughly by:
  a) checking them against the storyboards
  b) gaining feedback from another person. **p**₆ **p**₇

Make improvements based on your testing resulting from the formal review. **m**₃

Evaluate the products used in your animations, describing the good and bad points, and what you would use in the future and why. **d**₂

Task 3 (P1, P4)

The local high school has heard about the work Digital Myths does and has asked it to produce a series of posters explaining some of the principles of animation. The posters will be displayed in Year 10 and 11 classrooms to help students when they begin learning animation.

Create a series of posters to explain the following topics:

- persistence of vision **p**₁
- traditional techniques
- frames and key frames
- layers
- tweening. **p**₄

The posters must be appropriate to the target audience and visually appealing.

Task 4 (P2, M2, D1)

The local high school has asked your advice on what animation applications would be best to provide for students in Years 10 and 11 who are beginning to learn animation.

Write a short, concise report comparing animation applications.

- Describe three applications in detail. **p**₂
- Choose two of these three and compare the animation techniques used in them in detail. **m**₂
- Choose a software package and evaluate it to explain why it would be most appropriate for the school. **d**₁

Task 5 (P3, P5, M1, M4)

The local high school has one more task for you: to create a leaflet advising the students on the best file formats and management techniques to use for their animation work.

Create a leaflet to explain:

- the file formats available **m**₁
- the advantages and limitations of an animated GIF and one other format type **p**₃
- how to minimise the size of an animation **m**₄
- special considerations for animating for the web. **p**₅

The leaflet should be double-sided and designed to be folded if required. It should be appropriate for the target audience and be clear and concise. It should contain a comparison of two different animation techniques.

Glossary

8-bit   8-bit means that a single byte is used for each item of data. A byte has 8 bits, each of which can be set to a one or zero. This gives 256 different combinations of bit patterns.

absolute cell referencing   Absolute cell referencing allows you to copy or move a formula without the cell reference changing. You can make all or part of a cell reference absolute.

accessibility   Accessibility is the ease with which websites can be accessed by users, especially referring to those with particular technologies or special needs.

ActionScript   ActionScript is a language used in Flash animations, for example, to create buttons.

API   API stands for Application Programming Interface – it represents a collection of functions that can be used by programmers to access programs outside the application they are writing.

argument   An argument is a value or expression used within a function. It specifies what data is to be acted upon, the criteria that are to be applied or the resulting value that is required.

array   An array is a range of cells that covers more than one row and more than one column, e.g. A5:D9.

artifacts   Artifacts are unwanted visible elements in a picture or animation.

asset   An asset is any type of object within a multimedia product, such as an image, movie clip or sound file.

atomic   An atomic item is a single item of information. For example, someone's name is non atomic because it should be broken down into at least three fields – title, first name and last name. Breaking fields down in this way gives more flexibility as to how the data can be used.

autocrop   Autocrop is a function that trims unwanted edges from an image or animation.

back up   To back up means to copy computer work to another place so that it is kept safe in case of emergency such as file corruption, fire, flood or theft. Many users back up to CD-ROM then store these somewhere secure, such as a fireproof safe or off-site in another location.

bandwidth   Bandwidth is the capacity that a network connection can conduct at one time.

baseline plan   A baseline plan is a plan that is fixed and agreed at a key point in a project, often the start of a phase.

bespoke   A bespoke program is written especially for a client. Usually more expensive than 'off-the-shelf' software and more likely to have bugs when first delivered, bespoke is a good option where a client has software needs that are not easily met by commercial, off-the-shelf applications.

BIOS   BIOS stands for basic input output system. It is a chip on every PC motherboard that connects the operating system to hardware, as well as holding the boot program and start-up settings.

bitmap   A bitmap is literally a map of bits; each pixel is saved in its location. Bitmap graphics are made from lots of pixels, each with a colour. They are also called raster graphics.

black box testing   Black box testing is when a program is tested without taking into consideration the code inside the program. The program is the 'box' which is 'black', as the tester does not see anything inside it.

bureau   A bureau is an organisation that carries out services such as printing for other businesses or clients. A design studio may not have expensive specialist printing facilities, so sends work to a bureau to make use of their printing equipment.

business case   A business case is a proposal stating the objectives, costs and benefits of a project.

cache memory   Cache memory is very fast electronic memory between RAM and another device, used to make the system run faster.

calculated field   A calculated field is one that can be derived from other fields. For example, if age and date of birth are two fields, then age is a calculated field because you can always work out someone's age given today's date.

calling   Calling a function means accessing it from wherever it is stored and executing it.

cascade   Cascade means following up any changes in one table by making the changes to all other related tables.

case sensitive   Case sensitive languages need the right mix of capital and lower case letters. A case sensitive part of a program will see System and SYSTEM as very different.

categorical data   Categorical data has separate categories, and there is no natural ordering.

CCD   A CCD (charge-coupled device) is an image sensor used in digital cameras and other devices that converts the image to digital signals.

cel   A cel is a piece of transparent film that can be drawn on and then overlaid with other cels to create a composite image.

certificate-based authentication   Certificate-based authentication is a method of coding information so the people at either end are identified by a digital certificate, coupled with a digital signature. These can confirm the identity of the sender or recipient.

checkpoint   A checkpoint could have any criteria for which stakeholders feel that there should be a review.

checksum   A checksum is a calculation on data that is a form of validation, often used during transmissions. The calculation produces a result that is worked out before transmission then sent as a checksum in the last section of data. The receiving computer carries out the same calculation on the data received then compares it with the checksum – if it is different, the data is corrupted and needs to be resent.

cinematograph   The cinematograph was invented by the Lumière brothers in 1895 and used 35 mm celluloid film.

claymation   Claymation is where models or puppets are moved frame by frame to create an animation.

CLE   CLE (command line editor) enables you to edit text files using the command line.

CLI   CLI stands for command line interpreter (or command line interface) and is used to describe a non GUI operating system.

client side scripting   Client side scripting is when the script is executed on the user's computer. This is the opposite of server side scripting, which is executed on the web server. Server side scripting is used for more advanced interactive features, such as connecting to a database.

colorimeter A colorimeter is a device that can measure the colours of a device for calibration.

colour depth The colour depth is the number of bits used by the graphics system to hold the colour of each pixel on the screen. A 24-bit colour depth means the number of colours available on a computer system will be 16.7 million.

COM COM stands for component object model.

comment A comment is an uninterrupted line of code which describes what is happening and helps developers understand how the code works.

compression Compression is where a mathematical calculation is performed on a file in order to 'squash' it and make it smaller.

concatenated A concatenated field is one that is formed by combining the contents of two or more other fields, e.g. Full name might be a concatenation of First name and Last name.

concept designing Concept designing means outlining the overall design of the product. This gives the general feel of the website and the effect it should have on its users.

concept keyboard A concept keyboard (or overlay keyboard) has keys that have been preset to do specific functions. The keys often have images or symbols to guide the user. A concept keyboard can do anything a QWERTY keyboard and/or a mouse can do.

condition A condition is part of a statement which the program understands as representing True or False. For example, MyVar < 3 would give True if MyVar is a variable containing 2 or False if it contains 3.

connectedness Connectedness is the ease with which users move from one location to another.

constant A constant is similar to a variable in that it is a name in code that represents a value, but different in that the value does not change.

context-sensitive help Context-sensitive help means that the help system provides appropriate and different help information depending on where the user was when they asked for help.

continuous data Continuous data can take a value anywhere on a number line. For example, time is a continuous variable, as are height, length and weight.

control object A control object is an object or a form. It can have a variety of purposes, including for example, displaying titles or descriptions, accepting data, or performing an action.

controls Controls and objects are the parts of an event driven programming language that have events happen to them. A control is a visual object such as a button or a combo box. An object may be either visual or non-visual. An example of a non-visual object is the PrintDocument object of VB.NET which can be used by a program to produce hard copy on to paper.

cookies Cookies are packets of data exchanged between the client computer and the web server for authentication or personalisation of a website.

CPU The CPU (central processing unit) is another name for the processor. This is a chip that fits into a socket on the motherboard. Modern CPUs are often made by AMD or Intel. The AMD family of CPUs include Athlon and Opteron. Intel processors include Pentium and Celeron.

cross-cast check A cross-cast check involves doing a calculation in two different ways and checking that the two totals are the same.

CRT CRT (cathode ray tube) is a screen technology that uses a phosphor-coated glass tube to display images. The tube makes the unit quite deep, especially for large screens as electron rays need to be fired at the display from the back of the tube with room to spread out to the size of the display. This technology uses a lot of electricity and older models can produce some radiation, which concerns many users.

CSS CSS stands for cascading style sheets. This is a form of web language which can be used to standardise the layout throughout a website.

CSS CSS (Cascading Style Sheets) is a language used to create the formatting for web pages.

customer deliverables Customer deliverables are those that are useful to the customer.

cut-out Cut-out animation is where shapes are laid against a background and moved for each shot of the camera.

DAB DAB stands for digital audio broadcasting – these radios require no tuning and provide a clearer, crisper sound than traditional radios.

daisy-chained Daisy-chained is a term used to describe when a number of devices are connected together with a cable connecting each device to the next. Daisy-chained devices usually need a terminator at the two ends of the chain to keep the data signal inside the cabling.

data flow A data flow is movement of data from one area to another, often through a process.

data integrity Maintaining data integrity means keeping the data accurate.

data mining Data mining involves the automatic collection of large amounts of data and then analysing the data for trends and patterns. For example, all credit card transactions might be stored and then the data analysed to spot possible fraudulent activity.

data redundancy Data redundancy describes a situation where information (such as a supplier address) is duplicated in more than one table. It wastes space and can cause problems if all copies of the duplicated data are not updated at the same time, resulting in inconsistency within the database. In some cases, however, duplication can be acceptable if it speeds up processing.

data store A data store is a holding area within a system for data.

data type The data type of a field determines how the data will be stored in that field.

deadline A deadline is a date by which something must have happened.

delete query Instead of selecting all the records that fit the criteria of a query, a delete query will delete the records. So use with care!

delimiter A delimiter is a character used to separate fields when data is stored as plain text. The delimiter most often used is the comma, hence the term comma-delimited file.

deliverable A deliverable is a product or service that a project aims to produce.

depends on One field depends on another if you can find out the unique value of the second field knowing the value of the first one. For example, if you know a patient's reference number, you can find out their name or address or telephone number and so these fields depend on the reference number.

diagnostic software Diagnostic software attempts to diagnose a problem; it identifies possible faults and offers solutions.

dialogue box In Office applications, clicking on a menu item with three dots (…) after it will open a dialogue box. A dialogue box is a window that responds to a command and allows you to make choices.

discrete data Discrete data takes values, but not the values between them. For example: shoes sizes are 4, 4½, 5, 5½, 6, 6½, 7 and so on. There is no shoe size between a 4 and a 4½.

dithering Dithering is a technique which uses in-between colours to reduce the harsh contrast of two colours.

DIV A DIV is a method of defining a style for a block of HTML (HyperText Markup Language). It includes an automatic paragraph break.

DMA DMA (direct memory addressing) is the name given to circuits on the motherboard which are used to move large amounts of data from one part of the system to another.

DOM DOM (Document Object Model) is used to integrate styles, content and formatting for web pages.

DOS DOS stands for disk operating system, the name given to a family of operating systems produced for PCs. MS-DOS was the Microsoft product, PC-DOS was from IBM and DR-DOS by Digital Research.

drawn animation Drawn animation is where animators draw each frame of the film.

dynamic A dynamic website is one that is updated live online. Usually, there are scripting languages and/or databases.

dynamic website A dynamic website can involve any level of activity from a simple feedback form to a database that personalises the website for each individual visitor. Changes can be made on the fly.

ease The ease (also known as the fairing) is the speed at which a tween is performed.

E-D E-D stands for eDimensional. E-D glasses make computer games appear more vividly 3D.

entities Entities are the real world things that are represented in the database. Examples are products, customers and orders information. An entity is a thing about which an organisation wants to record information.

event An event is anything that happens to an object when the program is running.

event handler An event handler is the code that runs when an event occurs.

external entity An external entity sends data into or gets data from a system.

FAT The FAT (File Allocation Table) is held on the disk to connect names of files and folders to where they actually are on the disk. When a file is opened or saved, the disk address needs to be looked up in the FAT before the file can be found. FAT can be likened to a phone book holding the addresses of files on the disk.

field size The field size determines how much space should be set aside for that field.

firewall A firewall is a piece of software that protects the system from unauthorised access. This is especially important for web servers.

flip book A flip book is a very simple type of animation where drawings are put on separate pages and then flicked through to animate.

formula A formula is an expression written in terms of cell references and operators, which specifies a calculation that is to be done. The result of the calculation appears in the cell in which the formula is stored.

frame A frame is a single section of film that contains one image of the animation.

frame disposal Frame disposal determines whether the frame continues to be displayed through subsequent frames or is discarded.

frames per second (fps) Frames per second (fps) refers to the number of individual images that are shown every second.

FTP FTP (File Transfer Protocol) is the protocol used to upload web pages on to a web server. Unusually, the term is used as both a noun and a verb.

function A function is a command that results in a value being returned

Gantt chart A Gantt chart is a picture of how long all the tasks should take.

geons Geons are 2D images that are quickly recognisable by the user from almost any angle.

GIF GIF stands for Graphics Interchange Format. It is a bitmap image format that can support animations.

GOMS GOMS stands for goals, operators, methods and selection. It provides a model for how the user will behave when carrying out a series of well-known tasks.

GUI A GUI is the name given to a modern operating system such as Windows or Linux. GUI stands for graphical user interface, meaning that the operating system can be controlled with a mouse by clicking on buttons, menus or similar objects.

handles Handles are markers on a shape that show where a shape can be adjusted.

hardware Hardware is the physical part of a computer system, including components inside the system unit and peripherals such as monitor, printer and specialised devices such as a digital camera.

HCI HCI is the human–computer interface. HCI is the art of making programs easy and intuitive to use.

head The head of the web page is the part of the code where all the styling and other invisibles parts are written. The body is where the all the elements that are visible on the web page are coded.

head up displays Head up displays are worn on the head like glasses and can be used to watch DVDs or experience a virtual activity.

hexadecimal Hexadecimal is the numbering system using base 16 – i.e. 10 in hexadecimal represents 16 as we know it in denary (base 10). Hexadecimal is important to programmers because it is often used to represent binary values with 2 hexadecimal digits being an exact match for any 8-digit binary value.

house style House style is a standard design that is carried throughout an organisation's website. It can also be extended throughout the business, e.g. on promotional brochures, letterheads, etc. It can include logos, colour combinations and layouts.

HTML HTML (Hypertext Markup Language) is the language used as a basis for all web pages.

hyperlink A hyperlink is a method of connecting two pages together. It can be applied to text or an image. When clicked, it will take you to a predefined location.

IDE An IDE is an integrated development environment – it is the name given to a programming language that is open for creating and editing a program. Modern IDEs include a toolbox for adding new components, views for designing and coding the application, windows for properties of components and what disk files are in the project, as well as debugging tools and help screens.

identity theft Identity theft is where a victim's details are stolen and someone poses as the victim, applying for financial products and making purchases.

interactive whiteboard An interactive whiteboard is a screen which has a touch-sensitive display and can connect to the Internet, file servers and computer applications. Information can be written on the screen with a special marker pen and changes can be made and stored in the same way as when working on a computer.

interactivity Interactivity is two-way communication between user and computer.

interim deliverables Interim deliverables are those that appear part way through the project.

interpreted HTML is interpreted to convert the language the developer can understand to a language the computer understands.

joystick A joystick is an input device which can be used for playing video games.

JPEG JPEG stands for Joint Photographics Expert Group. It is a bitmap image format which can hold more than 16 million colours in an image.

kinetoscope The kinetoscope was invented by Thomas Edison and was an early projector using perforated film.

LCD LCD stands for liquid crystal display – used, for example, in cash machines and mobile phones.

limited animation Limited animation is where the same cels are used over and over again.

link A link is a reference to another workbook; it is sometimes called an external reference.

list A list is a series of worksheet rows that contain related data. The first row contains labels for the columns.

live A website goes live when it is uploaded to be viewed on the Internet.

logbook A logbook is a record of every important thing that happens on a project.

logical functions Logical functions return a value of True or False, depending on the conditions that you set up.

logical operators Logical operators return a value of True or False, depending on the logical values in the argument.

loop A loop is a piece of code that is executed over and over again until it fulfils a preset criterion.

lossless compression Lossless compression makes the file size smaller without losing the quality of the image. It allows the original image to be rebuilt from the compressed image.

lossy compression Lossy compression of images does not allow the original image to be rebuilt from the compressed image.

macro A macro is a series of commands and functions that are stored in a Microsoft Visual Basic module and can be run whenever the user needs to perform the task.

maintenance Program maintenance is the stage in the systems development life cycle (SDLC) when programs are tweaked to remove bugs that are found during use and to make small improvements.

man hour A man hour is the amount of work a person can be expected to do in one hour.

management review   A management review is a formal review, run on behalf of the customer.

mask   A mask is used to cover part or all of an image and can be moved to reveal the image beneath.

masking   Masking means selecting a certain area of an image to protect it from changes, such as applying colour, filters or other effects.

memo   Memo stands for memorandum and is a short note used within an organisation between colleagues.

method   A method is an action that can be performed by an object.

milestone   A milestone is a point where a project achieves an important measurable deliverable.

mood boards   Mood boards are a collage of images, textures and other items aimed at providing an idea of the look and feel of a product. They are usually A3 size.

navigation diagram   A navigation diagram shows how the different parts of a project will be arranged. In web design, it shows how different pages will interrelate.

normalisation   Normalisation is the process by which complex real world information used by an organisation is analysed and represented in a number of simple tables that can then be implemented using relational database software such as Microsoft Access.

object   An object is a special type of data that has properties and methods.

operator   An operator is a mathematical symbol used in a calculation or comparison.

ordinal data   Ordinal data may be discrete or continuous, but has a definite ordering, e.g. from smallest to largest, or oldest to newest.

parameter query   A parameter query prompts the user of a database to set the specific criteria for the field(s) selected for that query by the database designer.

parameters   Parameters act as local variables where values are passed into a subroutine or function. A parameter is usually inside brackets after the name where it is declared, e.g. Sub LoadData(FName) has FName as a parameter.

payback period   The payback period for a project is the length of time taken before the cash benefits exceed the cost.

PDA   PDA stands for personal digital assistant and is a hand-held computer.

performance capture   Performance capture is where human acting is 'captured' by a computer and then used by animators to create the images.

persistence of vision   Persistence of vision refers to the ability of the human eye to preserve the image it has just seen for a brief instant. Therefore, when the eye sees a series of images that follow each other, it retains each image and the brain processes the series as one continuous image.

PERT chart   A PERT (Program Evaluation and Review Technique) chart shows the dependencies between tasks. It depicts the task, its duration and dependency information.

phonograph   The phonograph was invented by Thomas Edison in 1877 to record the spoken word.

pivot   To pivot means to rotate about a point. In a spreadsheet, the point is a cell and the rows and columns become interchanged.

pixel   A pixel is a dot of colour on a screen or other output device. The word pixel is short for 'picture element'.

pixel perfect   Pixel perfect is a term used in the design field to describe graphics that are accurate down to the very last pixel.

plug-in   A plug-in is software which will play specific types of files. For example, modern versions of browsers like Internet Explorer come with Flash Player, which is a plug-in to allow the user to play Flash animation. Most browsers have a range of plug-ins automatically installed or available for download.

predictive model   A predictive model is an equation or calculation used to forecast an event.

process   A process is what changes data from one form to another.

project methodology   A project methodology is a standard, documented way of tackling a computer project.

properties   The properties of a field are the characteristics that are set by the database designer.

proprietary   Proprietary means owned, often by a company. In computing, proprietary often refers to the way a document file is structured, e.g. CorelDRAW uses a CDR format for its vector files, which are structured so that CorelDRAW can open them.

prototype   A prototype is a quickly and cheaply built version of a product that contains the main features and is close to the real thing.

pseudoclasses   Pseudoclasses are the states of a hyperlink that can be set in CSS: link, visited, hover and active.

public key encryption   Public key encryption is a method of coding information so only the people with the right key at both ends of the communication can decode it.

qualitative research   Qualitative research involves collecting information about people's opinions, views and preferences about something. It allows you to make 'quality' judgements about your findings.

quantitative research   Quantitative research involves collecting data that can be measured and counted. The data collected can usually be presented in the form of graphs, tables and charts. It is important to use a large enough sample to ensure that you have used sufficient 'quantity' for the results to be valid and not guesswork.

RAM   RAM stands for random access memory. It is the name given to the electronic memory plugged into the main motherboard inside the system unit. RAM is often 1 GB or more in a modern computer system. This component is often replaced when a PC has a memory upgrade.

real time   Real time transmission results in audio and video signals being transmitted almost instantaneously.

referential integrity   Referential integrity is a system of rules to ensure that relationships between records in related tables are valid, and that users do not accidentally delete or change related data.

relational database   A relational database contains a set of tables which are held together by the relationships between the tables. It is for this reason such a database is called relational.

relationship   A relationship is a link between entities.

relative cell reference   A relative cell reference in a formula is based on the relative positions of the cell that contains the formula and the cell the formula refers to. If the position of the cell that contains the formula changes (because you copy it or move it), the cell reference in the formula changes automatically. So, if you copy the formula across rows (or down columns), the reference automatically adjusts for you.

rendering   Rendering is the process combining audio and visual elements with any applied effects to produce a file that can be played in real time.

representative values   Representative values are single values that represent many items of data. Representative values include mean, mode and median, as well as other statistical values.

reserved word   A reserved word is a word that is already used in the programming language and therefore cannot be used as a variable name.

resolution   Resolution is the number of pixels on the screen or other output device. The resolution is usually written as two numbers, the number of pixels across then the number down, so a 1024×768 resolution has 1024 pixels across and 786 down, giving 786,432 dots on the screen.

review point   A review point is where the project manager and others meet to review the progress of the project.

risk   A risk is any event, foreseen or not, that may happen and that puts the success of the project in jeopardy.

risk assessment   A risk assessment is an analysis of a task against each of the steps that could be taken to achieve the task.

risk mitigation   Risk mitigation is the actions taken to reduce the effect of a risk if it should happen.

rollover buttons   Rollover buttons work as normal buttons on a web page, but when the mouse hovers over them, the image or text changes.

RSI   RSI stands for repetitive strain injury. This common complaint can result from overuse of a computer mouse.

scope The scope of a variable is how much of the program the variable is usable within.

screen design A screen design depicts the layout of a web page and should be drawn before starting to build it.

search engine visibility Search engine visibility is getting a website listed as high as possible on a search engine. This will increase the number of visitors to a site.

select query A select query is a query that selects the data from the fields that you specify and with the criteria that you set for those fields.

selector A selector is similar to the title of the style. The property is what is being changed. The value is the amount by which it is being changed.

signed Signed means that a number can be positive or negative. In programming, signed usually means that the most significant digit (MSD) of a binary number (the leftmost digit) is used to define whether the number is positive (MSD is 0) or negative (MSD is 1).

software Software is the collection of programs installed on the computer.

solid state A solid state device has no moving parts. USB pen drives are solid state because they store data on electronic circuits which hold their values even when unplugged. USB hard drives are not solid state because the hard disk spins (moves) when used.

spam Spam is the term used for junk email.

SPAN A SPAN is a method of defining a style for a block of HTML (HyperText Markup Language).

spider A spider is an automated bot used by search engines to find websites.

stakeholder A stakeholder is a person or organisation that is actively involved in a project or whose interests the project may affect.

static website A static website is one with no interactivity and is usually just a presentation of information. Changes have to be hard-coded into the site.

storyboard A storyboard shows the sequence of a project. In web design, it shows how different pages will interrelate. In animation, it shows how different frames and scenes will interrelate.

streaming Streaming means feeding the video file to the user's computer in a continuous smaller volume of data, buffered by temporarily storing it and feeding to the player gradually so it is displayed steadily on the screen.

structured walkthrough A structured walkthrough is a review by one or more developers who manually go through the main paths of a program or system simulating how the computer executes them.

style A style is a group of formatting decisions to be applied together as defined in the CSS. For example, to have text display as red and centred could be a style.

subroutine A subroutine is a self-contained section of program also known as a procedure. Subroutines in VB.NET must have Sub and the name of the subroutine in their first line with End Sub as their last line. The first line of a subroutine often has extra code to define how it is to be run.

subtotal A subtotal is the sum of some data, which together with other subtotals makes a grand total.

syntax Syntax is the structure and order of the language. In English, 'door to go the' is not understandable as the syntax is wrong, whereas 'go to the door' is very clear as the syntax is correct. Similarly, programming languages need the syntax to be correct or the code cannot be understood. Syntax is the grammar of a programming language – it sets out the order in which words must appear within the code.

TabIndex TabIndex is the property of controls that defines the sequence they are selected when the Tab key is used to navigate a form.

tags Tags are elements of web page code, either in HTML or CSS. Usually they are written between angle brackets < and > to indicate that they are code words.

text reader A text reader is software that translates text into speech.

tracing Tracing is the process of the individual pixels of a bitmap being converted into the mathematical algorithm of a vector.

trichromatic system The trichromatic system uses combinations of the three colours that are the basis of 3D vision: red, blue and green.

tweening Tweening (short for in betweening) is where the animator states where points A and B are and the computer fills in the intermediary movement.

Uncanny Valley Uncanny Valley is the theory that if animation looks too real, audiences will feel uncomfortable.

unsigned Unsigned means that a number is treated as positive. In programming unsigned usually means that the most significant digit (MSD) of a binary number (the leftmost digit) is simply part of the number.

uploading Uploading is the process of putting a website on to a web server so it can be distributed across the Internet.

USB USB stands for universal serial bus and enables files to be transferred and stored by inserting the flat end into a computer with a USB port.

validation Validation is the process of checking that data entered into a system is reasonable and in the correct format.

variable A variable is used to store data and is given a name, e.g. the data 'Fred' might be stored in variable 'firstname'.

variant Variant variables respond to the data given to them and adapt as the program runs to whatever is put inside them.

vector A vector is a range that covers one row or one column. It is an image which is saved as a mathematical algorithm. Each line is saved as co-ordinates of each point and details of colour, width, etc.

vector graphics Vector graphics define objects as coordinate points and use mathematics inside the software to calculate how to display the image on the screen or printer.

verification Verification is a method of checking that the data entered on to the system is correct and the same as that on the original source.

web server A web server is a server that distributes web pages on to the Internet.

white box testing White box testing is when a program is tested to make sure each line of the code works. The program is the 'box', which is 'white' as the tester does see inside it.

WiFi WiFi is an increasingly popular standard for wireless networking and connection of PCs and other devices such as printers. WiFi is based on the 802.11 standard for wireless transmissions.

WIMP WIMP stands for windows, icons, mouse, pointer and is used to describe a GUI system. The windows are used to show running programs, the icons to start programs, the mouse to control the system and the pointer is an arrow on screen to show the position of the mouse.

wire-framing Wire-framing is used to draw an image of a 3D object that shows only the edges of the object.

wizard A wizard is a programme that enables a user to carry out a complex task by following a series of simple steps using dialogue boxes.

zoetrope The zoetrope (also known as a daedalum) was invented by William Horner in 1834. It was a machine that spun a strip of images at high speed in order to show movement.

zoopraxiscope The zoopraxiscope was invented by Eadweard Muybridge and was a development of the zoetrope. It used light shone through images on glass.

Index

3D graphics 251
8-bit 251

CLE (command line editor) 130
CLI (command line interface) 164
client-side scripts 103–4, 200–1
clocks, JavaScript 120
collecting information 16–17
colorimeter 247
colour, perception of 139–40
colour balance 250
colour depth 228, 251
colour laser printers 236
colour schemes, websites 198
columns, CSS 100–1
COM (component object model) 74
comma delimited files 46
comments, scripting languages 122
compression 217, 243, 246
Computer Misuse Act (1990) 222
computer monitors 236
concept designing 196
concept keyboards 148
conflict management 11
connectedness 140
constants, event driven programming 176, 178–9
constraints 6
content area 98
context-sensitive help 27
continuous data 64
control objects 52–3
controls 158, 278–9
conversions *see* images, file format conversions
cookies 104
copyright 255–6, 290
Copyright, Designs and Patents Act (1988) 223
CorelTRACE 240
corrective action 11
cost–benefit analysis 66–7
counters, JavaScript 120
CPU (central processing unit) 230
critical path analysis 9
crop 250
cross-cast checks 68
CRT (cathode ray tube) 236
CSS (cascading style sheets)
    characteristics 96–9
    creating 213
    design considerations 202
    testing 124
    uses 99–101
    website design 111–12
customer deliverables 19
customisation
    Microsoft Access 55–6
    spreadsheets 86–9
cut-out animation 267

D

DAB (digital audio broadcasting) 149
daisy-chaining 232
data entry forms 44–5, 73
data flow modelling 17
data flows 17
data integrity 81; *see also* referential integrity
data mining 65
Data Protection Act (1998) 222
data redundancy 36
data sharing, spreadsheets 71
data stores 17
data types 38–9, 176
data validation, spreadsheets 88–9

deadlines 16
debugging, event driven programming 186
debugging tools, event driven programming 174–5
decision support 65
delete queries 51–2
delimiters 46
deliverables 4, 4–5, 19
DHTML (dynamic HTML) 272–3
diagnostic software 187
dial-up 218
dialogue boxes 130
digital cameras 235
digital card readers 230–1
dimensions, CSS 98
discrete data 64
dithering 275
DIV, HTML 198
DMA (direct memory addressing) 230
documentation
    animation 288–9
    project completion 23
    project phase deliverables 20
    scripting languages 122–3
    system design 18
    technical 27
    user guides 27–8
DOM (Document Object Model) 272
DOS 164
drawn animation 266
Dreamweaver *see* Adobe Dreamweaver
drop-down menus, CSS 114–16
DSL 218
DVI (Digital Visual Interface) 228
dye-sublimation printers 236
dynamic websites 102, 194

E

e-cards 283–4
E-D glasses 132
Edison, Thomas Alva 263–5
education, using animation 269–70
entertainment, animation 267–8
entities 17, 34
ERD (entity relationship diagrams) 34
event driven applications
    creating 185–6
    designing 182–5
    specifying 180
event driven languages 102–3
event driven programming
    advantages 160–3
    application examples 164–5
    characteristics 158–60
    data storage 176–9
    disadvantages 163
    programming languages 165–7
    testing 187–9
    tools and techniques 169–75
event handlers, event driven programming 159, 171
event handling, JavaScript 108
event loops 159–60
event testing 187
events, event driven programming 159
Excel
    add–ins 74
    data entry forms 73
    named ranges 70
    sharing workbooks 71
    toolbar modifications 88

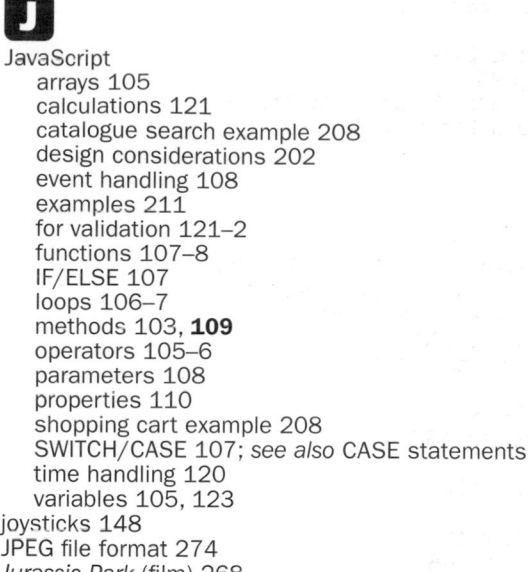

Let the web do the work!

Why not visit our website and see what it can do for you?

Free online support materials

You can download free support materials for many of our IT products. We even offer a special e-alert service to notify you when new content is posted.

Lists of useful weblinks

Our site includes lists of other websites, which can save you hours of research time.

Online ordering – 24 hours a day

It's quick and simple to order your resources online, and you can do it anytime – day or night!

Find your consultant

The website helps you find your nearest Heinemann consultant, who will be able to discuss your needs and help you find the most cost-effective way to buy.

It's time to save time – visit our website now!

www.harcourt.co.uk/vocational

And what's more, you can register now to receive our FREE information-packed eNewsletter. Register today at www.harcourt.co.uk/vocnews.

(t) 01865 888080 (f) 01865 314029 (e) orders@heinemann.co.uk (w) www.harcourt.co.uk

M872